THE THEORY OF THE POTENTIAL

MacMillan's

THEORETICAL MECHANICS

STATICS AND THE DYNAMICS OF
A PARTICLE

THE THEORY OF THE POTENTIAL

theoretical mechanics

THE THEORY OF THE POTENTIAL

By William Duncan MacMillan

Dover Publications, Inc., New York, New York.

Manufactuerd in United States of America

Dover Publications, Inc.
920 Broadway
New York 10, N. Y.

PREFACE

The purpose of the present volume is to give the reader a connected account of a certain field of mechanics which is very useful from the point of view of a physicist and very beautiful from the point of view of a mathematician. The book is not intended as a treatise, but it is hoped that the bird's-eye view which is here presented will serve as an introduction to this very attractive field and stimulate somewhat its cultivation.

The study of the theory of the potential may properly be said to have been initiated by Laplace in 1782 in the discovery that the potential function of every finite body satisfies a certain partial differential equation of the second order which is now known as Laplace's equation, and the theory of the potential is largely a study of the properties of the functions which satisfy it. Such functions were called harmonic functions by Lord Kelvin about the middle of the last century, and it is by this name that they are usually known.

Spherical harmonics were invented by Laplace in the paper above mentioned. These harmonic functions are associated with the sphere and are peculiarly adapted to the expansion of the potentials of bodies which differ but little from spheres, although the potential of every body is expansible in terms of spherical harmonics. The zonal harmonics, which had been developed previously by Legendre, are merely a particular type of the more general spherical harmonics of Laplace.

The next noteworthy advance in the theory was made by George Green in a very remarkable paper which was printed privately in 1828. Green was almost entirely a self-taught mathematician. He did not receive his degree of Bachelor of Arts until 1837, at which time he was forty-four years of age Notwithstanding these handicaps the brilliant originality of this paper marks it as one of the mathematical classics—a fact which should be stimulating to the more fortunate students of the present day. In this paper is to be found a fundamental theorem of mathematical analysis which is known as Green's theorem.

v

He also formulated the problem of electrical induction which later became celebrated under the name of Dirichlet's problem. It was in this paper that the term potential function was used for the first time.

Owing to the manner of its publication Green's paper was almost unknown for more than a decade. In the meantime many of his theorems had been rediscovered by Gauss, Charles, Sturm and others. In particular, Gauss' paper of 1841 covered somewhat the same ground as Green's paper of 1828, but the methods of Gauss were so different from those of Green that both papers are fundamental in this field. Although, apparently, Gauss was not familiar with Green's paper, he, too, used the term potential function—without, however, any claim of invention.

The theory of the potential was very popular during the middle decades of the nineteenth century. A vast literature was developed in which are to be found the names of many brilliant mathematicians. Interest in the subject has not yet died out, as is evidenced by the long list of titles of modern papers in this field. The properties of many of the functions which arise can be made to depend upon the solutions of integral equations, a fact that is of great interest to the mathematical students of this type of functional equations.

A knowledge of integral equations on the part of the student, however, is not assumed here. It seems more practical to leave this aspect of the theory of the potential to those who are devoted to the theory of integral equations than to assume too wide a knowledge of mathematical theory on the part of the student.

It is hoped that the presentation of the subject here given will be found useful both to students of mathematics and to students of mathematical physics.

W. D. MacMillan.

The University of Chicago,
March, 1930.

CONTENTS

CHAPTER III

VECTOR FIELDS. THEOREMS OF GREEN AND GAUSS

CHAPTER IV

THE ATTRACTIONS OF SURFACES AND LINES

Attractions of Surfaces

Attractions of Lines

CHAPTER V

SURFACE DISTRIBUTIONS OF MATTER

CHAPTER VI

TWO-LAYER SURFACES

The Methods of Neumann and Poincaré

CHAPTER VII

Spherical Harmonics

CHAPTER VIII

ELLIPSOIDAL HARMONICS

THE THEORY OF THE POTENTIAL

CHAPTER I

THE ATTRACTION OF FINITE BODIES

1. The Law of Gravitation.—Newton's law of gravitation states that

Every particle in the universe attracts every other particle with a force which is directly proportional to the product of the two masses and inversely proportional to the square of the distance between them; the direction of the force being in the line joining the two particles.

It will be observed that the law applies only to particles, and not to bodies of finite size.

2. The Attraction of Systems of Particles.—Since forces are vectors, it is evident that the attraction of many particles, of mass m_i, upon a single particle, of mass m_0, is the vector sum of the attractions of the individual particles (Fig. 1). In order to effect this sum, it is convenient to resolve the individual attractions into their compo-

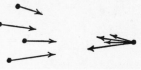

Fig. 1.

nents along three mutually perpendicular axes. The components of the resultant attraction, or the vector sum, along these three axes is then the algebraic sum of the individual components along these axes.

3. The Components of Attraction.—Let the coordinates of the particle of mass m_i with respect to a fixed set of rectangular axes be ξ_i, η_i, ζ_i; and let the coordinates of the particle of mass m_0 be x, y, z. The force acting on m_0 which is due to the attraction of the particle m_i is directed towards m_i and its intensity is

$$\frac{k^2 m_0 m_i}{r_i{}^2},$$

1

where
$$r_i = \sqrt{(\xi_i - x)^2 + (\eta_i - y)^2 + (\zeta - z)^2}.$$

The direction cosines of the line of the force are respectively

$$\frac{\xi_i - x}{r_i}, \qquad \frac{\eta_i - y}{r_i}, \qquad \frac{\xi_i - z}{r_i}.$$

Hence the components of the force along the three axes are

$$k^2 m_0 m_i \frac{\xi_i - x}{r_i^3}, \qquad k^2 m_0 m_i \frac{\eta_i - y}{r_i^3}, \qquad k^2 m_0 m_i \frac{\zeta_i - z}{r_i^3}.$$

If there are n particles m_i, and if X, Y, and Z are the components of the resultant attraction of the particles m_i upon the particle m_0, then

$$\left. \begin{aligned} X &= -k^2 m_0 \sum_{i=1}^{n} \frac{m_i(x - \xi_i)}{r_i^3}, \\ Y &= -k^2 m_0 \sum_{i=1}^{n} \frac{m_i(y - \eta_i)}{r_i^3}, \\ Z &= -k^2 m_0 \sum_{i=1}^{n} \frac{m_i(z - \zeta_i)}{r_i^3}. \end{aligned} \right\} \tag{1}$$

In the event that the system of particles m_i form a continuous body of density $\sigma(\xi, \eta, \zeta)$ these sums pass over into the definite integrals

$$\left. \begin{aligned} X &= -k^2 m_0 \int_B \frac{x - \xi}{r^3} dm, \\ Y &= -k^2 m_0 \int_B \frac{y - \eta}{r^3} dm, \\ Z &= -k^2 m_0 \int_B \frac{z - \zeta}{r^3} dm, \end{aligned} \right\} \tag{2}$$

where
$$r = \sqrt{(x - \xi)^2 + (y - \eta)^2 + (z - \zeta)^2},$$
and
$$dm = \sigma \, d\xi \, d\eta \, d\zeta.$$

The value of the gravitational constant k^2 in c.g.s. units is 6.66×10^{-8}. It is the force with which each of two unit particles attracts the other when the distance between them is 1 cm.

4. The Elements of Mass.—The volume density at a point is the limit of the ratio

$$\frac{\text{mass}}{\text{volume}}$$

at that point, the density of water at 4°C. being unity. The element of mass is

$$dm = \sigma \, d\xi \, d\eta \, d\zeta.$$

Similarly for thin sheets or plates, which are regarded as surfaces, the surface density at a point is the limit of the ratio

$$\frac{mass}{area}$$

at that point, or the mass per unit area if the density is constant. For a surface, the element of mass is

$$dm = \sigma \, d\xi \, d\eta.$$

In the case of fine wires, which are regarded as lines, the line density at a point in the limit of the ratio

$$\frac{mass}{length}$$

at that point, or the mass per unit length in case the density is constant. For a line the element of mass is

$$dm = \sigma \, d\xi.$$

5. Attraction on a Point.—The phrase "attraction of a body on a point" in itself has no meaning, but since the attraction is always proportional to the mass of the particle attracted it is convenient to assume that its mass is unity. Hence, by definition, *the attraction of a body on a point* means the attraction of the body on a unit particle at that point.

In the simple examples which follow, the general formulas of Sec. 3 are not used, as the examples are solved by simpler methods. Doubtless the student will find it interesting to verify these solutions by the integration of the formulas Eq. (3.2).

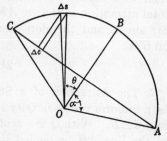

FIG. 2.

6. The Attraction of a Circular Arc on Its Center.—Given a fine uniform wire of mass σ per unit length bent into the form of a circular arc ABC (Fig. 2), which subtends an angle 2α at the center O. It is desired to find the attraction of the arc upon its center, the radius of the circle being r.

It is evident from symmetry that the resulting attraction lies in the bisector of the angle AOC, that is, along the line OB.

Hence it is necessary to consider only the components of attraction which are parallel to OB, the sum of the perpendicular components being zero.

Let the arc AC be divided into n parts each of length Δs. If n is very large, each part can be regarded as a particle of mass $\sigma\Delta s$. Let θ be the angle which the particle makes with the line OB. Then the component along OB of the attraction of the particle at Δs on the point O is

$$k^2\sigma\frac{\Delta s}{r^2}\cos\theta.$$

Imagine the chord AC to be a fine wire similar to the arc ABC. Let Δc be the projection on the chord of the length Δs. Then

$$\Delta c = \Delta s \cdot \cos\theta,$$

and the mass of the particle at Δc is

$$\sigma\,\Delta c = \sigma\,\Delta s\cos\theta.$$

If this particle were moved to the point B then its attraction on O along OB would be

$$k^2\frac{\sigma\,\Delta s\cos\theta}{r^2};$$

that is, it would be the same as the component of attraction of the particle at Δs along OB. But Δs is any particle of the arc, and Δc is the corresponding particle of the chord. Hence if every particle of the chord AC were placed at the point B their total attraction on the point O would be the same as the total attraction of the arc ABC. The total mass of the chord is $2\sigma r \sin\alpha$, and therefore the total attraction of the arc ABC on O is

$$2k^2\sigma\frac{\sin\alpha}{r}.$$

7. The Attraction of a Straight Line on a Point.—Let AB be a uniform rod of density σ, and let O be any point not in the line of AB. With O as a center draw a circle of radius r, tangent to the line AB (extended if necessary) at C. Draw the lines OA and OB cutting the circle in the points D and E respectively, and then imagine the arc of the circle DCE to be a rod similar to the rod AB. Let Δs be a portion of the rod AB so short that its mass can be regarded as a particle. Join the extremities of Δs to O. These lines cut out a portion of the circular rod Δc.

The attractions of the particles at Δs and Δc on the point O are equal; for, if θ is the angle which the line $O\Delta s$ makes with the line OC,

$$\Delta c = \Delta s \cos^2 \theta.$$

The distance $O\Delta s$ is equal to $r \sec \theta$. Hence, the attraction of the particle Δs on O is

$$\frac{k^2 \sigma \, \Delta s}{r^2 \sec^2 \theta} = \frac{k^2 \sigma \, \Delta s \cos^2 \theta}{r^2} = \frac{k^2 \sigma \, \Delta c}{r^2},$$

which is the same as the attraction of the particle Δc on O.

Since each particle of the rod has the same attraction for the point O as the corresponding particle of the circular arc, both

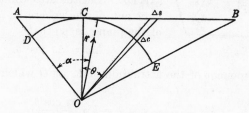

FIG. 3.

as the magnitude and direction, it follows that the total attraction of the rod is the same as the total attraction of the arc. If the angle subtended by the rod at the point O is 2α, the resultant attraction bisects this angle, and, by Sec. 6, its magnitude is

$$2k^2\sigma \, \frac{\sin \alpha}{r}, \tag{1}$$

where r is the perpendicular distance from O to the rod.

If the rod increases in length, its line remaining fixed, the angle α increases and has the limit $\pi/2$ for a rod which is infinite in both directions; and this limit is independent of the manner in which the limit is approached. Hence the attraction of an infinitely long rod for a particle, at a distance r from it, is

$$\frac{2k^2\sigma}{r};$$

that is, it is inversely as the distance, and not inversely as the square of the distance.

8. The Attraction of a Thin Sheet on Its Axis of Symmetry.— Consider the attraction of a thin, doubly symmetric, plane sheet upon a point in the axis of symmetry which is perpendicular to the sheet. By virtue of symmetry, the resultant attraction lies in the axis.

Let O (Fig. 4) be any point of the axis OP, other than the point of intersection of the axis with the sheet. With O as a center, describe a sphere of radius r, which is tangent to the sheet, and imagine that the plane sheet and the spherical sheet have the same surface density σ.

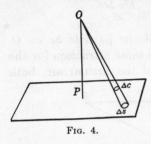

FIG. 4.

Take an infinitesimal cone of solid angle $\Delta\omega$ with its apex at O which intersects both the plane and the sphere, and which makes an angle θ with the axis OP. Let the area which this cone cuts out of the sphere be Δc, and out of the plane Δs, so that

$$\Delta c = \Delta s \cos^3 \theta.$$

The component of the attraction of Δs on O which lies in the axis OP is

$$k^2\sigma \frac{\Delta s}{r^2 \sec^2 \theta} \cos \theta = k^2\sigma \frac{\Delta s \cos^3\theta}{r^2}.$$

If the particle Δc were placed at P, its attraction on O would be

$$k^2\sigma \frac{\Delta c}{r^2} = k^2\sigma \frac{\Delta s \cos^3 \theta}{r^2}.$$

Its attraction, therefore, would be identical with the component of the attraction of Δs along OP. Therefore, the attraction of the entire plane sheet on O is the same as the attraction of the corresponding spherical sheet under the supposition that the mass of the spherical sheet is all concentrated at the point P. If the solid angle subtended at the point O by the plane sheet is ω (the apparent size at O of the plane sheet), the intensity of the attraction of the sheet on O is

$$k^2\sigma \frac{r^2\omega}{r^2} = k^2\sigma\omega. \tag{1}$$

The attraction depends only upon the apparent size at O and not at all upon its shape, except that it must be doubly symmetric. If the plane sheet is not doubly symmetric, the above argument still holds for that component of the attraction which is along OP, but the component of the attraction which is parallel to the plane sheet, in general, is not zero.

The limiting value of the component which is perpendicular to the sheet is $2k^2\pi\sigma$, if the sheet is extended indefinitely in all directions.

9. The Attraction of the Frustum of a Cone on Its Apex.—

If the plane sheet of the previous section is regarded as having a finite thickness Δa, the relation between its surface density σ and its volume density $\bar{\sigma}$ is

$$\sigma = \bar{\sigma}\Delta a.$$

Imagine the frustum of a homogeneous cone, the base of which is doubly symmetric, with the apex on the axis perpendicular to the base through the center of symmetry. Let the frustum be divided into n sheets, of equal thickness Δa (n very large). If the height of the frustum is h, then

$$h = n\Delta a.$$

By Eq. (8.1) the attraction of each sheet on the apex is

$$k^2\sigma\omega = k^2\bar{\sigma}\Delta a\omega$$

which has the same value for every sheet. Hence the total attraction of the frustum on the apex is

$$k^2\bar{\sigma}\omega n\Delta a = k^2\sigma h\omega,$$

where ω is the solid angle at the apex.

In the case of a right circular cone, the generator of which makes an angle α with the axis, the value of ω is

$$\omega = \int_0^\alpha \int_0^{2\pi} \sin\varphi \, d\varphi \, d\theta$$
$$= 2\pi(1 - \cos\alpha),$$

and the attraction is

$$A = 2\pi k^2\bar{\sigma}h(1 - \cos\alpha).$$

Frustums of equal height attract the apex equally.

Consider any homogeneous cone, that is, one with a plane base of any kind, and an infinitesimal solid angle $d\omega$ with its apex at the apex of the cone making an angle θ with the perpendicular h from the apex of the cone to the base. If the length of this infinitesimal cone is r, the area which it cuts out of the base is

$$da = r^2 d\omega \sec\theta.$$

Let $d\mu$ be an element of mass of this infinitesimal cone which lies between two planes parallel to the base at distances ρ and $\rho + d\rho$ measured along the cone from the apex. Since the thickness of this element $d\mu$ is $d\rho \cos \theta$ and its base area is $\rho^2 d\omega$ sec θ, its mass is

$$d\mu = \sigma\rho^2 d\omega d\rho,$$

and the attraction of this infinitesimal cone upon its apex is

$$A = \int_0^r \frac{r d\mu}{\rho^2} = \int_0^r \sigma \, d\omega \, d\rho = \sigma r \, d\omega$$

$$= \sigma \frac{da}{r} \cos \theta = \frac{\sigma h \, da}{r^2}.$$

The mass of the infinitesimal cone is

$$\mu = \frac{1}{3}\sigma h \, da,$$

so that

$$A = \frac{3\mu}{r^2}.$$

Hence the attraction of the homogeneous infinitesimal cone upon its apex is three times as great as it would be if all of its mass were distributed uniformly over its base. Since the height of every such infinitesimal cone has the same value h, their masses are all proportional to the areas of their bases. Since the proposition holds for each of them separately, it holds for all of them taken together. That is, the attrac-

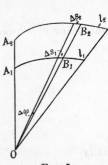

Fig. 5.

tion of a homogeneous cone upon its apex is three times as great, and in the same direction, as it would be if the mass of the cone were distributed uniformly in an infinitesimal layer over its base.

10. Perspectivity.—Two lines, l_1 and l_2, are in perspective with respect to the point O if the radius vector from O is intercepted by the two lines in a constant ratio; that is, if, in Fig. 5,

$$\frac{OB_1}{OB_2} = \frac{OA_1}{OA_2} = \rho,$$

for every position of the vector OB. If the ratio of perspectivity is ρ, the ratio of the length of the lines l_1 and l_2 also is ρ.

Likewise, two surfaces are in perspective with respect to the point O if the radius vector from the point O is intercepted by the two surfaces in a constant ratio. If the ratio of perspectivity is ρ, the ratio of the areas of the two surfaces is ρ^2.

Two solids are in perspective with respect to the point O if their corresponding surfaces are in perspective with the same ratio of perspectivity. Thus, if, in Fig. 6, the surfaces C_1 and C_2 are in perspective with the ratio ρ, and if the surfaces B_1 and B_2 also are in perspective with the ratio ρ, then the solid bounded by the surfaces B_1 and C_1 is in perspective with the solid which is bounded by the surfaces B_2 and C_2; and the ratio of the volumes of these solids is ρ^3.

Theorem I.—Two lines which are in perspective with respect to the point O and which have the same linear density attract the point O with forces which are in-versely proportional to their ratio of perspectivity (or, inversely propor-tional to their distances).

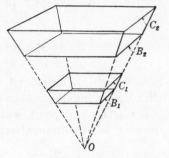

In Fig. 5 let l_1 and l_2 be in per-spective with the point O with the ratio of perspectivity ρ. Then

$$\frac{OB_1}{OB_2} = \rho.$$

Let $\Delta\omega$ be an infinitesimal plane angle which cuts out the arcs

Fig. 6.

Δs_1 and Δs_2. Let α_1 and α_2 be the attractions of the two particles Δs_1 and Δs_2 on the point O. Since the linear density of the two lines are equal, the masses of these two particles are proportional to the two lengths Δs_1 and Δs_2. Hence

$$\frac{\alpha_1}{\alpha_2} = \frac{m_1}{m_2} \cdot \frac{\overline{OB_2}^2}{\overline{OB_1}^2} = \frac{\Delta s_1}{\Delta s_2} \cdot \frac{1}{\rho^2} = \frac{1}{\rho}.$$

Since this constant ratio holds for every pair of corresponding points of the two lines, it holds for their sum, and therefore holds for the attraction of the lines themselves.

In a manner quite similar the two following theorems are proved.

Theorem II.—Two surfaces which are in perspective and have the same surface density attract the point of perspectivity equally.

Theorem III.—Two homogeneous solids of the same density which are in perspective attract their point of perspectivity with forces which have the same ratio as the ratio of perspectivity (or, which are directly proportional to their distances).

The Andromeda Nebula has about the same apparent size as the sun but it is 6×10^{10} times as far away. If it were spherical in shape with the same density as the sun, its attraction on the earth would be 6×10^{10} times that of the sun. Even though the density of the Nebula were the density of the sun divided by 6×10^{10}, the two attractions would be equal.

11. The Attraction of an Ellipsoidal Homoeoid upon an Interior Point.—A homogeneous shell bounded by two ellipsoids which are similar and similarly placed is called by Thompson and Tait an ellipsoidal homoeoid. For example, the two surfaces

$$\frac{x^2}{a^2} + \frac{y^2}{b^2} + \frac{z^2}{c^2} = 1,$$

and

$$\frac{x^2}{a^2} + \frac{y^2}{b^2} + \frac{z^2}{c^2} = (1 + \lambda)^2$$

bound such an ellipsoidal shell. It will be supposed at first that λ is an infinitesimal so that the shell is very thin.

Let P be any point within the shell. With P as a vertex describe an infinitesimal solid angle which cuts the shell at a_1

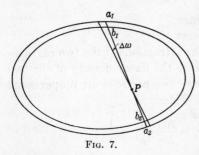

FIG. 7.

and a_2. Pass a plane through this line and the center of the shell. The cross section is an ellipse (Fig. 7), or rather, two similar concentric ellipses. The system of chords parallel to a_1a_2 is bisected by the conjugate diameter of this system, which is also the conjugate diameter of the system of chords b_1b_2 of the inner ellipse. Hence the chords b_1b_2 also are bisected by this conjugate diameter, so that

$$a_1b_1 = a_2b_2.$$

Let the measure of the solid angle be $\Delta\omega$. (The measure of a solid angle is the area which the solid angle cuts out of the unit sphere which has the apex of the solid angle as its center.) Since the volume density of the shell is constant, the mass of the particle which is cut out of the shell by the solid angle is proportional to its volume. Since the angle and the shell are infinitesimal, this volume is an oblique cylinder, the volume of which is equal to the product of the area of the base and the height of the cylinder; or, what comes to the same thing, the product of the area of a perpendicular cross-section of the cylinder and its slant height. This last formula is the one which is desired in the present case.

Let m_1 be the mass of the particle at a_1 and m_2 the mass of the particle at a_2. Then, if σ is the density,

$$m_1 = \sigma \cdot \overline{a_1 b_1} \cdot \overline{Pa_1}^2 \cdot \Delta\omega,$$

$$m_2 = \sigma \cdot \overline{a_2 b_2} \cdot \overline{Pa_2}^2 \cdot \Delta\omega.$$

The attractions of m_1 and m_2 on the point P are therefore

$$A_1 = k^2 \frac{m_1}{\overline{Pa_1}^2} = k^2\sigma \cdot \overline{a_1 b_1} \cdot \Delta\omega,$$

$$A_2 = k^2 \frac{m_2}{\overline{Pa_2}^2} = k^2\sigma \cdot \overline{a_2 b_2} \cdot \Delta\omega.$$

Since $\overline{a_1 b_1} = \overline{a_2 b_2}$, it follows that $A_1 = A_2$, and, since the two forces are oppositely directed, the resultant attraction of the two particles on P is zero. This is true for every infinitesimal cone which has its apex at P. It is, therefore, equally true for finite cones, and consequently for the entire shell for which the value of ω is 2π. It follows, therefore, that the resultant attraction of an infinitely thin ellipsoidal homoeoid on a particle anywhere in its interior is zero.

It will be zero for any number of such homoeoids, and is therefore zero for a shell of finite thickness. In particular, since a spherical shell is a special case of an ellipsoidal homoeoid, the attraction of a spherical shell, which is homogeneous in concentric layers, on a particle anywhere within its interior is zero.

12. The Attraction of a Spherical Shell on an Exterior Particle.—It will be shown in this section that a homogeneous spherical shell attracts an exterior particle just as though all of the mass of the shell were concentrated at its center. The method of proof used is due to Thompson and Tait.[1]

Let O in Fig. 8 be the center of the spherical shell of radius a and thickness Δa (infinitesimal), and let P be the attracted particle. On the line PO take the point A (the harmonic conjugate) so that

$$\overline{PO} \cdot \overline{OA} = a^2.$$

---

[1] "Natural Philosophy," Part II, §471.

This can be done graphically by drawing the two tangents to the shell from the point P and then drawing the chord which connects the two points of tangency. The intersection of this chord with the line PO is the point A which is required. For the chord C_1C_2 is perpendicular to the line PO, so that the triangles OC_1A and OC_1P are similar, and therefore

$$OC_1 : OP :: OA : OC_1;$$

from which follows at once

$$\overline{OP} \cdot \overline{OA} = a^2.$$

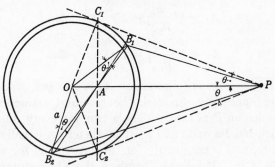

Fig. 8.

With the point A as a vertex construct any infinitesimal cone whose solid angle is $\Delta\omega$. If σ is the volume density of the shell, the masses of the two particles m_1 and m_2 which are cut out of the shell by the cone at B_1 and B_2 are

$$m_1 = \sigma \cdot \Delta\omega \cdot \overline{AB_1}^2 \cdot \Delta a \cdot \sec \theta,$$
$$m_2 = \sigma \cdot \Delta\omega \cdot \overline{AB_2}^2 \cdot \Delta a \cdot \sec \theta,$$

where θ is the value of the base angles in the triangle B_1OB_2. The attractions of these two particles upon the point P are

$$\left. \begin{aligned} A_1 &= k^2\sigma \cdot \Delta\omega \cdot \Delta a \cdot \sec \theta \cdot \left(\frac{AB_1}{B_1P}\right)^2, \\ A_2 &= k^2\sigma \cdot \Delta\omega \cdot \Delta a \cdot \sec \theta \cdot \left(\frac{AB_2}{B_2P}\right)^2. \end{aligned} \right\} \tag{1}$$

In the triangles OB_1A and OPB_1, the angle at O is common and the sides which include this angle are proportional, since

$$\frac{PO}{OB_1} = \frac{OB_1}{OA}, \quad \text{or} \quad \overline{PO} \cdot \overline{OA} = \overline{OB_1}^2 = a^2.$$

Hence, these two triangles are similar and the angle B_1PO is equal to θ.

Likewise, the triangles OB_2A and OPB_2 are similar, and the angle B_2PO is equal to θ.

Furthermore, from the similarity of the triangles,

$$\frac{AB_1}{B_1P} = \frac{OB_1}{OP} = \frac{a}{OP},$$

$$\frac{AB_2}{B_2P} = \frac{OB_2}{OP} = \frac{a}{OP}.$$

On substituting these ratios in Eq. (1), the expressions for the attractions become

$$A_1 = k^2\sigma \cdot \Delta\omega \cdot \Delta a \cdot \sec\theta \cdot \left(\frac{a}{OP}\right)^2,$$

$$A_2 = k^2\sigma \cdot \Delta\omega \cdot \Delta a \cdot \sec\theta \cdot \left(\frac{a}{OP}\right)^2,$$

and, therefore, in magnitude A_1 is equal to A_2. The resultant of the forces $\mathbf{A}_1$ and $\mathbf{A}_2$ lies along the bisector of the angle B_1PB_2, that is along PO, and its magnitude is equal to

$$A = \frac{2k^2\sigma \cdot \Delta\omega \cdot a^2\Delta a}{\overrightarrow{OP}^2}.$$

This formula holds for every solid angle $\Delta\omega$ whose vertex is at A, and therefore it holds for their sum, since the coefficient of $\Delta\omega$ is constant. Hence, on setting

$$\Sigma\Delta\omega = 2\pi,$$

the attraction of the entire shell is

$$A_s = \frac{4\pi \, k^2\sigma a^2\Delta a}{\overrightarrow{OP}^2} = \frac{k^2M_s}{\overrightarrow{OP}^2}.$$

Since the mass of the spherical shell is $4\pi\sigma a^2\Delta a$. But this is just what the formula would be, if the mass of the shell were all concentrated at its center.

If the point P is in the shell itself, only one nappe of the cone intersects the shell, and for this case

$$A_s = \frac{1}{2}\frac{k^2M_s}{\overrightarrow{OP}^2}.$$

This result, however, depends upon the manner in which the limit is attained. It is shown in Sec. 86 that the attraction of a surface for one of its own particles is quite indeterminate.

13. The Attraction of a Solid Sphere upon an Exterior Point.—
If m_s is the mass of a homogeneous shell and if the point P lies
outside of the shell at a distance r from its center, the attraction
of the shell on the point is directed towards the center of the
shell, and its intensity is

$$A_\text{shell} = \frac{k^2 m_s}{r^2}.$$

The resulting attraction of any number of such shells which
are concentric is directed towards their common center, and its
intensity is simply the sum of the intensities for the individual
shells. Hence, if M is the total mass of the sphere, its attraction
upon an exterior point is

$$A = \frac{k^2 M}{r^2}.$$

It is not necessary that the shells shall all have the same
volume density. It is sufficient that each shell separately shall
be homogeneous. It is evident that a solid sphere which is
homogeneous, or homogeneous in concentric layers, attracts an
exterior point just as though it were a particle of the same mass
located at the center of the sphere; and two such spheres will
attract each other just as though both were particles concentrated at their centers.

14. The Mutual Attraction of Two Straight Collinear Rods.—
The preceeding examples have been solved by special methods

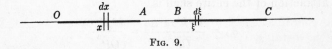

Fig. 9.

which appeal directly to the intuition. Some further examples
will be given which require the method of integration. Consider
first the attraction of a straight rod on an exterior point in the
line of the rod.

Let OA be a rod of length l_1 and of linear density σ_1. Let dx
be an element of length at a distance x from O. The mass of the
particle at dx is $\sigma_1 dx$. The attraction of this particle on a point
at a distance ξ from the point O is

$$\frac{\sigma_1 dx}{(\xi - x)^2},$$

and the attraction of the entire rod OA on the point ξ is the sum of the attractions of all of its elements. That is

$$\int_0^{l_1} \frac{\sigma_1 dx}{(\xi - x)^2} = \sigma_1\left(\frac{1}{\xi - l_1} - \frac{1}{\xi}\right),$$

This is the attraction of the rod on a unit particle at the point ξ. Suppose σ_2 is the linear density of the rod BC. Then the attraction of the rod OA on a particle $\sigma_2 d\xi$ of the rod BC located at the point ξ is

$$\sigma_1\sigma_2\left(\frac{1}{\xi - l_1} - \frac{1}{\xi}\right)d\xi.$$

Let the distance between the rods be a and the length of the second rod be l_2. Then the total attraction of the first rod on the second is the sum of the attractions on the individual elements. That is,

$$\sigma_1\sigma_2\int_{l_1+a}^{l_1+a+l_2}\left(\frac{1}{\xi - l_1} - \frac{1}{\xi}\right)d\xi = \sigma_1\sigma_2 \log\frac{(a + l_1)(a + l_2)}{a(a + l_1 + l_2)},$$

and this is intensity of the mutual attraction of the two rods.

15. The Attraction of a Circular Disk on Its Axis.—In Fig. 10 let the radius of the circular disk be r and let its surface density be σ. It is required to find the attraction of the disk upon a point of its axis, that is, the line which is perpendicular to the disk at its center O. Let O be the origin of a system of polar coordinates ρ, θ, and let z be the distance from O along the axis to the attracted point P. The mass of the particle of the disk whose polar coordinates are ρ, θ is

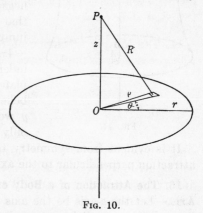

Fig. 10.

$$dm = \sigma \rho \, d\rho \, d\theta,$$

and its distance from the attracted particle is

$$R = \sqrt{\rho^2 + z^2}.$$

Hence, its attraction on the point P is

$$\frac{dm}{R^2} = \frac{k^2\sigma \rho \, d\rho \, d\theta}{\rho^2 + z^2};$$

and the component of this attraction along the axis is

$$-\frac{k^2\sigma\rho d\rho d\theta}{\rho^2 + z^2} \cdot \frac{z}{R} = -\frac{k^2\sigma z\rho d\rho d\theta}{(\rho^2 + z^2)^{\frac{3}{2}}}.$$

The total attraction of the disk is therefore

$$Z = -k^2\sigma z \int_0^r \int_0^{2\pi} \frac{\rho d\rho d\theta}{(\rho^2 + z^2)^{\frac{3}{2}}} = -2\pi k^2\sigma z \int_0^r \frac{\rho d\rho}{(\rho^2 + z^2)^{\frac{3}{2}}}$$

$$= +2\pi k^2\sigma \left[\frac{z}{\sqrt{z^2 + r^2}} - \frac{z}{\sqrt{z^2}} \right]. \tag{1}$$

The numerical value of the second term of the bracket is ± 1 according as z is negative or positive, for in extracting the square root of z^2 it is the positive root which is taken.

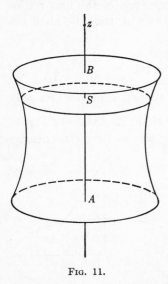

Fig. 11.

Since this expression changes sign with z but does not vanish with z, the attraction has a finite discontinuity, if $\sigma \neq 0$, as the attracted point passes through the disk. For a disk of infinite radius the attraction is independent of the distance z and has the constant numerical value $2\pi k^2\sigma$. In passing from the negative side to the positive side, that is, dz positive, there is a finite jump in the attraction equal to $-4\pi k^2\sigma$. If the earth were an indefinitely extended homogeneous plane, as some of the ancients believed, the acceleration of gravity g would be rigorously, instead of only approximately, constant.

It is evident from symmetry that there is no component of attraction perpendicular to the axis.

16. The Attraction of a Body of Revolution on a Point in Its Axis.—Let the z-axis be the axis of revolution. If the body is homogeneous, as will be supposed, the resultant attraction is along the z-axis, and it is necessary to compute only the z-component.

In Fig. 11, let AB be a figure of revolution. By the third formula of Eqs. (3.2)

$$Z = k^2\sigma \int \int \int_B \frac{\zeta - z}{r^3} d\xi d\eta d\zeta;$$

but the results of Sec. 15 can be utilized, thus eliminating two of the three integrations. Consider a thin cross-section of thickness $d\zeta$ at the distance ζ from the origin A. If σ is its volume density and σ_1 is its surface density, then

$$\sigma_1 = \sigma d\zeta.$$

If z is the coordinate of the attracted point, with $z > B$, Eq. (15.1) gives for the attraction of the disk at ζ

$$2\pi k^2\sigma\left[\frac{z - \zeta}{\sqrt{(z - \zeta)^2 + r^2}} - 1\right]d\zeta,$$

where r is the radius of the disk; and the attraction of the entire body is

$$Z = 2\pi k^2\sigma\int_A^B\left[\frac{z - \zeta}{\sqrt{(z - \xi)^2 + r^2}} - 1\right]d\zeta. \tag{1}$$

17. Example—The Oblate Spheroid.—Let the surface of the oblate spheroid be defined by the equation

$$\frac{\xi^2 + \eta^2}{a^2} + \frac{\zeta^2}{c^2} = 1.$$

The radius of the cross-section at the distance ζ from the origin is defined by the formula

$$r^2 = a^2 - \frac{a^2}{c^2}\zeta^2;$$

so that the expression for the attraction (Eq. (16.1)) becomes

$$Z = 2\pi k^2\sigma\left[\int_{-c}^{+c}\frac{(z - \zeta)d\zeta}{\sqrt{(z - \zeta)^2 + a^2 - \dfrac{a^2}{c_2}\zeta^2}} - 2c\right]. \tag{1}$$

Since

$$z - \zeta = -\frac{\left(-z + \zeta - \dfrac{a^2}{c^2}\zeta\right) + \dfrac{a^2}{c^2}z}{1 - \dfrac{a^2}{c^2}},$$

the integral of this expression can be resolved into the sum of the two integrals

$$+\frac{c^2}{a^2 - c^2}\int_{-c}^{+c}\frac{-z + \zeta - \dfrac{a^2}{c^2}\zeta}{\sqrt{(z - \zeta)^2 + a^2 - \dfrac{a^2}{c^2}\zeta^2}}d\zeta +$$

$$\frac{a^2z}{a^2 - c^2}\int_{-c}^{+c}\frac{d\zeta}{\sqrt{(z - \zeta)^2 + a^2 - \dfrac{a^2}{c^2}\zeta^2}}.$$

The first integral is the value of

$$\frac{c^2}{a^2 - c^2} \sqrt{(z - \zeta)^2 + a^2 - \frac{a^2}{c^2}\zeta^2},$$

between the limits $+c$ and $-c$. After substituting the values of the limits and subtracting, this value is found to be

$$-\frac{2c^3}{a^2 - c^2}.$$

The second integral can be written

$$\frac{a^2 cz}{(a^2 - c^2)^{\frac{3}{2}}} \int_{-c}^{+c} \frac{d\zeta}{\sqrt{\dfrac{a^2 c^2 (a^2 - c^2 + z^2)}{(a^2 - c^2)^2} - \left(\dfrac{zc^2}{a^2 - c^2} + \zeta\right)^2}}.$$

The value of the indefinite integral is

$$\sin^{-1} \frac{(a^2 - c^2)\zeta + zc^2}{ac\sqrt{a^2 - c^2 + z^2}},$$

which for the upper limit c has the value

$$\sin^{-1} \frac{a^2 - c^2 + cz}{a\sqrt{a^2 - c^2 + z^2}} = \tan^{-1} \frac{a^2 - c^2 + cz}{\sqrt{a^2 - c^2}\,(z - c)},$$

and for the lower limit

$$\sin^{-1} \frac{-a^2 + c^2 + cz}{a\sqrt{a^2 - c^2 + z^2}} = -\tan^{-1} \frac{a^2 - c^2 - cz}{\sqrt{a^2 - c^2}\,(z + c)}.$$

The value of the integral is therefore

$$\tan^{-1} \frac{a^2 - c^2 + cz}{\sqrt{a^2 - c^2}\,(z - c)} + \tan^{-1} \frac{a^2 - c^2 - cz}{\sqrt{a^2 - c_2}\,(z + c)}.$$

$$= \tan^{-1} \frac{2z\sqrt{a^2 - c^2}}{z^2 + c^2 - a^2} = 2\tan^{-1} \frac{\sqrt{a^2 - c^2}}{z}.$$

Hence,

$$Z = 4\pi k^2 \sigma \left[-c - \frac{c^3}{a^2 - c^2} + \frac{a^2 cz}{(a^2 - c^2)^{\frac{3}{2}}} \tan^{-1} \frac{\sqrt{a^2 - c^2}}{z} \right]$$

$$= \frac{4\pi k^2 \sigma a^2 c}{a^2 - c^2} \left[-1 + \frac{z}{\sqrt{a^2 - c^2}} \tan^{-1} \frac{\sqrt{a^2 - c^2}}{z} \right].$$

Since the mass of the spheroid is

$$M = \frac{4}{3}\pi \sigma a^2 c,$$

the expression for the attraction can also be written

$$Z = \frac{3k^2 M}{a^2 - c^2} \left[-1 + \frac{z}{\sqrt{a^2 - c^2}} \tan^{-1} \frac{\sqrt{a^2 - c^2}}{z} \right].$$

From the expansion

$$\tan^{-1} x = x - \frac{1}{3}x^3 + \frac{1}{5}x^5 - \frac{1}{7}x^7 + \cdots$$

it follows that

$$Z = k^2 M\left[-\frac{1}{z^2} + \frac{3}{5}\frac{(a^2 - c^2)}{z^4} - \frac{3}{7}\frac{(a^2 - c^2)^2}{z^6} + \cdots \right].$$

If this expression is compared with the expression for the sphere it is seen that the attraction of an oblate spheroid on a point of its axis is less than the attraction of a sphere of the same mass at the same distance.

18. The Attraction of a Uniform Rectangular Plate on a Point in Its Own Plane.—Let the sides of the rectangular plate be $2a$

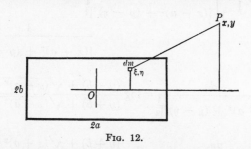

Fig. 12.

and $2b$, and its surface density be σ. Referred to a set of rectangular axes with origin at the center of the plate and the axes parallel to the sides of the plate, the element of mass of the plate is $\sigma d\xi d\eta$. Let the coordinates of the attracted point P be x, y. Since there is no symmetry in the situation, it is necessary to compute the X- and Y-components of the attraction separately.

The attraction of the element dm on the point P, which is assumed to lie outside of the plate, is directed along the line joining dm to P, and its intensity is

$$\frac{k^2 \sigma d\xi d\eta}{[(x - \xi)^2 + (y - \eta)^2]}.$$

The components of this element of force along the x- and y-axes are

$$-\frac{k^2 \sigma(x - \xi)d\xi d\eta}{[(x - \xi)^2 + (y - \eta)^2]^{\frac{3}{2}}}, \qquad -\frac{k^2 \sigma(y - \eta)d\xi d\eta}{[(x - \xi)^2 + (y - \eta)^2]^{\frac{3}{2}}};$$

and the total X- and Y-components of the attraction are

$$X = -k^2\sigma \int_{-b}^{+b} \int_{-a}^{+a} \frac{(x - \xi)d\eta d\xi}{[(x - \xi)^2 + (y - \eta)^2]^{\frac{3}{2}}},$$

$$Y = -k^2\sigma \int_{-a}^{+a} \int_{-b}^{+b} \frac{(y - \eta)d\xi d\eta}{[(x - \xi)^2 + (y - \eta)^2]^{\frac{3}{2}}}.$$

Let the integrations for the X-component be taken first. Since

$$\frac{(x - \xi)}{[(x - \xi)^2 + (y - \eta)^2]^{\frac{3}{2}}} = \frac{\partial}{\partial \xi}\left(\frac{1}{[(x - \xi)^2 + (y - \eta)^2]^{\frac{1}{2}}}\right),$$

it is evident that

$$X = -k^2\sigma \int_{-b}^{+b}\left[\frac{1}{[(x - a)^2 + (y - \eta)^2]^{\frac{1}{2}}} - \frac{1}{[(x + a)^2 + (y - \eta)^2]^{\frac{1}{2}}}\right]d\eta.$$

Now

$$\int_{-b}^{+b} \frac{-d\eta}{[(x - a)^2 + (y - \eta)^2]^{\frac{1}{2}}} = \log \frac{(y - b) + \sqrt{(x - a)^2 + (y - b)^2}}{(y + b) + \sqrt{(x - a)^2 + (y + b)^2}},$$

and

$$\int_{-b}^{+b} \frac{d\eta}{[(x + a)^2 + (y - \eta)^2]^{\frac{1}{2}}} = \log \frac{(y + b) + \sqrt{(x + a)^2 + (y + b)^2}}{(y - b) + \sqrt{(x + a)^2 + (y - b)^2}}.$$

Therefore

$$X = k^2\sigma \log \frac{\{(y - b) + \sqrt{(x - a)^2 + (y - b)^2}\}\{(y + b) + \sqrt{(x + a)^2 + (y + b)^2}\}}{\{(y + b) + \sqrt{(x - a)^2 + (y + b)^2}\}\{(y - b) + \sqrt{(x + a)^2 + (y - b)^2}\}},$$

and similarly,

$$Y = k^2\sigma \log \frac{\{(x - a) + \sqrt{(x - a)^2 + (y - b)^2}\}\{(x + a) + \sqrt{(x + a)^2 + (y + b)^2}\}}{\{(x + a) + \sqrt{(x + a)^2 + (y - b)^2}\}\{(x - a) + \sqrt{(x - a)^2 + (y + b)^2}\}}.$$

It is understood, of course, that in every term in which the radical occurs the positive square root is to be taken. Although it is not evident on the surface, it is not difficult to verify that X is an odd function of x and an even function of y, and that Y is an even function of x and an odd function of y. That is

$$X(x) = -X(-x), \quad X(y) = +X(-y),$$
$$Y(x) = +Y(-x), \quad Y(y) = -Y(-y).$$

These properties merely state that the field of force has the same properties of symmetry with respect to the x- and y-axes that the plate itself has.

It is interesting to note also that the attraction increases indefinitely if the attracted point approaches the edge of the plate anywhere.

19. The Attraction between Two Rigid Bodies.—Let the two bodies be denoted by B_1 and B_2. Let σ_1 be the density of the body B_1 at the point ξ_1, η_1, ζ_1, and let σ_2 be the density of the body B_2 at the point ξ_2, η_2, ζ_2. If the densities are not constants, it will be assumed that they are continuous functions of the coordinates. The component of attraction in the x-direction of the body B_1 on the point ξ_2, η_2, ζ_2, is by Sec. 3,

$$\int\int\int_{B_1}\frac{k^2\sigma_1(\xi_1 - \xi_1)d\xi_1 d\eta_1 d\zeta_1}{[(\xi_1 - \xi_2)^2 + (\eta_1 - \eta_2)^2 + (\zeta_1 - \zeta_2)^2]^{\frac{3}{2}}},$$

where $dm_1 = \sigma_1 d\xi_1 d\eta_1 d\zeta_1$ is an element of mass of B_1.

If $dm_2 = \sigma_2 d\xi_2 d\eta_2 d\zeta_2$ is an element of mass of the body B_2, the x-component X of the mutual attraction of the two bodies is evidently

$$\int\int\int_{B_1}\int\int\int_{B_2}\frac{k^2\sigma_1\sigma_2(\xi_1 - \xi_2)d\xi_1 d\eta_1 d\zeta_1 d\xi_2 d\eta_2 d\zeta_2}{[(\xi_1 - \xi_2)^2 + (\eta_1 - \eta_2)^2 + (\zeta_1 - \zeta_2)^2]^{\frac{3}{2}}}.$$

There are similar expressions for the other two components of the attraction. Thus the determination of the three components of attraction of two solid bodies requires the evaluation of 18 definite integrals. These integrals are not sufficient, however, to determine the line of action of the resulting force.

Problems

1. Three particles of mass m_1, m_2 and m_3 are placed at the vertices of an equilateral triangle of which the side is s. The center of gravity of the three particles is at the point P. Show that the resultant attraction of any two of the particles upon the third lies in a line which passes through P. Show that this is still true if the law of attraction varies inversely as the nth power of the distance.

2. Show that for spheres which are homogeneous the attraction of the sphere for a point upon its surface is

$$\frac{4}{3}\pi k^2\sigma r.$$

3. A small hole of negligible diameter is bored along a radius into a sphere which is homogeneous in concentric layers. It is found that the attraction of the sphere for a point in the hole is independent of the distance of the point from the center of the sphere. What is the law of density of the sphere?

4. Show that the attraction of a homogeneous cylinder of length $2l$, radius r, and density σ on a point in the axis of the cylinder at a distance z from the center of the cylinder is

$$2\pi k^2 \sigma \{ \sqrt{(l+z)^2 + r^2} - \sqrt{(l-z)^2 + r^2} - 2z \}$$

if the point is inside of the cylinder, and

$$2\pi k^2 \sigma \{ \sqrt{(l+z)^2 + r^2} - \sqrt{(l-z)^2 + r^2} \mp 2l \}$$

if the point is outside the cylinder. The negative sign before the term $2l$ is to be taken if z is positive and the lower sign if z is negative. Thus the attraction all along the axis of the cylinder is a continuous function of z.

5. Given a straight rod of length l and density σ. Show that the attraction of the rod on a point whose distances from the ends of the rod are r_1 and r_2, Eq. (7.1), can be written

$$A = \frac{2k^2\sigma l}{r_1 r_2},$$

and therefore the equation of the surface, in bipolar coordinates, on which the intensity of the attraction is everywhere the same is

$$r_1 r_2 = \text{constant}.$$

6. If a spherical segment is cut off a sphere of radius a and density σ by a plane at a distance x from the center, the attraction of the segment on the center point of its base is

$$\frac{2\pi k^2 \sigma}{3x^2} [(a^3 - x^3) - (a^2 - x^2)^{\frac{3}{2}}];$$

and if the segment is a hemisphere the attraction is

$$\pi k^2 \sigma a.$$

7. Show that the attraction of the above spherical segment upon its vertex, or its highest point, is

$$2\pi\sigma(x - a)\left[1 - \frac{1}{3}\sqrt{\frac{2(a-x)}{a}} \right].$$

8. A straight rod of linear density σ is bent into the form of a rectangle of which the sides are $2a$ and $2b$. Show that its attraction on a point in the line which is perpendicular to the plane of the rectangle through its center is

$$\frac{-4\pi\sigma z}{\sqrt{a^2 + b^2 + z^2}}\left[\frac{a}{b^2 + z^2} + \frac{b}{a^2 + z^2} \right].$$

9. The base of a homogeneous isosceles triangular plate lies on the x-axis and the vertex of the triangle lies on the y-axis. The length of its base is $2a$ and the tangent of its base angle θ is α. Show that the components of the attraction of the plate upon a point x, y, outside of the plate, but lying in its plane, are

$$X = k^2\sigma \sin\theta \log A \cdot B, \qquad Y = k^2\sigma \cos\theta \log C \cdot D \cdot E,$$

where

$$A = \frac{a\alpha^2 - x + \alpha y + \sqrt{[\alpha(a+x) - y]^2 + [a\alpha^2 - x - \alpha y]^2}}{-a - x - \alpha y + \sqrt{[\alpha(a+x) - y]^2 + [a + x + \alpha y]^2}},$$

$$B = \frac{-a + x - \alpha y + \sqrt{[\alpha(a-x) - y]^2 + [a - x + \alpha y]^2}}{a\alpha^2 + x - \alpha y + \sqrt{[\alpha(a-x) - y]^2 + [a\alpha^2 + x - \alpha y]^2}},$$

$$C = \left[\frac{a + x + \sqrt{(a+x)^2 + y^2}}{a - x + \sqrt{(a-x)^2 + y^2}}\right]^{\sec\alpha},$$

$$D = \frac{-a\alpha^2 - x + \alpha y + \sqrt{[a\alpha - x\alpha - y]^2 + [a\alpha^2 + x - \alpha y]^2}}{+a - x + \alpha y + \sqrt{[a\alpha - \alpha x - y]^2 + [a - x + \alpha y]^2}},$$

$$E = \frac{a + x + \alpha y + \sqrt{[\alpha(a+x) - y]^2 + [a + x + \alpha y]^2}}{-a\alpha^2 + x + \alpha y + \sqrt{[\alpha(a+x) - y]^2 + [a\alpha^2 - x - \alpha y]^2}}.$$

Show that the attraction is infinite at the edges of the plate, and that it is finite and determined along the lines which are the continuations of the edges of the plate.

10. Show that the attraction of a uniform rectangular plate on a point in the line perpendicular to the plate through its center is

$$-4\pi k^2\sigma \frac{z}{\sqrt{z^2}} \sin^{-1} \frac{a}{\sqrt{a^2 + z^2}} \cdot \frac{b}{\sqrt{b^2 + z^2}},$$

where $2a$ and $2b$ are the lengths of the edges of the plate and z is the distance of the point from the plate.

11. Matter is distributed on the curved part of the surface of a cone for which the length of a generator is R in such a way that the density is inversely proportional to the distance from the apex. Show that the attraction of the cone for a particle on its axis at a distance z from the apex and ρ from its base edge is directed toward the apex and is proportional to $R/(\rho z)$. For an infinite cone the attraction is inversely as the distance from the apex.

CHAPTER II

THE NEWTONIAN POTENTIAL FUNCTION

20. The Potential Function Defined.—In the formulas for the attraction of a finite body on a point, the three components of the attraction are given by means of three triple integrals, making nine integrals altogether. It is a remarkably interesting fact that these nine integrals can be replaced by one triple integral and three differentiations.

Let x, y, z, be the coordinates of the attracted point and ξ, η, ζ be the coordinates of a point of the attracting body, of which dm is an element of mass. Then

$$dm = \sigma \, d\xi \, d\eta \, d\zeta,$$

where σ is the density of the body at the points ξ, η, ζ, and is, therefore, in general, a function of the letters ξ, η, ζ. Let the function V be defined by the definite integral.

$$\left. \begin{aligned} V &= k^2 \int_B \frac{dm}{\rho}, \\ \rho &= \sqrt{(\xi - x)^2 + (\eta - y)^2 + (\zeta - z)^2}, \end{aligned} \right\} \tag{1}$$

the integration to be extended over the entire body.

The constant k^2 depends upon the intensity of the force at a unit distance and the system of units employed. As it enters always as a linear factor, it will be convenient to drop it, and this will be done hereafter, with the understanding that it is to be restored whenever necessary.

The function V thus defined is a function of the coordinates x, y, z (not ξ, η, ζ); that is, V is a function of the position of the attracted point. It can therefore be differentiated with respect to these letters; that is

$$\frac{\partial V}{\partial x} = \frac{\partial}{\partial x} \int_B \frac{dm}{\rho}, \qquad \text{etc.} \tag{2}$$

If the attracted point lies outside of the body, ρ does not vanish and therefore $1/\rho$ is always finite within the region of integration. Under these conditions[1] it is permissible to inter-change the order of differentiation and integration in Eq. (2) and write

$$\frac{\partial V}{\partial x} = \int_B \frac{\partial}{\partial x}\left(\frac{1}{\rho}\right)dm = -\int_B \frac{x - \xi}{\rho^3}dm = X, \quad \text{Eq. (3.2)}$$

$$\frac{\partial V}{\partial y} = \int_B \frac{\partial}{\partial y}\left(\frac{1}{\rho}\right)dm = -\int_B \frac{y - \eta}{\rho^3}dm = Y,$$

$$\frac{\partial V}{\partial z} = \int_B \frac{\partial}{\partial z}\left(\frac{1}{\rho}\right)dm = -\int_B \frac{z - \zeta}{\rho^3}dm = Z.$$

If the function V were known, the components of attraction of the body on outside points could be obtained by the differentiation of V with respect to the coordinates x, y and z; and V is defined by a triple integral. It will be shown immediately that V exists even if the attracted point is inside the attracting body, and that even for an inside point the components of attraction are the derivatives of V with respect to x, y and z.

21. The Significance of the Potential Function.—It is easy to see the physical significance of the potential function. Let the attracted point be given a displacement of which the components are dx, dy, dz. The element of work which is done in effecting this displacement is

$$dW = Xdx + Ydy + Zdz$$
$$= \frac{\partial V}{\partial x}dx + \frac{\partial V}{\partial y}dy + \frac{\partial V}{\partial z}dz$$
$$= dV,$$

and, therefore, the work done in effecting any finite displacement against the attraction of the body is

$$W = V(x_1, y_1, z_1) - V(x_2, y_2, z_2),$$

where $x_1 y_1 z_1$ is the original position and x_2, y_2, z_2 is the displaced position. Stated in words, the amount of work done in moving a particle from one position to another against the attraction of the given body is equal to the difference in the values of the potential function for these two positions.

The potential function is a scalar function of position. Its derivatives are the components of a vector, namely the attraction of the body. If A is the magnitude of this vector,

$$A^2 = X^2 + Y^2 + Z^2.$$

---

[1] HARNACK's "Calculus," translation by Cathcart, p. 267. Also GOURSAT-HEDRICK, "Mathematical Analysis," p. 193.

whatever be the orientation of the coordinate system. If a system of axes is chosen so that the x-axis is parallel to the vector A, then

$$\frac{\partial V}{\partial x} = A,$$

and the perpendicular components are zero. From this one concludes that the total attraction lies in the line for which the derivative of V is a maximum.

22. The Potential Function Exists.—It will be assumed that the density of the attracting body is generally a continuous function, but that there may be a finite number of surfaces across which the density is discontinuous. Such would be the case in a sphere if one hemisphere were made of iron and the other hemisphere were made of lead. If the number of surfaces of discontinuity is finite the body can be resolved into a finite number of smaller bodies B_K for each of which the density is continuous, and then

$$V = \int_B \frac{dm}{\rho} = \sum_K \int_{B_K} \frac{dm}{\rho} ;$$

under these conditions each integral

$$\int\int\int_{B_K} \frac{\sigma}{\rho} d\xi\, d\eta\, d\zeta$$

exists if the attracted point lies outside of the body[1] for the function $\bar\sigma/\rho$ is continuous over the region of integration. Since each integral separately exists their sum exists, and therefore V exists. Furthermore, since the integrand is everywhere positive, if r is the minimum distance from the attracting body to the attracted point, and R is the maximum distance, Fig. 13,

$$\int_B \frac{dm}{r} > \int_B \frac{dm}{\rho} > \int_B \frac{dm}{R}$$

and, therefore, if M is the total mass of the body,

$$\frac{M}{r} > V > \frac{M}{R}.$$

As the attracted point recedes from the attracting body, both r and R increase indefinitely and therefore V *has the limit zero at infinity* in every direction.

If the attracted point is in the attracting body let the variables be changed to polar coordinates by the substitution

[1] GOURSAT, HEDRICK, "Mathematical Analysis," p. 296.

$$\left. \begin{aligned} \xi &= x + \rho \cos \varphi \cos \theta, \\ \eta &= y + \rho \cos \varphi \sin \theta, \\ \zeta &= z + \rho \sin \varphi, \\ dm &= \sigma \rho^2 \cos \varphi \, d\varphi \, d\theta \, d\rho, \end{aligned} \right\} \qquad (1)$$

so that the origin of the polar system of coordinates is at the attracted point. The integral which defines V then becomes

$$V = \iiint_B \sigma \rho \cos \varphi \, d\varphi \, d\theta \, d\rho,$$

and by the same argument as for the exterior point it is seen that V exists. Let σ_0 be the maximum value of σ in B. With the attracted point as a center and a radius R equal to the distance of the most remote point of the attracting body, describe a sphere which will wholly enclose the attracting body. Imagine this sphere filled with matter of the constant density σ_0. Then since all of the elements of the integrals are positive

$$\int_S \frac{dm}{\rho} > \int_B \frac{dm}{\rho}.$$

But

$$\int_S \frac{dm}{\rho} = \sigma_0 \int_{-\frac{\pi}{2}}^{+\frac{\pi}{2}} \int_0^{2\pi} \int_0^R \cos \varphi \, d\varphi \, d\theta \, d\rho$$

$$= 4\pi \sigma_0 R^2$$

Hence, for any interior point

$$V \leqq 4\pi \sigma_0 R^2.$$

23. Existence of Derivatives of the Potential.—Owing to the importance of the derivatives of the potential in the general theory a direct proof will be given not only that the derivatives exist, but that these derivatives are equal to the component of the attraction in the direction in which the derivative is taken. In making the proof, however, it is necessary to distinguish between the interior and the exterior points, and to make the proof for each class separately.

24. Existence of Derivatives at Exterior Points.—As a first step certain upper limits for the derivatives of

$$\frac{1}{\rho} = \frac{1}{\sqrt{(x - \xi)^2 + (y - \eta)^2 + (z - \zeta)^2}}$$

will be indicated.   Thus

$$\frac{\partial}{\partial x}\left(\frac{1}{\rho}\right) = -\frac{x-\xi}{\rho^3}, \qquad \text{therefore,} \qquad \left|\frac{\partial}{\partial x}\left(\frac{1}{\rho}\right)\right| < \frac{1}{\rho^2},$$

$$\frac{\partial^2}{\partial x^2}\left(\frac{1}{\rho}\right) = \frac{3(x-\xi)^2}{\rho^5} - \frac{1}{\rho^3}, \qquad \left|\frac{\partial^2}{\partial x^2}\left(\frac{1}{\rho}\right)\right| < \frac{4}{\rho^3},$$

$$\frac{\partial^3}{\partial x^3}\left(\frac{1}{\rho}\right) = -15\frac{(x-\xi)^3}{\rho^7} + 9\frac{x-\xi}{\rho^5}, \qquad \left|\frac{\partial^3}{\partial x^3}\left(\frac{1}{\rho}\right)\right| < \frac{24}{\rho^4},$$

etc.

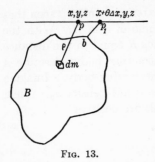

Fig. 13.

Let B, Fig. 13, be the attracting body of which dm is an element. Let $d\tau$ be the volume of dm, σ its density and ξ, η, ζ the coordinates of its center of gravity. Let x, y, z be the coordinates of the attracted point p. The element dm exerts upon p an attraction of which the x-component is

$$-\frac{(x-\xi)dm}{\rho^3},$$

and, therefore, for the entire body,

$$X = -\int_B \frac{(x-\xi)}{\rho^3}dm = \int_B \frac{\partial}{\partial x}\left(\frac{1}{\rho}\right)dm,$$

and likewise,

$$Y = -\int_B \frac{(y-\eta)}{\rho^3}dm = \int_B \frac{\partial}{\partial y}\left(\frac{1}{\rho}\right)dm,$$

$$Z = -\int_B \frac{(z-\zeta)}{\rho^3}dm = \int_B \frac{\partial}{\partial z}\left(\frac{1}{\rho}\right)dm.$$

By definition, the potential is

$$V = \int_B \frac{dm}{\rho}.$$

It is desired to prove that

$$\frac{\partial V}{\partial x} = \int_B \frac{\partial}{\partial x}\left(\frac{1}{\rho}\right)dm.$$

For convenience of notation, let

$$\frac{1}{\rho} = \varphi(x, y, z),$$

so that

$$V = \int_B \varphi(x, y, z)dm.$$

By the definition of a derivative

$$\frac{\partial V}{\partial x} = \lim_{\Delta x = 0} \frac{1}{\Delta x}\left[\int_B \varphi(x + \Delta x, y, z)dm - \int_B \varphi(x, y, z)dm\right]$$

$$= \lim_{\Delta x = 0}\int_B\left[\frac{\partial \varphi}{\partial x} + \frac{1}{2}\Delta x \cdot \frac{\partial^2 \varphi}{\partial x^2}(x + \theta\Delta x)\right]dm.$$

Where θ is some number lying between 0 and 1; therefore,

$$\frac{\partial V}{\partial x} = \int_B\frac{\partial\varphi}{\partial x}dm + \lim_{\Delta x = 0}\frac{1}{2}\Delta x\int_B\frac{\partial^2}{\partial x^2}\varphi(x + \theta\Delta x)dm.$$

It is not difficult to see that

$$\lim_{\Delta x = 0}\frac{1}{2}\Delta x\int_B\frac{\partial^2}{\partial x^2}\varphi(x + \theta\Delta x)dm = 0,$$

for

$$\frac{\partial^2}{\partial x^2}\varphi(x + \Delta x) < \frac{4}{\rho^3},$$

where ρ is the distance from the element dm to the point p_1 $(x + \theta\Delta x, y, z)$. Suppose b is the closest point of B to p_1 and that the distance $bp_1 = l$. Then l is the smallest possible value of ρ, and

$$\frac{1}{2}\Delta x\int_B\frac{\partial^2}{\partial x^2}\varphi(x + \theta\Delta x)dm < \int_B\frac{2\Delta x}{l^3}dm = \frac{2m}{l^3}\Delta x.$$

As Δx tends towards zero the point p_1 moves towards p and the minimum distance of p_1 to the body l may change. But since p lies outside of B, there exists a minimum value of l, say $l_0 > 0$, if Δx is sufficiently small. Hence

$$\lim\frac{1}{2}\Delta x\int_B\frac{\partial^2}{\partial x^2}\varphi(x + \theta\Delta x)dm < \frac{2M}{l_0^3}\Delta x,$$

which vanishes with Δx. Therefore,

$$\frac{\partial V}{\partial x} = \int_B\frac{\partial}{\partial x}\left(\frac{1}{\rho}\right)dm = X,$$

from which the conclusion follows that the derivative exists and that its value is the component of the attraction.

25. Existence of Derivatives at Interior Points.—It was shown in Sec. 22 that the potential exists at interior points. It is easy to show in the same manner that the component of the attraction

exists. Using the transformation (Eq. (22.1)), the expression
for the x-component of attraction becomes

$$X = -\int_B \frac{x - \xi}{\rho^3} dm = \int_B \frac{\partial}{\partial x}\left(\frac{1}{\rho}\right) dm$$

$$= \int\int\int_B \sigma \cos^2 \varphi \, \cos \theta \, d\varphi \, d\theta \, d\rho.$$

Inasmuch as the integrand is continuous over the entire region
of integration, if σ is continuous, it is evident that this last integral exists.

It is desired to show that the derivative of V exists at interior
points, just as for exterior points, and that its value is X.

Let the attracted point p lie within B. With p as a center
describe a sphere of radius r which lies wholly within B.

This spherical surface divides the body B into two bodies
namely, the sphere S and the remainder of the body B_1. Let
the coordinates of p be x, y, z, and let $\bar{p}$ be a neighboring point
with the coordinates $x + \Delta x, y, z$. Let V be the value of the
potential at p and $\bar{V}$ the value of the potential at $\bar{p}$. Then

$$\frac{\partial V}{\partial x} = \lim_{\Delta x = 0} \frac{\bar{V} - V}{\Delta x}.$$

It will be shown that if X is the x-component of the attracting
force at the point p, the value of Δx can be taken so small that
the value of

$$\left|\frac{\bar{V} - V}{\Delta x} - X\right| < \epsilon,$$

where ϵ is any small number given in advance.

Let X, X_S, X_{B_1} be the components of attraction, and V,
V_S, V_{B_1} the values of the potentials at p, due respectively to the
body B, the sphere, and the body B_1. Likewise, let $\bar{X}, \bar{X}_S, \bar{X}_{B_1}$;
$\bar{V}, \bar{V}_S, \bar{V}_{B_1}$, be the corresponding values at the point $\bar{p}$. Then

$$V = V_S + V_{B_1}, \qquad X = X_S + X_{B_1},$$
$$\bar{V} = \bar{V}_S + \bar{V}_{B_1}, \qquad \bar{X} = \bar{X}_S + \bar{X}_{B_1};$$

so that

$$\left[\frac{\bar{V} - V}{\Delta x} - X\right] = \left[\frac{\bar{V}_S - V_S}{\Delta x} - X_S\right] + \left[\frac{\bar{V}_{B_1} - V_{B_1}}{\Delta x} - X_{B_1}\right].$$

Since p and $\bar{p}$ are both exterior to B_1, it follows from the results of Sec. 24 that, whatever value r may have, $|\Delta x| < r$ can be taken so small that

$$\left| \frac{\overline{V}_{B_1} - V_{B_1}}{\Delta x} - X_{B_1} \right| < \frac{1}{2}\epsilon.$$

There remains then for consideration

$$\frac{\overline{V}_S - V_S}{\Delta x} - X_S.$$

Let $d\tau$ be the volume of the element of mass dm, and let σ_0 be the upper limit of the density within S. Then since

$$X_S = -\int_S \frac{(x - \xi)}{\rho^3} \sigma \, d\tau,$$

it follows that

$$|X_S| < \sigma_0 \int_S \frac{d\tau}{\rho^2} = 4\pi\sigma_0 r,$$

so that

$$|X_S| < 4\pi\sigma_0 r.$$

An upper limit for the value of

$$\frac{\overline{V}_S - V_S}{\Delta X}$$

also can be found. From their definitions it follows that

$$\overline{V}_S - V_S = \int_S \left(\frac{1}{\bar{\rho}} - \frac{1}{\rho} \right) \sigma \, d\tau.$$

Now

$$\frac{1}{\bar{\rho}} - \frac{1}{\rho} = \frac{\rho - \bar{\rho}}{\rho\bar{\rho}},$$

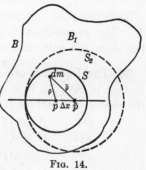

Fig. 14.

and, as is seen from the triangle in Fig. 14,

$$|\rho - \bar{\rho}| < |\Delta x|.$$

Also, since

$$\left(\frac{1}{\rho} - \frac{1}{\bar{\rho}} \right)^2 > 0,$$

it follows that

$$\frac{1}{\rho\bar{\rho}} < \frac{1}{\rho^2} + \frac{1}{\bar{\rho}^2},$$

so that

$$\left| \overline{V}_S - V_S \right| < \left| \Delta x \right| \cdot \sigma_0 \left[\int_S \frac{d\tau}{\rho^2} + \int_S \frac{d\tau}{\bar{\rho}^2} \right]. \tag{1}$$

It has already been observed that

$$\int_S \frac{d\tau}{\rho^2} = 4\pi r.$$

With $^-$ as a center describe a sphere S_2 with a radius equal to $r + |\Delta x|$. This second sphere will then contain the first, and therefore

$$\int_S \frac{d\tau}{\bar{\rho}^2} < \int_{S_2} \frac{d\tau}{\bar{\rho}^2} = 4\pi(r + |\Delta x|) < 8\pi r.$$

It follows at once that

$$\left| \frac{\overline{V}_S - V_S}{\Delta X} \right| < 12\pi\sigma_0 r,$$

and

$$\left| \frac{\overline{V}_S - V_S}{\Delta x} - X_S \right| < 16\pi\sigma_0 r.$$

For values of r sufficiently small this expression is less than $\epsilon/2$, and therefore

$$\left| \frac{\overline{V} - V}{\Delta X} - X \right| < \epsilon.$$

Therefore, the derivative of V exists, and its value is equal to X. The proposition is entirely general, and it holds whether the attracted point lies inside or outside of the attracting body.

26. The Equation of Laplace.—In a manner quite analogous to that of Sec. 24, it is a relatively simple matter to prove that the second derivatives of V exist at all external points, and that

$$\frac{\partial^2 V}{\partial x^2} = \int_B \frac{\partial^2}{\partial x^2}\left(\frac{1}{\rho}\right)dm, \qquad \frac{\partial^2 V}{\partial y^2} = \int_B \frac{\partial^2}{\partial y^2}\left(\frac{1}{\rho}\right)dm,$$

$$\frac{\partial^2 V}{\partial z^2} = \int_B \frac{\partial^2}{\partial z^2}\left(\frac{1}{\rho}\right)dm.$$

But

$$\frac{\partial^2}{\partial x^2}\left(\frac{1}{\rho}\right) = \frac{3(x - \xi)^2}{\rho^5} - \frac{1}{\rho^3},$$

$$\frac{\partial^2}{\partial y^2}\left(\frac{1}{\rho}\right) = \frac{3(y - \eta)^2}{\rho^5} - \frac{1}{\rho^3},$$

$$\frac{\partial^2}{\partial z^2}\left(\frac{1}{\rho}\right) = \frac{3(z - \zeta)}{\rho^5} - \frac{1}{\rho^3},$$

and

$$\text{their sum} = \frac{3}{\rho^3} - \frac{3}{\rho^3} = 0.$$

Hence,

$$\int_B \left[\frac{\partial^2}{\partial x^2}\left(\frac{1}{\rho}\right) + \frac{\partial^2}{\partial y^2}\left(\frac{1}{\rho}\right) + \frac{\partial^2}{\partial z^2}\left(\frac{1}{\rho}\right) \right] dm = 0,$$

and therefore

$$\frac{\partial^2 V}{\partial x^2} + \frac{\partial^2 V}{\partial y^2} + \frac{\partial^2 V}{\partial z^2} = 0, \tag{1}$$

a partial differential equation of the second order which must be satisfied by the potential of every finite body at all exterior points. The left member of Eq. (1) is called the *Laplacian* of V. It has been designated by different writers by the symbols ΔV, $\Delta^2 V$, ∇V and $\nabla^2 V$. In the present volume it will be denoted by the symbol ΔV.

This equation was first given by Laplace in 1782 in polar coordinates in the form

$$r\frac{\partial^2 (rV)}{\partial r^2} + \frac{1}{\sin\theta}\frac{\partial}{\partial\theta}\left(\sin\theta\frac{\partial V}{\partial\theta}\right) + \frac{1}{\sin^2\theta}\frac{\partial^2 V}{\partial\varphi^2} = 0, \tag{2}$$

but several years later, 1787, he gave the corresponding expression in rectangular coordinates.

Since the form for the expression for ρ

$$\rho = \sqrt{(x-\xi)^2 + (y-\eta)^2 + (z-\zeta)^2}$$

is independent of the particular rectangular system to which it is referred, it is natural to suspect that the same is true of Laplace's equation. The suspicion is easily justified by a change of variables,

$$x_1 = x_0 + \alpha_1 x + \alpha_2 y + \alpha_3 z,$$
$$y_1 = y_0 + \beta_1 x + \beta_2 y + \beta_3 z,$$
$$z_1 = z_0 + \gamma_1 x + \gamma_2 y + \gamma_3 z.$$

where

$$\alpha_1{}^2 + \alpha_2{}^2 + \alpha_3{}^2 = 1, \qquad \alpha_1\beta_1 + \alpha_2\beta_2 + \alpha_3\beta_3 = 0,$$
$$\beta_1{}^2 + \beta_2{}^2 + \beta_3{}^2 = 1, \qquad \beta_1\gamma_1 + \beta_2\gamma_2 + \beta_3\gamma_3 = 0,$$
$$\gamma_1{}^2 + \gamma_2{}^2 + \gamma_3{}^2 = 1, \qquad \gamma_1\alpha_1 + \gamma_2\alpha_2 + \gamma_3\alpha_3 = 0.$$

Since

$$\frac{\partial V}{\partial x} = \frac{\partial V}{\partial x_1}\alpha_1 + \frac{\partial V}{\partial y_1}\beta_1 + \frac{\partial V}{\partial z_1}\gamma_1,$$

it follows that

$$\frac{\partial^2 V}{\partial x^2} = \alpha_1{}^2\frac{\partial^2 V}{\partial x_1{}^2} + \beta_1{}^2\frac{\partial^2 V}{\partial y_1{}^2} + \gamma_1{}^2\frac{\partial^2 V}{\partial z_1{}^2}$$
$$+ 2\alpha_1\beta_1\frac{\partial^2 V}{\partial x_1\partial y_1} + 2\beta_1\gamma_1\frac{\partial^2 V}{\partial y_1\partial z_1} + 2\gamma_1\alpha_1\frac{\partial^2 V}{\partial z_1\partial x_1},$$

$$\frac{\partial^2 V}{\partial y^2} = \alpha_2{}^2 \frac{\partial^2 V}{\partial x_1{}^2} + \beta_2{}^2 \frac{\partial^2 V}{\partial y_1{}^2} + \gamma_2{}^2 \frac{\partial^2 V}{\partial z_1{}^2}$$
$$+ 2\alpha_2\beta_2 \frac{\partial^2 V}{\partial x_1 \partial y_1} + 2\beta_2\gamma_2 \frac{\partial^2 V}{\partial y_1 \partial z_1} + 2\gamma_2\alpha_2 \frac{\partial^2 V}{\partial z_1 \partial x_1},$$

$$\frac{\partial^2 V}{\partial z^2} = \alpha_3{}^2 \frac{\partial^2 V}{\partial x_1{}^2} + \beta_3{}^2 \frac{\partial^2 V}{\partial y_1{}^2} + \gamma_3{}^2 \frac{\partial^2 V}{\partial z_1{}^2}$$
$$+ 2\alpha_3\beta_3 \frac{\partial^2 V}{\partial x_1 \partial y_1} + 2\beta_3\gamma_3 \frac{\partial^2 V}{\partial y_1 \partial z_1} + 2\gamma_3\alpha_3 \frac{\partial^2 V}{\partial z_1 \partial x_1}.$$

On taking the sum of these three expressions it is found that

$$\frac{\partial^2 V}{\partial x^2} + \frac{\partial^2 V}{\partial y^2} + \frac{\partial^2 V}{\partial z^2} = \frac{\partial^2 V}{\partial x_1{}^2} + \frac{\partial^2 V}{\partial y_1{}^2} + \frac{\partial^2 V}{\partial z_1{}^2} = 0. \tag{3}$$

That is, Laplace's equation is invariant under a change of rectangular axes. The same thing is true for Laplace's equation in two variables.

27. Equipotential Surfaces, or Level Surfaces.

—If the potential function is set equal to a constant

$$V(x, y, z) = C, \tag{1}$$

there is defined a surface which is called an *equipotential* surface, since the potential has the same value at every point on this surface. If the constant C is regarded as a parameter, an entire family of such surfaces is defined. Since by its definition V is a single valued function of x, y, z, it cannot have two values at the same point and, therefore, no two surfaces of the family intersect.

These surfaces are also called *level surfaces* for a reason which will appear in the next paragraph.

Lines of Force.—If x, y, z, is a point on the surface Eq. (27.1), the equation of the tangent plane at the point x, y, z is

$$\frac{\partial V}{\partial x}(\xi - x) + \frac{\partial V}{\partial y}(\eta - y) + \frac{\partial V}{\partial z}(\zeta - z) = 0,$$

where ξ, η, ζ are the running coordinates of the plane. The direction cosines of the normal to this plane are

$$\cos \alpha = \frac{1}{R} \frac{\partial V}{\partial x}, \qquad \cos \beta = \frac{1}{R} \frac{\partial V}{\partial y}, \qquad \cos \gamma = \frac{1}{R} \frac{\partial V}{\partial z},$$
$$R = \sqrt{\left(\frac{\partial V}{\partial x}\right)^2 + \left(\frac{\partial V}{\partial y}\right)^2 + \left(\frac{\partial V}{\partial z}\right)^2}.$$

But

$$\frac{\partial V}{\partial x} = X, \qquad \frac{\partial V}{\partial y} = Y, \qquad \frac{\partial V}{\partial z} = Z,$$

are the components of the attraction at the point x, y, z, and the direction cosines of the resultant attraction are

$$\frac{X}{R}, \quad \frac{Y}{R}, \quad \frac{Z}{R}, \quad R = \sqrt{X^2 + Y^2 + Z^2}.$$

These expressions are identical with those of the corresponding direction cosines of the normal to the equipotential surface at the point x, y, z. Hence the direction of the attraction of a body at any point is perpendicular to the equipotential surface which passes through that point.

Consider a line which is orthogonal to every equipotential surface which it intersects. At each of its points it has the direction of the attractive force, and for this reason such a line is called a *line of force*.

The surface of a free liquid at rest is always normal to the force which is acting upon it. Hence it coincides with an equipotential surface, and therefore equipotential surfaces are level surfaces. If a drop of water could be placed upon an equipotential surface and be freed from surface tension, it would distribute itself over the entire surface.

28. The Logarithmic Potential.—In Sec. 7 it was found that an infinitely long, homogeneous, straight rod attracts an exterior point in a direction which is perpendicular to the rod with an intensity which is equal to $2\sigma_0/\rho$ where σ_0 is the mass of the rod per unit length and ρ is the perpendicular distance of the attracted point. Imagine this rod parallel to the z-axis and piercing the x,y-plane in a point whose coordinates are ξ, η. Let the coordinates of the attracted point be x, y. Then the rod attracts the point x, y just as though it were a particle of mass $\sigma = 2\sigma_0$ placed at the point ξ, η with a law of attraction σ/ρ which is inversely proportional to the distance, instead of inversely proportional to the square of the distance. The components of this attraction are

$$X = -\sigma\frac{x - \xi}{\rho^2}, \qquad Y = -\sigma\frac{y - \eta}{\rho^2}, \qquad Z = 0.$$

A bundle of such rods, not necessarily all alike, would attract just like an area (the cross-section of the bundle) with the surface density σ and the inverse first power of the distance. That is, for such a bundle

$$X = -\int_A \frac{x - \xi}{\rho^2} dm, \qquad Y = -\int_A \frac{y - \eta}{\rho^2} dm,$$
$$\rho = \sqrt{(x - \xi)^2 + (y - \eta)^2}.$$

For this law of attraction the expression for the potential becomes

$$\left.\begin{aligned} V &= -\int_A \log \rho \, dm, \\ V &= \int_A \log \frac{\rho_0}{\rho} \, dm \end{aligned}\right\} \tag{1}$$

or

if preferred, where ρ_0 is an arbitrary constant. It will be verified without difficulty that

$$X = \frac{\partial V}{\partial x}, \qquad Y = \frac{\partial V}{\partial y}. \tag{2}$$

The potential in this case, for obvious reasons, is called the *logarithmic potential.* As can easily be verified, for exterior points it satisfies the equation of Laplace in two variables

$$\frac{\partial^2 V}{\partial x^2} + \frac{\partial^2 V}{\partial y^2} = 0.$$

The logarithmic potential exists at interior points also, and Eqs. (1) and (2) are still valid.

29. The Potential of a Spherical Shell.—Let O, Fig. 15, be the center of a homogeneous spherical shell of radius a, Δa its

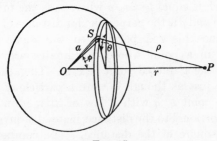

FIG. 15.

thickness and σ its density. Let P be the attracted point, and the line OP be drawn. Let the radius OS make an angle φ with the line OP, and the plane OSP make an angle θ with the plane of the paper.

Consider an element of mass dm of the attracting surface at S. Expressed in terms of its coordinates of position

$$dm = \sigma a^2 \Delta a \sin \varphi \, d\varphi \, d\theta,$$

and therefore

$$V = \sigma a^2 \Delta a \int_0^\pi \int_0^{2\pi} \frac{\sin \varphi \, d\varphi \, d\theta}{\rho},$$

$$= 2\pi \sigma a^2 \Delta a \int_0^\pi \frac{\sin \varphi \, d\varphi}{\rho},$$

since

$$\rho = \sqrt{a^2 - 2ar \cos \varphi + r^2}$$

is independent of θ.

On differentiating this expression for ρ, bearing in mind that a and r are constants, it is found that

$$\frac{\sin \varphi \, d\varphi}{\rho} = \frac{d\rho}{ar},$$

and therefore

$$V = 2\pi \sigma \frac{a \Delta a}{r} \int d\rho.$$

The limits of the integral depend upon whether the point P is outside the shell, or inside the shell. If the point P is outside the shell,

$$\left.\begin{aligned} V_O &= 2\pi \sigma \frac{a \Delta a}{r} \int_{r-a}^{r+a} d\rho, \\ &= 4\pi \sigma \frac{a^2 \Delta a}{r} = \frac{M}{r}, \end{aligned}\right\} \tag{1}$$

the last equality holding since the mass of the shell M is

$$M = 4\pi \sigma a^2 \Delta a.$$

If the point P is inside the shell,

$$\left.\begin{aligned} V_I &= 2\pi \sigma \frac{a \Delta a}{r} \int_{a-r}^{a+r} d\rho \\ &= 4\pi \sigma a \Delta a = \frac{M}{a}. \end{aligned}\right\} \tag{2}$$

From these expressions it follows that the potential of a homogeneous, infinitely thin, spherical shell is constant within the shell, and that it varies inversely as the distance from the center of the shell on the outside. The limiting value of the potential as the attracted point approaches the shell either from the inside or from the outside is M/a, and therefore the potential is continuous across the shell.

If the shell is of finite thickness, bounded by a sphere of radius a on the outside and a sphere of radius b on the inside, it is necessary to integrate Eqs. (1) and (2) again with respect to the radius; thus

$$V_O = \frac{4\pi\sigma}{r} \int_b^a a^2 da$$

$$= \frac{4}{3} \frac{\pi\sigma}{r} (a^3 - b^3) = \frac{M}{r},$$

and

$$V_I = 4\pi\sigma \int_b^a a \, da$$

$$= 2\pi\sigma(a^2 - b^2),$$

which is not conveniently expressible in terms of the mass of the shell.

For a solid sphere the radius of the interior surface is zero and $V_O = M/r$ just as for the shell. The limiting value of the potential in the hollow-interior of the shell as the radius of the inner boundary diminishes is

$$V_I = 2\pi\sigma a^2 = \frac{3}{2} \frac{M}{a}.$$

For a point between the two spheres which bound the shell at a distance r from the center, pass a concentric sphere through the attracted point. This sphere, which has a radius r, divides the shell into two shells for which the bounding spheres are b and r for the inner shell, and r and a for the outer shell. The potential of the entire shell is the sum of the potentials of the inner and outer shells, that is

$$V = \frac{4}{3} \pi\sigma \frac{r^3 - b^3}{r} + 2\pi\sigma(a^2 - r^2)$$

$$= 4\pi\sigma\left(\frac{1}{2} a^2 - \frac{1}{3} \frac{b^3}{r} - \frac{1}{6} r^2\right).$$

This expression has the limiting value $2\pi\sigma(a^2 - b^2)$ on the inner boundary and $\frac{4}{3}\pi\sigma(a^3 - b^3)$ on the outer boundary. As these are the limiting values of the potential as the attracted point approaches the inner surface from within the hollow, and the outer surface from the outside of the shell respectively, it is clear that the potential of the shell is continuous everywhere, although in different regions of space it is represented by different analytic functions.

In each of these expressions the only variable which occurs is r, the distance from the center. Hence, wherever the attracted point may be the attraction is always directed towards this center. Its intensity is given by the first derivative of V with respect to r, namely

$$A = \frac{\partial V}{\partial r}.$$

In the hollow of the shell V is constant; the first derivative is zero, and, therefore, the attraction is zero everywhere.

Between the boundaries of the shell

$$A = \frac{4}{3}\pi\sigma\left(\frac{b^3}{r^2} - r\right).$$

This expression vanishes on the inner boundary, and has the value

$$\frac{4}{3}\pi\sigma\left(\frac{b^3 - a^3}{a^2}\right) = -\frac{M}{a^2}$$

on the outer boundary.

Outside of the sphere

$$A = -\frac{M}{r^2},$$

which also has the value $-M/a^2$ on the outer boundary of the shell. Hence the first derivative of the potential function is continuous everywhere and in particular across the bounding surfaces of the shell. That is, the attraction of the shell is a continuous function of the position of the attracted point.

It is not the same, however, with the second derivative. Within the hollow, the second derivative is zero everywhere. Between the boundaries of the shell

$$\frac{\partial^2 V}{\partial r^2} = -\frac{4}{3}\pi\sigma\left(\frac{2b^3}{r^3} + 1\right).$$

This is a continuous function of r within this region. It does not vanish on the inner boundary, however, but has the value $-4\pi\sigma$. Hence the second derivative has a finite discontinuity $4\pi\sigma$ across the inner boundary. On the outer boundary the second derivative has the value

$$-\frac{4}{3}\pi\sigma\left(\frac{2b^3}{a^3} + 1\right).$$

On the outside of the shell the second derivative is

$$\frac{\partial^2 V}{\partial r^2} = +\frac{8}{3}\pi\sigma\frac{a^3 - b^3}{r^3},$$

which is continuous everywhere on the outside and takes the value

$$-\frac{4}{3}\pi\sigma\left(\frac{2b^3}{a^3} - 2\right)$$

on the boundary. Thus in crossing the outer boundary from the inside the second derivative has the finite discontinuity $+4\pi\sigma$ (see Fig. 16).

This study of the potential of a finite spherical shell is valuable because the integrals involved are easily evaluated, and the

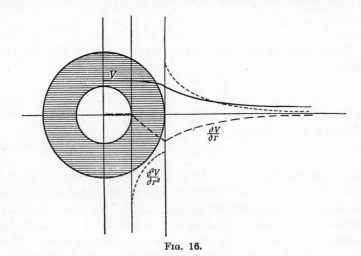

FIG. 16.

properties exhibited are characteristic of potentials and their derivatives in general. The results are summarized in the following table.

POTENTIAL OF A FINITE, HOMOGENEOUS SPHERICAL SHELL

Region	$r < b$	$b < r < a$	$r > a$
V	$2\pi\sigma(a^2 - b^2)$	$4\pi\sigma\left(\dfrac{1}{2}a^2 - \dfrac{1}{3}\dfrac{b^3}{r} - \dfrac{1}{6}r^2\right)$	$\dfrac{4}{3}\pi\sigma\dfrac{a^3 - b^3}{r}$
$\dfrac{\partial V}{\partial r}$	0	$\dfrac{4}{3}\pi\sigma\dfrac{b^3 - r^3}{r^2}$	$-\dfrac{4}{3}\pi\sigma\dfrac{a^3 - b^3}{r^2}$
$\dfrac{\partial^2 V}{\partial r^2}$	0	$-\dfrac{4}{3}\pi\sigma\left(2\dfrac{b^3}{r^3} + 1\right)$	$+\dfrac{8}{3}\pi\sigma\dfrac{a^3 - b^3}{r^3}$

30. Potential of a Uniform Circular Disk along Its Axis.—
Let O, Fig. 17, be the center of the disk, OP its axis, a the radius
and σ the surface density. Let the angle θ be measured from
a fixed line in the disk. Then in polar coordinates

$$dm = \sigma r dr d\theta,$$

and

$$V = \sigma \int_0^a \int_0^{2\pi} \frac{r dr d\theta}{\rho} = 2\pi\sigma \int_0^a \frac{r dr}{\rho}. \tag{1}$$

But, since

$$\rho^2 = r^2 + x^2,$$

and x is constant in the integration,

$$\rho d\rho = r dr,$$

and therefore

$$\frac{r dr}{\rho} = d\rho.$$

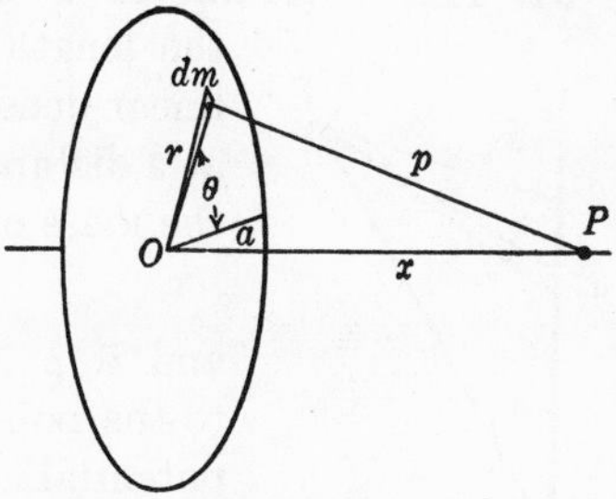

Hence

Fig. 17.

$$V = 2\pi\sigma \int_{\sqrt{x^2}}^{\sqrt{a^2+x^2}} d\rho,$$

or

$$V = 2\pi\sigma[\sqrt{a^2 + x^2} - \sqrt{x^2}]. \tag{2}$$

Attention is again called to the fact that in every case the
positive square root is taken, so that V is a function of x^2, as is
evident from the form of the potential when expressed as an
integral, Eq. (1).

The attraction of the disk for a point on its axis is given
by the formula

$$X = \frac{\partial V}{\partial x} = 2\pi\sigma\left[\frac{1}{\sqrt{a^2 + x^2}} - \frac{1}{\sqrt{x^2}}\right]x. \tag{3}$$

This is an odd function of x, as evidently it should be. The
limiting value of the attraction as x approaches zero from the
positive side is $-2\pi\sigma$; and as it aproaches zero from the negative
side it is $+2\pi\sigma$. There is, therefore, a discontinuity in the
attraction equal to $-4\pi\sigma$ as the attracted point passes through
the disk from the negative side to the positive side, and the
magnitude of the discontinuity is independent of the size of the
disk. It is not independent, however, of its density.

If the radius of the disk is very great, the first term of Eq.
(3) is negligible. The second term is constant on either side

of the disk, but opposite in sign on the two sides. Thus, if the earth were an indefinitely extended plane, as it was thought to be by the ancients, with the surface density σ, then the acceleration of gravity would be

$$g = 2\pi\sigma,$$

and would be independent of distance from the earth's surface.

31. The Potential of a Homogeneous Straight Rod.—Let

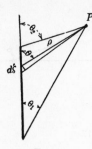

FIG. 18.

the length of rod be $2l$, Fig. 18, and let its linear density be σ. Let an element of the rod at a distance ζ from the center be $d\zeta$. Then the mass of this element is

$$dm = \sigma d\zeta,$$

and if ρ is the distance from this element to the point $P(x, z)$ at which the value of the potential is to be computed, then

$$V = \int \frac{dm}{\rho} = \sigma \int_{-l}^{+l} \frac{d\zeta}{\rho}.$$

Let θ be the angle formed by the rod and the line ρ. It is clear from the diagram that

$$d\zeta \sin \theta = \rho d\theta,$$

and therefore,

$$\left.\begin{aligned} V &= \sigma \int_{\theta_1}^{\theta_2} \frac{d\theta}{\sin \theta} \\ &= \sigma \log \frac{\tan \frac{1}{2}\theta_2}{\tan \frac{1}{2}\theta_1} \end{aligned}\right\} \qquad (1)$$

Since θ always lies in the first or second quadrant, the trigonometric identity

$$\tan \frac{1}{2}\theta = \sqrt{\frac{1}{\tan^2 \theta} + 1} - \frac{1}{\tan \theta}. \qquad (2)$$

holds. Now

$$\tan \theta_1 = \frac{x}{z + l}, \qquad \tan \theta_2 = \frac{x}{z - l}. \qquad (3)$$

By means of Eqs. (2) and (3) the potential can be expressed explicitly in terms of x and z; namely,

$$V = \sigma \log \frac{-(z - l) + \sqrt{(z - l)^2 + x^2}}{-(z + l) + \sqrt{(z + l)^2 + x^2}},$$

or, if ρ_1 and ρ_2 are the lines drawn from the point P to the ends of the rod,

$$V = \sigma \log \frac{-z + l + \rho_2}{-z - l + \rho_1} = \sigma \log \frac{\rho_1 + \rho_2 + 2l}{\rho_1 + \rho_2 - 2l}.$$

The components of attraction are now easily found. They are

$$X = \frac{\partial V}{\partial x} = \frac{\sigma}{x}\left[\left(\frac{1}{\rho_2} - \frac{1}{\rho_1}\right)z - \left(\frac{1}{\rho_2} + \frac{1}{\rho_1}\right)l\right],$$

$$Z = \frac{\partial V}{\partial z} = \sigma\left(\frac{1}{\rho_1} - \frac{1}{\rho_2}\right).$$

Imagine two particles each of the same mass as a unit length of the rod placed at the two ends of the rod. Then the component of the attraction of the rod at the point P which is parallel to the rod has the curious property that it is equal to the difference of the potentials of the two particles at the point P.

Equipotential Surfaces.—On an equipotential surface V is constant. Let

$$C = e^{-\frac{V}{\sigma}} < 1. \tag{4}$$

Then on an equipotential surface

$$\tan \frac{1}{2}\theta_1 = C \tan \frac{1}{2}\theta_2. \tag{5}$$

From the formula for the tangent of a half angle,

$$\tan \theta = \frac{2 \tan \frac{1}{2}\theta}{1 - \tan^2 \frac{1}{2}\theta},$$

it is found that

$$\frac{2}{\tan \theta_1} = \frac{1}{\tan \frac{1}{2}\theta_1} - \tan \frac{1}{2}\theta_1,$$

or, by virtue of Eq. (5),

$$\frac{2}{\tan \theta_1} = \frac{1}{C \tan \frac{1}{2}\theta_2} - C \tan \frac{1}{2}\theta_2,$$

and similarly

$$\frac{2}{\tan \theta_2} = \frac{1}{\tan \frac{1}{2}\theta_2} - \tan \frac{1}{2}\theta_2.$$

If the first of these equations is multiplied by C and then subtracted from the second; and then the second is multiplied by C and the first is subtracted from it, there results the two equations

$$\frac{1}{\tan \theta_2} - \frac{C}{\tan \theta_1} = -\frac{(1 - C^2)}{2} \tan \frac{1}{2}\theta_2,$$

$$\frac{C}{\tan \theta_2} - \frac{1}{\tan \theta_1} = -\frac{(1 - C^2)}{2C} \cdot \frac{1}{\tan \frac{1}{2}\theta_2}.$$

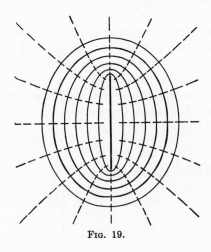

Fig. 19.

The product of these two equations eliminates the half angle, and gives

$$\left(\frac{1}{\tan \theta_2} - \frac{C}{\tan \theta_1}\right)\left(\frac{C}{\tan \theta_2} - \frac{1}{\tan \theta_1}\right) = \frac{(1 - C^2)^2}{4C},$$

which reduces, by the substitutions of Eqs. (3), to

$$\frac{(1 - C)^2}{(1 + C)^2}\frac{z^2}{l^2} + \frac{(1 - C)^2}{4C}\frac{x^2}{l^2} = 1.$$

This equation, by the substitutions,

$$\frac{4Cl^2}{(1 - C)^2} = \kappa, \qquad \frac{(1 + C)^2}{(1 - C)^2}l^2 = l^2 + \kappa, \tag{6}$$

becomes the equation for confocal conics, Fig. (19),

$$\frac{z^2}{l^2 + \kappa} + \frac{x^2}{\kappa} = 1. \tag{7}$$

On replacing the value of C from Eq. (4), it is found from Eq. (6) that

$$\kappa = \frac{l^2}{\sinh^2 \dfrac{V}{2\sigma}} > 0.$$

For positive values of κ these curves are ellipses, and from its definition κ must be positive. But the equation

$$\frac{z^2}{l^2 - \kappa} - \frac{x^2}{\kappa} = 1, \qquad 0 < \kappa < l^2, \tag{8}$$

represents the orthogonal confocal family of hyperbolas[1] which, by virtue of the property of orthogonality, are the lines of force, Sec. 28.

The parametric equations

$$x = \frac{l \sin \varphi}{\sinh \omega}, \qquad z = \frac{l \cos \varphi}{\tanh \omega},$$

represents a family of ellipses if ω is constant, and the family of orthogonal hyperbolas if φ is constant.

The equation of the equipotential surfaces in three dimensions is

$$\frac{z^2}{l^2 + \kappa} + \frac{x^2 + y^2}{\kappa} = 1$$

which represents prolate spheroids. The orthogonal system of surfaces is represented by

$$\frac{z^2}{l^2 - \kappa} - \frac{x^2 + y^2}{\kappa} = 1,$$

and are hyperboloids of two sheets. The lines of force are the intersections of the hyperboloids with the family of planes which intersect in the z-axis,

$$y = \lambda x,$$

where λ is a parameter.

32. The Potential of a Homogeneous Solid Ellipsoid for Interior Points.—Let the surface of the given ellipsoid be defined by the equation

$$\frac{\xi^2}{a^2} + \frac{\eta^2}{b^2} + \frac{\zeta^2}{c^2} = 1, \tag{1}$$

---

[1] "Statics and the Dynamics of a Particle," p. 356.

and let the interior point for which the potential is to be computed be $P(x, y, z)$. On taking P as the origin of a system of polar coordinates ρ, φ, θ, with the equations of transformation

$$\left.\begin{array}{l} \xi = x + \rho \cos \varphi \cos \theta, \\ \eta = y + \rho \cos \varphi \sin \theta, \\ \zeta = z + \rho \sin \varphi, \\ dm = \sigma \rho^2 \cos \varphi \, d\varphi d\theta d\rho, \end{array}\right\} \qquad (2)$$

then the value of the potential at the point P is

$$V = \sigma \int_E \frac{dm}{\rho} = \sigma \int_{-\frac{\pi}{2}}^{+\frac{\pi}{2}} \int_0^{2\pi} \int_0^{\rho_1} \rho \cos \varphi \, d\varphi d\theta d\rho. \qquad (3)$$

The upper limit ρ_1 of the integration with respect to ρ is a function of φ and θ, since the integration is from P to a point on the surface of the ellipsoid.

If Eqs. (2) are substituted in Eq. (1) the surface of the ellipsoid is found to be represented by an equation of the second degree in ρ_1. This equation can be written

$$A\rho_1^2 + 2B\rho_1 + C = 0. \qquad (4)$$

where

$$\left.\begin{array}{l} A = \dfrac{\cos^2 \varphi \cos^2 \theta}{a^2} + \dfrac{\cos^2 \varphi \sin^2 \theta}{b^2} + \dfrac{\sin^2 \varphi}{c^2}, \\[2mm] B = \dfrac{x \cos \varphi \cos \theta}{a^2} + \dfrac{y \cos \varphi \sin \theta}{b^2} + \dfrac{z \sin \varphi}{c^2}, \\[2mm] C = \dfrac{x^2}{a^2} + \dfrac{y^2}{b^2} + \dfrac{z^2}{c^2} - 1. \end{array}\right\} \qquad (5)$$

The solution of Eq. (4) which belongs to the present problem is

$$\rho_1 = \frac{-B + \sqrt{B^2 - AC}}{A},$$

for A is necessarily positive and for interior points C is negative. Hence $B^2 - AC$ is positive and greater than B^2. Since ρ_1 must be positive, the positive sign must be taken before this radical. From this expression for ρ_1 is obtained

$$\rho_1^2 = \frac{2B^2 - AC - 2B\sqrt{B^2 - AC}}{A^2},$$

so that Eq. 3 becomes

$$V = \frac{1}{2}\sigma \int_{-\frac{\pi}{2}}^{+\frac{\pi}{2}} \int_0^{2\pi} \frac{2B^2 - AC - 2B\sqrt{B^2 - AC}}{A^2} \cos \varphi \, d\varphi d\theta. \quad (6)$$

Consider first the part of this integral which depends upon the radical

$$R = \int_{-\frac{\pi}{2}}^{+\frac{\pi}{2}} \int_0^{2\pi} \frac{B\sqrt{B^2 - AC}}{A^2} \cos\varphi \, d\varphi \, d\theta.$$

The elements of this surface integral can be taken in pairs the two elements being equal numerically but of opposite sign. At the points P_1 and P_2, let

$$(P_1) \quad \theta = \theta_0, \ \varphi = \varphi_0; \quad \text{and} \quad (P_2) \quad \theta = \theta_0 + \pi, \ \varphi = -\varphi_0,$$

so that on a unit sphere P_1 and P_2 are diametrically opposite points. At the points P_1 and P_2 the quantities A and C have the same values while B merely changes sign at these two points. Hence, the integral of

$$\frac{B\sqrt{B^2 - AC}}{A^2} d\omega,$$

where $d\omega$ is an element of area on the unit sphere, taken over any hemisphere is equal numerically, but opposite in sign, to the same integral taken over the other hemisphere. That is, the integral taken over the entire sphere is zero. Hence,

$$R = 0,$$

and the integral (Eq. (6)) reduces to

$$V = \frac{1}{2}\sigma \int_{-\frac{\pi}{2}}^{+\frac{\pi}{2}} \int_0^{2\pi} \frac{2B^2 - AC}{A^2} \cos\varphi \, d\varphi \, d\theta. \tag{7}$$

If the values of A, B, and C from Eqs. (5) are substituted in Eq. (7), there results

$$V = \sigma \int_{-\frac{\pi}{2}}^{+\frac{\pi}{2}} \int_0^{2\pi} \left\{ \frac{\cos^2\varphi \cos^2\theta}{a^2} \cdot \frac{x^2}{a^2} + \frac{\cos^2\varphi \sin^2\theta}{b^2} \cdot \frac{y^2}{b^2} + \right.$$

$$\left. \frac{\sin^2\varphi}{c^2} \cdot \frac{z^2}{c^2} \right\} \frac{\cos\varphi \, d\varphi \, d\theta}{A^2}$$

$$+ 2\sigma \int_{-\frac{\pi}{2}}^{+\frac{\pi}{2}} \int_0^{2\pi} \left\{ \frac{xy \cos^2\varphi \sin\theta \cos\theta}{a^2 b^2} + \frac{yz \cos\varphi \sin\varphi \sin\theta}{b^2 c^2} \right.$$

$$\left. + \frac{zx \cos\varphi \sin\varphi \cos\theta}{c^2 a^2} \right\} \frac{\cos\varphi \, d\varphi \, d\theta}{A^2} - \frac{1}{2}C\sigma \int_{-\frac{\pi}{2}}^{+\frac{\pi}{2}} \int_0^{2\pi} \frac{\cos\varphi \, d\varphi \, d\theta}{A}.$$

By properly pairing the elements in the second integral its value is seen to be zero. For example, in the integral

$$\sigma xy \int_{-\frac{\pi}{2}}^{+\frac{\pi}{2}} \int_0^{2\pi} \frac{\cos^2 \varphi \sin \theta \cos \theta}{a^2 b^2 A^2} d\omega$$

it is seen that at the points P_1 and P_2, where

$$(P_1) \quad \theta = \theta_0, \quad \varphi = \varphi_0, \quad \text{and} \quad (P_2) \quad \theta = -\theta_0, \quad \varphi = \varphi_0,$$

the integrand has values which are equal numerically but opposite in sign. Hence the integral is zero; and in a similar way it can be shown that the other two terms of the second integral also are zero. Hence,

$$V = \sigma \int_{-\frac{\pi}{2}}^{+\frac{\pi}{2}} \int_0^{2\pi} \left\{ \frac{\cos^2 \varphi \cos^2 \theta}{a^2} \cdot \frac{x^2}{a^2} + \frac{\cos^2 \varphi \sin^2 \theta}{b^2} \cdot \frac{y^2}{b^2} + \frac{\sin^2 \varphi}{c^2} \cdot \frac{z^2}{c^2} \right\}$$

$$\times \frac{\cos \varphi d\varphi d\theta}{A^2} - \frac{1}{2}\sigma C \int_{-\frac{\pi}{2}}^{+\frac{\pi}{2}} \int_0^{2\pi} \frac{\cos \varphi d\varphi d\theta}{A}. \quad (8)$$

Now let

$$W = \frac{1}{2}\sigma \int_{-\frac{\pi}{2}}^{+\frac{\pi}{2}} \int_0^{2\pi} \frac{\cos \varphi d\varphi d\theta}{A}.$$

W is a function of the three semi-axes, a, b, and c, but is independent of the coordinates x, y, and z of the attracted points. If it is written

$$W = \frac{1}{2}\sigma \int_{-\frac{\pi}{2}}^{+\frac{\pi}{2}} \int_0^{2\pi} \frac{\cos \varphi d\varphi d\theta}{\frac{\cos^2 \varphi \cos^2 \theta}{a^2} + \frac{\cos^2 \varphi \sin^2 \theta}{b^2} + \frac{\sin^2 \varphi}{c^2}}, \quad (9)$$

it is readily verified that Eq. (8) can be written

$$V = \frac{1}{a} \frac{\partial W}{\partial a} x^2 + \frac{1}{b} \frac{\partial W}{\partial b} y^2 + \frac{1}{c} \frac{\partial W}{\partial c} z^2 - CW,$$

or, again, on substituting the value of C,

$$V = \left(\frac{1}{a} \frac{\partial W}{\partial a} - \frac{W}{a^2} \right) x^2 + \left(\frac{1}{b} \frac{\partial W}{\partial b} - \frac{W}{b^2} \right) y^2 + \left(\frac{1}{c} \frac{\partial W}{\partial c} - \frac{W}{c^2} \right) z^2 + W.$$

$$(10)$$

Since W is a function of a, b, and c alone (and therefore its derivatives also), the coefficients of x^2, y^2, and z^2 are functions of a, b, and c only. It is evident at once that W is the value of the potential at the center of the ellipsoid.

There still remains the problem of evaluating W. For this purpose, let

$$M = \frac{\cos^2 \varphi}{a^2} + \frac{\sin^2 \varphi}{c^2}, \qquad N = \frac{\cos^2 \varphi}{b^2} + \frac{\sin^2 \varphi}{c^2}. \qquad (11)$$

Then Eq. (9) becomes

$$W = \frac{1}{2}\sigma \int_{-\frac{\pi}{2}}^{+\frac{\pi}{2}} \cos \varphi d\varphi \int_0^{2\pi} \frac{d\theta}{M \cos^2 \theta + N \sin^2 \theta},$$

$$= 4\sigma \int_0^{\frac{\pi}{2}} \cos \varphi d\varphi \int_0^{\frac{\pi}{2}} \frac{\sec^2 \theta d\theta}{M + N \tan^2 \theta},$$

$$= 2\pi\sigma \int_0^{\frac{\pi}{2}} \frac{\cos \varphi d\varphi}{\sqrt{MN}}.$$

On replacing the values of M and N in this integral from Eqs. (11), it is found that

$$W = 2\pi\sigma abc^2 \int_0^{\frac{\pi}{2}} \frac{\cos \varphi d\varphi}{\sqrt{(a^2 \sin^2 \varphi + c^2 \cos^2 \varphi)(b^2 \sin^2 \varphi + c^2 \cos^2 \varphi)}},$$

an expression which is not symmetric in the letters a, b, and c. The symmetry can be restored however by the substitution

$$\sin \varphi = \frac{c}{\sqrt{c^2 + s}},$$

where s is the new variable of integration. The result of this substitution is

$$W = \pi\sigma abc \int_0^\infty \frac{ds}{\sqrt{(a^2 + s)(b^2 + s)(c^2 + s)}}, \qquad (12)$$

and if this form of W is used in Eq. (10), the expression for the potential becomes

$$V = \pi\sigma abc \int_0^\infty \left(1 - \frac{x^2}{a^2 + s} - \frac{y^2}{b^2 + s} - \frac{z^2}{c^2 + s}\right)$$

$$\times \frac{ds}{\sqrt{(a^2 + s)(b^2 + s)(c^2 + s)}}. \qquad (13)$$

For purposes of numerical computation W is reduced at Legendre's normal form of an elliptic integral of the first kind by the substitution

$$\sin \varphi = \frac{c \tan \omega}{\sqrt{a^2 - c^2}}, \qquad \text{or} \qquad s = a^2 \cot^2 \omega - c^2 \csc^2 \omega,$$

provided
$$a > b > c,$$
and becomes
$$W = \frac{2\pi\sigma abc}{\sqrt{a^2 - c^2}} \int_0^{\cos^{-1}\frac{c}{a}} \frac{d\omega}{\sqrt{1 - k^2 \sin^2 \omega}},$$
where
$$k^2 = \frac{a^2 - b^2}{a^2 - c^2}.$$

33. The Equipotential Surfaces.—The equation for the potential V at an internal point of a homogeneous ellipsoid can be written in the form, from Eq. (32.13),

$$\frac{W - V}{\pi\sigma abc} = \frac{x^2}{\alpha^2} + \frac{y^2}{\beta^2} + \frac{z^2}{\gamma^2}. \tag{1}$$

where

$$\left.\begin{aligned}
\frac{1}{\alpha^2} &= \int_0^\infty \frac{ds}{(a^2 + s)\sqrt{(a^2 + s)(b^2 + s)(c^2 + s)}}, \\
\frac{1}{\beta^2} &= \int_0^\infty \frac{ds}{(b^2 + s)\sqrt{(a^2 + s)(b^2 + s)(c^2 + s)}}, \\
\frac{1}{\gamma^2} &= \int_0^\infty \frac{ds}{(c^2 + s)\sqrt{(a^2 + s)(b^2 + s)(c^2 + s)}}.
\end{aligned}\right\} \tag{2}$$

If V is a constant, the equipotential, or level, surface also is an ellipsoid with axes which are proportional to α, β, and γ. By forming the differences between these expressions (Eq. (2)), it is readily proved that

$$\frac{1}{\alpha^2} < \frac{1}{\beta^2} < \frac{1}{\gamma^2},$$

and therefore

$$\alpha^2 > \beta^2 > \gamma^2.$$

In a manner quite similar it is also proved that

$$\frac{\alpha^2}{a^2} < \frac{\beta^2}{b^2} < \frac{\gamma^2}{c^2}.$$

These inequalities show that the level surface, which is an ellipsoid co-axial with the given ellipsoid, has its longest axis coinciding with the longest axis of the given ellipsoid and its shortest axis coinciding with the shortest axis of the given ellipsoid, so that the two ellipsoids are similarly oriented, but since

$$\frac{\alpha}{a} < \frac{\beta}{b} < \frac{\gamma}{c},$$

it follows that the level surface is not similar to the given ellipsoid, but is more nearly spherical. Hence the surface of the given ellipsoid is not itself a level surface. If surface tensions can be neglected water placed upon the surface of a homogeneous ellipsoid and subject to no other force than the attraction of the ellipsoid will flow towards the ends of the shortest axis of the ellipsoid.

34. The Components of Attraction at an Interior Point.— Since

$$X = \frac{\partial V}{\partial x}, \qquad Y = \frac{\partial V}{\partial y}, \qquad Z = \frac{\partial V}{\partial z},$$

it follows at once from Eq. (32.13) that

$$\left. \begin{aligned} X &= -x \int_0^\infty \frac{2\pi\sigma abcds}{(a^2 + s)\sqrt{(a^2 + s)(b^2 + s)(c^2 + s)}}, \\ Y &= -y \int_0^\infty \frac{2\pi\sigma abcds}{(b^2 + s)\sqrt{(a^2 + s)(b^2 + s)(c^2 + s)}}, \\ Z &= -z \int_0^\infty \frac{2\pi\sigma abcds}{(c^2 + s)\sqrt{(a^2 + s)(b^2 + s)(c^2 + s)}}. \end{aligned} \right\} \quad (1)$$

The resultant of the vectors X, Y and Z, is, of course, a vector which is perpendicular to the level surface through the point x, y, z. It represents the total attraction of the ellipsoid at that point.

Consider the attraction of a second ellipsoid which is similar and similarly placed upon the same point x, y, z. The axes of this second ellipsoid are λa, λb, and λc. Then if X_2 is the x-component of its attraction on x, y, z

$$X_2 = -x \int_0^\infty \frac{2\pi\sigma\lambda^3 abcds}{(\lambda^2 a^2 + s)\sqrt{(\lambda^2 a^2 + s)(\lambda^2 b^2 + s)(\lambda^2 c^2 + s)}}$$

or, if the variable of integration be changed by the substitution

$$s = \lambda\tau,$$

it becomes

$$\begin{aligned} X_2 &= -x \int_0^\infty \frac{2\pi\sigma abcd\tau}{(a^2 + \tau)\sqrt{(a^2 + \tau)(b^2 + \tau)(c^2 + \tau)}}, \\ &= X; \end{aligned}$$

and, similarly, for Y and Z. Hence the attraction on the inside of a homogeneous, ellipsoidal shell which is bounded by two similar and similarly placed ellipsoids is zero, a proposition which was proved in a different manner in Sec. 11. The potential, however, is not zero in the interior. If $\lambda > 1$ is the ratio of similitude, the value of the potential in the interior has the constant value

$$(\lambda^2 - 1)W.$$

where W is defined in Eq. (32.12).

35. The Attraction of a Homogeneous Solid Ellipsoid upon an Exterior Particle—Ivory's Method.

—If the point for which the potential is computed $P(x, y, z)$ is exterior to the ellipsoid the limits of the integral which corresponds to Eq. (32.3) are complicated and it is not practical to carry through the integration in the manner of Sec. 32. A beautiful method of obtaining the components of attraction on an exterior point was given by Ivory in 1809. The method is based upon a comparison of the integrals for an exterior point with the integrals for a corresponding interior point. The integrals for the interior points being known, the corresponding integrals for the exterior point can be derived.

Let the surface of the attracting ellipsoid E_1 be defined by the equation

$$\frac{x_1^2}{a_1^2} + \frac{y_1^2}{b_1^2} + \frac{z_1^2}{c_1^2} = 1, \qquad (E_1)$$

and let the attracted point be denoted by P_2 with coordinates x_2, y_2, z_2. Through the point P_2 pass an ellipsoid E_2 confocal with E_1. The surface of the ellipsoid E_2 is defined by the equation

$$\frac{x_2^2}{a_2^2} + \frac{y_2^2}{b_2^2} + \frac{z_2^2}{c_2^2} = 1; \qquad (E_2)$$

but since it is confocal with E_1 the axes of the two ellipsoids are related by the equations

$$a_2^2 = a_1^2 + \kappa, \qquad b_2^2 = b_1^2 + \kappa, \qquad c_2^2 = c_1^2 + \kappa, \qquad (1)$$

where κ is the algebraically largest root of the equation

$$\frac{x_2^2}{a_1^2 + \kappa} + \frac{y_2^2}{b_1^2 + \kappa} + \frac{z_2^2}{c_1^2 + \kappa} = 1. \qquad (2)$$

(The three roots of this equation are real.)[1]

Let $\bar{x}_1, \bar{y}_1, \bar{z}_1$ be any point within or on the surface of E_1 and let $\bar{x}_2, \bar{y}_2, \bar{z}_2$ be any point within or on the surface of E_2.

[1] " Statics and the Dynamics of a Particle," p. 355.

A one to one correspondence between the points of E_1 and E_2 is established by the equations

$$\frac{\bar{x}_1}{a_1} = \frac{\bar{x}_2}{a_2}, \qquad \frac{\bar{y}_1}{b_1} = \frac{\bar{y}_2}{b_2}, \qquad \frac{\bar{z}_1}{c_1} = \frac{\bar{z}_2}{c_2}. \tag{3}$$

Let P_1 be the point on E_1 which corresponds to P_2 on E_2. Then P_1 is interior to E_2, and E_2 can be regarded as a homogeneous solid with the same density as E_1. Let X_2, Y_2, Z_2 be the components of attraction of E_1 on P_2, and X_1, Y_1, Z_1 be the components of attraction of E_2 on P_1. Then

$$X_1 = -\sigma \iiint_{E_2} \frac{\bar{x}_2 - x_1}{\bar{\rho}_1} d\bar{x}_2 d\bar{y}_2 d\bar{z}_2,$$

$$X_2 = -\sigma \iiint_{E_1} \frac{\bar{x}_1 - x_2}{\bar{\rho}_2} d\bar{x}_1 d\bar{y}_1 d\bar{z}_1,$$

where

$$\bar{\rho}_1 = \sqrt{(\bar{x}_2 - x_1)^2 + (\bar{y}_2 - y_1)^2 + (\bar{z}_2 - z_1)^2},$$

$$\bar{\rho}_2 = \sqrt{(\bar{x}_1 - x_2)^2 + (\bar{y}_1 - y_2)^2 + (\bar{z}_1 - z_2)^2};$$

and similar expressions for the other components. These integrals can also be written

$$X_1 = \iiint_{E_2} \frac{\partial}{\partial \bar{x}_2} \left(\frac{1}{\bar{\rho}_1} \right) d\bar{x}_2 d\bar{y}_2 d\bar{z}_2,$$

$$X_2 = \iiint_{E_1} \frac{\partial}{\partial \bar{x}_1} \left(\frac{1}{\bar{\rho}_2} \right) d\bar{x}_1 d\bar{y}_1 d\bar{z}_1.$$

Integration of these expressions with respect to the x-variable sums up the X-components of the attraction along an elementary cylinder of cross section $dydz$ parallel to the x-axis between the two points where this cylinder intersects the surface of the ellipsoid to which it belongs. Hence

$$\left. \begin{aligned} X_1 &= \iint \left(\frac{1}{\rho_{11}} - \frac{1}{\rho_{12}} \right) d\bar{y}_2 d\bar{z}_2, \\ X_2 &= \iint \left(\frac{1}{\rho_{21}} - \frac{1}{\rho_{22}} \right) d\bar{y}_1 d\bar{z}_1. \end{aligned} \right\} \tag{4}$$

where ρ_{11} and ρ_{12} are the two lines joining the point P_1 to the two points where the elementary cylinder intersects the surface of E_2, and ρ_{21} and ρ_{22} are the two lines which join P_2 to the extremities of the elementary cylinder which terminates in the surface of E_1. It will be assumed that these two cylinders are corresponding cylinders in the sense of Eq. (3), and therefore the termini of these cylinders are corresponding points on the surfaces of the ellipsoids.

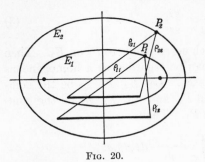

FIG. 20.

Lemma.—*If R_1 and S_1 are any two points on the surface of E_1 and R_2 and S_2 are the corresponding points on the surface of E_2, then the distances $\overline{R_1S_2}$ and $\overline{R_2S_1}$ are equal.*

In order to prove this lemma let the coordinates of R_1 and R_2 be l_1, m_1, n_1 and l_2, m_2, n_2 respectively, and let the coordinates of S_1 and S_2 be λ_1, μ_1, ν_1 and λ_2, μ_2, ν_2. Then

$$\overline{R_1S_2}^2 = (l_1 - \lambda_2)^2 + (m_1 - \mu_2)^2 + (n_1 - \nu_2)^2,$$

and

$$\overline{R_2S_1}^2 = (l_2 - \lambda_1)^2 + (m_2 - \mu_1)^2 + (n_2 - \nu_1)^2.$$

But since

$$l_1 = \frac{a_1}{a_2}l_2, \qquad \lambda_1 = \frac{a_1}{a_2}\lambda_2, \qquad \text{etc.,}$$

the difference between these two quantities is

$$\overline{R_1S_2}^2 - \overline{R_2S_1}^2 = \left(\frac{a_1^2}{a_2^2} - 1\right)l_2^2 + \left(\frac{b_1^2}{b_2^2} - 1\right)m_2^2 + \left(\frac{c_1^2}{c_2^2} - 1\right)n_2^2$$

$$+ \left(1 - \frac{a_1^2}{a_2^2}\right)\lambda_2^2 + \left(1 - \frac{b_1^2}{b_2^2}\right)\mu_2^2 + \left(1 - \frac{c_1^2}{c_2^2}\right)\nu_2^2$$

$$= -\kappa\left(\frac{l_2^2}{a_2^2} + \frac{m_2^2}{b_2^2} + \frac{n_2^2}{c_2^2}\right) + \kappa\left(\frac{\lambda_2^2}{a_2^2} + \frac{\mu_2^2}{b_2^2} + \frac{\nu_2^2}{c_2^2}\right)$$

$$= -\kappa + \kappa = 0.$$

Hence, the distance $\overline{R_1S_2}$ is equal to the distance $\overline{R_2S_1}$.

Since all of the conditions of the lemma are satisfied, it follows that in Eqs. (4)

$$\rho_{11} = \rho_{21}, \qquad \rho_{12} = \rho_{22},$$

and, therefore, at corresponding points the integrands of these two integrals are equal. Let the variables $\bar{y}_1$ and $\bar{z}_1$ in X_2 be changed by the substitution

$$d\bar{y}_1 = \frac{b_1}{b_2}d\bar{y}_2, \qquad d\bar{z}_1 = \frac{c_1}{c_2}d\bar{z}_2.$$

The limits of the integral will be altered and will become the same as the limits for the integral in X_1; and it is evident that

$$X_2 = \frac{b_1 c_1}{b_2 c_2} X_1,$$

and similarly,

$$Y_2 = \frac{c_1 a_1}{c_2 a_2} Y_1,$$

$$Z_2 = \frac{a_1 b_1}{a_2 b_2} Z_1.$$

Hence, if the components of attraction of E_2 on the interior point P_1, that is X_1, Y_1, Z_1, are known, then the attraction of E_1 on the exterior point P_2 can be computed. Using the values of these components as given in Sec. 34 with the proper subscripts, it is seen that

$$X_2 = -2\pi\sigma a_2 b_1 c_1 x_1 \int_0^\infty \frac{ds_2}{(a_2{}^2 + s_2)\sqrt{(a_2{}^2 + s_2)(b_2{}^2 + s_2)(c_2{}^2 + s_2)}},$$

$$Y_2 = -2\pi\sigma a_1 b_2 c_1 y_1 \int_0^\infty \frac{ds_2}{(b_2{}^2 + s_2)\sqrt{(a_2{}^2 + s_2)(b_2{}^2 + s_2)(c_2{}^2 + s_2)}},$$

$$Z_2 = -2\pi\sigma a_1 b_1 c_2 z_1 \int_0^\infty \frac{ds_2}{(c_2{}^2 + s_2)\sqrt{(a_2{}^2 + s_2)(b_2{}^2 + s_2)(c_2{}^2 + s_2)}}.$$

In the factors preceding the integral signs

$$a_2 x_1 = a_1 x_2, \qquad b_2 y_1 = b_1 y_2, \qquad c_2 z_1 = c_1 z_2;$$

under the integral signs the semi-axes of E_2 can be eliminated by the substitutions

$$a_2{}^2 = a_1{}^2 + \kappa, \qquad b_2{}^2 = b_1{}^2 + \kappa, \qquad c_2{}^2 = c_1{}^2 + \kappa,$$

and then the substitution

$$s_2 + \kappa = s_1$$

gives the desired forms of the integrals. Dropping all of the subscripts, which are no longer necessary, the components of the attraction of the given ellipsoid upon an exterior point are

$$\left.\begin{aligned}
X &= -2\pi\sigma abcx \int_\kappa^\infty \frac{ds}{(a^2 + s)\sqrt{(a^2 + s)(b^2 + s)(c^2 + s)}}, \\
Y &= -2\pi\sigma abcy \int_\kappa^\infty \frac{ds}{(b^2 + s)\sqrt{(a^2 + s)(b^2 + s)(c^2 + s)}}, \\
Z &= -2\pi\sigma abcz \int_\kappa^\infty \frac{ds}{(c^2 + s)\sqrt{(a^2 + s)(b^2 + s)(c^2 + s)}},
\end{aligned}\right\} \quad (5)$$

where a, b, c are the semi-axes of the given ellipsoid and x, y, z are the coordinates of the exterior point. The lower limit κ is the algebraically largest root of the equation

$$\frac{x^2}{a^2 + \kappa} + \frac{y^2}{b^2 + \kappa} + \frac{z^2}{c^2 + \kappa} = 1. \tag{6}$$

36. The Potential of a Homogeneous Solid Ellipsoid at Exterior Points.

—The forms of the expressions for the components of attraction of a homogeneous solid ellipsoid upon an exterior point, Eqs. (35.5), are identical with the corresponding expressions for an interior point, (Eqs. (34.1)) with the exception that for an exterior point the lower limit of the integrals is κ, and for an interior point it is zero. This similarity of form leads to the suspicion that the same similarity holds for the potentials also, and that

$$V = \pi\sigma abc \int_\kappa^\infty \left(1 - \frac{x^2}{a^2 + s} - \frac{y^2}{b^2 + s} - \frac{z^2}{c^2 + s}\right)$$
$$\times \frac{ds}{\sqrt{(a^2 + s)(b^2 + s)(c^2 + s)}} \tag{1}$$

is the potential of the ellipsoid at an exterior point. In order to prove that this surmize is correct, it is necessary to show that

$$\frac{\partial V}{\partial x} = X, \qquad \frac{\partial V}{\partial y} = Y, \qquad \frac{\partial V}{\partial z} = Z.$$

If this condition is satisfied, V can differ from the potential only by an additive constant.

Now

$$\frac{\partial V}{\partial x} = -2\pi\sigma abc x \int_\kappa^\infty \frac{ds}{(a^2 + s)\sqrt{(a^2 + s)(b^2 + s)(c^2 + s)}}$$
$$- \left(1 - \frac{x^2}{a^2 + \kappa} - \frac{y^2}{b^2 + \kappa} - \frac{z^2}{c^2 + \kappa}\right)\frac{\pi\sigma abc\frac{\partial \kappa}{\partial x}}{\sqrt{(a^2 + \kappa)(b^2 + \kappa)(c^2 + \kappa)}},$$

the first term of which is equal to X, Eqs. (35.5), and the second term vanishes by Eq. (35.6). Hence the condition

$$\frac{\partial V}{\partial x} = X$$

is satisfied, and similarly with the other derivatives.

In order to show that the additive constant is zero, it is sufficient to show that V vanishes at infinity, a property which is possessed by every finite body (Sec. 22).

Just as in Sec. 35, let the ellipsoid which is defined by a given κ be denoted by E_2. The greatest distance from the origin to the surface E_2 is $r = \sqrt{a^2 + \kappa}$, assuming that

$$a > b > c,$$

and the shortest distance is $r = \sqrt{c^2 + \kappa}$. Hence for any point on E_2

$$c^2 + \kappa \leqq r^2 \leqq a^2 + \kappa,$$

which shows that if r tends towards infinity so also does κ, and conversely.

Now

$$\int_\kappa^\infty \frac{ds}{\sqrt{(a^2 + s)(b^2 + s)(c^2 + s)}} < \int_\kappa^\infty \frac{ds}{s^{\frac{3}{2}}} = \frac{2}{\sqrt{\kappa}},$$

and

$$\int_\kappa^\infty \frac{ds}{(a^2 + s)\sqrt{(a^2 + s)(b^2 + s)(c^2 + s)}} <$$

$$\int_\kappa^\infty \frac{ds}{(b^2 + s)\sqrt{(a^2 + s)(b^2 + s)(c^2 + s)}}$$

$$< \int_\kappa^\infty \frac{ds}{(c^2 + s)\sqrt{(a^2 + s)(b^2 + s)(c^2 + s)}} < \int_\kappa^\infty \frac{ds}{s^{\frac{5}{2}}} = \frac{2}{3}\frac{1}{\kappa^{\frac{3}{2}}}.$$

Hence

$$-\left(\frac{2}{\kappa^{\frac{1}{2}}} + \frac{2}{3}\frac{x^2 + y^2 + z^2}{\kappa^{\frac{3}{2}}}\right) < \frac{V}{\pi \sigma abc} < +\left(\frac{2}{\kappa^{\frac{1}{2}}} + \frac{2}{3}\frac{x^2 + y^2 + z^2}{\kappa^{\frac{3}{2}}}\right)$$

or, since

$$x^2 + y^2 + z^2 \leqq a^2 + \kappa,$$

$$-\frac{1}{\sqrt{\kappa}}\left(\frac{8}{3} + \frac{2}{3}\frac{a^2}{\kappa}\right) < \frac{V}{\pi \sigma abc} < +\frac{1}{\sqrt{\kappa}}\left(\frac{8}{3} + \frac{2}{3}\frac{a^2}{\kappa}\right).$$

Consequently as κ tends towards infinity V tends towards zero, which proves that V as defined in Eq. (1) is the potential of the ellipsoid at exterior points.

For $\kappa = 0$ the ellipsoid E_2 which passes through the attracted point x, y, z coincides with the surface of the attracting ellipsoid. Thus the limit of the potential as the attracted point approaches the surface of the attracting ellipsoid is the same whether the approach is from the inside (Eq. (32.13)) or from the outside

(Eq. (1)), and the potential is continuous across the surface. It is therefore continuous throughout all space.

It should be observed that the factor $\pi\sigma abc$ which appears in Eq. (1) is simply the mass M of the ellipsoid.

37. Evaluation of the Elliptic Integrals.—By the transformation

$$w = \sqrt{\frac{a^2 - c^2}{a^2 + s}}, \qquad a > b > c,$$

where w is a new variable, the integral

$$v = \frac{1}{2}\sqrt{a^2 - c^2} \int_s^\infty \frac{ds}{\sqrt{(a^2 + s)(b^2 + s)(c^2 + s)}}$$

becomes

$$v = \int_0^{\sqrt{\frac{a^2-c^2}{a^2+s}}} \frac{dw}{\sqrt{(1 - w^2)(1 - k^2 w^2)}},$$

where

$$k^2 = \frac{a^2 - b^2}{a^2 - c^2};$$

or, if

$$w = \sin \varphi,$$

the integral takes the form

$$v = \int_0^{\omega_s} \frac{d\varphi}{\sqrt{1 - k^2 \sin^2 \varphi}} = F(\omega_s, k) \tag{1}$$

where

$$\sin \omega_s = \sqrt{\frac{a^2 - c^2}{a^2 + s}}.$$

Thus the integral $v = F(\omega_s, k)$ is Legendre's elliptic integral of the first kind. The upper limit of the last form ω_s is called the amplitude of v, and $\sin \omega_s$ is called $\sin \mathrm{am}\, v$, which is usually written $\mathrm{sn}\, v$. Similarly

$$\cos \mathrm{am}\, v = \mathrm{cn}\, v = \sqrt{1 - \mathrm{sn}^2 v},$$
$$\mathrm{delta\ am}\, v = \mathrm{dn}\, v = \sqrt{1 - k^2 \mathrm{sn}^2 v}.$$

From these definitions it is evident that

$$\mathrm{sn}\, v = \sqrt{\frac{a^2 - c^2}{a^2 + s}},$$

and

$$\frac{ds}{\sqrt{(a^2 + s)(b^2 + s)(c^2 + s)}} = -\frac{2}{\sqrt{a^2 - c^2}} dv.$$

By means of these relations it is not difficult to show that

$$\int_\kappa^\infty \frac{ds}{\sqrt{(a^2+s)(b^2+s)(c^2+s)}} = \frac{2}{(a^2-c^2)^{\frac{1}{2}}}\int_0^{v_\kappa} dv,$$

$$\int_\kappa^\infty \frac{ds}{(a^2+s)\sqrt{(a^2+s)(b^2+s)(c^2+s)}} = \frac{2}{(a^2-c^2)^{\frac{3}{2}}}\int_0^{v_\kappa} \mathrm{sn}^2 v\, dv,$$

$$\int_\kappa^\infty \frac{ds}{(b^2+s)\sqrt{(a^2+s)(b^2+s)(c^2+s)}} = \frac{2}{(a^2-c^2)^{\frac{3}{2}}}\int_0^{v_\kappa} \frac{\mathrm{sn}^2 v}{\mathrm{dn}^2 v}dv,$$

$$\int_\kappa^\infty \frac{ds}{(c^2+s)\sqrt{(a^2+s)(b^2+s)(c^2+s)}} = \frac{2}{(a^2-c^2)^{\frac{3}{2}}}\int_0^{v_\kappa} \frac{\mathrm{sn}^2 v}{\mathrm{cn}^2 v}dv,$$

where

$$\mathrm{sn}\, v_\kappa = \sqrt{\frac{a^2-c^2}{a^2+\kappa}},$$

$$\mathrm{am}\, v_\kappa = \omega_\kappa = \sin^{-1}\sqrt{\frac{a^2-c^2}{a^2+\kappa}}.$$

The substitution of these expressions in Eq. (35.1) gives

$$V = \frac{2\pi\sigma abc}{(a^2-c^2)^{\frac{3}{2}}}\int_0^{v_\kappa}\left[(a^2-c^2)-x^2\mathrm{sn}^2 v - y^2\frac{\mathrm{sn}^2 v}{\mathrm{dn}^2 v} - z^2\frac{\mathrm{sn}^2 v}{\mathrm{cn}^2 v}\right]dv.$$

The last three of the above integrals introduce Legendre's elliptic integral of the second kind, namely,

$$E(\omega_\kappa,\, k) = \int_0^{\omega_\kappa}\sqrt{1-k^2\sin^2\varphi}\,d\varphi. \tag{2}$$

Since

$$\frac{d\,\mathrm{sn}\, v}{dv} = +\mathrm{cn}\, v\, \mathrm{dn}\, v,$$

$$\frac{d\,\mathrm{cn}\, v}{dv} = -\mathrm{sn}\, v\, \mathrm{dn}\, v,$$

$$\frac{d\,\mathrm{dn}\, v}{dv} = -k^2\, \mathrm{sn}\, v\, \mathrm{cn}\, v,$$

it can be proved simply by differentiation that

$$\int_0^{v_\kappa} \mathrm{sn}^2 v\, dv = \frac{1}{k^2}[v_\kappa - E(\omega_\kappa)],$$

$$\int_0^{v_\kappa} \frac{\mathrm{sn}^2 v}{\mathrm{dn}^2 v}dv = \frac{E(\omega_\kappa)}{k^2(1-k^2)} - \frac{1}{1-k^2}\frac{\mathrm{sn}\, v_\kappa\, \mathrm{cn}\, v_\kappa}{\mathrm{dn}\, v_\kappa} - \frac{v_\kappa}{k^2},$$

$$\int_0^{v_\kappa} \frac{\mathrm{sn}^2 v}{\mathrm{cn}^2 v}dv = \frac{1}{1-k^2}\left[\frac{\mathrm{sn}\, v_\kappa\, \mathrm{dn}\, v_\kappa}{\mathrm{cn}\, v_\kappa} - E(\omega_\kappa)\right].$$

Since

$$v_\kappa = F(\omega_\kappa), \qquad \operatorname{sn} v_\kappa = \sqrt{\frac{a^2 - c^2}{a^2 + \kappa}},$$

$$\operatorname{dn} v_\kappa = \sqrt{\frac{b^2 + \kappa}{c^2 + \kappa}}, \qquad \operatorname{cn} v_\kappa = \sqrt{\frac{c^2 + \kappa}{a^2 + \kappa}},$$

the expression for V becomes

$$V = \frac{2\pi\sigma abc}{\sqrt{a^2 - c^2}} \left\{ \left[1 - \frac{x^2}{a^2 - b^2} + \frac{y^2}{a^2 - b^2} \right] F(\omega_\kappa, k) \right.$$

$$+ \left[\frac{x^2}{a^2 - b^2} - \frac{(a^2 - c^2)y^2}{(a^2 - b^2)(b^2 - c^2)} + \frac{z^2}{b^2 - c^2} \right] E(\omega_\kappa) \quad (3)$$

$$+ \left[\frac{c^2 + \kappa}{b^2 - c^2} y^2 - \frac{b^2 + \kappa}{b^2 - c^2} z^2 \right] \frac{\sqrt{a^2 - c^2}}{\sqrt{(a^2 + \kappa)(b^2 + \kappa)(c^2 + \kappa)}} \right\}.$$

It has already been observed in Sec. 35 that the derivative of this expression with respect to κ vanishes, and therefore in forming the derivatives

$$X = \frac{\partial V}{\partial x}, \qquad Y = \frac{\partial V}{\partial y}, \qquad Z = \frac{\partial V}{\partial z},$$

it is not necessary to regard κ as a function of x, y, and z. It is sufficient to differentiate only in so far as x, y, and z occur explicitly in V. The components of attraction are, therefore, very easily derived and it will not be necessary to write them.

38. MacLaurin's Theorem.—Let E_1 and E_2 be two confocal ellipsoids with semi-axes a_1, b_1, c_1 and a_2, b_2, c_2 respectively, each of which is homogeneous, but not necessarily of the same density. Let x, y, z be a point exterior to both of them. Let

$$\frac{x^2}{a_1{}^2 + \kappa_1} + \frac{y^2}{b_1{}^2 + \kappa_1} + \frac{z^2}{c_1{}^2 + \kappa_1} = 1$$

and

$$\frac{x^2}{a_2{}^2 + \kappa_2} + \frac{y^2}{b_2{}^2 + \kappa_2} + \frac{z^2}{c_2{}^2 + \kappa_2} = 1$$

represent the same ellipsoid, confocal to E_1 and E_2, through the point x, y, z. Then the equations

$$a_2{}^2 = a_1{}^2 + \kappa, \qquad b_2{}^2 = b_1{}^2 + \kappa, \qquad c_2{}^2 = c_1{}^2 + \kappa, \qquad (1)$$

define the value of κ by means of which E_2 can be referred to E_1, and, therefore,

$$\kappa + \kappa_2 = \kappa_1.$$

Consider the two integrals

$$I_1 = \int_{\kappa_1}^{\infty} \frac{ds_1}{\sqrt{(a_1^2 + s_1)^i(b_1^2 + s_1)^j(c_1^2 + s_1)^k}}$$

and

$$I_2 = \int_{\kappa_2}^{\infty} \frac{ds_2}{\sqrt{(a_2^2 + s_2)^i(b_2^2 + s_2)^j(c_2^2 + s)^k}},$$

where i, j, and k are any positive integers.

If a_2^2, b_2^2, c_2^2 in the second of these two integrals are replaced by their values from Eq. (1) there results

$$I_2 = \int_{\kappa_2}^{\infty} \frac{ds_2}{\sqrt{(a_1^2 + \kappa + s_2)^i(b_1^2 + \kappa + s_2)^j(c_1^2 + \kappa + s_2)^k}};$$

and if the substitution

$$s_2 + \kappa = s_1$$

is made this integral becomes

$$I_2 = \int_{\kappa_1}^{\infty} \frac{ds_1}{\sqrt{(a_1^2 + s_1)^i(b_1^2 + s_1)^j(c_1^2 + s_1)^j}} = I_1.$$

All of the integrals which appear in the expressions for the potential Eq. (36.1) and for the components of attraction Eq. (35.5) are included under these forms. Hence if V_1 and V_2 are the potentials of E_1 and E_2 at the point x, y, z which is external to both ellipsoids and if M_1 and M_2 are their masses, it is evident at once that

$$\frac{V_1}{M_1} = \frac{V_2}{M_2};$$

and similarly

$$\frac{X_1}{M_1} = \frac{X_2}{M_2}, \qquad \frac{Y_1}{M_1} = \frac{Y_2}{M_2}, \qquad \frac{Z_1}{M_1} = \frac{Z_2}{M_2}.$$

This proves a very beautiful theorem due originally to Mac-Laurin, namely

MacLaurin's Theorem.—Two homogeneous, confocal ellipsoids attract a particle which is exterior to both of them with forces which have the same direction and which in magnitude are proportional to the masses of the attracting ellipsoids.

MacLaurin proved this proposition for the attraction of ellipsoids of revolution for points on their axes of revolution. Legendre extended the proof to any points external to the ellipsoids of revolution. The complete theorem as given above was first established by Laplace, although his method is not the same as that which is given here.

It follows also that a homogeneous ellipsoidal shell, finite or infinitesimal in thickness, bounded by two confocal ellipsoids, attracts an exterior particle just as though it were a solid ellipsoid of the same mass and homogeneous throughout. Likewise, an ellipsoid which is homogeneous in confocal layers attracts an exterior particle just as though it were of the same mass and homogeneous throughout. Thus the earth increases in density from the surface towards the center, but if the distribution of matter within the earth is such that it is homogeneous in confocal layers, the attraction of the earth for an exterior particle is just the same as though it were homogeneous throughout, provided the total mass is the same in the two cases.

39. The Potential of Spheroids at Exterior Points.—The integrals which are involved in the expressions for the potential and the components of attraction of the general ellipsoid are all elliptic of the first or second kind. They all reduce to integrals of an elementary character, however, if two of the axes of the ellipsoid are equal; that is, if the ellipsoid is either an oblate or a prolate spheroid. If, for example,

$$a = b > c,$$

the ellipsoid is an oblate spheroid, and the expression for the potential is

$$V = \pi\sigma a^2 c \int_{\kappa}^{\infty} \frac{ds}{(a^2 + s)\sqrt{c^2 + s}} - \pi\sigma a^2 c(x^2 + y^2)$$

$$\times \int_{\kappa}^{\infty} \frac{ds}{(a^2 + s)^2\sqrt{c^2 + s}} - \pi\sigma a^2 c z^2 \int_{\kappa}^{\infty} \frac{ds}{(a^2 + s)(c^2 + s)^{\frac{3}{2}}}. \quad (1)$$

The evaluation of these integrals gives

$$V = \frac{2\pi\sigma a^2 c}{\sqrt{a^2 - c^2}}\left(1 - \frac{x^2 + y^2 - 2z^2}{2(a^2 - c^2)}\right)\sin^{-1}\sqrt{\frac{a^2 - c^2}{a^2 + \kappa}}$$

$$+ \frac{\pi\sigma a^2 c\sqrt{c^2 + \kappa}}{a^2 - c^2}\frac{x^2 + y^2}{a^2 + \kappa} - \frac{\pi\sigma a^2 c}{a^2 - c^2}\frac{2z^2}{\sqrt{c^2 + \kappa}}, \quad (2)$$

where κ satisfies the equation

$$\frac{x^2 + y^2}{a^2 + \kappa} + \frac{z^2}{c^2 + \kappa} = 1. \quad (3)$$

Although κ is a function of x, y, and z, it is not necessary to regard it as such in forming the first partial derivatives of V

with respect to x, y, and z; for it was shown in Sec. 36 that even for the general ellipsoid the derivative of the potential with respect to x, y, or z, in so far as these variables are involved implicitly through κ, vanishes. It is useless, therefore, to form it, and

$$X = \frac{\partial V}{\partial x}, \qquad Y = \frac{\partial V}{\partial y}, \qquad Z = \frac{\partial V}{\partial z},$$

are obtained from Eq. (2) just as though κ were a constant. If, however, the substitution

$$\frac{x^2 + y^2}{a^2 + \kappa} = 1 - \frac{z^2}{c^2 + \kappa}.$$

from Eq. (3) should be made in the second line of Eq. (2), although the expression for V would be simplified slightly, κ could no longer be regarded as a constant in forming the first derivatives.

If the ellipsoid of revolution is prolate, so that $c > a$, Eq. (2) becomes imaginary in form though not in reality. If it is borne in mind that

$$\sqrt{a^2 - c^2} = i\sqrt{c^2 - a^2}, \qquad i = \sqrt{-1},$$

and that

$$-i \sin^{-1} i\theta = \sinh^{-1} \theta,$$

it is readily seen from Eq. (2) that the expression for the potential of a prolate spheroid $c > a$ is

$$V = \pi\sigma a^2 c\left(1 + \frac{x^2 + y^2 - 2z^2}{2(c^2 - a^2)}\right)\frac{2}{\sqrt{c^2 - a^2}} \sinh^{-1}\sqrt{\frac{c^2 - a^2}{a^2 + \kappa}}$$
$$- \frac{\pi\sigma a^2 c\sqrt{c^2 + \kappa}}{c^2 - a^2}\frac{x^2 + y^2}{a^2 + \kappa} + \frac{\pi\sigma a^2 c}{c^2 - a^2}\frac{2z^2}{\sqrt{c^2 + \kappa}}. \qquad (4)$$

Where κ is defined by Eq. (3) just as before. In obtaining the components of attraction from Eq. (4) by differentiation κ can be regarded as a constant. It will be remembered that for interior points κ is zero.

The expression for the potential of an oblate spheroid, Eq. (2) above, was derived directly from the definite integrals in Eq. (1). It could have been derived with equal ease by limiting processes directly from Eq. (37.3), by letting b^2 approach a^2. The potential of the prolate spheroid is obtained by letting b^2 approach c^2.

40. The Attraction of a Spheroid on the Surface.—If the derivatives of the potential of an oblate spheroid Eq. (39.2) are formed and then κ is set equal to zero, the resulting expressions are the components of the attraction of the spheroid for points on its surface.   They are

$$X = -\frac{3M}{2a^3e^3\sqrt{1-e^2}}[-e + e^3 + \sqrt{1-e^2}\sin^{-1}e]x,$$

$$Y = -\frac{3M}{2a^3e^3\sqrt{1-e^2}}[-e + e^3 + \sqrt{1-e^2}\sin^{-1}e]y,$$

$$Z = -\frac{3M}{a^3e^3\sqrt{1-e^2}}[+e - 0 - \sqrt{1-e^2}\sin^{-1}e]z;$$

where $M = \frac{4}{3}\pi\sigma a^2 c$ is the mass of the spheroid and $e = \frac{\sqrt{a^2-c^2}}{a}$

is the eccentricity of a meridian section.

The intensity of the attraction is a function of the latitude but not of the longitude, since the spheroid is a figure of revolution.   For a point in the xz-plane

$$x = a\cos E, \qquad y = 0, \qquad z = a\sqrt{1-e^2}\sin E.$$

where E is the eccentric angle corresponding to the point x, y, z. If e is replaced by $e = \sin\epsilon$ the intensity of the attraction $F = \sqrt{X^2 + Y^2}$ is

$$F = \frac{3M}{2a^2\sin^3\epsilon}[(\epsilon - \sin\epsilon\cos\epsilon)^2 + \{4(\epsilon\cos\epsilon - \sin\epsilon)^2 - (\epsilon - \sin\epsilon\cos\epsilon)^2\}\sin^2 E]^{\frac{1}{2}}.$$

If a sphere of radius R has the same mass and density as the spheroid, its radius must satisfy the relationship

$$M = \frac{4}{3}\pi\sigma a^3\cos\epsilon = \frac{4}{3}\pi\sigma R^3,$$

and therefore

$$R = a\cos^{\frac{1}{3}}\epsilon.$$

The intensity of the attraction on the surface of this sphere is

$$G = \frac{M}{R^2} = \frac{M}{a^2\cos^{\frac{2}{3}}\epsilon}.$$

so that

$$F = \frac{3}{2}G\frac{\cos^{\frac{2}{3}}\epsilon}{\sin^3\epsilon}[(\epsilon - \sin\epsilon\cos\epsilon)^2 + \{4(\epsilon\cos\epsilon - \sin\epsilon)^2 - (\epsilon - \sin\epsilon\cos\epsilon)^2\}\sin^2 E]^{\frac{1}{2}}. \quad (1)$$

On the equator of the spheroid, E is zero, and

$$F_{\text{Eq.}} = \frac{3}{2} \frac{\cos^{\frac{2}{3}} \epsilon}{\sin^3 \epsilon} (\epsilon - \sin \epsilon \cos \epsilon) G,$$

$$= G\left(1 - \frac{\epsilon^2}{30} + \cdots \right).$$

For small values of ϵ the attraction on the equator of the spheroid is less than attraction on the sphere, and it is not difficult to verify that it is less for all values of $\epsilon < \pi/2$.

At the poles of the spheroid $E = \pi/2$ and

$$F_{\text{Pole}} = 3G \frac{\cos^{\frac{2}{3}} \epsilon}{\sin^3 \epsilon} (\sin \epsilon - \epsilon \cos \epsilon),$$

$$= G\left(1 + \frac{\epsilon^2}{15} + \cdots \right),$$

so that the attraction at the pole is greater than the attraction on the sphere if ϵ is small. The coefficient of G, however, has a maximum which is defined by the equation

$$\epsilon = \frac{9 - 7 \sin^2 \epsilon}{9 - 4 \sin^2 \epsilon} \tan \epsilon,$$

the solution of which is

$$\epsilon = 44° 5', \qquad \therefore e = .6958.$$

For this value of ϵ

$$F_{\text{Pole}} = 1.022G, = \frac{46}{45} G \text{ approx.},$$

and for larger values of ϵ the coefficient of G diminishes and has the limit zero.

Since the attraction on the spheroid at the pole is greater than the attraction on the sphere for small values of ϵ, while at the equator it is less, there is some latitude for which it is just equal to the attraction on the surface of the sphere. This latitude is found by setting F equal to G in Eq. (1) and then solving for $\sin^2 E$. The result is

$$\left. \begin{array}{l} \sin^2 E = \dfrac{\dfrac{4}{9} \dfrac{\sin^6 \epsilon}{\cos^{\frac{4}{3}} \epsilon} - (\epsilon - \sin \epsilon \cos \epsilon)^2}{4(\sin \epsilon - \epsilon \cos \epsilon)^2 - (\epsilon - \sin \epsilon \cos \epsilon)^2} \\[2em] = \dfrac{1}{3} + \dfrac{119}{315}\epsilon^2 + \cdots . \end{array} \right\} \tag{2}$$

The limiting value of this expression for $\epsilon = 0$ is

$$\sin^2 E = \frac{1}{3}, \quad \text{or} \quad E = 35° \ 15' \ 52'',$$

and for $\epsilon = 0$ the eccentric angle is the same as the latitude.

If the first term of the numerator of the right member of Eq. (2) is equal to the first term of the denominator, then $\sin^2 E = 1$ and $E = 90°$. This condition is

$$\frac{1}{3} \frac{\sin^3 \epsilon}{\cos^3 \epsilon} = \sin \epsilon - \epsilon \cos \epsilon$$

the solution of which is

$$\epsilon = 59° \ 4' \ 10''.$$

If ϵ is greater than this value there is no latitude for which the attraction on the spheroid is as great as the attraction on the sphere. It is everywhere less. This limiting spheroid and the corresponding sphere is shown in Fig. 21.

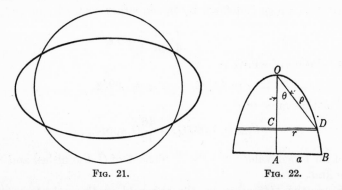

Fig. 21.   Fig. 22.

41. The Attraction is a Maximum.—It might be imagined that of all homogeneous figures of revolution the attraction of the body on the point where the axis pierces the surface is a maximum for a sphere, but the results of the preceeding section show that this is not so. It will be of interest therefore to inquire *for what figure of revolution of given volume and density is the attraction upon the point where the axis pierces the surface a maximum.*

Let Fig. 22 be a homogeneous solid of revolution with a base the radius of which is $AB = a$, and a height $AO = h$. Let CD be a thin cross-section of radius r at a distance s from the apex O, where the axis pierces the surface. Then, by Eq. (16.1), the numerical value of the attraction of the solid upon the point O is

$$F = 2\pi\sigma \int_0^h \left[1 - \frac{s}{\sqrt{r^2 + s^2}}\right] ds.$$

The sign is reversed since the magnitude of F only is of importance. The problem is to find the curve ODB which makes F a maximum *for a given volume*. That is, the condition

$$\int_0^h r^2 ds = \text{const.}$$

also must be satisfied.

On making h and r vary, it is found that the conditions which must be satisfied are

$$\int_0^h \frac{sr\,\delta r}{(a^2 + s^2)^{\frac{3}{2}}} ds + \left(1 - \frac{h}{\sqrt{a^2 + h^2}}\right)\delta h = 0, \tag{1}$$

and

$$\int_0^h 2r\,\delta r ds + a^2 \delta h = 0. \tag{2}$$

Let Eq. (1) be multiplied by the undetermined multiplier $2\lambda^2$ and then subtracted from Eq. (2). There results

$$\int_0^h \left(2 - \frac{2\lambda^2 s}{(r^2 + s^2)^{\frac{3}{2}}}\right) r\,\delta r ds + \left(a^2 - 2\lambda^2\left\{1 - \frac{h}{\sqrt{a^2 + h^2}}\right\}\right)\delta h = 0.$$

If λ is chosen so that the coefficient of δh vanishes, there remains

$$\int_0^h \left(2 - \frac{2\lambda^2 s}{(r^2 + s^2)^{\frac{3}{2}}}\right) r\,\delta r ds = 0;$$

and since this must vanish for every δr, it follows that

$$\frac{\lambda^2 s}{(r^2 + s^2)^{\frac{3}{2}}} = 1; \tag{3}$$

also

$$2\lambda^2 = \frac{a^2}{1 - \dfrac{h}{\sqrt{a^2 + h^2}}} = (a^2 + h^2) + h\sqrt{a^2 + h^2}. \tag{4}$$

Equation (3) is the equation of the curve sought in rectangular coordinates. In polar coordinates with O as the pole and OA as the polar axis

$$s = \rho \cos \theta, \qquad s^2 + r^2 = \rho^2,$$

and the equation is

$$\rho = \lambda\sqrt{\cos \theta}. \tag{5}$$

At the point B Eq. (3) gives

$$\lambda^2 h = (h^2 + a^2)^{\frac{3}{2}}. \qquad (6)$$

If λ^2 is eliminated between Eqs. (6) and (4) and the resulting expression is then rationalized, it is found that

$$(h^2 + a^2)(3h^2 + 4a^2)a^2 = 0,$$

and therefore a is zero. Equation (4) then gives

$$\lambda = h.$$

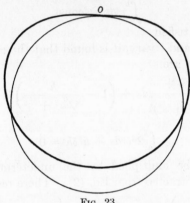

FIG. 23.

The radius of the sphere of equal volume R is given by the formula

$$\pi \int_0^h r^2 ds = \frac{4}{3}\pi R^3,$$

or

$$\int_0^{\frac{\pi}{2}} \cos^{\frac{3}{2}} \theta \, \sin^3 \theta \, d\theta = \frac{8}{9}\frac{R^3}{h^3};$$

from which it follows that

$$h = R\sqrt[3]{5} = 1.71 \cdots R.$$

A meridian section of the solid of revolution of maximum surface attraction and the sphere of equal volume is given in Fig. 23.

The intensity of the attraction upon the point O is

$$\begin{aligned}
F &= 2\pi\sigma \int_0^h \left(1 - \frac{s}{\sqrt{r^2 + s^2}}\right) ds \\
&= 2\pi\sigma h \left(1 - \frac{3}{2}\int_J^{\frac{\pi}{2}} \cos^{\frac{3}{2}} \theta \, \sin \theta \, d\theta\right) \\
&= \frac{4}{5}\pi\sigma h.
\end{aligned}$$

The attraction upon the sphere of equal volume is

$$G = \frac{4}{3}\pi\sigma R.$$

Hence,

$$\frac{F}{G} = \frac{3}{5}\frac{h}{R} = \frac{3}{5}\sqrt[3]{5} = 1.0260 \cdots = \frac{39}{38} \text{ approx.,}$$

and the attraction of the solid of revolution of maximum attraction upon the point O exceeds the attraction of the sphere of equal volume by one part in 38 approximately. It was seen in Sec. 40 that the maximum attraction at the pole of an oblate spheroid exceeds the attraction of a sphere of equal volume by about one part in 45.

It is interesting to observe that this surface furnishes also the solution of another problem, namely; a particle is attracted towards a fixed point by a force which varies inversely as the square of the distance. It is required to find the locus of the points for which the z-component of the attraction is constant. The z-component of attraction is

$$-\frac{k^2 z}{(x^2 + y^2 + z^2)^{\frac{3}{2}}},$$

where k^2 is the force of attraction at a unit distance. On comparing this expression with Eq. (3) it is seen that the solution is the surface drawn in Fig. 23.

42. The Potential of a Homogeneous Elliptic Cylinder.— Instead of computing the potential of elliptic cylinders directly from the definite integrals the desired result will be obtained by letting the longest axis of the ellipsoid approach infinity. The ellipsoid, then, approaches an elliptic cylinder for which the equation is

$$\frac{y^2}{b^2} + \frac{z^2}{c^2} = 1, \qquad b^2 > c^2.$$

Equation (35.6) becomes

$$\frac{y^2}{b^2 + \kappa} + \frac{z^2}{c^2 + \kappa} = 1,$$

which is the equation of a confocal cylinder.

The first factor in the expression for the potential of an ellipsoid Eq. (36.3),

$$\frac{2\pi\sigma abc}{\sqrt{a^2 - c^2}},$$

has the limiting value $2\pi\sigma bc$.

The amplitude of the elliptic integrals F and E is ω_κ, where

$$\sin \omega_\kappa = \sqrt{\frac{a^2 - c^2}{a^2 + \kappa}}.$$

Since κ remains finite as $a \to \infty$, the limit of ω_κ is $\pi/2$. The limit of the modulus,

$$k^2 = \frac{a^2 - b^2}{a^2 - c^2},$$

as a^2 tends towards infinity, is evidently $+1$. Hence, the limit of $E(\omega_\kappa, k)$ is, Eq. (36.2),

$$E\left(\frac{\pi}{2}, 1\right) = \int_0^{\frac{\pi}{2}} \sqrt{1 - \sin^2 \varphi} \, d\varphi = +1;$$

and the limit of $F(\omega_\kappa, k)$ is

$$F\left(\frac{\pi}{2}, 1\right) = \int_0^{\frac{\pi}{2}} \frac{d\varphi}{\sqrt{1 - \sin^2 \varphi}} = +\infty \cdot$$

It is evident that the term in the potential which is explicitly independent of x^2, y^2, and z^2 increases indefinitely as the length of the ellipsoid increases. It will be shown immediately that the remaining terms have a finite limit, and, therefore, the limit of V is infinite. This is not surprising for the mass of the limiting cylinder is infinite. This term corresponds to the constant term of the potential, for it drops out when V is differentiated with respect to x, y, or z in so far as these variables occur explicitly.

The coefficient of the term in x^2 is

$$\frac{1}{a^2 - b^2}[+E(\omega_\kappa, k) - F(\omega_\kappa, k)]$$

$$= \frac{1}{b^2 - c^2} \cdot \frac{(1 - k^2)}{k^2}[E(\omega_\kappa, k) - F(\omega_\kappa, k)].$$

The limit of $(1 - k^2)E$, as k^2 approaches $+1$, is evidently zero. As for the limit of $(1 - k^2)F$,

$$F(\omega_\kappa, k) = \int_0^{\omega_\kappa} \frac{d\varphi}{\sqrt{1 - k^2 \sin^2 \varphi}} < \int_0^{\omega_\kappa} \frac{d\varphi}{\sqrt{1 - k^2}} = \frac{\omega_\kappa}{\sqrt{1 - k^2}}$$

so that

$$(1 - k^2)F(\omega_\kappa, k) < \omega_\kappa \sqrt{1 - k^2},$$

which has the limit zero as $k^2 \to 1$. The coefficient of the term in x^2 therefore vanishes.

Likewise, the term

$$\frac{y^2}{a^2 - b^2} F(\omega_\kappa, k^2)$$

has the limit zero; and, since the limit of E is $+1$, the limit of the remaining terms can be written down at once.

A true potential does not exist, but the variable part is

$$V_{\text{var.}} = \frac{2\pi\sigma bc}{b^2 - c^2} \left\{ y^2 \left(\sqrt{\frac{c^2 + \kappa}{b^2 + \kappa}} - 1 \right) + z^2 \left(1 - \sqrt{\frac{b^2 + \kappa}{c^2 + \kappa}} \right) \right\}.$$

Now

$$\sqrt{\frac{c^2 + \kappa}{b^2 + \kappa}} - 1 = \frac{\sqrt{c^2 + \kappa} - \sqrt{b^2 + \kappa}}{\sqrt{b^2 + \kappa}}$$

$$= \frac{(\sqrt{c^2 + \kappa})^2 - (\sqrt{b^2 + \kappa})^2}{\sqrt{b^2 + \kappa}(\sqrt{b^2 + \kappa} + \sqrt{c^2 + \kappa})} =$$

$$-\frac{b^2 - c^2}{b^2 + \kappa + \sqrt{(b^2 + \kappa)(c^2 + \kappa)}};$$

and likewise

$$1 - \sqrt{\frac{b^2 + \kappa}{c^2 + \kappa}} = -\frac{b^2 - c^2}{c^2 + \kappa + \sqrt{(b^2 + \kappa)(c^2 + \kappa)}},$$

so that

$$V_{\text{var.}} = -2\pi\sigma bc \left(\frac{y^2}{b^2 + \kappa + \sqrt{(b^2 + \kappa)(c^2 + \kappa)}} \right.$$

$$\left. + \frac{z^2}{c^2 + \kappa + \sqrt{(b^2 + \kappa)(c^2 + \kappa)}} \right),$$

from which the factor $b^2 - c^2$ has disappeared.

The components of attraction are

$$Y = \frac{-4\pi\sigma bcy}{b^2 + \kappa + \sqrt{(b^2 + \kappa)(c^2 + \kappa)}},$$

$$Z = \frac{-4\pi\sigma bcz}{c^2 + \kappa + \sqrt{(b^2 + \kappa)(c^2 + \kappa)}}.$$

If the point x, y, z is in the interior or on the surface of the cylinder, κ is zero and the expressions for the components of attraction become

$$Y_i = -4\pi\sigma\frac{cy}{b+c}, \qquad Z_i = -4\pi\sigma\frac{bz}{b+c}.$$

If $b = c$ the cylinder is circular, and the expressions for the components of attraction become

$$Y = -\frac{2\pi\sigma c^2 y}{c^2 + \kappa}, \qquad Z = -\frac{2\pi\sigma c^2 z}{c^2 + \kappa}.$$

or, since in this case, $c^2 + \kappa = y^2 + z^2$, for exterior particles,

$$Y = -2\pi\sigma c^2\frac{y}{y^2 + z^2}, \qquad Z = -2\pi\sigma c^2\frac{z}{y^2 + z^2}.$$

These expressions are the derivatives of the logarithmic potential

$$V = -2\pi\sigma c^2 \log \sqrt{y^2 + z^2},$$

which satisfies the partial differential equation, Sec. 28,

$$\frac{\partial^2 V}{\partial x^2} + \frac{\partial^2 V}{\partial y^2} = 0.$$

The functions which satisfy this equation are closely related to the functions of a complex variable*

$$w = y + iz, \qquad i = \sqrt{-1}.$$

It will be observed that the logarithmic potential becomes infinite at infinity.

43. The Potential of a Homogeneous, Rectangular Parallelopiped.—Let the origin of a rectangular coordinate system be taken with the origin at the center of the parallelopiped and the axes parallel to its edges. Let the edges of the parallelopiped be $2a$, $2b$, and $2c$ and, for convenience of notation, let the density σ be taken equal to unity. Let the coordinates of the attracted point be x, y, z and the running coordinates of the element of mass of the parallelopiped be ξ, η, ζ. Then

$$V = \int_B \frac{dm}{\rho} = \int_{-c}^{+c}\int_{-b}^{+b}\int_{-a}^{+a}\frac{d\xi d\eta d\zeta}{\rho},$$

or, after multiplying numerator and denominator by

$$\rho^2 = [(\xi - x)^2 + (\eta - y)^2 + (\zeta - z)^2],$$

* PICARD, "Traite d'Analyze," Vol. II.

there results

$$2V = \int_{-c}^{+c}\int_{-b}^{+b}\int_{-a}^{+a}\left[\frac{(\eta - y)^2 + (\zeta - z)^2}{\rho^3} + \frac{(\zeta - z)^2 + (\xi - x)^2}{\rho^3} + \frac{(\xi - x)^2 + (\eta - y)^2}{\rho^3}\right]d\xi d\eta d\zeta.$$

From this last form it is readily seen that

$$2V = \int_{-c}^{+c}\int_{-b}^{+b}\int_{-a}^{+a}\left[\frac{\partial}{\partial\xi}\left(\frac{\xi - x}{\rho}\right) + \frac{\partial}{\partial\eta}\left(\frac{\eta - y}{\rho}\right) + \frac{\partial}{\partial\zeta}\left(\frac{\zeta - z}{\rho}\right)\right]d\xi d\eta d\zeta. \quad (1)$$

Since each term of the integrand is an exact derivative, it is possible to integrate each of them once. Before doing so, however, it is desirable to define a notation as to the limiting values of ρ. Let

$$\rho_{100} = \sqrt{(a + x)^2 + (\eta - y)^2 + (\zeta - z)^2},$$
$$\rho_{200} = \sqrt{(a - x)^2 + (\eta - y)^2 + (\zeta - z)^2},$$
$$\rho_{110} = \sqrt{(a + x)^2 + (b + y)^2 + (\zeta - z)^2},$$
$$\rho_{120} = \sqrt{(a + x)^2 + (b - y)^2 + (\zeta - z)^2},$$
$$\text{etc.,}$$

the subscript 1 being associated with the positive sign and the subscript 2 with the negative sign.

With this notation the expression for V becomes after integrating once

$$2V = \int_{-c}^{+c}\int_{-b}^{+b}\left[\frac{x + a}{\rho_{100}} - \frac{x - a}{\rho_{200}}\right]d\eta d\zeta$$
$$+ \int_{-c}^{+c}\int_{-a}^{+a}\left[\frac{y + b}{\rho_{010}} - \frac{y - b}{\rho_{020}}\right]d\zeta d\xi$$
$$+ \int_{-b}^{+b}\int_{-a}^{+a}\left[\frac{z + c}{\rho_{001}} - \frac{z - c}{\rho_{002}}\right]d\xi d\eta. \quad (2)$$

The numerators in these expressions are all constants with respect to the variables of integration, and the six integrals are all of the same type. It will be sufficient to integrate one of them and then derive the others from it. The first integral is

$$
\left.\begin{aligned}
(x+a)\int_{-c}^{+c}\int_{-b}^{+b}\frac{d\eta d\zeta}{\rho_{100}} &= (x+a)\int_{-c}^{+c}\int_{-b}^{+b}\left[\frac{(x+a)^2+(\eta-y)^2}{\rho^3_{100}}\right. \\
&\qquad \left.+\frac{(x+a)^2+(\zeta-z)^2}{\rho^3_{100}}-\frac{(x+a)^2}{\rho^3_{100}}\right]d\eta d\zeta \\
&= (x+a)\int_{-c}^{+c}\int_{-b}^{+b}\left[\frac{\partial}{\partial\zeta}\left(\frac{\zeta-z}{\rho_{100}}\right)+\frac{\partial}{\partial\eta}\left(\frac{\eta-y}{\rho_{100}}\right)-\frac{(x+a)^2}{\rho^3_{100}}\right]d\eta d\zeta \\
&= (x+a)\int_{-b}^{+b}\left[\frac{z+c}{\rho_{101}}-\frac{z-c}{\rho_{102}}\right]d\eta+(x+a)\int_{-c}^{+c}\left[\frac{y+b}{\rho_{110}}-\frac{y-b}{\rho_{120}}\right]d\zeta
\end{aligned}\right\} \quad (3)
$$

$$
-(x+a)^3\int_{-c}^{+c}\int_{-b}^{+b}\frac{d\eta d\zeta}{\rho^3_{100}}. \quad (4)
$$

Since, in general,

$$
\int\frac{dx}{\rho}=\int\frac{dx}{\sqrt{m^2+x^2}}=-\log(\rho-x),
$$

the sum of the four simple integrals in the above expression is

$$
(x+a)(z+c)\log\frac{\rho_{111}+(y+b)}{\rho_{121}+(y-b)}
$$
$$
-(x+a)(z-c)\log\frac{\rho_{112}+(y+b)}{\rho_{122}+(y-b)}
$$
$$
+(x+a)(y+b)\log\frac{\rho_{111}+(z+c)}{\rho_{112}+(z-c)}
$$
$$
-(x+a)(y-b)\log\frac{\rho_{121}+(z+c)}{\rho_{122}+(z-c)}.
$$

Now
$$
\rho^2_{111}=(x+a)^2+(y+b)^2+(z+c)^2,
$$
$$
\rho^2_{121}=(x+a)^2+(y-b)^2+(z+c)^2,
$$
so that
$$
\rho^2_{111}-\rho^2_{121}=4by.
$$
Therefore
$$
\frac{\rho_{111}+(y+b)}{\rho_{121}+(y-b)}=\frac{4b\rho_{111}+\rho^2_{111}-\rho^2_{121}+4b^2}{4b\rho_{121}+\rho^2_{111}-\rho^2_{121}-4b^2}
$$
$$
=\frac{(\rho_{111}+2b)^2-\rho^2_{121}}{\rho^2_{111}-(\rho_{121}-2b)^2}=\frac{\rho_{111}+\rho_{121}+2b,}{\rho_{111}+\rho_{121}-2b},
$$

and the sum of the four simple integrals can also be written

$$
(x+a)(z+c)\log\frac{\rho_{111}+\rho_{121}+2b}{\rho_{111}+\rho_{121}-2b}
$$
$$
-(x+a)(z-c)\log\frac{\rho_{112}+\rho_{122}+2b}{\rho_{112}+\rho_{122}-2b}
$$

$$+ (x + a)(y + b) \log \frac{\rho_{111} + \rho_{112} + 2c}{\rho_{111} + \rho_{112} - 2c}$$

$$- (x + a)(y - b) \log \frac{\rho_{121} + \rho_{122} + 2c}{\rho_{121} + \rho_{122} - 2c}. \quad (5)$$

Consider the face of the parallelopiped which is perpendicular to the x-axis and at the distance $x = -a$ from the origin. This face contains four edges, two of which are parallel to the y-axis and two parallel to the z-axis. Through the attracted point $P(x, y, z)$ pass a plane perpendicular to the y-axis. Any line L which is parallel to the y-axis will pierce this plane at a certain point O. The x- and z-coordinates of the point P with respect to the point O will be called for brevity the coordinates of the point P with respect to the line L; and a similar convention will be adopted if L is parallel to either of the other two axes. Any one of the four terms which occurs in Eq. (5) is the potential of one of the four edges considered as a straight line of unit density (Sec. 31) multiplied by the product of the coordinates of P with respect to that edge.

Each one of the six integrals in Eq. (2) gives rise to four of these edge potentials, making 24 in all; but as there are only 12 edges it is evident that each edge potential occurs twice, so that in the final result the terms in Eq. (5) are multiplied by the factor 2.

There remains the double integral (Eq. (4))

$$- (x + a)^3 \int_{-c}^{+c} \int_{-b}^{+b} \frac{d\eta d\zeta}{\rho^3_{100}},$$

which is the integral of $1/\rho^3$ taken over the face of the parallelopiped $x = -a$. Consider the infinitesimal cone which has the rectangle $d\eta d\zeta$ as its base and the point $P(xyz)$ as its apex. Let dA be the area cut out of the sphere which has P as its center and is tangent to the face $x = -a$, Fig. 4, by this infinitesimal cone. Since the radius of this sphere is $x + a$ it is evident that

$$\frac{(x + a)^3}{\rho^3} d\eta d\zeta = dA,$$

and, therefore, the integral

$$D = (x + a)^3 \int_{-c}^{+c} \int_{-b}^{+b} \frac{d\eta d\zeta}{\rho^3_{100}}$$

is simply the projection of the face $x = -a$ upon the sphere which has its center at P and is tangent to the plane of the face $x = -a$. (Fig. 24.)

In order to evaluate it, it will be observed that

$$\frac{\partial}{\partial \eta}\left(\frac{\eta - y}{\rho_{100}}\right) = \frac{(x + a)^2 + (\zeta - z)^2}{\rho^3{}_{100}},$$

so that

$$D = \int_{-c}^{+c}\left[\frac{(x + a)^3}{(x + a)^2 + (\zeta - z)^2} \cdot \frac{\eta - y}{\rho_{100}}\right]_{-b}^{+b} d\zeta;$$

or

$$D = \int_{-c}^{+c} \frac{(x + a)^3}{(x + a)^2 + (\zeta - z)^2} \cdot \frac{b - y}{\rho_{120}} d\zeta$$
$$+ \int_{-c}^{+c} \frac{(x + a)^3}{(x + a)^2 + (\zeta - z)^2} \cdot \frac{b + y}{\rho_{110}} d\zeta.$$

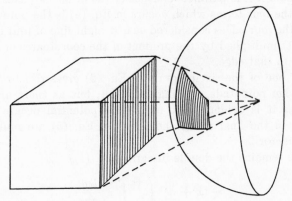

FIG. 24.

Now, since

$$\int \frac{xy}{x^2 + z^2} \cdot \frac{dz}{\rho} = \tan^{-1}\frac{yz}{x\rho},$$

where

$$\rho = \sqrt{x^2 + y^2 + z^2},$$

the fully integrated expression for D is

$$D = (x + a)^2\left[\tan^{-1}\frac{(z + c)(y + b)}{(x + a)\rho_{111}} - \tan^{-1}\frac{(y + b)(z - c)}{(x + a)\rho_{112}}\right.$$
$$\left. - \tan^{-1}\frac{(y - k)(z + c)}{(x + a)\rho_{121}} + \tan^{-1}\frac{(y - b)(z - c)}{(x + a)\rho_{122}}\right].$$

Since there are four $\tan^{-1}$'s for each face and there are six faces, there are 24 such expressions in the complete potential.

If x, y, z, ρ are the coordinates of a point P_1, and if

$$w_1 = \tan^{-1}\frac{yz}{x\rho}$$

it is easy to interpret w_1 upon the sphere, which has the origin as its center and passes through the point P_1. Let Fig. 25 be such a sphere. Then,

$$\tan \varphi = \frac{y}{x}, \qquad \sin \omega = \frac{z}{\rho},$$

from which it follows that

$$\tan w_1 = \tan \varphi \sin \omega.$$

In the spherical triangle P_1Q_1Y, the angle at Q_1 is a right angle, so that

$$\tan (90° - P_1) = \tan \varphi \sin \omega,$$

and consequently

$$w_1 = 90° - P_1.$$

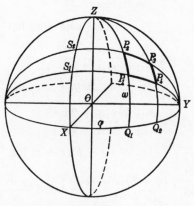

Fig. 25.

It is, therefore, the spherical excess of the spherical quadrilateral $XQ_1P_1S_1$, and the area of this quadrilateral is

$$\text{area } XQ_1P_1S_1 = \rho^2 w_1.$$

The area of the spherical quadrilateral $P_1P_2P_3P_4$ evidently is

$$\text{area } P_1P_2P_3P_4 = \rho^2(w_1 + w_3 - w_2 - w_4).$$

The second integral of Eq. (2) can be obtained from the first by first changing the sign of a in the first integral and then changing the sign of all of the terms. A circular permutation of the letters x, y, z and a, b, c in the first two integrals will then give all of the others. In this way the complete potential of the homogeneous right parallelopiped of unit density is found to be:

$$V = (x + a)(y + b) \log \frac{\rho_{111} + \rho_{112} + 2c}{\rho_{111} + \rho_{112} - 2c}$$

$$- (x + a)(y - b) \log \frac{\rho_{121} + \rho_{122} + 2c}{\rho_{121} + \rho_{122} - 2c}$$

$$+ (x + a)(z + c) \log \frac{\rho_{111} + \rho_{121} + 2b}{\rho_{111} + \rho_{121} - 2b}$$

$$- (x + a)(z - c) \log \frac{\rho_{112} + \rho_{122} + 2b}{\rho_{112} + \rho_{122} - 2b}$$

$$+ (x - a)(y - b) \log \frac{\rho_{221} + \rho_{222} + 2c}{\rho_{221} + \rho_{222} - 2c}$$

$$- (x - a)(y + b) \log \frac{\rho_{211} + \rho_{212} + 2c}{\rho_{211} + \rho_{212} - 2c}$$

$$+ (x - a)(z - c) \log \frac{\rho_{212} + \rho_{222} + 2b}{\rho_{212} + \rho_{222} - 2b}$$

$$- (x - a)(z + c) \log \frac{\rho_{211} + \rho_{221} + 2b}{\rho_{211} + \rho_{221} - 2b}$$

$$+ (y + b)(z + c) \log \frac{\rho_{111} + \rho_{211} + 2a}{\rho_{111} + \rho_{211} - 2a}$$

$$- (y + b)(z - c) \log \frac{\rho_{112} + \rho_{212} + 2a}{\rho_{112} + \rho_{212} - 2a}$$

$$+ (y - b)(z - c) \log \frac{\rho_{122} + \rho_{222} + 2a}{\rho_{122} + \rho_{222} - 2a}$$

$$- (y - b)(z + c) \log \frac{\rho_{121} + \rho_{221} + 2a}{\rho_{121} + \rho_{221} - 2a}$$

$$+ \frac{1}{2}(x + a)^2 \left[\tan^{-1} \frac{(y + b)(z - c)}{(x + a)\rho_{112}} - \tan^{-1} \frac{(y + b)(z + c)}{(x + a)\rho_{111}} \right.$$

$$\left. + \tan^{-1} \frac{(y - b)(z + c)}{(x + a)\rho_{121}} - \tan^{-1} \frac{(y - b)(z - c)}{(x + a)\rho_{122}} \right]$$

$$+ \frac{1}{2}(x - a)^2 \left[\tan^{-1} \frac{(y + b)(z + c)}{(x - a)\rho_{211}} - \tan^{-1} \frac{(y + b)(z - c)}{(x - a)\rho_{212}} \right.$$

$$\left. + \tan^{-1} \frac{(y - b)(z - c)}{(x - a)\rho_{222}} - \tan^{-1} \frac{(y - b)(z + c)}{(x - a)\rho_{221}} \right]$$

$$+ \frac{1}{2}(y + b)^2 \left[\tan^{-1} \frac{(x - a)(z + c)}{(y + b)\rho_{211}} - \tan^{-1} \frac{(x + a)(z + c)}{(y + b)\rho_{111}} \right.$$

$$\left. + \tan^{-1} \frac{(x + a)(z - c)}{(y + b)\rho_{112}} - \tan^{-1} \frac{(x - a)(z - c)}{(y + b)\rho_{212}} \right]$$

$$+ \frac{1}{2}(y-b)^2 \left[\tan^{-1}\frac{(x+a)(z+c)}{(y-b)\rho_{121}} - \tan^{-1}\frac{(x-a)(z+c)}{(y-b)\rho_{221}} \right.$$

$$\left. + \tan^{-1}\frac{(x-a)(z-c)}{(y-b)\rho_{222}} - \tan^{-1}\frac{(x+a)(z-c)}{(y-b)\rho_{122}} \right]$$

$$\frac{1}{2}(z+c)^2 \left[\tan^{-1}\frac{(x+a)(y-b)}{(z+c)\rho_{121}} - \tan^{-1}\frac{(x+a)(y+b)}{(z+c)\rho_{111}} \right.$$

$$\left. + \tan^{-1}\frac{(x-a)(y+b)}{(z+c)\rho_{211}} - \tan^{-1}\frac{(x-a)(y-b)}{(z+c)\rho_{221}} \right]$$

$$+ \frac{1}{2}(z-c)^2 \left[\tan^{-1}\frac{(x+a)(y+b)}{(z-c)\rho_{112}} - \tan^{-1}\frac{(x+a)(y-b)}{(z-c)\rho_{122}} \right.$$

$$\left. + \tan^{-1}\frac{(x-a)(y-b)}{(z-c)\rho_{222}} - \tan^{-1}\frac{(x-a)(y+b)}{(z-c)\rho_{212}} \right].$$

44. The Components of Force for the Right Parallelopiped.—
The components of the force due to the attraction of a right
parallelopiped X, Y, Z are, of course, the partial derivatives
of the potential with respect to the coordinates x, y, and z. On
the face of it this differentiation is such a discouraging task that a
resort to the integration formulas

$$\left. \begin{aligned} X = \frac{\partial V}{\partial x} &= \int\int\int \frac{\partial}{\partial x}\left(\frac{1}{\rho}\right)d\xi d\eta d\zeta = -\int\int\int \frac{\partial}{\partial \xi}\left(\frac{1}{\rho}\right)d\xi d\eta d\zeta \\ &= \int_{-c}^{+c}\int_{-b}^{+b}\left(\frac{1}{\rho_{100}} - \frac{1}{\rho_{200}}\right)d\eta d\zeta, \\ &\qquad\qquad \text{etc.,} \end{aligned} \right\} \quad (1)$$

seems preferable. As a matter of fact, however, it is not necessary
to differentiate with respect to the coordinates in so far as these
coordinates appear under the log and $\tan^{-1}$ symbols. It is
sufficient to differentiate as though these functions were constants,
and a recognition of this fact makes the differentiation a very
simple matter.

In order to prove this it will be observed that Eq. (1) is simply
$\partial(2V)/\partial x$ in so far as x appears explicitly in Eq. (43.2). The
terms in $2V$ which arise from the first integral carry either $x + a$
or $x - a$ as factors, and in order to produce Eq. (1) by differentiation only these terms should be used. The terms in Eq. (5)
carry $(x + a)$ linearly and they are duplicated by terms in the
second and third integrals. Hence, when the factor 2 is removed
the same terms appear in V not duplicated. Similar remarks
hold for the terms which carry $x - a$ as a factor. All of these

terms contain logarithms. The terms which carry arc-tangents do not reappear in the terms of the second and third integrals, but a second factor $(x + a)$ appears, which, when divided by 2, gives the factor $(x + a)^2/2$. The derivative of this factor is just the same as the derivative of the product $(x + a)(x + a)$ when only one of the factors is differentiated. Hence, the correct value of $\partial V/\partial x$ is obtained by differentiating V with respect to x only in so far as x occurs in the factors which are the coefficients of the logarithms and arc-tangents.

45. A Generalization Regarding Derivatives of a Potential.—
It will be remembered that a similar phenomenon appeared in the potential of the ellipsoid where κ, the root of a cubic equation, could be regarded as constant in the process of differentiation. The phenomenon is not peculiar to these two potentials, however, but appears in general for homogeneous bodies.   By its definition

$$V = \sigma \int \int \int \frac{d\xi d\eta d\zeta}{\rho},$$

and

$$2V = \sigma \int \int \int \left[\frac{(\eta - y)^2 + (\zeta - z)^2}{\rho^3} + \frac{(\zeta - z)^2 + (\xi - x)^2}{\rho^3} + \frac{(\xi - x)^2 + (\eta - y)^2}{\rho^3} \right] d\xi d\eta d\zeta.$$

$$= \sigma \int \int \int \left[\frac{\partial}{\partial \xi}\left(\frac{\xi - x}{\rho} \right) + \frac{\partial}{\partial \eta}\left(\frac{\eta - y}{\rho} \right) + \frac{\partial}{\partial \zeta}\left(\frac{\zeta - z}{\rho} \right) \right] d\xi d\eta d\zeta.$$

or

$$2V = \sigma \int \int \left[\frac{\xi - \bar{x}}{\rho} \right]_{\xi_1}^{\xi_2} d\eta d\zeta + \sigma \int \int \left[\frac{\eta - \bar{y}}{\rho} \right]_{\eta_1}^{\eta_2} d\zeta d\xi + \sigma \int \int \left[\frac{\zeta - \bar{z}}{\rho} \right]_{\zeta_1}^{\zeta_2} d\xi d\eta. \quad (1)$$

Let the letters $x, y,$ and z *in so far as they occur explicitly* in Eq. (1) be marked by a dash, $\bar{x}, \bar{y}, \bar{z}$, so that they can be identified in the integration process.   Then

$$\left.\begin{aligned} \frac{\partial (2V)}{\partial \bar{x}} &= -\sigma \int \int \left[\frac{1}{\rho} \right]_{\xi_1}^{\xi_2} d\eta d\zeta, \\ \frac{\partial (2V)}{\partial \bar{y}} &= -\sigma \int \int \left[\frac{1}{\rho} \right]_{\eta_1}^{\eta_2} d\zeta d\xi, \\ \frac{\partial (2V)}{\partial \bar{z}} &= -\sigma \int \int \left[\frac{1}{\rho} \right]_{\zeta_1}^{\zeta_2} d\xi d\eta. \end{aligned}\right\} \quad (2)$$

The components of force X, Y, and Z are given by the formulas

$$
\left.
\begin{aligned}
X = \frac{\partial V}{\partial x} &= \sigma \int \int \int \frac{\partial}{\partial x}\left(\frac{1}{\rho}\right) d\xi d\eta d\zeta \\
&= -\sigma \int \int \int \frac{\partial}{\partial \xi}\left(\frac{1}{\rho}\right) d\xi d\eta d\zeta \\
&= -\sigma \int \int \left[\frac{1}{\rho}\right]_{\xi_1}^{\xi_2} d\eta d\zeta.
\end{aligned}
\right\}
\tag{3}
$$

and similarly

$$
Y = -\sigma \int \int \left[\frac{1}{\rho}\right]_{\eta_1}^{\eta_2} d\zeta d\xi, \qquad Z = -\sigma \int \int \left[\frac{1}{\rho}\right]_{\zeta_1}^{\zeta_2} d\xi d\eta, \tag{4}
$$

where the distinction indicated by the dashes does not occur. A comparison of Eqs. (3) and (4) with Eqs. (2) shows that

$$
X = \frac{\partial(2V)}{\partial \bar{x}}, \qquad Y = \frac{\partial(2V)}{\partial \bar{y}}, \qquad Z = \frac{\partial(2V)}{\partial \bar{z}}.
$$

Since

$$
X = \frac{\partial V}{\partial x}
$$

wherever x occurs, marked and not marked, and since

$$
X = 2\frac{\partial V}{\partial \bar{x}},
$$

it follows that the derivative of V with respect to x in so far as x is marked is exactly equal to the derivative of V with respect to x in so far as x is not marked; and, similarly, with respect to the letters y and z.

46. The Potential of a Body at a Distant Point.—Only in relatively simple cases can the expression for the potential of a body be obtained in a closed (finite) form on account of the difficulties in carrying out the required integrations, and recourse must be had to expansions in series. Indeed, for points which are at a great distance relative to the size of the body the first few terms of the expansion are sufficient for many purposes, and as they are simpler than the closed form they are to be preferred even when the closed form of the potential is known.

In Fig. 26, let B be any body of finite dimensions. Let O be any point within or without the body which is taken as the origin of a coordinate system. Let G be the center of gravity of B, and P any point distant from B. Let $\sigma d\tau = dm$ be an element of mass of B, at a distance ρ from P and r from O; and finally let $OP = R$. Then the potential of B at P is

$$V = \int_B \frac{\sigma d\tau}{\rho}.$$

If the angle between r and R is denoted by α, then
$$\rho^2 = R^2 - 2rR \cos \alpha + r^2,$$

and

$$\frac{1}{\rho} = \frac{1}{R}\left(1 - 2\frac{r}{R} \cos \alpha + \frac{r^2}{R^2}\right)^{-\frac{1}{2}}.$$

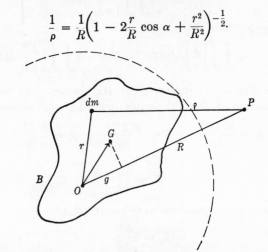

Fig. 26.

The binomial theorem gives the formula
$$(1 - x)^{-\frac{1}{2}} = 1 + \frac{1}{2}x + \frac{1 \cdot 3}{2 \cdot 4}x^2 + \frac{1 \cdot 3 \cdot 5}{2 \cdot 4 \cdot 6}x^3 + \cdots,$$

and by taking

$$x = 2\frac{r}{R} \cos \alpha - \frac{r^2}{R^2} \cdots,$$

and then rearranging in powers of r/R, it is found that

$$\frac{1}{\rho} = \frac{1}{R} + \frac{r}{R^2} \cos \alpha + \frac{1}{2}\frac{r^2}{R^3}(3 \cos^2 \alpha - 1)$$
$$+ \frac{1}{2}\frac{r^3}{R^4}(5 \cos^3 \alpha - 3 \cos \alpha)$$
$$+ \frac{1}{8}\frac{r^4}{R^5}(35 \cos^4 \alpha - 30 \cos^2 \alpha + 3) + \cdots. \quad (1)$$

The coefficients of this expression evidently are polynomials in $\cos \alpha$ and are known as *Legendre's polynomials*, the coefficient of r^n/R^{n+1} being denoted by $P_n(\cos \alpha)$.

This expansion can be derived in another way which is useful in proving the convergence of the series. If r/R is denoted by the letter h, the factors of ρ^2 are

$$\rho^2 = R^2(1 - 2h \cos \alpha + h^2)$$
$$= R^2(1 - he^{i\alpha})(1 - he^{-i\alpha}), \qquad i = \sqrt{-1};$$

and

$$\frac{1}{\rho} = \frac{1}{R}(1 - he^{i\alpha})^{-\frac{1}{2}}(1 - he^{-i\alpha})^{-\frac{1}{2}}.$$

The expansions for $(1 - he^{i\alpha})^{-\frac{1}{2}}$ and $(1 - he^{-i\alpha})^{-\frac{1}{2}}$ in powers of h are absolutely convergent provided

$$|he^{i\alpha}| < 1 \qquad \text{and} \qquad |he^{-i\alpha}| < 1$$

respectively, and since

$$|e^{i\alpha}| = |e^{-i\alpha}| = 1.$$

for all real values of α, both conditions are satisfied if

$$|h| < 1;$$

and the expansions are absolutely and uniformly convergent if

$$|h| < h_0 < 1.$$

With O as a center and a radius a trifle greater than the distance of the most remote point of B from O (the trifle can be as small as is desired), describe a sphere S. The body B will lie wholly within S, and the expansion Eq. (1) is absolutely and uniformly convergent for every point P which lies outside of S. It can, therefore, be integrated term by term and the resulting series is convergent and represents V. Therefore

$$V = \int_B \frac{dm}{R} + \frac{1}{R^2}\int_B r \cos \alpha \, dm + \frac{1}{2R^3}\int_B (3r^2 \cos^2 \alpha - r^2)dm$$

$$+ \frac{1}{2R^4}\int_B (5r^3 \cos^3 \alpha - 3r^3 \cos \alpha)dm + \cdots . \quad (2)$$

If M is the total mass of B and g is the projection of OG on R, it is evident at once, that

$$\int_B \frac{dm}{R} = \frac{M}{R}, \qquad \text{and} \qquad \int_B \frac{r \cos \alpha}{R^2}dm = \frac{Mg}{R^2}.$$

If $\cos^2 \alpha$ in the third integral of Eq. (2) is replaced by $1 - \sin^2 \alpha$, it is seen that the third integral can be written

$$\frac{1}{R^3}\int_B r^2 dm - \frac{3}{2R^3}\int r^2 \sin^2 \alpha \, dm.$$

But $\int_B r^2 dm$ is the moment of inertia of the body B with respect to the origin O, and $\int_B r^2 \sin^2 \alpha \, dm$ is the moment of inertia of the body with respect to the line $OP = R$. If these moments of inertia are denoted by I_O and I_R respectively, the first three terms of the series (2) can be written

$$V = \frac{M}{R} + \frac{Mg}{R^2} + \frac{2I_O - 3I_R}{R^3} + \cdots . \qquad (3)$$

When the origin is taken at the center of gravity, g is zero and the expression is

$$V = \frac{M}{R} + \frac{2I_O - 3I_R}{R^3} + \cdots . \qquad (4)$$

If the point P is very remote, the second and higher terms are very small and the potential is reduced essentially to its first term, which is the potential of a sphere of the same mass M. It is evident from Eq. (3) that for every finite body

$$\lim_{R=\infty} RV = M, \qquad (5)$$

a limiting value which is often useful.

Expansion for the Logarithmic Potential.—For a logarithmic potential

$$V = \int_A \log \frac{1}{\rho} \cdot \sigma d\omega,$$

the integral being taken over a given area for which σ is the density and $d\omega$ an element of surface, so that $dm = \sigma d\omega$.

Using the same notation as above and Fig. 26,

$$\frac{1}{\rho} = \frac{1}{R}(1 - he^{i\alpha})^{-\frac{1}{2}}(1 - he^{-i\alpha})^{-\frac{1}{2}},$$

and

$$\log \frac{1}{\rho} = \log \frac{1}{R} - \frac{1}{2}\log(1 - he^{i\alpha}) - \frac{1}{2}\log(1 - he^{-i\alpha}).$$

Since

$$-\log(1 - x) = x + \frac{x^2}{2} + \frac{x^3}{3} + \cdots ,$$

it is found very simply that

$$-\frac{1}{2}\log(1 - he^{i\alpha}) - \frac{1}{2}\log(1 - he^{-i\alpha}) =$$

$$h\cos\alpha + \frac{1}{2}h^2\cos 2\alpha + \frac{1}{3}h^3\cos 3\alpha + \cdots .$$

Hence, since

$$h = \frac{r}{R},$$

$$\log \frac{1}{\rho} = \log \frac{1}{R} + \frac{r}{R} \cos \alpha + \frac{1}{2} \frac{r^2}{R^2} \cos 2\alpha + \frac{1}{3} \frac{r^3}{R^3} \cos 3\alpha + \cdots ,$$

and

$$V = \int_A \log \frac{1}{R} \cdot dm + \frac{1}{R}\int_A r \cos \alpha \cdot dm + \frac{1}{2R^2}\int_A r^2 \cos 2\alpha \cdot dm + \cdots ;$$

or

$$V = M \log \frac{1}{R} + \frac{Mg}{R} + \frac{I_0 - 2I_R}{2R^2} + \cdots . \tag{6}$$

Thus V can be written

$$V = M \log \frac{1}{R} + \frac{M_1}{R},$$

the limiting value of M_1 being Mg.

47. The Terms of Higher Degrees.—The second and third integrals of Eq. (46.2) are readily interpreted as integrals of the center of gravity and moments of inertia respectively; the center of gravity being the integrals which involve the coordinates of the elements of mass linearly, and the moments of inertia those which involve the coordinates of mass in the second degree. These integrals are functions of the body and the system of rectangular coordinates which are chosen, but they do not depend upon the point P. The terms of higher degrees depend upon integrals

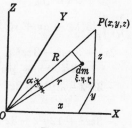

Fig. 27.

which involve the coordinates of the elements of mass in the same way but in higher degrees, and these integrals, also, are independent of the coordinates x, y, z of the point P.

Let Fig. 27 represent a coordinate system with the origin at the point O. Let dm be an element of mass of the body B at a distance r from O with the coordinates ξ, η, ζ. Let λ, μ, ν be the direction cosines of the line R, so that

$$\lambda = \frac{x}{R}, \qquad \mu = \frac{y}{R}, \qquad \nu = \frac{z}{R}. \tag{1}$$

The angle α is the angle between the lines R and r, so that $r \cos \alpha$ is the projection of the distance r upon the line of R. Hence

$$r \cos \alpha = \lambda\xi + \mu\eta + \nu\zeta.$$

The second integral of Eq. (46.2) can be written

$$\left.\begin{aligned}
\frac{1}{R^2}\int_B r\cos\alpha\,dm &= \frac{\lambda}{R^2}\int_B \xi\,dm + \frac{\mu}{R^2}\int_B \eta\,dm + \frac{\nu}{R^2}\int \zeta\,dm \\
&= \frac{x}{R^3}\int_B \xi\,dm + \frac{y}{R^3}\int_B \eta\,dm + \frac{z}{R^3}\int_B \zeta\,dm.
\end{aligned}\right\} \quad (2)$$

The third integral is

$$\left.\begin{aligned}
\frac{1}{2R^3}\int_B (3r^2\cos^2\alpha - r^2)\,dm &= \frac{1}{2R^3}\int_B [3(\lambda\xi + \mu\eta + \nu\zeta)^2 \\
&\qquad - (\xi^2 + \eta^2 + \zeta^2)]\,dm \\
= \frac{(2x^2 - y^2 - z^2)}{2R^5}\int_B \xi^2\,dm &+ \frac{(-x^2 + 2y^2 - z^2)}{2R^5}\int_B \eta^2\,dm \\
+ \frac{(-x^2 - y^2 + 2z^2)}{2R^5}&\int_B \zeta^2\,dm \\
- \frac{3xy}{R^5}\int_B \xi\eta\,dm &- \frac{3yz}{R^5}\int_B \eta\zeta\,dm - \frac{3xz}{R^5}\int_B \zeta\xi\,dm.
\end{aligned}\right\} \quad (3)$$

The fourth integral can be written

$$\left.\begin{aligned}
\frac{1}{2R^4}\int_B [5r^3\cos^3\alpha - 3r^2\cdot r\cos\alpha]\,dm &= \\
\frac{1}{2R^4}\int_B [5(\lambda\xi + \mu\eta + \nu\zeta)^3 - 3(\xi^2 + \eta^2 + \zeta^2)(\lambda\xi + \mu\eta + \nu\zeta)]\,dm& \\
= \frac{2x^3 - 3xy^2 - 3xz^2}{2R^7}\int_B \xi^3\,dm + \frac{-3x^2y + 2y^3 - 3yz^2}{2R^7}\int_B \eta^3\,dm& \\
+ \frac{-3x^2z - 3y^2z + 2z^3}{2R^7}\int \zeta^3\,dm + \frac{12x^2y - 3y^3 - 3yz^2}{2R^7}\int_B \xi^2\eta\,dm& \\
+ \frac{-3zx^2 + 12y^2z - 3z^3}{2R^7}\int_B \eta^2\zeta\,dm& \\
+ \frac{-3x^3 - 3xy^2 + 12xz^2}{2R^7}\int \zeta^2\xi\,dm& \\
+ \frac{12x^2z - 3y^2z - 3z^3}{2R^7}\int_B \xi^2\zeta\,dm +& \\
+ \frac{-3x^3 + 12xy^2 - 3xz^2}{2R^7}\int_B \xi\eta^2\,dm& \\
+ \frac{-3x^2y - 3y^3 + 12yz^2}{2R^7}\int_B \eta\zeta^2\,dm + 15\frac{xyz}{R^7}\int_B \xi\eta\zeta\,dm.&
\end{aligned}\right\} \quad (4)$$

The coefficient of $\int_B \xi^i\eta^j\zeta^k\,dm$ in the above expressions is a perfectly definite function of x, y, and z altogether independent of the body itself, and in Eq. (204.4) there is given a formula which is valid for any integral values of i, j, and k.

If a homogeneous body has the xy-, yz-, and zx-planes as three planes of symmetry, the integral $\int_B \xi^i \eta^j \zeta^k dm$ vanishes if either $i, j,$ or k is odd. For such bodies all of the integrals in Eqs. (2) and (4) vanish and the expansion of the potential is very much simplified. It will be left to the student as an exercise to prove that the terms of the fifth integral which do not vanish for such triply symmetric bodies are as follows:

Let

$$A = \int_B \xi^4 dm, \qquad D = \int_B \xi^2 \eta^2 dm,$$

$$B = \int_B \eta^4 dm, \qquad E = \int_B \eta^2 \zeta^2 dm,$$

$$C = \int_B \zeta^4 dm, \qquad F = \int_B \zeta^2 \xi^2 dm.$$

Then

$$\frac{1}{8R^5} \int_B r^4 (35 \cos^4 \alpha - 30 \cos^2 \alpha + 3) dm =$$

$$\frac{1}{8R^9} \Big\{ (8A + 3B + 3C - 24D + 6E - 24F)x^4$$

$$+ (-24A - 24B + 6C + 162D - 18E - 18F)x^2y^2$$
$$+ (3A + 8B + 3C - 24D - 24E + 16F)y^4$$
$$+ (+6A - 24B - 24C - 18D + 162E - 18F)y^2z^2$$
$$+ (3A + 3B + 8C + 6D - 24E - 24F)z^4$$
$$+ (-24A + 6B - 24C - 18D - 18E + 162F)z^2x^2 \Big\}.$$

48. The Expansion for the Homogeneous Ellipsoid.—In the case of a homogeneous ellipsoid referred to its own axes as coordinates axes, it is easily found that

$$\left. \begin{array}{lll} \displaystyle\int \xi^2 dm = \frac{1}{5} Ma^2, & \displaystyle\int \eta^2 dm = \frac{1}{5} Mb^2, & \displaystyle\int \zeta^2 dm = \frac{1}{5} Mc^2, \\[2mm] \displaystyle\int \xi^4 dm = \frac{3}{35} Ma^4, & \displaystyle\int \eta^4 dm = \frac{3}{35} Mb^4, & \displaystyle\int \zeta^4 dm = \frac{3}{35} Mc^4, \\[2mm] \displaystyle\int \xi^2 \eta^2 dm = \frac{1}{35} Ma^2 b^2, & & \displaystyle\int \eta^2 \zeta^2 dm = \frac{1}{35} Mb^2 c^2, \\[2mm] & \displaystyle\int \zeta^2 \xi^2 dm = \frac{1}{35} Mc^2 a^2, & \end{array} \right\} \quad (1)$$

the terms with odd exponents vanishing. The terms in Eq. (47.3) become

$$\frac{1}{10R^5}[(2a^2 - b^2 - c^2)x^2 + (-a^2 + 2b^2 - c^2)y^2 + (-a^2 - b^2 + 2c^2)z^2].$$

This expression is simplified somewhat by introducing the eccentricities of the meridian sections of the ellipsoid by the substitutions

$$b^2 = a^2(1 - e_1^2), \qquad c^2 = a^2(1 - e_2^2),$$

when it becomes

$$\frac{a^2}{10R^5}[(e_1^2 + e_2^2)x^2 + (e_2^2 - 2e_1^2)y^2 + (e_1^2 - 2e_2^2)z^2];$$

and, similarly, with the terms in x, y, and z of the fourth order. Up to and including the terms of the fourth order, the expansion is

$$\left.\begin{aligned}
V &= \frac{M}{R} + \frac{Ma^2}{10R^5}[(e_1^2 + e_2^2)x^2 + (e_2^2 - 2e_1^2)y^2 + (e_1^2 - 2e_2^2)z^2] \\
&+ \frac{Ma^4}{280R^9}[(9e_1^4 + 6e_1^2e_2^2 + 9e_2^4)x^4 \\
&\qquad\qquad + (-72e_1^4 - 18e_1^2e_2^2 + 18e_2^4)x^2y^2 \\
&+ (24e_1^4 - 24e_1^2e_2^2 + 9e_2^4)y^4 \\
&\qquad\qquad + (-72e_1^4 + 162e_1^2e_2^2 - 72e_2^4)y^2z^2 \\
&+ (9e_1^4 - 24e_1^2e_2^2 + 24e_2^4)z^4 \\
&\qquad\qquad + (+18e_1^4 - 18e_1^2e_2^2 - 72e_2^2)z^2x^2] + \cdots.
\end{aligned}\right\} \quad (2)$$

49. The Right Parallelepiped.—For the right parallelepiped, the edges of which are $2a$, $2b$, and $2c$, the integrals corresponding to Eqs. (48.1) have the values

$$\frac{1}{3}Ma^2, \qquad \frac{1}{3}Mb^2, \qquad \frac{1}{3}Mc^2,$$

$$\frac{1}{5}Ma^4, \qquad \frac{1}{5}Mb^4, \qquad \frac{1}{5}Mc^4,$$

$$\frac{1}{9}Ma^2b^2, \qquad \frac{1}{9}Mb^2c^2, \qquad \frac{1}{9}Mc^2a^2,$$

so that the expansion of the potential is

$$V = \frac{M}{R} + \frac{M}{6R^5}[(2a^2 - b^2 - c^2)x^2 + (-a^2 + 2b^2 - c^2)y^2$$
$$+ (-a^2 - b^2 + 2c^2)z^2]$$

$$+ \frac{M}{72R^9}[(8a^4 + 3b^4 + 3c^4 - 24a^2b^2 + 6b^2c^2 - 24c^2a^2)x^4$$

$$+ (3a^4 + 8b^4 + 3c^4 - 24a^2b^2 - 24b^2c^2 + 6c^2a^2)y^4$$
$$+ (3a^4 + 3b^4 + 8a^4 + 6a^2b^2 - 24b^2c^2 - 24c^2a^2)z^4$$
$$+ (-24a^4 - 24b^4 + 6c^4 + 162a^2b^2 - 18b^2c^2 - 18c^2a^2)x^2y^2$$
$$+ (+6a^4 - 24b^4 - 24c^4 - 18a^2b^2 + 162b^2c^2 - 18c^2a^2)y^2z^2$$
$$+ (-24a^4 + 6b^4 - 24c^4 - 18a^2b^2 - 18b^2c^2 + 162c^2a^2)z^2x^2]$$
$$+ \cdots\cdots\cdots\cdots\cdots\cdots\cdots\cdots\cdots\cdots\cdots\cdots\cdots\cdots$$

For the cube $a = b = c$, and the terms of the second order vanish. The terms of the fourth order reduce to

$$-\frac{7Ma^4}{18R^9}[x^4 + y^4 + z^4 + 3x^2y^2 + 3y^2z^2 + 3z^2x^2],$$

which shows that at large distances the potential of the cube is less than that of a sphere of the same mass.

50. The Inertial Integrals.—It is evident from the preceeding discussion that the expansion of the potential in powers of $1/R$ is a fixed form so far as the letters x, y, and z are concerned. The coefficients of this fixed form are groups of integrals of the type

$$\int_B \xi^i \eta^j \zeta^k dm,$$

which belong to the geometry of the body and nothing else. As the center of gravity integrals and the integrals of the various moments of inertia belong to this class, the entire class will be called the *inertial integrals*.

Since the general term of the expansion of the potential can be written down in terms of these integrals (see Sec. 204), the general term of the expansion can be written down explicitly providing the general inertial integral can be written explicitly. This can be done for the three homogeneous solids which have three planes of symmetry, namely:

For the parallelepiped bounded by the six planes

$$x^2 = a^2, \qquad y^2 = b^2, \qquad z^2 = c^2,$$

$$\sigma \int \int \int \xi^{2p} \eta^{2q} \zeta^{2r} d\xi d\eta d\zeta = M \frac{a^{2p}b^{2q}c^{2r}}{(2p + 1)(2q + 1)(2r + 1)};$$

for the ellipsoid bounded by the surface

$$\frac{x^2}{a^2} + \frac{y^2}{b^2} + \frac{z^2}{c^2} = 1,$$

$$\sigma \int \int \int \xi^{2p} \eta^{2q} \zeta^{2r} d\xi d\eta d\zeta = 3M \frac{[2p - 1][2q - 1][2r - 1]}{[2p + 2q + 2r + 3]} a^{2p}b^{2q}c^{2r},$$

where

$$[2s - 1] = 1 \cdot 3 \cdot 5 \cdot \cdots \cdot (2s - 1),$$

except when $s = 0$, when the value is unity; for the octahedron which is bounded by the eight planes

$$\pm \frac{x}{a} \pm \frac{y}{b} \pm \frac{z}{c} = 1,$$

$$\sigma \iiint \xi^{2p} \eta^{2q} \zeta^{2r} d\xi d\eta d\zeta = 6M \frac{(2p)!(2q)!(2r)!}{(2p + 2q + 2r + 3)!} a^{2p} b^{2q} c^{2r}.$$

These integrals are examples of a general class which can be evaluated for homogeneous bodies. Consider the integral

$$\int_B x^{p-1} y^{q-1} z^{r-1} dx\, dy\, dz$$

taken over a body which is bounded by the surface

$$\left(\frac{x}{a}\right)^\alpha + \left(\frac{y}{b}\right)^\beta + \left(\frac{z}{c}\right)^\gamma = 1.$$

If the substitution

$$\left(\frac{x}{a}\right)^\alpha = \xi, \qquad \left(\frac{y}{b}\right)^\beta = \eta, \qquad \left(\frac{z}{c}\right)^\gamma = \zeta,$$

is made, then

$$\frac{dx}{x} = \frac{d\xi}{\alpha\xi}, \qquad \frac{dy}{y} = \frac{d\eta}{\beta\eta}, \qquad \frac{dz}{z} = \frac{d\zeta}{\gamma\zeta},$$

also

$$x^p = a^p \xi^{\frac{p}{\alpha}}, \qquad y^q = b^q \eta^{\frac{q}{\beta}}, \qquad z^r = c^r \zeta^{\frac{r}{\gamma}};$$

so that

$$I = \iiint_B x^{p-1} y^{q-1} z^{r-1} dx dy dz =$$

$$\frac{a^p b^q c^r}{\alpha\beta\gamma} \iiint \xi^{\frac{p}{\alpha}-1} \eta^{\frac{q}{\beta}-1} \zeta^{\frac{r}{\gamma}-1} d\xi d\eta d\zeta,$$

which is the well-known Dirichlet integral,[1] the integral in the right member being taken over the tetrahedron which is bounded by the four planes

$$\xi = 0, \qquad \eta = 0, \qquad \zeta = 0, \qquad \xi + \eta + \zeta = 1.$$

Hence

$$I = \frac{a^p b^q c^r}{\alpha\beta\gamma} \frac{\Gamma\left(\frac{p}{\alpha}\right) \Gamma\left(\frac{q}{\beta}\right) \Gamma\left(\frac{r}{\gamma}\right)}{\Gamma\left(\frac{p}{\alpha} + \frac{q}{\beta} + \frac{r}{\gamma} + 1\right)}.$$

[1] DIRICHLET, "Werke," p. 375, 391. Also GOURSAT-HEDRICK, "Mathematical Analysis," Vol. I, p. 308.

For the volume itself,

$$p = q = r = 1,$$

therefore,

$$\text{Vol.} = \frac{abc}{\alpha\beta\gamma} \frac{\Gamma\left(\frac{1}{\alpha}\right)\Gamma\left(\frac{1}{\beta}\right)\Gamma\left(\frac{1}{\gamma}\right)}{\Gamma\left(\frac{1}{\alpha} + \frac{1}{\beta} + \frac{1}{\gamma} + 1\right)}.$$

Hence the general inertial integral of the body, if its mass is M, is

$$\int x^p y^q z^r dm = M a^p b^q c^r \frac{\Gamma\left(\frac{p+1}{\alpha}\right)\Gamma\left(\frac{q+1}{\beta}\right)\Gamma\left(\frac{r+1}{\gamma}\right)\Gamma\left(\frac{1}{\alpha} + \frac{1}{\beta} + \frac{1}{\gamma} + 1\right)}{\Gamma\left(\frac{1}{\alpha}\right)\Gamma\left(\frac{1}{\beta}\right)\Gamma\left(\frac{1}{\gamma}\right)\Gamma\left(\frac{p+1}{\alpha} + \frac{q+1}{\beta} + \frac{r+1}{\gamma} + 1\right)}.$$

51. The Inertial Integrals Cannot All Vanish.—It has been pointed out that if a body has three perpendicular planes of symmetry all of the inertial integrals with odd exponents vanish. Even though negative (but not zero) masses are admitted, not all of the inertial integrals can vanish. In order to prove this it will be assumed that the body is composed of a finite number of discrete particles instead of a continuous mass. The ultimate nature of bodies, of course, is not known but the ideal of a very large number of discrete particles is more nearly in harmony with our notions as to the structure of matter than the ideal of continuity, and for the present purpose is simpler. The proof will be made in three steps.

(A) *The inertial integrals of a system of discrete particles placed on a straight line are not all zero.*

For a set of discrete particles on a straight line the inertial integrals are finite sums, namely

$$\sum_{i=1}^{n} m_i x_i{}^p \qquad p = 0, 1, 2, \cdots, \infty.$$

Even though negative masses are admitted, these sums cannot all vanish. Consider the first n such sums set equal to zero:

$$m_1 x_1{}^p + m_2 x_2{}^p + \cdots + m_n x_n{}^p = 0,$$

for

$$p = 0, 1, 2, \cdots, n - 1. \tag{1}$$

It is assumed that the particles are all distinct, that is, that no two of the x's are equal, and that none of the masses is zero. Equations (1) however are linear and homogeneous in the masses.

Therefore, either the masses are all zero, or the determinant vanishes. That is

$$\Delta = \begin{vmatrix} 1 & 1 & \cdots & 1 \\ x_1 & x_2 & \cdots & x_n \\ x_1^2 & x_2^2 & \cdots & x_n^2 \\ x_1^{n-1} & x_2^{n-1} & \cdots & x_n^{n-1} \end{vmatrix} = 0;$$

This well known determinant has the value

$$\Delta = \Pi(x_i - x_j), \qquad i \neq j,$$

that is the product of the differences of the x's. It cannot vanish, since all of the x's are distinct by hypothesis. Hence, Eqs. (1) cannot all be true, and even the first n of the inertial integrals cannot all vanish.

(B) *The inertial integrals of a system of discrete particles lying in a plane are not all zero.*

For a set of discrete particles, n in number, lying in a plane the inertial integrals are

$$\sum_{i=1}^{n} m_i x_i^p y_i^q \qquad p, q = 0, 1, 2, \cdots, \infty.$$

For any fixed integer p, consider the sums

$$(m_1 x_1^p) y_1^q + (m_2 x_2^p) y_2^q + \cdots + (m_n x_n^p) y_n^q = 0,$$
$$q = 0, \cdots, (n-1). \quad (2)$$

There is nothing to prevent the y's from being equal in groups. Therefore it will be supposed that

$$y_1 = y_2 = \cdots = \cdots = y_{\alpha_1} = \eta_1,$$
$$y_{\alpha_1+1} = y_{\alpha_1+2} = \cdots = y_{\alpha_2} = \eta_2,$$
$$y_{\alpha_{s-1}+1} = y_{\alpha_{s-1}+2} = \cdots = y_n = \eta_s,$$

and that the η's are all distinct. Let

$$m_1 x_1^p \quad + \cdots + m_{\alpha_1} x^p{}_{\alpha_1} = \mu_1,$$
$$m_{\alpha_1+1} x^p{}_{\alpha_1+1} + \cdots + m_{\alpha_2} x^p{}_{\alpha_2} = \mu_2,$$
$$\cdots \cdots \cdots \cdots \cdots \cdots \cdots \cdots \cdots \cdots$$
$$m_{\alpha_{s-1}+1} x_{\alpha_{s-1}+1}^p + \cdots + m_n x_n^p = \mu_s.$$

Then Eqs. (2) become

$$\mu_1 \eta_1^q + \mu_2 \eta_2^q + \cdots + \mu_s \eta_s^q = 0. \qquad q = 0, \cdots, n-1.$$

The determinant of the first s equations of this set linear homogeneous is the product of the differences of the η's which cannot vanish since the η's are all distinct. Therefore, all of the μ's must vanish. This cannot be true either, since

$$\mu_1 = m_1 x_1{}^p + m_2 x_2{}^p + \cdots + m_{\alpha_1} x^p{}_{\alpha_1}$$

cannot vanish for every p, by A. Hence Eqs. (2) cannot hold for every p, and proposition B is proved.

(*C*) *The inertial integrals of a system of discrete particles in a closed volume are not all zero.*

The inertial integrals are

$$\sum_{i=1}^{n} m_i x_i{}^p y_i{}^q z_i{}^r \qquad p, q, r = 0, 1, 2, \cdots, \infty.$$

For any pair of fixed integers p and q, consider the n simultaneous equations

$$(m_1 x_1{}^p y_1{}^q) z_1{}^r + (m_2 x_2{}^p y_2{}^q) z_2{}^r + \cdots + (m_n x_n{}^p y_n{}^q) z_n{}^r = 0,$$
$$r = 0, 1, \cdots, n - 1. \quad (3)$$

If equalities exist among the z's, let

$$z_1 = z_2 = \cdots = z_{\alpha_1} = \zeta_1,$$
$$z_{\alpha_1+1} = z_{\alpha_1+2} = \cdots = z_{\alpha_2} = \zeta_2,$$
$$\cdots\cdots\cdots\cdots\cdots\cdots\cdots\cdots\cdots$$
$$z_{\alpha_{s-1}+1} = z_{\alpha_{s-1}+2} = \cdots = z_n = \zeta_s;$$

and let

$$m_1 x_1{}^p y_1{}^q + m_2 x_2{}^p y_2{}^q + \cdots + m_{\alpha_1} x^p{}_{\alpha_1} y^q{}_{\alpha_1} = \mu_1,$$
$$m_{\alpha_1+1} x_{\alpha_1+1}{}^p y_{\alpha_1+1}{}^q + \cdots + m_{\alpha_2}{}^p x_{\alpha_2} y^q{}_{\alpha_2} = \mu_2,$$
$$\cdots\cdots\cdots\cdots\cdots\cdots\cdots\cdots\cdots$$
$$m_{\alpha_{s-1}+1} x^p{}_{\alpha_{s-1}+1} y^q{}_{\alpha_{s-1}+1} + \cdots + m_n x_n{}^p y_n{}^q = \mu_s.$$

Then Eqs. (3) become

$$\mu_1 \zeta_1{}^r + \mu_2 \zeta_2{}^r + \cdots + \mu_s \zeta_s{}^r = 0, \qquad r = 0, 1, \cdots, n - 1.$$

Since the determinant of the first s of these equations is not zero all of the μ's are zero. But $\mu_1, \mu_2, \ldots$ cannot vanish for every pair of integers, by B. Hence, Eqs. (3) cannot hold for every triple of integers p, q, r, and not all of the inertial integrals can vanish. Proposition C is therefore established.

In the case of a single particle located at the origin all of the initial integrals vanish except the first one, namely

$$\Sigma m_i x_i{}^0 y_i{}^0 z_i{}^0$$

which is equal to the mass of the single particle, which by hypothesis is not zero. With this single exception, it is possible to go farther and state that there does not exist a finite sub-set of inertial integrals which are different from zero, if all of the rest of the inertial integrals are zero.

Since the subset is finite, the exponents p, q, r are bounded. Let
$$p < u, \qquad q < v, \qquad r < w,$$
for every integral in the subset I_1, and consider the subset I_2,
$$I_2 = \sum_{i=1}^{n} m_i x_i^{u+\alpha} y_i^{v+\beta} z_i^{w+\gamma} = 0, \qquad \alpha, \beta, \gamma = 0, 1, \cdots, \infty. \quad (4)$$
By writing
$$\mu_i = m_i x_i^u y_i^v z_i^w \qquad i = 1, \cdots, n,$$
Eqs. (4) becomes
$$\sum_{i=1}^{n} \mu_i x_i^\alpha y_i^\beta z_i^\gamma = 0 \qquad \alpha, \beta, \gamma = 0, 1 \cdots, \infty.$$

This is a complete set of inertial integrals for a system of particles μ_i. A repetition of the previous argument shows that every μ_i must vanish, and since the masses of the particles are not zero, at least one of the coordinates is zero, and all of the particles lie in the coordinate planes. A repetition of the argument for the planes shows that they must lie on the axes, and finally, a repetition for the axes show that the only possibility is a single particle at the origin.

52. A Body Is Uniquely Defined by Its Inertial Integrals.— By means of the results in the previous section, it is possible to show that a body is uniquely defined by its set of inertial integrals. Suppose a body B_1 and its set of inertial integrals I is given, and suppose B_2 is a second body which has the same set of inertial integrals I. Then $B_1 - B_2$ is a body, with possibly positive and negative masses, which has all of its inertial integrals zero. But such a body cannot exist unless all of its particles are of mass zero. Hence the body B_2 is identical with the body B_1 and is not distinct from it.

A complete set of inertial integrals cannot be written down at random for the integrals are not independent, but if a complete set of integrals of n particles is given it is possible, at least theoretically, to determine their masses and their locations. The proof is too long for insertion here.

Problems

1. Let the density of a straight rod AB be chosen so that the potential of the rod at a point P in the line of the rod, but outside of it, and at a distance c from the end is equal to one. If the end A, the point P and the potential at P are kept fixed while the length of the rod increases indefinitely, show that the limit of the potential is one everywhere, except on the rod itself.

2. A particle of mass unity is placed at each of the three vertices A, B, C of an equilateral triangle, the center of the triangle being at the point D, and the radius of the circumscribing circle being equal to a. Show that there are three equilibrium points on the circle which has D as a center and radius $r = .2847a$; and that the value of the potential at these three points is $3.123a$.

3. Show that the expansion of the potential in the neighborhood of the point D in the preceding problem is

$$V = \frac{3}{a} + \frac{3(x^2 + y^2 - 2z^2)}{4a^3} + \cdots$$

4. Show that the potential of a uniform circular disk at one of its own points p is

$$V = 4aE\left(k, \frac{\pi}{2}\right)$$

where E is Legendre's complete elliptic integral of the second kind for the modulus $k = r/a$, a being the radius of the disk and r the distance of p from the center.

5. Show that the value of the potential of a uniform elliptical disk, which is defined by the equations

$$x = a \cos \varphi, \qquad y = b \sin \varphi,$$

at a point of its edge is

$$V = \frac{4b}{e}\left[\cos \varphi \tan^{-1} \frac{ae \cos \varphi}{\sqrt{a^2 \sin^2 \varphi + b^2 \cos^2 \varphi}} + \right.$$

$$\left. \sin \varphi \tanh^{-1} \frac{ae \sin \varphi}{\sqrt{a^2 \sin^2 \varphi + b^2 \cos^2 \varphi}} \right],$$

and at the center is

$$V = 4bK\left(e, \frac{\pi}{2}\right)$$

where K is Legendre's complete elliptic integral of the first kind for the modulus $k = e$, the eccentricity of the ellipse.

6. Show that the potential of a homogeneous right circular cone referred to a set of axes which has its origin at the center of gravity of the cone and its z-axis coinciding with the axis of the cone is

$$V = \frac{M}{R} + \frac{3}{40}M\left(a^2 - \frac{1}{4}h^2\right)\frac{x^2 + y^2 - 2z^2}{R^5}$$

$$+ \frac{M(3a^2 + h^2)h}{320} \cdot \frac{2z^3 - 3z(x^2 + y^2)}{R^7} + \cdots,$$

where h is the height of the cone, a is the radius of the base, and M is the total mass.

7. If α, β, and γ are the semi-axes of the interior equipotential surface of the homogeneous ellipsoid whose semi-axes are a, b, and c, show that

$$\frac{1}{\alpha^2} + \frac{1}{\beta^2} + \frac{1}{\gamma^2} = \frac{2}{abc}.$$

CHAPTER III

VECTOR FIELDS

THEOREMS OF GREEN AND GAUSS

53. Definitions.—If at each point of a region R, which may be either a volume, an area, or a line, a vector is uniquely defined, then R and its associated vectors is called a *field of vectors*.

Suppose there are given three functions of x, y, and z, *viz.*, F, G, and H, which are single-valued and continuous. These three functions can be regarded as the components of a vector W at each point M of space, for at the point M, x, y, and z are definite numbers and so also are F, G, and H. Hence, F, G, and H can be regarded as the x-, y-, and z-components of a perfectly definite vector. In the region R in which these things are defined, there is a field of vectors.

The functions F, G, and H are scalar functions, that is, they are numbers which depend upon the coordinates x, y, z. If they are three quite independent functions, the vector W is said to be a *triply scalar vector*.

Suppose $\varphi(x, y, z)$ and its first derivatives are continuous in R and $\psi(x, y, z)$ is any other continuous function. A vector W can be defined also by the relations

$$F = \psi\frac{\partial\varphi}{\partial x}, \qquad G = \psi\frac{\partial\varphi}{\partial y}, \qquad H = \psi\frac{\partial\varphi}{\partial z}.$$

The expression $Fdx + Gdy + Hdz$ admits an integrating factor, and

$$\frac{1}{\psi}(Fdx + Gdy + Hdz) = d\varphi$$

is an exact differential. In this event the vector W is defined by means of two scalar functions, and the vector is said to be a *doubly scalar* vector.

If the function ψ is equal to $+1$, and

$$F = \frac{\partial\varphi}{\partial x}, \qquad G = \frac{\partial\varphi}{\partial y}, \qquad H = \frac{\partial\varphi}{\partial z},$$

the vector W is defined by means of a single function φ, and it is said to be a *singly scalar vector*.

96

54. The Normal Derivative.—Let there be given a single valued function $\varphi(x, y, z)$ which admits unique derivatives with respect to $x, y,$ and z in a certain volume V; and let there be given also a certain surface S defined by the equation

$$f(x, y, z) = 0,$$

which lies wholly within V. Let P_1 be any point on S; λ, μ, ν the direction cosines of the normal to S at P_1, directed outward if S is a closed surface; and P_2 a point on the normal near P_1. If φ_1 and φ_2 are the values of $\varphi(x, y, z)$ at the points P_1 and P_2

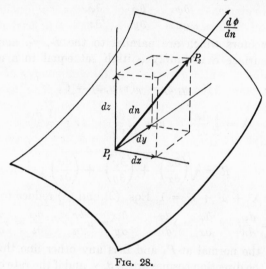

Fig. 28.

respectively, the derivative of $\varphi(x, y, z)$ normal to the surface S at the point P_1 is the limit of

$$\frac{\varphi_2 - \varphi_1}{P_1 P_2}$$

as the point P_2 approaches P_1 along the normal. That is, the normal derivative of φ at the point P_1 is the rate of change of the value of φ in the direction of the normal.

If the coordinates of P_1 and P_2 are $x, y, z,$ and $x + dx, y + dy, z + dz$ respectively, and if the distance $P_1 P_2$ is dn, then it is evident from Fig. 28 that

$$dx = \lambda dn, \qquad dy = \mu dn, \qquad dz = \nu dn. \qquad (1)$$

Also

$$\lim (\varphi_2 - \varphi_1) = d\varphi = \frac{\partial \varphi}{\partial x} dx + \frac{\partial \varphi}{\partial y} dy + \frac{\partial \varphi}{\partial z} dz.$$

Or, after replacing the values of dx, dy, and dz from Eq. (1),

$$d\varphi = \left(\lambda\frac{\partial\varphi}{\partial x} + \mu\frac{\partial\varphi}{\partial y} + \nu\frac{\partial\varphi}{\partial z}\right)dn;$$

that is

$$\frac{d\varphi}{dn} = \lambda\frac{\partial\varphi}{\partial x} + \mu\frac{\partial\varphi}{\partial y} + \nu\frac{\partial\varphi}{\partial z}. \tag{2}$$

Thus, the normal derivative $d\varphi/dn$ is a vector which has the direction of the normal and the magnitude of which is given by Eq. (2). The derivatives

$$\frac{\partial\varphi}{\partial x}, \qquad \frac{\partial\varphi}{\partial y}, \qquad \frac{\partial\varphi}{\partial z},$$

also are vectors which are parallel to the x-, y-, and z-axes.

If the surface S is simply φ itself set equal to a constant, that is

$$f(x, y, z) = \varphi(x, y, z) = C,$$

then

$$\lambda = \frac{1}{R}\frac{\partial\varphi}{\partial x}, \qquad \mu = \frac{1}{R}\frac{\partial\varphi}{\partial y}, \qquad \nu = \frac{1}{R}\frac{\partial\varphi}{\partial z}, \tag{3}$$

where

$$R = \sqrt{\left(\frac{\partial\varphi}{\partial x}\right)^2 + \left(\frac{\partial\varphi}{\partial y}\right)^2 + \left(\frac{\partial\varphi}{\partial z}\right)^2};$$

and, since $\lambda^2 + \mu^2 + \nu^2 = 1$, Eqs. (2) and (3) reduce to

$$R = \frac{d\varphi}{dn}, \qquad \frac{\partial\varphi}{\partial x} = \lambda\frac{d\varphi}{dn}, \qquad \frac{\partial\varphi}{\partial y} = \mu\frac{d\varphi}{dn}, \qquad \frac{\partial\varphi}{\partial z} = \nu\frac{d\varphi}{dn}. \tag{4}$$

If N is the normal at P_1 and L is any other line through P_1 for which the direction cosines are α, β, γ, and if the rate of change of φ along L is denoted by $d\varphi/dl$, then

$$\frac{d\varphi}{dl} = \alpha\frac{\partial\varphi}{\partial x} + \beta\frac{\partial\varphi}{\partial y} + \gamma\frac{\partial\varphi}{\partial z};$$

and since

$$\frac{\partial\varphi}{\partial x} = \lambda\frac{d\varphi}{dn}, \qquad \frac{\partial\varphi}{\partial y} = \mu\frac{d\varphi}{dn}, \qquad \frac{\partial\varphi}{\partial z} = \nu\frac{d\varphi}{dn},$$

it can be written

$$\frac{d\varphi}{dl} = \frac{d\varphi}{dn}(\alpha\lambda + \beta\mu + \gamma\nu)$$

$$= \frac{d\varphi}{dn}\cos(\widehat{LN}),$$

from which it is evident that the rate of change of a function is most rapid in the direction which is normal to the surface along which the function is constant.

If the vector $d\varphi/dn$ at the point P_1 on the surface $\varphi = C$ is taken as the diameter of a sphere, the derivative in any other direction is the length of the chord of the sphere which passes through P_1 in the given direction (Fig. 29).

55. Relations between Certain Volume- and Surface-Integrals.— Suppose there is given a closed surface S which may be composed of one or many parts. An element of the enclosed volume V will be denoted by the symbol $d\tau$, and an element of the surface S by the symbol $d\omega$. The direction cosines

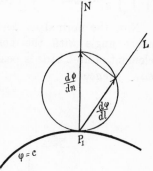

Fig. 29.

of the normal to the surface at the element $d\omega$ will be denoted by α, β, and γ.

Let F be a given function of x, y, and z, and consider the integral over the volume V

$$\int_V \frac{\partial E}{\partial x} d\tau = \int \int \int \frac{\partial F}{\partial x} dx dy dz$$
$$= \int \int dy dz \int \frac{\partial F}{\partial x} dx.$$

On integrating first with respect to x, the function F is obtained as the indefinite integral. In this integration y and z are constants so that the integral

$$\left[\int \frac{\partial F}{\partial x} dx \right] dy dz$$

represents the sum of the elements of a rectangular parallelepiped of cross-section $dy dz$ parallel to the x-axis, Fig. 30. This elementary parallelepiped enters the volume V at the element of surface $d\omega_1$ and emerges at $d\omega_2$, re-enters at $d\omega_3$ and emerges again at $d\omega_4$, and so on. Since the surface is closed it emerges as often as it enters.

Let F_1 be the value of F at the element $d\omega_1$ and α_1, β_1, γ_1 the direction cosines of the normal *directed outward;* let F_2 be the value of F at $d\omega_2$ and α_2, β_2, γ_2 the direction cosines of the normal, and so on. Then the value of the definite integral is

$$\int \frac{\partial F}{\partial x} dx = (F_1 - F_2) + (F_3 - F_4) + \cdots ,$$

and

$$\iiint \frac{\partial F}{\partial x} dx dy dz = \iint [(F_1 - F_2) + (F_3 - F_4) + \cdots] dy dz.$$

Now the normal at $d\omega_1$ directed outward from V makes an acute angle with the positive direction of the x-axis. The element of area $dydz$ is positive, so also is the element of surface $d\omega_1$. Hence

$$dydz = +\alpha_1 d\omega_1.$$

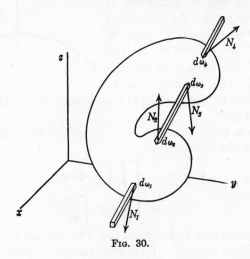

Fig. 30.

But at the element $d\omega_2$ the normal directed outward from V makes an obtuse angle with the x-axis. Since $dydz$ and $d\omega_2$ are both positive, it follows that

$$dydz = -\alpha_2 d\omega_2,$$

and so on. Consequently

$$\iiint \frac{\partial F}{\partial x} dx dy dz = \iint [F_1 - F_2 + F_3 - F_4 + \cdots] dy dz$$

$$= \int_S [+ \alpha_1 F_1 d\omega_1 + \alpha_2 F_2 d\omega_2 + \alpha_3 F_3 d\omega_3 + \alpha_4 F_4 d\omega_4 + \cdots]$$

$$= \int_S \alpha F d\omega.$$

Hence

$$\int_V \frac{\partial F}{\partial x} d\tau = \int_S \alpha F d\omega, \qquad (1)$$

and the original integral taken over a volume is reduced to an integral taken over a surface; that is, a triple integral is reduced to a double integral. In a similar manner it is proved that

$$\int_V \frac{\partial G}{\partial y} d\tau = \int_S \beta G d\omega, \tag{2}$$

$$\int_V \frac{\partial H}{\partial z} d\tau = \int_S \gamma H d\omega. \tag{3}$$

On taking the sum of Eqs. (1), (2) and (3) there results the important formula

$$\int_V \left(\frac{\partial F}{\partial x} + \frac{\partial G}{\partial y} + \frac{\partial H}{\partial z} \right) d\tau = \int_S (\alpha F + \beta G + \gamma H) d\omega. \tag{4}$$

Examples.—If the function F is a constant, say unity, Eq. (1) reduces to

$$0 = \int_S \alpha d\omega,$$

which expresses the obvious fact that the algebraic sum of the projections of any closed surface upon the yz-plane is zero.

If F is taken equal to x simply, Eq. (1) becomes

$$\int_V d\tau = \int_S \alpha x d\omega;$$

that is the volume itself is expressed as a surface integral.

56. A Vector Interpretation.— If F, G, and H are single valued functions of x, y, and z, they can be regarded as the components of a vector W which is uniquely defined at each point of space. Suppose there is given a closed surface S in the region R in which the vector W is defined. Let $d\omega$ be an element of this surface at the point M, and let MN be the

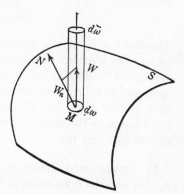

Fig. 31.

normal to S drawn outward, and α, β, γ its direction cosines. Let W_n be the projection of W on the normal. Then

$$W_n = \alpha F + \beta G + \gamma H. \tag{1}$$

and Eq. (55.4) becomes

$$\int_V \left(\frac{\partial F}{\partial x} + \frac{\partial G}{\partial y} + \frac{\partial H}{\partial z} \right) d\tau = \int_S W_n d\omega. \tag{2}$$

Let W represent the velocity of a fluid and $d\omega$ a small hole in S through which the fluid is flowing. Let $d\overline{\omega}$ be the projection of $d\omega$ on a plane perpendicular to W. Then, Fig. 31,

$$W d\overline{\omega} = W_n d\omega$$

represents the amount of fluid which flows across the element $d\omega$ per unit of time. Hence

$$W_n d\omega = (\alpha F + \beta G + \gamma H) d\omega$$

is called *the element of flux* across $d\omega$, or simply the flux; and the integral

$$\int_S W_n d\omega$$

represents the total flux across the surface.

The quantity

$$E = \frac{\partial F}{\partial x} + \frac{\partial G}{\partial y} + \frac{\partial H}{\partial z} \tag{3}$$

also has physical significance. By Eq. (2)

$$\int_V E d\tau = \int_S W_n d\omega \tag{4}$$

for every closed surface S. Let the volume be limited to a single element so that

$$E d\tau = \int_S W_n d\omega.$$

The right side of this equation is the amount of fluid which leaves the element of volume per unit time. Hence E is the amount of fluid which leaves the volume per unit time per unit volume, and is called the *divergence* of the vector W. Equation (4) then merely says that the amount of fluid which escapes from the volume is the same as the amount of fluid which crosses the surface per unit time.

57. Generalized Orthogonal Coordinates.—The normal component and the divergence of the vector W have a meaning which is quite independent of the coordinate system in terms of which they are expressed.

Let q_1, q_2, q_3 be the coordinates in any triply orthogonal system; by which is meant that the tangent planes of the surfaces $q_1 = c_1$, $q_2 = c_2, q_3 = c_3$, where c_1, c_2 and c_3 are constants, at their common point of intersection are mutually perpendicular. Then the coordinates of a point p are related by the equations.

$$x = f_1(q_1, q_2, q_3), \qquad y = f_1(q_1, q_2, q_3), \qquad z = f_3(q_1, q_2, q_3).$$

If the coordinates q_1, q_2, q_3 are given infinitesimal increments, the point p undergoes a displacement of which the components are

$$\left.\begin{aligned}
ds_1 &= \sqrt{\left(\frac{\partial x}{\partial q_1}\right)^2 + \left(\frac{\partial y}{\partial q_1}\right)^2 + \left(\frac{\partial z}{\partial q_1}\right)^2}\, dq_1 = R_1 dq_1, \\
ds_2 &= \sqrt{\left(\frac{\partial x}{\partial q_2}\right)^2 + \left(\frac{\partial y}{\partial q_2}\right)^2 + \left(\frac{\partial z}{\partial q_2}\right)^2}\, dq_2 = R_2 dq_2, \\
ds_3 &= \sqrt{\left(\frac{\partial x}{\partial q_3}\right)^2 + \left(\frac{\partial y}{\partial q_3}\right)^2 + \left(\frac{\partial z}{\partial q_3}\right)^2}\, dq_3 = R_3 dq_3.
\end{aligned}\right\} \quad (5)$$

The directions of these components, which are mutually at right angles, will be called the q_1-, q_2-, and q_3-directions at the point p. The arc element ds is

$$ds = \sqrt{R_1^2 dq_1^2 + R_2^2 dq_2^2 + R_3^2 dq_3^2}.$$

The elements of area on the surfaces $q_1 = c_1$, $q_2 = c_2$, $=$ and $q_3 = c_3$, respectively, are

$$d\omega_1 = R_2 R_3 dq_2 dq_3, \qquad d\omega_2 = R_3 R_1 dq_3 dq_1, \qquad d\omega_3 = R_1 R_2 dq_1 dq_2;$$

and the element of volume is

$$d\tau = R_1 R_2 R_3 dq_1 dq_2 dq_3.$$

Returning now to the vector W, let the components of W at the point p in the q_1-, q_2- and q_3-directions be W_1, W_2, and W_3; and, if p is on the given surface, let the direction cosines of the normal, directed outward, with respect to the q_1-, q_2- and q_3-directions be ν_1, ν_2, and ν_3. Then the normal component of W is

$$W_n = \nu_1 W_1 + \nu_2 W_2 + \nu_3 W_3.$$

Consider now

$$\int_S \nu_1 W_1 d\omega = \int_S W_1 (\nu_1 d\omega).$$

The cosine of the angle between the normal and the q_1 direction is ν_1.
Hence

$$\pm \nu_1 d\omega = d\omega_1 = R_2 R_3 dq_2 dq_3$$

and

$$\int_S \nu_1 W_1 d\omega = \int_S R_2 R_3 W_1 dq_2 dq_3.$$

Consider also the volume integral

$$\int_V \frac{1}{R_1 R_2 R_3} \frac{\partial}{\partial q_1} (R_2 R_3 W_1) d\tau = \int_V \frac{\partial}{\partial q_1} (R_2 R_3 W_1) dq_1 dq_2 dq_3.$$

A repetition of the argument in Sec. 55 shows that

$$\int_V \frac{1}{R_1 R_2 R_3} \frac{\partial}{\partial q_1}(R_2 R_3 W_1) d\tau = \int_S \nu_1 W_1 d\omega,$$

and similarly

$$\int_V \frac{1}{R_1 R_2 R_3} \frac{\partial}{\partial q_2}(R_3 R_1 W_2) d\tau = \int_S \nu_2 W_2 d\omega,$$

$$\int_V \frac{1}{R_1 R_2 R_3} \frac{\partial}{\partial q_3}(R_1 R_2 W_3) d\tau = \int_S \nu_3 W_3 d\omega.$$

On taking the sum of these three expressions, there results

$$\int_V \frac{1}{R_1 R_2 R_3} \left[\frac{\partial}{\partial q_1}(R_2 R_3 W_1) + \frac{\partial}{\partial q_2}(R_3 R_1 W_2) + \frac{\partial}{\partial q_3}(R_1 R_2 W_3) \right] d\tau = \int_S W_n d\omega. \quad (6)$$

If it is borne in mind that this expression holds whatever the volume may be, a comparison with Eq. (2) shows that

$$\frac{\partial F}{\partial x} + \frac{\partial G}{\partial y} + \frac{\partial H}{\partial z} = \frac{1}{R_1 R_2 R_3} \left[\frac{\partial}{\partial q_1}(R_2 R_3 W_1) + \frac{\partial}{\partial q_2}(R_3 R_1 W_2) + \frac{\partial}{\partial q_3}(R_1 R_2 W_3) \right], \quad (7)$$

and the right member of this equation is the divergence of W expressed in terms of any triply orthogonal system of coordinates.

If W is a singly scalar vector U, then

$$\frac{\partial U}{\partial x} = F, \qquad \frac{\partial U}{\partial y} = G, \qquad \frac{\partial U}{\partial z} = H,$$

and (Eqs. (5))

$$\frac{1}{R_1} \frac{\partial U}{\partial q_1} = W_1, \qquad \frac{1}{R_2} \frac{\partial U}{\partial q_2} = W_2, \qquad \frac{1}{R_3} \frac{\partial U}{\partial q_3} = W_3.$$

Therefore

$$\frac{\partial^2 U}{\partial x^2} + \frac{\partial^2 U}{\partial y^2} + \frac{\partial^2 U}{\partial z^2} = \Delta U \qquad (8)$$

$$= \frac{1}{R_1 R_2 R_3} \left[\frac{\partial}{\partial q_1}\left(\frac{R_2 R_3}{R_1} \frac{\partial U}{\partial q_1} \right) + \frac{\partial}{\partial q_2}\left(\frac{R_3 R_1}{R_2} \frac{\partial U}{\partial q_2} \right) + \frac{\partial}{\partial q_3}\left(\frac{R_1 R_2}{R_3} \frac{\partial U}{\partial q_3} \right) \right]$$

is the expression for the Laplacian in generalized orthogonal coordinates. This formula is due to Lamé.[1]

58. Green's Theorem.—Since doubly scalar vectors form a sub-class of triply scalar vectors, the results of Secs. 55 and 56

[1] LAMÉ, *Journal de l'Ecole Polytechnique*, Vol. 23, p. 215, (1833).

hold also for doubly scalar vectors. Suppose φ and ψ are any two functions of x, y, and z which are continuous together with their first derivatives and which admit second derivatives. Let

$$F = \psi\frac{\partial\varphi}{\partial x}, \qquad G = \psi\frac{\partial\varphi}{\partial y}, \qquad H = \psi\frac{\partial\varphi}{\partial z}; \qquad (1)$$

and for brevity of notation, let

$$\Delta\varphi = \frac{\partial^2\varphi}{\partial x^2} + \frac{\partial^2\varphi}{\partial y^2} + \frac{\partial^2\varphi}{\partial z^2}. \qquad (2)$$

Then the expression for E becomes

$$E = \frac{\partial F}{\partial x} + \frac{\partial G}{\partial y} + \frac{\partial H}{\partial z}$$

$$= \psi\Delta\varphi + \frac{\partial\psi}{\partial x}\frac{\partial\varphi}{\partial x} + \frac{\partial\psi}{\partial y}\frac{\partial\varphi}{\partial y} + \frac{\partial\psi}{\partial z}\frac{\partial\varphi}{\partial z};$$

and Eq. (55.4) becomes

$$\int_V\left[\psi\Delta\varphi + \frac{\partial\psi}{\partial x}\frac{\partial\varphi}{\partial x} + \frac{\partial\psi}{\partial y}\frac{\partial\varphi}{\partial y} + \frac{\partial\psi}{\partial z}\frac{\partial\varphi}{\partial z}\right]d\tau$$

$$= \int_S\psi\left(\alpha\frac{\partial\varphi}{\partial x} + \beta\frac{\partial\varphi}{\partial y} + \gamma\frac{\partial\varphi}{\partial z}\right)d\omega.$$

or, since

$$\alpha\frac{\partial\varphi}{\partial x} + \beta\frac{\partial\varphi}{\partial y} + \gamma\frac{\partial\varphi}{\partial z} = \frac{\partial\varphi}{\partial n},$$

that is, the normal derivative of φ, Eq. (54.2),

$$\int_V\psi\Delta\varphi d\tau + \int_V\left(\frac{\partial\psi}{\partial x}\frac{\partial\varphi}{\partial x} + \frac{\partial\psi}{\partial y}\frac{\partial\varphi}{\partial y} + \frac{\partial\psi}{\partial z}\frac{\partial\varphi}{\partial z}\right)d\tau = \int_S\psi\frac{\partial\varphi}{\partial n}d\omega. \qquad (3)$$

This formula, which holds for any two functions that satisfy the above condition, is known as *Green's theorem.*

If φ and ψ are interchanged in this formula and the result is subtracted from Eq. (3), the second integral will disappear, since it is symmetrical in φ and ψ. There results the very important formula

$$\int_V(\psi\Delta\varphi - \varphi\Delta\psi)d\tau = \int_S\left(\psi\frac{\partial\varphi}{\partial n} - \varphi\frac{\partial\psi}{\partial n}\right)d\omega, \qquad (4)$$

which is Green's theorem in its second form.

If ψ is a constant, say equal to unity, the vector W is singly scalar and Eq. (4) reduces to

$$\int_V\Delta\varphi d\tau = \int_S\frac{\partial\varphi}{\partial n}d\omega. \qquad (5)$$

Reduction to Two Dimensions.—Green's theorem still holds if volumes are replaced by areas and surfaces by contours. Triple integrals become double integrals, and double integrals become single integrals. Three dimensions are reduced to two, and two dimensions are reduced to one. Equation (3) becomes

$$\int_{\text{Area}} \psi\left(\frac{\partial^2 \varphi}{\partial x^2} + \frac{\partial^2 \varphi}{\partial y^2}\right) d\omega + \int_{\text{Area}} \left(\frac{\partial \psi}{\partial x}\frac{\partial \varphi}{\partial y} + \frac{\partial \psi}{\partial y}\frac{\partial \varphi}{\partial y}\right) d\omega = \int_C \psi\frac{\partial \varphi}{\partial n} d\lambda, \quad (6)$$

where $d\omega = dxdy$ is an element of area and $d\lambda = \sqrt{dx^2 + dy^2}$ is an element of a closed contour. Similarly, Eq. (4) becomes

$$\int_A \left[\psi\left(\frac{\partial^2 \varphi}{\partial x^2} + \frac{\partial^2 \varphi}{\partial y^2}\right) - \varphi\left(\frac{\partial^2 \psi}{\partial x^2} + \frac{\partial^2 \psi}{\partial y^2}\right)\right] d\omega$$

$$= \int_C \left(\psi\frac{\partial \varphi}{\partial n} - \varphi\frac{\partial \psi}{\partial n}\right) d\lambda, \quad (7)$$

and Eq. (5) becomes

$$\int_A \left(\frac{\partial^2 \varphi}{\partial x^2} + \frac{\partial^2 \varphi}{\partial y^2}\right) d\omega = \int_C \frac{\partial \varphi}{\partial n} d\lambda. \quad (8)$$

59. The Potential of Homogeneous Bodies.—Let ξ, η, ζ be a point of a homogeneous body of density σ, and x, y, z, an outside point, and let

$$\rho = \sqrt{(\xi - x)^2 + (\eta - y)^2 + (\zeta - z)^2}.$$

Then

$$\frac{\partial \rho}{\partial \xi} = \frac{\xi - x}{\rho}, \qquad \frac{\partial^2 \rho}{\partial \xi^2} = \frac{1}{\rho} - \frac{(\xi - x)^2}{\rho^3},$$

$$\frac{\partial \rho}{\partial \eta} = \frac{\eta - y}{\rho}, \qquad \frac{\partial^2 \rho}{\partial \eta^2} = \frac{1}{\rho} - \frac{(\eta - y)^2}{\rho^3},$$

$$\frac{\partial \rho}{\partial \zeta} = \frac{\zeta - z}{\rho}, \qquad \frac{\partial^2 \rho}{\partial \zeta^2} = \frac{1}{\rho} - \frac{(\zeta - z)^2}{\rho^3};$$

and therefore

$$\Delta\rho = \frac{\partial^2 \rho}{\partial \xi^2} + \frac{\partial^2 \rho}{\partial \eta^2} + \frac{\partial^2 \rho}{\partial \zeta^2} = \frac{2}{\rho}. \quad (1)$$

In Eq. (58.4) identify ψ with σ and φ with ρ, which can be done since ρ is continuous within the body, and σ is constant. It then becomes

$$\int_V \sigma\Delta\rho d\tau = 2\sigma \int_V \frac{d\tau}{\rho} = \sigma \int_S \frac{\partial \rho}{\partial n} d\omega,$$

or, after removing the factor 2,

$$\sigma \int_V \frac{d\tau}{\rho} = \frac{1}{2}\sigma \int_S \frac{\partial \rho}{\partial n} d\omega. \quad (2)$$

The left member of Eq. (2) is the potential of the body in its usual form. The right member is the surface integral of the normal derivative of ρ multiplied by $\sigma/2$. Thus, the potential of every homogeneous body can be reduced to a surface integral, which involves only double integrals instead of triple integrals. This theorem is due to Gauss, although Gauss' proof follows a very different line of thought.

It is a simple matter to extend this theorem of Gauss to cases where σ is a function which satisfies the equation of Laplace, namely,

$$\Delta\sigma = \frac{\partial^2\sigma}{\partial\xi^2} + \frac{\partial^2\sigma}{\partial\eta^2} + \frac{\partial^2\sigma}{\partial\zeta^2} = 0;$$

for in this event Eq. (58.4) becomes

$$\int_V \frac{\sigma}{\rho}d\tau = \frac{1}{2}\int_S\left(\sigma\frac{\partial\rho}{\partial n} - \rho\frac{\partial\sigma}{\partial n}\right)d\omega \tag{3}$$

if σ is identified with ψ and ρ with φ. The left member of Eq. (3) is the potential in its usual form, while the right member is a surface integral.

60. Example—A Non-homogeneous Spherical Shell.—Consider the potential of a spherical shell of which the radius of the outer surface is a and the inner surface is b, and the density of which is

$$\sigma = \frac{\sigma_0}{r},$$

where

$$r = \sqrt{\xi^2 + \eta^2 + \zeta^2}.$$

Since σ satisfies the equation of Laplace, the potential at the point x, y, z, provided the point x, y, z does not lie within the shell itself, nor on the surfaces, is

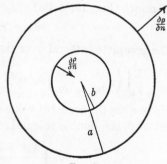

FIG. 32.

$$V = \frac{\sigma_0}{2}\int_S\left[\frac{1}{r}\frac{\partial\rho}{\partial n} - \rho\frac{\partial}{\partial n}\left(\frac{1}{r}\right)\right]d\omega.$$

The surface of the shell consists of two spheres, one of radius a and the other of radius $b < a$. The normal derivative on the sphere of radius a is directed away from the center, while over the sphere of radius b it is directed toward the center (Fig. 32). In both cases it is outward with respect to the volume between the two surfaces, that is the volume of the shell.

Since the radius of the sphere is always normal to the surface

$$\frac{\partial \rho}{\partial n} = \pm \frac{\partial \rho}{\partial r}, \qquad \frac{\partial \sigma}{\partial n} = \pm \frac{\partial \sigma}{\partial r},$$

the positive sign to be taken on the outer sphere and the negative sign on the inner sphere.

Now

$$\rho^2 = (\xi - x)^2 + (\eta - y)^2 + (\zeta - z)^2$$
$$= r^2 - 2rR \cos \varphi + R^2,$$

where

$$R^2 = x^2 + y^2 + z^2,$$

and φ is the angle between the lines r and R.   Hence

$$\frac{\partial \rho}{\partial r} = \frac{r - R \cos \varphi}{\rho}, \qquad \frac{\partial \sigma}{\partial r} = -\frac{\sigma_0}{r^2};$$
$$\sigma \frac{\partial \rho}{\partial r} - \rho \frac{\partial \sigma}{\partial r} = \frac{\sigma_0(r^2 - rR \cos \varphi + \rho^2)}{r^2 \rho}$$
$$= \frac{\sigma_0(3\rho^2 + r^2 - R^2)}{2r^2 \rho}.$$

The element of surface $d\omega$ is

$$d\omega = r^2 \overline{d\omega}$$

where $\overline{d\omega}$ is the corresponding element on the unit sphere, and therefore (Fig. 15, p. 36)

$$d\omega = r^2 \sin \varphi \, d\varphi \, d\theta.$$

The complete integral over the outer sphere is

$$\frac{1}{2} \int \left(\sigma \frac{\partial \rho}{\partial n} - \rho \frac{\partial \sigma}{\partial n} \right) d\omega = \frac{\sigma_0}{2} \int \int \frac{3\rho^2 + r^2 - R^2}{2\rho} \sin \varphi \, d\varphi \, d\theta,$$

where r has the constant value a.   Since the integrand is independent of θ, the double integral reduces at once to the single integral

$$\pi \sigma_0 \int \frac{3\rho^2 + a^2 - R^2}{2\rho} \sin \varphi \, d\varphi.$$

The variables ρ, a, R, and φ are related on the sphere by the equation

$$\rho^2 = a^2 - 2aR \cos \varphi + R^2;$$

and, since a and R are constant,

$$\rho d\rho = aR \sin \varphi \, d\varphi,$$

or

$$\frac{\sin \varphi d\varphi}{\rho} = \frac{d\rho}{aR}.$$

Hence, on the outer sphere

$$\frac{1}{2}\int\left(\sigma\frac{\partial\rho}{\partial n} - \rho\frac{\partial\sigma}{\partial n}\right)d\omega = \pi\sigma_0\int_{R-a}^{R+a}\frac{3\rho^2 + a^2 - R^2}{2aR}d\rho,$$

or

$$\frac{1}{2}\int\left(\sigma\frac{\partial\rho}{\partial n} - \rho\frac{\partial\sigma}{\partial n}\right)d\omega = \pi\sigma_0\int_{a-R}^{a+R}\frac{3\rho^2 + a^2 - R^2}{2aR}d\rho,$$

according as the point x, y, z lies outside of the sphere of radius a or inside of the sphere of radius b. In the first case the value of the integral is

$$\frac{2\pi\sigma_0}{R}(R^2 + a^2),$$

and in the second case

$$4\pi\sigma_0 a.$$

The corresponding integrals taken over the inner sphere are

$$-\frac{2\pi\sigma_0}{R}(R^2 + b^2), \qquad \text{and} \qquad -4\pi\sigma_0 b.$$

Hence

$$V = \frac{1}{2}\sigma_0\int\left(\sigma\frac{\partial\rho}{\partial n} - \rho\frac{\partial\sigma}{\partial n}\right)d\omega$$

$$= \frac{2\pi\sigma_0(a^2 - b^2)}{R}, \qquad \text{or} \qquad 4\pi\sigma_0(a - b).$$

The mass M of the shell is

$$M = \sigma_0\int_b^a 4\pi r dr = 2\pi\sigma_0(a^2 - b^2).$$

Hence

$$V = \frac{M}{R}, \qquad \text{or} \qquad V = \frac{2M}{(a + b)},$$

according as the point x, y, z is on the outside of the shell, or within the hollow enclosed by the shell.   Within the hollow, the potential is constant.

61. Existence of Higher Derivatives of Potential Functions.— The potential function of any body is

$$V = \int_B \frac{\sigma d\tau}{\rho},$$

where

$$\rho = \sqrt{(\xi - x)^2 + (\eta - y)^2 + (\zeta - z)^2}.$$

The existence of first derivatives was proved in Secs. 24 and 25, and for either internal or external points

$$\frac{\partial V}{\partial x} = \int_B \frac{\partial}{\partial x}\left(\frac{1}{\rho}\right)\sigma d\tau = -\int_B \frac{\partial}{\partial \xi}\left(\frac{1}{\rho}\right) \cdot \sigma d\tau. \tag{1}$$

An interesting proof of the existence of derivatives of all orders, due to Riemann, can be made by the use of the formulas which were established in Sec. 55. By Eq. (55.1),

$$\int_B \frac{\partial F}{\partial \xi} d\tau = \int_S \alpha F d\omega,$$

provided F and its first derivatives are continuous within B and on its surface. If F is taken to be

$$F = \frac{\sigma}{\rho},$$

in this formula it becomes

$$\frac{\partial V}{\partial x} = -\int_B \frac{\partial}{\partial \xi}\left(\frac{1}{\rho}\right)\sigma d\tau = -\int_S \frac{\alpha\sigma}{\rho}d\omega + \int_B \frac{\partial \sigma}{\partial \xi}\frac{d\tau}{\rho}. \tag{2}$$

If the point p (x, y, z) is outside the body, $1/\rho$ is continuous within B and Eq. (2) is valid. If it is inside, let a small sphere Σ of radius ϵ be described around the point p. The function $1/\rho$ is continuous within the volume B_1 bounded by the surfaces S and Σ. Then

$$\frac{\partial V}{\partial x} = \lim_{\epsilon=0}\left[-\int_S \frac{\alpha\sigma}{\rho}d\omega - \int_\Sigma \frac{\alpha\sigma}{\rho}d\omega + \int_{B_1} \frac{\partial \sigma}{\partial \xi}\frac{d\tau}{\rho} \right]$$

If the partial derivatives of σ exist they are functions of ξ, η, ζ, and they can be regarded as density functions. Hence, the last integral

$$\int_{B_1} \frac{\partial \sigma}{\partial \xi}\frac{d\tau}{\rho} = \int_{B_1} \frac{\bar{\sigma}d\tau}{\rho}$$

is a Newtonian potential for a certain distribution of matter within B, and it is known from Sec. 22 that

$$\lim_{\epsilon=0}\int_{B_1} \frac{\bar{\sigma}d\tau}{\rho} = \int_B \frac{\bar{\sigma}d\tau}{\rho}.$$

For the surface integral over the sphere Σ, the function ρ has the constant value ϵ. Let

$$d\omega = \epsilon^2 d\bar{\omega},$$

where $d\overline{\omega}$ is an infinitesimal solid angle. The maximum value of α is $+1$, since it is a cosine. Let σ_0 be the maximum value of $|\sigma|$ within Σ. Then

$$\int_\Sigma \frac{\alpha\sigma}{\rho}d\omega = \epsilon \int_\Sigma \alpha\sigma d\overline{\omega} < 4\pi\sigma_0\epsilon,$$

which vanishes with ϵ. Since the surface integral over S does not depend upon ϵ, it follows that

$$\frac{\partial V}{\partial x} = \int_B \frac{\partial\sigma}{\partial\xi}\frac{d\tau}{\rho} - \int_S \frac{\alpha\sigma}{\rho}d\omega, \qquad (3)$$

even when the point $p(x, y, z)$ lies within the body.

From Eq. (3) it is seen that $\partial V/\partial x$ is the sum of two potentials, one of which is a volume potential and the other is a surface potential, for it represents the potential of a certain distribution of matter upon the surface of the body. The first has derivatives everywhere, while the second has derivatives everywhere except on the surface itself. Therefore V has second derivatives everywhere except on the surface. If $\sigma(\xi, \eta, \zeta)$ has derivatives of all orders, it is possible to proceed step by step and show that V likewise has derivatives of all orders except on the surface.

62. Harmonic Functions.—If the function $\varphi(x, y, z)$ and its first derivatives are single valued and continuous within and on the boundaries of a certain region R, if second derivatives exist, and if the function φ satisfies the equation of Laplace

$$\Delta\varphi = \frac{\partial^2\varphi}{\partial x^2} + \frac{\partial^2\varphi}{\partial y^2} + \frac{\partial^2\varphi}{\partial z^2} = 0,$$

then $\varphi(x, y, z)$ is said to be *harmonic* within the region R.

Let S be any closed surface within R, and φ and ψ any two harmonic functions. Then by Green's theorem, Eq. (57.4),

$$\int_S \left(\psi\frac{\partial\varphi}{\partial n} - \varphi\frac{\partial\psi}{\partial n}\right)d\omega = 0. \qquad (1)$$

If ψ is equal to a constant, say $+1$, this equation reduces to

$$\int_S \frac{\partial\varphi}{\partial n}d\omega = 0; \qquad (2)$$

that is, the surface integral of the normal derivative of an harmonic function over any closed surface is zero.

63. An Extension of Green's Theorem for Harmonic Functions.—Let S be any surface enclosing a volume B. Let ξ, η, ζ

be the coordinates of a point of B, and let x, y, z be the coordinates of a point p located anywhere. Then the function

$$\frac{1}{\rho} = \frac{1}{\sqrt{(\xi - x)^2 + (\eta - y)^2 + (\zeta - z)^2}}$$

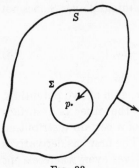

is harmonic in B if the point p lies outside of B, since it satisfies all of the conditions of Sec. 62. If φ is any other function which is harmonic in B

$$\int_S \left[\frac{1}{\rho} \frac{\partial \varphi}{\partial n} - \varphi \frac{\partial}{\partial n}\left(\frac{1}{\rho}\right) \right] d\omega = 0. \quad (1)$$

Interior Point.—If the point p lies within B the conditions of the theorem are not satisfied and Eq. (1) is not applicable. It is possible, however, to describe a small sphere Σ of radius ϵ with its center at p (Fig. 33) and apply

Fig. 33.

Eq. (1) to the volume B_1 which is bounded by the surfaces S and Σ, but the integral must be extended over both surfaces. That is

$$\int_S \left[\frac{1}{\rho} \frac{\partial \varphi}{\partial n} - \varphi \frac{\partial}{\partial n}\left(\frac{1}{\rho}\right) \right] d\omega + \int_\Sigma \left[\frac{1}{\rho} \frac{\partial \varphi}{\partial n} - \varphi \frac{\partial}{\partial n}\left(\frac{1}{\rho}\right) \right] d\omega = 0,$$

the normal derivative to be taken outward with respect to B_1 on both surfaces.

If the normal derivative in the second integral be taken outward with respect to Σ it merely changes the sign of the second integral, and the equation becomes

$$\int_S \left[\frac{1}{\rho} \frac{\partial \varphi}{\partial n} - \varphi \frac{\partial}{\partial n}\left(\frac{1}{\rho}\right) \right] d\omega = \int_\Sigma \left[\frac{1}{\rho} \frac{\partial \varphi}{\partial n} - \varphi \frac{\partial}{\partial n}\left(\frac{1}{\rho}\right) \right] d\omega, \quad (2)$$

normal derivatives *outward* with respect to both surfaces. Since the left member of Eq. (2) is independent of ϵ, the radius of Σ, the right number also is independent of ϵ.

The first integral of the right member is

$$\int_\Sigma \frac{1}{\rho} \frac{\partial \varphi}{\partial n} d\omega = \frac{1}{\epsilon} \int_\Sigma \frac{\partial \varphi}{\partial n} d\omega = 0,$$

by Eq. (62.2), since φ is harmonic in Σ. In the second integral

$$\frac{\partial}{\partial n}\left(\frac{1}{\rho}\right) = \frac{\partial}{\partial \rho}\left(\frac{1}{\rho}\right) = -\frac{1}{\rho^2},$$

and, since $\rho = \epsilon$ on the surface of Σ, the second integral reduces to

$$-\int_\Sigma \varphi \frac{\partial}{\partial n}\left(\frac{1}{\rho}\right)d\omega = +\frac{1}{\epsilon^2}\int_\Sigma \varphi d\omega.$$

Let M and m be the maximum and minimum values of φ on Σ. Then

$$4\pi m \leqq \frac{1}{\epsilon^2}\int_\Sigma \varphi d\omega = \int_\Sigma \varphi d\overline{\omega} \leqq 4\pi M,$$

where $d\overline{\omega}$ is an infinitesimal solid angle, and $d\omega = \epsilon^2 d\overline{\omega}$.

Since φ is continuous and ϵ is as small as is desired, m and M can be made to differ from the value of φ at the point p by as small a quantity as is desired; and, since the integral is independent of ϵ, its value is rigorously

$$-\int_\Sigma \varphi \frac{\partial}{\partial n}\left(\frac{1}{\rho}\right)d\omega = +4\pi\varphi(x, y, z).$$

Therefore, Eq. (2) becomes

$$\frac{1}{4\pi}\int_S\left[\frac{1}{\rho}\frac{\partial \varphi}{\partial n} - \varphi\frac{\partial}{\partial n}\left(\frac{1}{\rho}\right)\right]d\omega = \varphi(x, y, z). \tag{3}$$

Stated in words, Eq. (3) says that if a function φ is harmonic in a volume which is bounded by a closed surface S, and if the value of φ and its normal derivative at all points of S are given, then the value of φ at any interior point of S is defined by Eq. (3).

Corollary I.—If φ and φ_1 are harmonic within a closed surface S, aside from the fact that φ_1 has a single pole within S, so that

$$\varphi_1 = \frac{1}{\rho} + H, \quad \text{where} \quad H \quad \text{is harmonic,} \quad \text{then}$$

$$\varphi(x, y, z) = \frac{1}{4\pi}\int_S\left[\varphi_1\frac{\partial \varphi}{\partial n} - \varphi\frac{\partial \varphi_1}{\partial n}\right]d\omega.$$

Corollary II.—If φ_1 and φ_2 are harmonic within a closed surface, aside from the fact that φ_1 has a single pole at the point p_1 and φ_2 has a single pole at the point p_2, so that

$$\varphi_1 = \frac{1}{\rho_1} + H_1, \qquad \varphi_2 = \frac{1}{\rho_2} + H_2,$$

then

$$\frac{1}{4\pi}\int_S\left(\varphi_1\frac{\partial \varphi_2}{\partial n} - \varphi_2\frac{\partial \varphi_1}{\partial n}\right)d\omega = \varphi_2(p_1) - \varphi_1(p_2),$$

where $\varphi_1(p_2)$ means the value of the function φ_1 at the point p_2.

Exterior Point.—If the function $\varphi(\xi, \eta, \zeta)$ is harmonic outside of S, and if it vanishes at infinity in such a way that

$$r\varphi, \qquad r^2\frac{\partial\varphi}{\partial\xi}, \qquad r^2\frac{\partial\varphi}{\partial\eta}, \qquad r^2\frac{\partial\varphi}{\partial\zeta},$$

$$r = \sqrt{\xi^2 + \eta^2 + \zeta^2}$$

remain finite for $r = \infty$, a similar theorem holds for values of φ at points outside of S.

Assuming that these conditions on φ are satisfied, let the point $p(x, y, z)$ lie outside of S. Describe a sphere Σ of radius R about the point p as a center large enough to enclose S, and let the volume which is inside of Σ and outside of S be denoted by B. Since p lies within B, Eq. (3) is applicable and

$$4\pi\varphi(x, y, z) = \int_S\left[\frac{1}{\rho}\frac{\partial\varphi}{\partial n} - \varphi\frac{\partial}{\partial n}\left(\frac{1}{\rho}\right)\right]d\omega + \int_\Sigma\left[\frac{1}{\rho}\frac{\partial\varphi}{\partial n} - \varphi\frac{\partial}{\partial n}\left(\frac{1}{\rho}\right)\right]d\omega,$$

where the normal derivatives are outward with respect to B. It cannot be stated this time that the integral

$$\frac{1}{\rho}\int_\Sigma\frac{\partial\varphi}{\partial n}d\omega$$

vanishes, because it is not known that the continuity condition on φ is satisfied inside of S which is within Σ. But for very large values of R

$$\varphi \text{ and } \frac{1}{\rho} \text{ are of the order } \frac{1}{R},$$

$$\frac{\partial\varphi}{\partial n} \text{ and } \frac{\partial}{\partial n}\left(\frac{1}{\rho}\right) \text{ are of the order } \frac{1}{R^2},$$

and $d\omega$ is of the order R^2.

Hence, the integral $\int_\Sigma\left[\frac{1}{\rho}\frac{\partial\varphi}{\partial n} - \varphi\frac{\partial}{\partial n}\left(\frac{1}{\rho}\right)\right]d\omega$ is of the order $1/R$ and vanishes at infinity. It is evident, too, that this integral is independent of R, so that it is always zero. Therefore, if φ is harmonic outside of S and vanishes at infinity in the order of $1/r$, if its value and the value of its normal derivative is specified at every point on S, and if the point $p(x, y, z)$ lies outside of S, then the value of φ at the point p is defined by the integral

$$\varphi(x, y, z) = \frac{1}{4\pi}\int_S\left[\frac{1}{\rho}\frac{\partial\varphi}{\partial n} - \varphi\frac{\partial}{\partial n}\left(\frac{1}{\rho}\right)\right]d\omega, \qquad (4)$$

the normal derivatives being taken *inward* with respect to S.

64. Reduction to Two Dimensions.—It is evident from Sec. 58 that if φ and ψ are two functions of x and y which are continuous, together with their first and second derivatives, in an area A which is bounded by a closed contour c, Green's theorem in its second form holds; that is

$$\int_A (\psi\Delta\varphi - \varphi\Delta\psi)d\omega = \int_c \left(\psi\frac{\partial\varphi}{\partial n} - \varphi\frac{\partial\psi}{\partial n}\right)d\lambda, \tag{1}$$

where

$$\Delta\varphi = \frac{\partial^2\varphi}{\partial x^2} + \frac{\partial^2\varphi}{\partial y}, \qquad \Delta\psi = \frac{\partial^2\psi}{\varphi x^2} + \frac{\partial^2\psi}{\partial y^2}. \tag{2}$$

If φ and ψ satisfy also the conditions

$$\Delta\varphi = 0, \qquad \Delta\psi = 0. \tag{3}$$

then

$$\int_c \left(\psi\frac{\partial\varphi}{\partial n} - \varphi\frac{\partial\psi}{\partial n}\right)d\lambda = 0; \tag{4}$$

and in particular if ψ is a constant

$$\int_c \frac{\partial\varphi}{\partial n}d\lambda = 0; \tag{5}$$

that is, *the line integral of the normal derivative of an harmonic function around any closed plane contour is zero.*

Extension of the Theorem.—Let the point $p(x, y)$ lie within A, and let $\rho = \sqrt{(\xi - x)^2 + (\eta - y)^2}$. Describe a small circle γ of radius ϵ with the point p as a center, and denote the area lying inside the contour c and outside the circle γ by A_1. Let φ be any function which is harmonic (in two dimensions) inside of c, and let $\psi = \log \rho$. Then both φ and ψ satisfy Eq. (3) in A_1, and Eq. (4) becomes

$$\int_c \left[\frac{\partial\varphi}{\partial n}\log \rho - \varphi\frac{\partial}{\partial n}(\log \rho)\right]d\lambda = \int_\gamma \left[\frac{\partial\varphi}{\partial n}\log \rho - \varphi\frac{\partial}{\partial n}(\log \rho)\right]d\lambda, \tag{6}$$

the normal derivatives being outward with respect to c and outward with respect to γ.

On the circle γ the function ρ is constant and equal to ϵ, while the normal derivative of $\log \rho$ is equal to $1/\epsilon$. Since

$$\log \epsilon \int_\gamma \frac{\partial\varphi}{\partial n}d\lambda = 0,$$

by Eq. (5), the right member of Eq. (6) reduces to

$$-\frac{1}{\epsilon}\int_\gamma \varphi d\lambda,$$

and since $d\lambda = \epsilon d\theta$ on γ, where $d\theta$ is an infinitesimal angle, this integral becomes

$$-\int_0^{2\pi} \varphi d\theta = -2\pi\varphi(x, y).$$

Hence, if φ is harmonic inside of A and $p(x, y)$ lies within A,

$$\varphi(x, y) = \frac{1}{2\pi}\int_c\left[\varphi\frac{\partial}{\partial n}(\log \rho) - \frac{\partial\varphi}{\partial n}\log \rho\right]d\lambda. \tag{7}$$

Corollary I.—If

$$G = \log \rho + H,$$

where H is harmonic inside of A, it is still true that

$$\varphi(x, y) = \frac{1}{2\pi}\int_c\left[\varphi\frac{\partial G}{\partial n} - G\frac{\partial\varphi}{\partial n}\right]d\lambda. \tag{8}$$

This follows readily from Eqs. (7) and (4).

If the point p lies outside of A and $\varphi = V$ is a logarithmic potential which is harmonic outside of A, so that, at large distances, Eq. (46.6),

$$V = M \log \frac{1}{R} + \frac{M_1}{R},$$

where M_1 is a function of $1/R$ that has a finite limit as R increases, then

$$V(x, y) = \frac{-1}{2\pi}\int_c\left[V\frac{\partial}{\partial n}(\log \rho) - \log \rho \cdot \frac{\partial V}{\partial n}\right]d\lambda. \tag{9}$$

In order to prove this, describe a small circle γ about the point p and a large circle Σ of radius R about any convenient point as a center, the circle Σ being large enough to include A and p wholly within it. Since V and $\log \rho$ are harmonic inside of the area which lies inside of Σ and outside of γ and c, Eq. (4) gives

$$\int_c\left[V\frac{\partial}{\partial n}(\log \rho) - \log \rho\frac{\partial V}{\partial n}\right]d\lambda + \int_\gamma\left[V\frac{\partial}{\partial n}(\log \rho) - \log \rho\frac{\partial V}{\partial n}\right]d\lambda$$

$$= \int_\Sigma\left[V\frac{\partial}{\partial n}(\log \rho) - \log \rho\frac{\partial V}{\partial n}\right]d\lambda. \tag{10}$$

Since V is harmonic inside of γ, the second of these integrals is equal to $+2\pi V(x, y)$, just as before. As for the third integral, for very large values of R,

$$\log \rho = -\log \frac{1}{R} - \frac{N}{R} \cdots,$$

$$\frac{\partial}{\partial n}(\log \rho) = \frac{1}{R} + \frac{N_1}{R_2} \cdots.$$

Hence

$$V\frac{\partial}{\partial n}(\log \rho) - \log \rho \frac{\partial V}{\partial n} = -\frac{1}{R^2}(MN_1 - M_1)(1 + \log R) + \cdots,$$

and the third integral becomes

$$-\int_0^{2\pi}\left[(MN_1 - M_1)\frac{1 + \log R}{R} + \cdots \right]d\theta,$$

which is of the order of $1/R$ and, therefore, vanishes. Equation (10), therefore, reduces to Eq. (9), which establishes the theorem.

Corollary II.—*If U and V are the logarithmic potentials of two masses M and N which lie in a plane area which is bounded by a closed contour c, then*

$$\int_c\left(U\frac{\partial V}{\partial n} - V\frac{\partial U}{\partial n}\right)d\lambda = 0. \tag{11}$$

Corollary III.—*If U and V have the same definitions as in Corollary II, if ρ is measured from a point p which lies outside of c, and if*

$$G = \log\frac{1}{\rho} + V,$$

then

$$U(p) = -\frac{1}{2\pi}\int_c\left(U\frac{\partial G}{\partial n} - G\frac{\partial U}{\partial n}\right)d\lambda.$$

65. Analogy with Cauchy's Theory of Residues.—Equation (64.7) bears a striking resemblance to Cauchy's equation in the theory of the complex variable.

$$f(z) = \frac{1}{2\pi i}\int_c\frac{f(\zeta)}{\zeta - z}d\zeta,$$

where $f(\zeta)$ is holomorphic within the contour c, and $z = x + iy$ is a point in the complex plane lying within c. The connection between the two theorems is traced by Poincaré as follows:[1]

Consider an area A bounded by a contour c in the plane of the complex variable $\zeta = \xi + i\eta$. Let $f(\zeta)$ be a function of ζ which is holomorphic in A. Let $f(\zeta)$ be separated into its real and imaginary parts

$$f(\zeta) = F_1(\xi, \eta) + iF_2(\xi, \eta).$$

[1] "Théorie du Potentiel Newtonien," p. 149, (1899).

The functions F_1 and F_2 of the real variables ξ and η satisfy the equations

$$\frac{\partial F_1}{\partial \xi} = \frac{\partial F_2}{\partial \eta}, \qquad \frac{\partial F_1}{\partial \eta} = -\frac{\partial F_2}{\partial \xi}, \tag{1}$$

$$\frac{\partial^2 F_1}{\partial \xi^2} + \frac{\partial^2 F_1}{\partial \eta^2} = 0, \qquad \frac{\partial^2 F_2}{\partial \xi^2} + \frac{\partial^2 F_2}{\partial \eta^2} = 0. \tag{2}$$

The function

$$\log\left(\frac{1}{\zeta - z}\right) = L_1(\xi, \eta) + iL_2(\xi, \eta)$$

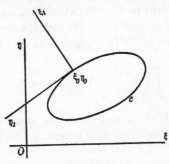

Fig. 34.

also can be separated into its real and imaginary parts; and if $\zeta - z$ is expressed in polar coordinates,

$$\zeta - z = \rho e^{i\theta},$$

then

$$L_1 = -\log \rho, \qquad L_2 = -\theta,$$

where

$$\rho = \sqrt{(\xi - x)^2 + (\eta - y)^2}, \qquad \theta = \tan^{-1}\frac{\eta - y}{\xi - x}.$$

Now, let Eq. (64.7) be applied to the functions F_1 and F_2, which are harmonic within A, with the recollection that $\log \rho = -L_1$. There results the two equations

$$F_1(x, y) = \frac{1}{2\pi}\int_c \left(L_1\frac{\partial F_1}{\partial n} - F_1\frac{\partial L_1}{\partial n}\right)d\lambda, \\ F_2(x, y) = \frac{1}{2\pi}\int_c \left(L_1\frac{\partial F_2}{\partial n} - F_2\frac{\partial L_1}{\partial n}\right)d\lambda. \tag{3}$$

Now imagine a change of coordinate systems, Fig. 34,

$$\xi = \xi_0 - \xi_1 \sin \alpha - y_1 \cos \alpha, \\ \eta = \eta_0 + \xi_1 \cos \alpha - y_1 \sin \alpha, \tag{4}$$

in which $\xi_0\eta_0$ is a point of the contour c, and α is chosen so that the ξ_1-axis is normal to the contour directed outward and the η_1-axis is tangent to it, directed forward.

Then *at the origin*

$$\frac{\partial F_k}{\partial \xi_1} = \frac{\partial F_k}{\partial n}, \qquad \frac{\partial F_k}{\partial \eta_1} = \frac{\partial F_k}{\partial \lambda}, \qquad k = 1, 2. \tag{5}$$

By virtue of the change of variables, Eqs. (1) become

$$\left(\frac{\partial F_1}{\partial \eta_1} + \frac{\partial F_2}{\partial \xi_1}\right) \cos \alpha + \left(\frac{\partial F_1}{\partial \xi_1} - \frac{\partial F_2}{\partial \eta_1}\right) \sin \alpha = 0,$$

$$\left(\frac{\partial F_1}{\partial \eta_1} + \frac{\partial F_2}{\partial \xi_1}\right) \sin \alpha - \left(\frac{\partial F_1}{\partial \xi_1} - \frac{\partial F_2}{\partial \eta_1}\right) \cos \alpha = 0;$$

and therefore, since the determinant is equal to minus one,

$$\frac{\partial F_1}{\partial \xi_1} = \frac{\partial F_2}{\partial \eta_1}, \qquad \frac{\partial F_1}{\partial \eta_1} = -\frac{\partial F_2}{\partial \xi_1}.$$

Equations (5) then show that at the origin

$$\frac{\partial F_1}{\partial n} = \frac{\partial F_2}{\partial \lambda}, \qquad \frac{\partial F_1}{\partial \lambda} = -\frac{\partial F_2}{\partial n};$$

and these relations hold all along the contour, independent of the coordinate system. Likewise

$$\frac{\partial L_1}{\partial n} = \frac{\partial L_2}{\partial \lambda}, \qquad \frac{\partial L_1}{\partial \lambda} = -\frac{\partial L_2}{\partial n}.$$

Equations (3), therefore, can be written

$$\left.\begin{aligned}
F_1(x, y) &= \frac{1}{2\pi} \int_c (+L_1 dF_2 - F_1 dL_2), \\
F_2(x, y) &= \frac{1}{2\pi} \int_c (-L_1 dF_1 - F_2 dL_2),
\end{aligned}\right\} \tag{6}$$

the two integrals being taken in the positive direction around c.

The function $L_2 = -\tan^{-1}\dfrac{\eta - y}{\xi - x}$ is not single valued, but $L_1 = -\log \rho$ is single valued since it is real. The functions F_1 and F_2 are single valued by hypothesis. Hence

$$\int_c d(L_1 F_1) = 0, \qquad \int_c d(L_1 F_2) = 0;$$

and

$$\int_c L_1 dF_1 = -\int_c F_1 dL_1, \qquad \int_c L_1 dF_2 = -\int_c F_2 dL_1;$$

so that Eqs. (6) can be written

$$F_1(x, y) = -\frac{1}{2\pi}\int_c (F_2 dL_1 + F_1 dL_2),$$

$$F_2(x, y) = +\frac{1}{2\pi}\int_c (F_1 dL_1 - F_2 dL_2).$$

Now

$$\log\frac{1}{\zeta - z} = L_1 + iL_2 \qquad \text{and} \qquad \frac{-d\zeta}{\zeta - z} = dL_1 + idL_2;$$

also

$$\frac{f(\zeta)}{\zeta - z}d\zeta = -(F_1 + iF_2)(dL_1 + idL_2).$$

Therefore,

$$\frac{1}{2\pi i}\int_c \frac{f(\zeta)}{\zeta - z}d\zeta = \frac{i}{2\pi}\int_c (F_1 dL_1 - F_2 dL_2) - \frac{1}{2\pi}\int (F_2 dL_1 + F_1 dL_2)$$

$$= F_1(x, y) + iF_2(x, y).$$

That is

$$\frac{1}{2\pi i}\int_c \frac{f(\zeta)}{\zeta - z}d\zeta = f(z)$$

which is Cauchy's theorem. The formula is applicable only if z lies within the contour c.

66. The Surface Integral of the Normal Derivative of $1/\rho$.—
Let there be given a closed surface S and a point O. With the

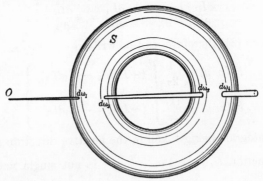

Fig. 35.

point O as a vertex, take a cone with the infinitesimal solid angle $d\omega$, which cuts out of the surface S the elements $d\omega_1$, $d\omega_2$, . . . ,
(Fig. 35). Let the normal to S at the element $d\omega_i$, directed outward, make an angle φ_i with the axis of the cone directed away from the point O. The projection of $d\omega_i$ upon a plane perpen-

dicular to the axis of the cone is $\rho_i^2 d\bar{\omega}$, where ρ_i is the distance along the axis of the cone from the point O to the element of surface $d\omega_i$. Since the angle between the plane which is tangent to S at $d\omega_i$ and the plane which is perpendicular to the axis of the cone is the same as the angle between the normal at $d\omega_i$ and the axis of the cone, φ_i, it follows that

$$\rho_i^2 d\omega = d\omega_i \cos \varphi_i, \qquad \text{or} \qquad d\bar{\omega} = \frac{d\omega_i \cos \varphi_i}{\rho_i^2}.$$

If the point O lies outside of S, the infinitesimal cone cuts the surface an even number of times; the angles φ_i are alternately obtuse and acute, and the $\cos \varphi_i$ alternately negative and positive. Since the elements of S, $d\omega_i$, are all positive, it follows that

$$\frac{d\omega_i \cos \varphi_i}{\rho_i^2}$$

is alternately negative and positive, $\mp d\bar{\omega}$. Hence, if 2κ is the number of times the infinitesimal cone pierces S,

$$\sum_{i=1}^{2\kappa} \frac{d\omega_i \cos \varphi_i}{\rho_i^2} = 0.$$

Since this is true for every infinitesimal angle $d\bar{\omega}$, it is true for the sum of all such angles, and therefore

$$\int_S \frac{\cos \varphi}{\rho^2} \cdot d\omega = 0.$$

If the point O lies inside of S, the infinitesimal cone pierces the surface an odd number of times, $2\kappa + 1$, and

$$\sum_{i=1}^{2\kappa+1} \frac{\cos \varphi_i \cdot d\omega_i}{\rho_i^2} = d\bar{\omega}.$$

and since this is true for every such infinitesimal solid angle, it follows that

$$\int_S \frac{\cos \varphi}{\rho^2} d\omega = \int_S d\bar{\omega} = 4\pi.$$

If the point O lies in S itself, at an ordinary point of the surface, it is evident that

$$\int_S \frac{\cos \varphi}{\rho^2} d\omega = \int_S d\bar{\omega} = 2\pi,$$

since in the neighborhood of O the surface lies entirely on one side of the tangent plane.

If x, y, z are the coordinates of the point O and ξ, η, ζ are the coordinates of a point on S at which the direction cosines of the normal are α, β, γ, then

$$\rho = \sqrt{(\xi - x)^2 + (\eta - y)^2 + (\zeta - z)^2},$$

and

$$\cos \varphi = \alpha \frac{\xi - x}{\rho} + \beta \frac{\eta - y}{\rho} + \gamma \frac{\zeta - z}{\rho},$$

$$= \alpha \frac{\partial \rho}{\partial \xi} + \beta \frac{\partial \rho}{\partial \eta} + \gamma \frac{\partial \rho}{\partial \zeta}.$$

Therefore, Eq. (54.2),

$$\cos \varphi = \frac{\partial \rho}{\partial n}, \tag{1}$$

$$\frac{\cos \varphi}{\rho^2} = \frac{1}{\rho^2} \frac{\partial \rho}{\partial n} = -\frac{\partial}{\partial n}\left(\frac{1}{\rho}\right),$$

and

$$\int_S \frac{\cos \varphi \, d\omega}{\rho^2} = -\int_S \frac{\partial}{\partial n}\left(\frac{1}{\rho}\right) d\omega.$$

Hence

$$\int_S \frac{\partial}{\partial n}\left(\frac{1}{\rho}\right) d\omega = \left\{ \begin{array}{l} 0 \text{ if } O \text{ is outside of } S, \\ -2\pi \text{ if } O \text{ is the surface } S, \\ -4\pi \text{ if } O \text{ is inside of } S, \end{array} \right\} \tag{2}$$

the normal derivative being taken outward with respect to S. If O is on the surface the value is -2π, if it is at an ordinary point of S. At a conical point of S its value is the solid angle of the enveloping cone taken negatively.

67. The Contour Integral of the Normal Derivative of Log ρ.—Let there be given a plane area A bounded by a closed contour c. Let O be any point in the plane and $d\theta$ any infinitesimal angle in the plane with its vertex at O, which cuts across the contour c (Fig. 36). If O is outside of c it will cut across the boundary an even number of times, but if it is inside the number of crossings will be odd. Let $d\lambda$, $d\lambda_2$, . . . be the elements of the contour intercepted by the angle $d\theta$ at

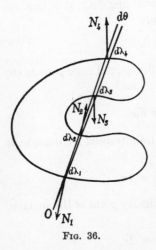

Fig. 36.

the distances ρ_1, ρ_2, . . . from O, and let φ_1, φ_2, . . . be the angles which the outward directed normals make with the axis of the angle $d\theta$ directed away from O. Then

$$\pm d\theta = \frac{d\lambda_i \cos \varphi_i}{\rho_i}, \qquad i = 1, 2, \cdots. \tag{1}$$

The angles φ_1, φ_2, . . . are alternately obtuse and acute. If

$d\lambda_i$ and ρ_i are regarded as always positive, the values in Eq. (1) are alternately positive and negative, although numerically equal. Hence

$$\sum_i \frac{d\lambda_i \cos \varphi_i}{\rho_i} = \begin{cases} 0 \text{ if } O \text{ is outside of } c, \\ d\theta \text{ if } O \text{ is on the contour or inside of } c. \end{cases}$$

Since this result is true for each infinitesimal angle $d\theta$, it is true for their sum, so that

$$\int_c \frac{\cos \varphi}{\rho} d\lambda = \begin{cases} 0 \text{ if } O \text{ is outside of } c, \\ 2\pi \text{ if } O \text{ is inside of } c. \end{cases}$$

If O is on the boundary c, the value is π at an ordinary point, but if O is at a cusp, the value of the integral is the angle between the two tangents at the cusp.

As in Sec. 66,

$$\cos \varphi = \frac{\partial \rho}{\partial n}, \tag{2}$$

and

$$\frac{\cos \varphi}{\rho} = \frac{1}{\rho} \frac{\partial \rho}{\partial n} = -\frac{\partial}{\partial n} \log \frac{1}{\rho}.$$

Hence

$$\int \frac{\partial}{\partial n} \left(\log \frac{1}{\rho} \right) d\lambda = 0, \text{ or } -2\pi, \tag{3}$$

according as the point O is outside or inside of the boundary.

68. A Theorem of Gauss.—By means of the integrals which have just been established, it is an easy matter to prove a certain theorem which is due to Gauss.

Suppose there is given a closed surface S and a point O. At the point O there is placed a particle of mass m. If p is a point of S at a distance ρ from O, the attraction of m on the point p is $-m/\rho^2$ and the component of this attraction along the exterior normal is

$$-\frac{m \cos \varphi}{\rho^2} = \frac{\partial}{\partial n} \left(\frac{m}{\rho} \right).$$

The surface integral of this normal component, or the flux of the gravitational force due to m across S is

$$\int_S \frac{\partial}{\partial n} \left(\frac{m}{\rho} \right) d\omega = \begin{cases} 0 \text{ if } m \text{ is outside of } S, \\ -4m\pi \text{ if } m \text{ is inside of } S. \end{cases} \tag{1}$$

If there are many such particles and M_i is the total mass inside of S, and M_o is the total mass outside of S, then

$$\int_S \frac{\partial}{\partial n} \left(\sum \frac{m_i}{\rho_i} \right) d\omega = -4\pi M_i, \tag{2}$$

which is independent of M_o. If the distribution of mass $M_i + M_o$ is a continuous one, the finite sum becomes a definite integral,

$$\lim \sum \frac{m_i}{\rho_i} = \int \frac{dm}{\rho} = V,$$

where V is the potential of the given distribution of mass, and Eq. (2) becomes

$$\int_S \frac{\partial V}{\partial n} d\omega = -4\pi M_i. \tag{3}$$

Expressed in full, Gauss' theorem states that *if there is any distribution of matter which may be partly within and partly without a closed surface S, and if M_i is the total mass within S, the surface integral of the normal component of the attraction toward the exterior, or the surface integral of the exterior normal derivative of the potential due to the entire mass $M_o + M_i$, is equal to $-4\pi M_i$.*

A similar theorem holds in two dimensions for the logarithmic potential. If M_i and M_o have the same significance as before, and V is the logarithmic potential,

$$\int_c \frac{\partial V}{\partial n} d\lambda = -2\pi M_i. \tag{4}$$

69. Poisson's Equation.—Suppose $V(\xi, \eta, \zeta)$ is any function of ξ, η, and ζ which is continuous in a volume B which is bounded by a closed surface S, and, likewise, its first derivatives. Then by Green's theorem, Eq. (58.5),

$$\int_B \Delta V d\tau = \int_S \frac{\partial V}{\partial n} d\omega. \tag{1}$$

The conditions imposed upon V are satisfied if V is a potential function of any finite continuous distribution of matter. Suppose V is such a potential function. Then by Gauss' theorem, Sec. 68,

$$\int_S \frac{\partial V}{\partial n} d\omega = -4\pi M_i,$$

and therefore

$$\int_B \Delta V d\tau = -4\pi M_i. \tag{2}$$

Suppose $\sigma(\xi, \eta, \zeta)$ is the density function which represents the distribution of matter in the volume B. Then

$$M_i = \int_B \sigma d\tau,$$

and Eq. (2) can be written

$$\int_B (\Delta V + 4\pi\sigma)d\tau = 0.$$

This equation holds whatever the volume B may be, and therefore the integrand vanishes identically. That is,

$$\Delta V + 4\pi\sigma = 0; \tag{3}$$

or

$$\frac{\partial^2 V}{\partial \xi^2} + \frac{\partial^2 V}{\partial \eta^2} + \frac{\partial^2 V}{\partial \zeta^2} = -4\pi\sigma(\xi, \eta, \zeta), \tag{4}$$

which is Poisson's equation.

An illuminating derivation of Poisson's equation can be obtained as follows. Let O be any point of the body and let σ_0 be the density at O. Let a small sphere Σ be described about the point O. The potential of the body can be separated into the sum of two potentials,

$$V = V_0 + V_1,$$

one of which, V_0, is the potential of the sphere at O, and the other V_1 is the potential of the remainder of the body. Let the sphere Σ be taken so small that the density within it can be regarded as constant. If its radius is a, then by Sec. 25

$$V_0 = 2\pi\sigma_0\left[a^2 - \frac{1}{3}(\xi^2 + \eta^2 + \zeta^2)\right],$$

and

$$\Delta V_0 = -4\pi\sigma_0.$$

Since O lies outside of the volume for which V_1 is the potential, it follows from Laplace's equation that $\Delta V_1 = 0$, and therefore at the point O,

$$\Delta V = -4\pi\sigma_0,$$

which is Poisson's equation.

Poisson's equation holds whatever the surface S may be and whatever the distribution of matter may be, provided only that σ is an integrable function. It can therefore be regarded as holding throughout all space. It includes Laplace's equation, for, outside of the body, the density σ is zero and Poisson's equation reduces to Laplace's equation.

If it is written in the form

$$\sigma = -\frac{1}{4\pi}\left(\frac{\partial^2 V}{\partial x^2} + \frac{\partial^2 V}{\partial y^2} + \frac{\partial^2 V}{\partial z^2}\right), \tag{5}$$

it is seen that Poisson's equation answers the question "What distribution of matter will produce a given potential, assuming that the potential is defined at all points of space."

In ordinary solid bodies the surface is a surface of discontinuity in the density, since at the surface the density changes abruptly from a certain finite value on the inside to zero on the outside. Equation (5) shows that at least one of the second derivatives of V for such a body also is discontinuous at the surface, and the sum of the discontinuities of the three second derivatives is -4π times the discontinuity in the density at the surface.

70. Poisson's Equation in Two Dimensions.—If φ and ψ are functions of the two variables x and y which, together with their first derivatives, are continuous in a plane area A which is bounded by a closed contour c, by Green's theorem, Eq. (64.1)

$$\int_A (\psi\Delta\varphi - \varphi\Delta\psi)d\omega = \int_c \left(\psi\frac{\partial\varphi}{\partial n} - \varphi\frac{\partial\psi}{\partial n}\right)d\lambda;$$

and if $\psi = 1$,

$$\int_A \Delta\varphi d\omega = \int_c \frac{\partial\varphi}{\partial n}d\lambda.$$

The conditions on φ are satisfied by the logarithmic potential V of any continuous distribution of matter over an area. Hence

$$\int_A \Delta V d\omega = \int_c \frac{\partial V}{\partial n}d\lambda,$$

and by Gauss' theorem, Eq. (68.4)

$$\int_c \frac{\partial V}{\partial n}d\lambda = -2\pi M_i$$

$$= -2\pi \int_A \sigma d\omega.$$

Hence

$$\int_A (\Delta V + 2\pi\sigma)d\omega = 0,$$

and therefore

$$\Delta V = -2\pi\sigma.$$

71. An Extension of Gauss' Theorem.—Gauss' theorem can be deduced from Green's theorem, but it is just as simple to give a generalization of it.

Let $\varphi(x, y, z)$ be any function which is harmonic within a volume B which is bounded by a closed surface S, and let

$V(x, y, z)$ be a Newtonian potential within S, that is the potential of a body B_1 bounded by a surface S_1, Fig. 37. The body B_1 may lie partly within S and partly without, or wholly within, or wholly without. Then by Green's theorem, Eq. (58.4),

$$\int_B (\varphi \Delta V - V \Delta \varphi) d\tau = \int_S \left(\varphi \frac{\partial V}{\partial n} - V \frac{\partial \varphi}{\partial n} \right) d\omega, \tag{1}$$

the normal derivatives taken outward.

Since φ is harmonic in B and V is a Newtonian potential,

$$\Delta \varphi = 0, \qquad \text{and} \qquad \Delta V = -4\pi\sigma,$$

inside of B. Hence, Eq. (1) becomes

$$\int_S \left(\varphi \frac{\partial V}{\partial n} - V \frac{\partial \varphi}{\partial n} \right) d\omega = -4\pi \int_B \varphi \sigma d\tau = -4\pi \int_B \varphi dm, \tag{2}$$

where $\sigma d\tau = dm$. Gauss' theorem follows at once by taking φ equal to unity, so that Eq. (2) is a generalization of Gauss' theorem. If the body B_1 consists of a single particle of mass m, so that

$$V = \frac{m}{\rho},$$

and if this particle is located inside of S, Eq. (2) reduces to Eq. (63.3) as of course it should. If the body B_1 is a set of discrete particles

$$V = \sum \frac{m_i}{\rho_i},$$

Eq. (2) becomes

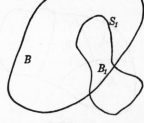

FIG. 37.

$$\int_S \left(\varphi \frac{\partial V}{\partial n} - V \frac{\partial \varphi}{\partial n} \right) d\omega = -4\pi \sum_i \varphi_i m_i, \tag{3}$$

where φ_i is the value of φ at the particle m_i and the sum in the right member is extended over all of the particles which lie inside of S. Eqs. (2) and (3) can be regarded as generalizations of Eq. (63.3).

Reduction to Two Dimensions.—A similar theorem holds in two dimensions. If $\varphi(x, y)$ is harmonic in an area A which is bounded by a closed contour c, and if V is a logarithmic potential of any continuous distribution of matter over an area A_1, which may lie wholly outside of A, wholly inside, or partly outside and partly inside, then

$$\int_c \left(\varphi \frac{\partial V}{\partial n} - V \frac{\partial \varphi}{\partial n} \right) d\lambda = -2\pi \int_A \varphi \cdot \sigma d\omega. \tag{4}$$

Or, if

$$V = \sum m_i \log \frac{1}{\rho_i},$$

is the potential for a discrete set of particles

$$\int_c \left(\varphi \frac{\partial V}{\partial n} - V \frac{\partial \varphi}{\partial n} \right) d\lambda = -2\pi \sum m_i \varphi_i, \qquad (5)$$

where φ_i is the value of φ at the point ξ_i, η_i at which the particle m_i is located, and the sum Σ is extended over all of the points inside of A. If the area A is divided into sub-areas $A_1, A_2, \ldots$ bounded by a finite number of contours, Fig. 38, and if the density, although discontinuous across a contour, is continuous in each sub-area A_i, Eq. (4) is still true, for it can be applied to each sub-area separately. If the sum of the results is taken, it is found that Eq. (4) reappears for the entire area A, since the division lines appear

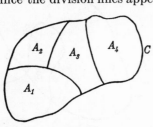

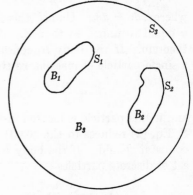

FIG. 38.   FIG. 39.

twice in the sum, the contour integrals being taken in opposite directions in the two cases. Since φ, V and their derivatives are continuous across these dividing lines, the two integrals taken along them, but in opposite directions, are numerically equal though opposite in sign. Hence, in the sum the integrals taken along the dividing lines cancel out, leaving only the integral along the outside contour c.

72. Green's Theorem Applied to Two Potential Functions.— Let V_1 be the potential function of a body B_1 which has a surface S_1 and a density σ_1. Let V_2, B_2, S_2 and σ_2 be the corresponding symbols for a second body. Let S_3 be any spherical surface which contains B_1 and B_2 wholly within its interior, and let B_3 be the volume which lies inside of S_3 and outside of B_1, and therefore includes the volume of B_2, so that the volume of B_2 is a part of the volume B_3.

Since V_1, V_2 and their first derivatives are continuous within B_3, Green's theorem in its first form, Eq. (58.3), applied to the volume B_3, gives

$$\int_{B_3} V_2 \Delta V_1 d\tau + \int_{B_3} \left(\frac{\partial V_1}{\partial x} \frac{\partial V_2}{\partial x} + \frac{\partial V_1}{\partial y} \frac{\partial V_2}{\partial y} + \frac{\partial V_1}{\partial z} \frac{\partial V_2}{\partial z} \right) d\tau$$
$$= \int_{S_1} V_2 \frac{\partial V_1}{\partial n} d\omega + \int_{S_3} V_2 \frac{\partial V_1}{\partial n} d\omega; \quad (1)$$

the normal derivative is outward with respect to B_3, and therefore on S_1 it is inward with respect to S_1.

The second integral in the right member of Eq. (1) can be evaluated. If the center of S_3 is kept fixed and its radius R is very large, V_2 is of the order M_2/R and

$$\frac{\partial V_1}{\partial n} = \frac{\partial V_1}{\partial R} = -\frac{M_1}{R^2} \text{ approx.,}$$

where M_1 and M_2 are the masses of B_1 and B_2 respectively. Thus, neglecting the higher terms of the expansion, since $d\omega = R^2 d\bar{\omega}$, the integral becomes

$$\int_{S_3} V_2 \frac{\partial V_1}{\partial n} d\omega = -M_1 M_2 \int_{S_3} \frac{d\bar{\omega}}{R} = -4\pi \frac{M_1 M_2}{R},$$

which vanishes with $R = \infty$. Hence, if B_3 represents all space outside of B_1, and $\partial V_1/\partial n_i$ represents the normal derivative of V_1 taken inward with respect to S_1, Eq. (1) becomes

$$\int_{B_3} V_2 \Delta V_1 d\tau + \int_{B_3} \left(\frac{\partial V_1}{\partial x} \frac{\partial V_2}{\partial x} + \frac{\partial V_1}{\partial y} \frac{\partial V_2}{\partial y} + \frac{\partial V_1}{\partial z} \frac{\partial V_2}{\partial z} \right) d\tau =$$
$$\int_{S_1} V_2 \frac{\partial V_1}{\partial n_i} d\omega. \quad (2)$$

Applied to the volume B_1, Green's theorem gives

$$\int_{B_1} V_2 \Delta V_1 d\tau + \int_{B_1} \left(\frac{\partial V_1}{\partial x} \frac{\partial V_2}{\partial x} + \frac{\partial V_1}{\partial y} \frac{\partial V_2}{\partial y} + \frac{\partial V_1}{\partial z} \frac{\partial V_2}{\partial z} \right) d\tau =$$
$$\int_{S_1} V_2 \frac{\partial V_1}{\partial n_e} d\omega, \quad (3)$$

where $\partial V_1/\partial n_e$ means the normal derivative outward with respect to S_1, and consequently is the negative of $\partial V_1/\partial n_i$. On adding Eqs. (2) and (3) it is found that

$$\int_\infty V_2 \Delta V_1 d\tau + \int_\infty \left(\frac{\partial V_1}{\partial x} \frac{\partial V_2}{\partial x} + \frac{\partial V_1}{\partial y} \frac{\partial V_2}{\partial y} + \frac{\partial V_1}{\partial z} \frac{\partial V_2}{\partial z} \right) d\tau = 0, \quad (4)$$

the integration being extended over all space; and this equation can also be written

$$-4\pi \int_\infty V_2\sigma_1 d\tau + \int_\infty \left(\frac{\partial V_1}{\partial x}\frac{\partial V_2}{\partial x} + \frac{\partial V_1}{\partial y}\frac{\partial V_2}{\partial y} + \frac{\partial V_1}{\partial z}\frac{\partial V_2}{\partial z}\right)d\tau = 0, (5)$$

if it is understood that σ_1 is zero outside of S_1.

On permuting V_1 and V_2 and then subtracting, there results

$$\int_\infty (V_1\Delta V_2 - V_2\Delta V_1)d\tau = 0, \tag{6}$$

or

$$\int_\infty (\sigma_1 V_2 - \sigma_2 V_1)d\tau = 0,$$

the integration being extended over all space. But since $\sigma_1 = 0$ outside of B_1 and $\sigma_2 = 0$ outside of B_2, this can be written just as well

$$\int_{B_1} \sigma_1 V_2 d\tau = \int_{B_2} \sigma_2 V_1 d\tau. \tag{7}$$

73. Characteristic Properties of a Potential Function.—In the preceeding pages it has been proved that the potential function V of any finite distribution of matter in a closed volume, or on a limited surface, has the following properties:

1. V is continuous throughout all space.

2. The first derivatives of V exist and are continuous everywhere, except possibly on a given surface S on which there may be a surface distribution of matter. On crossing this surface there may be discontinuities in the derivatives, that is, they tend towards definite limits on both sides as the surface is approached along the normal, but the two limits are different. The tangential components are continuous.

3. On the exterior of S, $\Delta V = 0$.

4. On the interior of S, ΔV is arbitrary.

5. V vanishes at infinity.

Conversely, if there is given a function $V(x, y, z)$ which satisfies these five conditions and for which ΔV within S and the discontinuities in the normal derivatives on S are specified, then, there exists one and only one distribution of matter for which V is the potential.

To prove this, let

$$\Delta V = -4\pi\sigma(\xi, \eta, \zeta)$$

within S, and let the discontinuities in the normal derivative on S be $-4\pi\bar{\sigma}(\xi, \eta, \zeta)$. Since the function V is given, by hypothesis, it can be supposed that the functions σ and $\bar{\sigma}$ also are given. Let

$$\rho = \sqrt{(\xi - x)^2 + (\eta - y)^2 + (\zeta - z)^2}.$$

and let the functions V_1 and V_2 be defined by the integrals

$$V_1 = \int_B \frac{\sigma}{\rho} d\tau, \qquad V_2 = \int_S \frac{\bar{\sigma}}{\rho} d\omega,$$

the first of which is a volume integral and the second is a surface integral. The function V_1 is the potential of a distribution of matter within S which has the volume density σ, and V_2 is the potential of a distribution of matter on S which has the surface density $\bar{\sigma}$. Hence the function $V_1 + V_2$ is the potential of a distribution of matter which satisfies all five of the given conditions.

It remains to be shown that this is the only possible distribution which satisfies the five given conditions. Suppose there existed another distribution of matter, the potential V of which also satisfied all five conditions. Let

$$W = V - (V_1 + V_2).$$

Then, on admitting negative masses, W also is the potential of a distribution of matter which vanishes at infinity, for which ΔW is zero everywhere, and normal derivatives are continuous across S.

In Sec. 72 the letters V_1 and V_2 denoted any two potential functions. In Eq. (72.4) let

$$V_1 = V_2 = W.$$

Then

$$\int_\infty W\Delta W d\tau + \int_\infty \left[\left(\frac{\partial W}{\partial x}\right)^2 + \left(\frac{\partial W}{\partial y}\right)^2 + \left(\frac{\partial W}{\partial z}\right)^2\right] d\tau = 0,$$

the integration being extended over all space. The first integral vanishes since W is everywhere finite and ΔW is everywhere zero. The second integral, therefore, also is zero, which compels

$$\frac{\partial W}{\partial x} = \frac{\partial W}{\partial y} = \frac{\partial W}{\partial z} = 0$$

everywhere. Hence, W is a constant, and since it vanishes at infinity, it vanishes everywhere, so that

$$V = V_1 + V_2,$$

instead of being different as was assumed. Consequently there is no other distribution of matter possible.

74. The Average Value of a Potential over a Sphere.— According to the extension of Green's theorem, Eq. (63.3), if φ is harmonic within a volume which is bounded by a closed surface S, and if ρ is the distance from a point x, y, z which is within S, then

$$\frac{1}{4\pi}\int_S\left[\frac{1}{\rho}\frac{\partial\varphi}{\partial n} - \varphi\frac{\partial}{\partial n}\left(\frac{1}{\rho}\right)\right]d\omega = \varphi(x, y, z). \tag{1}$$

If the surface S is a sphere and the point x, y, z is at its center, ρ and its normal derivative are constant on S; and Eq. (1) becomes

$$\frac{1}{4\pi\rho}\int_S\frac{\partial\varphi}{\partial n}d\omega + \frac{1}{4\pi\rho^2}\int_S\varphi d\omega = \varphi(x, y, z). \tag{2}$$

If, in addition to these assumptions, $\varphi = V$ is the potential of a body which is wholly exterior to the sphere, then by Gauss' theorem, Eq. (68.3),

$$\frac{1}{4\pi}\int_S\frac{\partial V}{\partial n}d\omega = -M_i,$$

and the first integral of Eq. (2) vanishes, since there is no matter within S. There remains then

$$\frac{1}{4\pi\rho^2}\int_S V d\omega = V(x, y, z). \tag{3}$$

This can be expressed in words as follows:

Theorem.—The average value of the potential function over any spherical surface which does not contain any of the attracting matter is equal to the value of the potential function at the center of the sphere.

This theorem holds also if V is merely harmonic within S.

If the matter lies wholly within the given sphere, let a second sphere S_2 concentric with the first be described and apply Green's theorem to the volume between S and S_2. If ψ and φ are two functions which are harmonic within this region

$$\int_S\left(\psi\frac{\partial\varphi}{\partial n} - \varphi\frac{\partial\psi}{\partial n}\right)d\omega = \int_{S_2}\left(\psi\frac{\partial\varphi}{\partial n} - \varphi\frac{\partial\psi}{\partial n}\right)d\omega,$$

the normal derivatives being outward with respect to the center on both spheres. If ρ is the distance from the center of the two spheres, ψ is taken to be $1/\rho$, and φ is taken to be the potential

V of a mass which lies wholly within S, then φ and ψ are harmonic in the volume between S and S_2, and

$$\int_S \left[\frac{1}{\rho} \frac{\partial V}{\partial n} - V \frac{\partial}{\partial n} \left(\frac{1}{\rho} \right) \right] d\omega = \int_{S_2} \left[\frac{1}{\rho} \frac{\partial V}{\partial n} - V \frac{\partial}{\partial n} \left(\frac{1}{\rho} \right) \right] d\omega.$$

If the radius R_2 of the sphere S_2 is very large, then, on S_2, V and $1/\rho$ are of the order $1/R_2$, $\partial V/\partial n$ and $\partial(1/\rho)/\partial n$ are of the order $1/R_2{}^2$, and $d\omega$ is of the order $R_2{}^2$. Hence, the entire integral in the right member is of the order $1/R_2$ and therefore vanishes. Hence

$$\int_S \left[\frac{1}{\rho} \frac{\partial V}{\partial n} + \frac{1}{\rho^2} V \right] d\omega = 0;$$

and, since ρ is constant on S,

$$\frac{1}{\rho^2} \int_S V d\omega = -\frac{1}{\rho} \int_S \frac{\partial V}{\partial n} d\omega = +4\pi \frac{M}{\rho}.$$

Therefore

$$\frac{1}{4\pi\rho^2} \int_S V d\omega = \frac{M}{\rho}. \tag{4}$$

which, expressed in words, states

Theorem.—*The average value of the potential of any distribution of matter over any sphere which includes all of the matter in its interior is the same as though all of the matter were concentrated in a particle at the center of the sphere.*

Reduction to Two Dimensions.—It is proved in a like manner that analogous theorems hold in two dimensions for a circle and the logarithmic potential.

75. Maxima and Minima of Harmonic Functions.—If $\varphi(x, y, z)$ is harmonic in a volume B which is bounded by a closed surface S, then, by Eq. (62.2),

$$\int_S \frac{\partial \varphi}{\partial n} d\omega = 0. \tag{1}$$

Suppose φ has a maximum at the point p, by which it is meant that the function $\varphi(x, y, z)$ has a greater value at the point p than at any point in the neighborhood of p. If a small sphere Σ is described with p as its center, it is evident that the normal derivative of φ is everywhere negative on Σ, since the function φ has a maximum value at p. Therefore, the integral

$$\int_\Sigma \frac{\partial \varphi}{\partial n} d\omega$$

is negative. But since φ is harmonic within Σ this integral must vanish by Eq. (1). This contradiction shows that if φ is harmonic in a volume which is bounded by a closed surface, it cannot have a maximum in that volume, and a similar argument shows also that it cannot have a minimum either.

Theorem I.—The potential function cannot have a maximum or a minimum at any point in empty space.

This theorem follows at once from the fact that the potential function is harmonic in empty space. The theorem does not, however, prevent all of the first derivatives of the potential from vanishing in empty space; and, since the first derivatives are the components of attraction, it does not prevent the existence of equilibrium points (*e.g.*, the center of a uniform anchor ring). Such a point which is neither a maximum nor a minimum is called a minimax, for it is a maximum with respect to some directions and a minimun with respect to others (like the seat of a saddle). When such points exist they are always points of unstable equilibrium.

If a function is harmonic within a volume B and constant everywhere on the bounding surface S, then it has the same constant value everywhere in B. If it were not constant throughout B, it would certainly have a maximum or a minimum point somewhere within B, which is impossible. Therefore, it is constant.

Similarly if a function is harmonic everywhere outside of S and has the same constant value everywhere on S and at infinity, it is constant everywhere outside of S. From this it follows, by allowing S to shrink up to a point, that a function which is harmonic everywhere, including infinity, is a mere constant.

If two functions V_1 and V_2 are harmonic within B and take the same values everywhere on the bounding surface S, they are identical everywhere within B. For their difference $V = V_1 - V_2$ is harmonic within B and equal to zero everywhere on S. Therefore, it is equal to zero everywhere within B.

From these properties of harmonic functions in general, there follow the two theorems:

Theorem II.—If a potential is constant over a closed surface which contains none of the attracting mass it has the same constant value throughout its interior, and

Theorem III.—If the potential due to any distribution of mass has a constant value throughout any finite volume B, it has the same value at every point of space which can be reached by any continuous path from B which does not pass through the attracting matter.

In order to show that this last theorem is true let B, Fig. 40, be a region of empty space in which the potential is constant and suppose further that the space in the neighborhood of B also is empty, but that the potential outside of B does not have the same value that it does inside. Take a point C near the boundary of B and describe about it a small sphere which lies mostly inside of B but partly outside of it. Since V and all of its derivatives are continuous in empty space, it would be possible to take C so near the boundary and the radius of the sphere so small that over the portion of the sphere which was outside of B the value of the potential would be everywhere greater (or everywhere less) than the value within B. This, however, is impossible, since the average value over the sphere is the value at the center C. Hence the boundary of the region of constant potential can be extended until the above argument fails, and it will fail only when attracting matter is encountered.

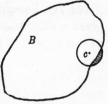

Fig. 40.

It will be observed that if matter is distributed over a closed surface in such a way as to have a constant potential within and on the surface there is nothing in the above argument to prevent the surface density from vanishing at isolated points or along certain lines, but it could not vanish over a finite area.

Theorem IV.—The potential function cannot have a minimum in the interior of attracting matter, but it can have a maximum.

Let p be an interior point of the mass, and let Σ be a small sphere with p at its center. By Gauss' theorem the integral

$$\int_{\Sigma} \frac{\partial V}{\partial n} d\omega = -4\pi M_i$$

is necessarily negative. In order that p might be a minimum $\partial V/\partial n$ would have to be positive everywhere on Σ and therefore the integral would be positive. Since the integral is always negative, a minimum within the attracting mass is excluded and the potential function cannot have a minimum anywhere, except at infinity.

There is nothing to prevent the existence of a maximum, however, in the interior of the attracting mass. The potential at a distance r from the center of a homogeneous sphere of radius a, Sec. 29, has the value $4\pi\sigma\left(\frac{1}{2}a^2 - \frac{1}{6}r^2\right)$, from which it is seen that the potential of a homogeneous sphere has a maximum at its center.

Reduction to Two Dimensions.—All of the above theorems have their analogies for the logarithmic potential and harmonic functions in two dimensions.

76. The Potential Energy of a Finite Mass.—Suppose there is given n discrete particles $m_1, \ldots, m_n$. The potential function of this system of particles is

$$W = \frac{1}{2} \sum_{i=1}^{n} \sum_{j=1}^{n} \frac{m_i m_j}{\rho_{ij}}, \qquad i \neq j,$$

where

$$\rho_{ij} = \sqrt{(x_i - x_j)^2 + (y_i - y_j)^2 + (z_i - z_j)^2}.$$

The factor $1/2$ is necessary since in the double sum as it is written each element occurs twice, as is easily verified by writing out the terms of the sum in a rectangular array.

If T is the kinetic energy of the system,

$$T - W = E$$

the total energy of the system, and $-W$ is the potential energy. Gravitational potential energy is always negative, so that as the particles come closer together the potential energy decreases. The function W represents the amount of work which must be done upon the system in order to effect an infinite dispersion of the particles. It was called the exhaustion of potential energy by Thompson and Tait, because it represents the loss in potential energy from a state of infinite dispersion.

If

$$V_i = \sum_{j=1}^{n} \frac{m_j}{r_{ij}} \qquad j \neq i,$$

is the potential of all of the other particles on the ith particle, the expression for W can be written

$$W = \frac{1}{2}(m_1V_1 + m_2V_2 + \cdots + m_nV_n)$$

$$= \frac{1}{2}\sum_{i=1}^{n} m_iV_i.$$

If the particles form a continuous mass, this expression passes over into the definite integral

$$W = \frac{1}{2}\int_B V\,dm = \frac{1}{2}\int_B V\sigma\,d\tau, \tag{1}$$

where V is the potential of the body upon one of its own elements $dm = \sigma\,d\tau$.

If the system of particles is regarded as forming two distinct bodies, which will be distinguished by the subscripts 1 and 2, so that V_1 is the potential due to the first body at any point x, y, z of space and V_2 is the potential due to the second body, the limit of the double sum becomes

$$W = \frac{1}{2}\int_{B_1} V_1\,dm_1 + \frac{1}{2}\int_{B_2} V_2\,dm_2 + \frac{1}{2}\int_{B_1} V_2\,dm_1 + \frac{1}{2}\int_{B_2} V_1\,dm_2 \tag{2}$$

The last two integrals are merely two different limiting expressions for precisely the same terms in the finite sum, and are, therefore, equal. This fact amounts merely to a verification of Eq. (72.7). Their sum represents the exhaustion of potential energy, due to the fact that the two bodies are not infinitely far apart.

Since by Poisson's theorem, Eq. (70.5),

$$\sigma = -\frac{1}{4\pi}\Delta V,$$

Eq. (1) can be written

$$W = -\frac{1}{8\pi}\int_\infty V \cdot \Delta V \cdot d\tau,$$

the integral being taken over all space. On setting $V_1 = V_2 = V$ in Eq. (72.4), it is seen that the expression for W can be written also

$$W = \frac{1}{8\pi}\int_\infty \left[\left(\frac{\partial V}{\partial x}\right)^2 + \left(\frac{\partial V}{\partial y}\right)^2 + \left(\frac{\partial V}{\partial z}\right)^2\right]d\tau,$$

the integral being taken over all space. But since

$$F^2 = \left(\frac{\partial V}{\partial x}\right)^2 + \left(\frac{\partial V}{\partial y}\right)^2 + \left(\frac{\partial V}{\partial z}\right)^2,$$

is the square of the attractive force due to the body, there results finally

$$W = \frac{1}{8\pi} \int_\infty F^2 d\tau. \tag{3}$$

If in Eq. (2) the sum of the last two integrals is denoted by W_{12}, it is seen immediately from Eq. (72.5) that

$$\left.\begin{array}{l} W_{12} = \int_\infty V_2 \sigma_1 d\tau = \int_\infty V_1 \sigma_2 d\tau \\[2mm] = \frac{1}{4\pi} \int_\infty \left[\frac{\partial V_1}{\partial x}\frac{\partial V_2}{\partial x} + \frac{\partial V_1}{\partial y}\frac{\partial V_2}{\partial y} + \frac{\partial V_1}{\partial z}\frac{\partial V_2}{\partial z} \right] d\tau, \end{array}\right\} \tag{4}$$

the integral being taken over all space.

According to Lord Kelvin and Tait[1] it was upon a proper interpretation of the formulas relating to the exhaustion of potential energy of two bodies that Green founded the whole structure of his general theorems regarding attraction.

77. The Potential Energy of a Homogeneous Sphere.—In the interior of a homogeneous sphere the attraction of the whole sphere on a point is due to the mass of a concentric sphere, the surface of which passes through the point. That is

$$F_i = \frac{-M_r}{r^2} = -\frac{4}{3}\pi\sigma r.$$

On the outside of the sphere

$$F_e = -\frac{M}{r^2}.$$

Hence, if the radius of the sphere is a,

$$8\pi W = \int F_i{}^2 d\tau + \int F_e{}^2 d\tau.$$

Since the force is a function of r alone, let the element of volume $d\tau$ be taken as the space between two infinitely close concentric spheres. Then

$$d\tau = 4\pi r^2 dr,$$

and

$$\left.\begin{array}{l} W = \frac{1}{2}\int_0^a F_i{}^2 r^2 dr + \frac{1}{2}\int_a^\infty F_e{}^2 r^2 dr \\[2mm] = \frac{8}{9}\pi^2\sigma^2 \int_0^a r^4 dr + \frac{1}{2}M^2 \int_a^\infty \frac{dr}{r^2} \\[2mm] = \frac{8}{45}\pi^2\sigma^2 a^5 + \frac{1}{2}\frac{M^2}{a} \\[2mm] = \frac{3}{5}\frac{M^2}{a}. \end{array}\right\} \tag{1}$$

[1] "Treatise on Natural Philosophy," Part II, p. 93.

78. The Heat of the Sun.—According to the theory published by Helmholtz, in 1854, it is the energy released in the process of contraction that is the source of the radiant energies of the stars. On this hypothesis the total amount of heat radiated by the sun in the past can be computed. Assuming that the sun is uniform in density, the total amount of work done in contracting from a state of infinite dispersion is

$$W = \frac{3}{5}k^2\frac{M^2}{a} \text{ ergs,}$$

where $k^2 = 6.66 \times 10^{-8}$ is the gravitation constant (Sec. 20), $M = 1.99 \times 10^{33}$ grams, and $a = 6.96 \times 10^{10}$ cm. Hence

$$W = 2.28 \times 10^{48} \text{ ergs,}$$
$$= 5.44 \times 10^{40} \text{ calories}$$

since 1 calorie is equal to 4.19×10^7 ergs. The sun radiates 2.95×10^{33} calories per year, or approximately 1.5 calories per gram per year. Hence, at the present rate of radiation, the energy released in the process of contraction would be sufficient to last for 18,-000,000 years.

This theory of the origin of the sun's heat was the dominant one during the latter half of the nineteenth century and the first two decades of the twentieth century. Both on astronomical and geological grounds it is now recognized as altogether inadequate.[1] It seems much more probable that the source of the sun's heat is to be found in the electrostatic potential of the electrons within the atom rather than in their gravitational potentials. The electrostatic potential energy of two electrons of opposite sign is

$$V = \frac{e^2}{\rho}$$

where ρ is the distance between the electrons and e the electric charge, is equal to 4.774×10^{-10} electrostatic units. A gram of matter is equivalent to 6.06×10^{23} such pairs of electrons. Hence, the electrostatic potential energy of a gram of matter is

$$V_1 = \frac{1.38 \times 10^5}{\rho} \text{ ergs.}$$

If it is assumed that when the distance between the two electrons is equal to the radius of the positive electron, which,

---

[1] MacMillan, On Stellar Evolution. *Astrophysical Journal*, Vol. XLVIII, p. 35, (1918). Some Mathematical Aspects of Cosmology. *Science*, Vol. LXII, Nos. 1595–1597, (1925).

according to Millikan, is approximately 10^{-16}, the two electrical fields are superposed and neutralized, the property of mass disappears and the potential energy takes the kinetic form of radiation, it is seen that 1 gram of matter is equivalent to 1.38×10^{21} ergs of energy, or approximately 3×10^{13} calories, a result which is approximately equal to that given by the modern theory of relativity, namely 9×10^{20} ergs, without any consideration of models.

This hypothesis does not furnish any basis for estimating the present age of the sun, but if one gram of matter is equivalent to 3×10^{13} calories and the sun is expending 1.5 calories per gram per year, it is evident that the sun contains a reserve of energy in its present mass sufficient to last 2×10^{13} years at its present rate of radiation, or 20,000 billion years. It is not possible to estimate how much additional matter the sun will gather in from space in that length of time.

79. Relation between Certain Surface and Line Integrals.— It will be supposed that at every point $m(x, y, z)$ of a certain region $\overline{R}$, a vector K is defined whose components P, Q, R are

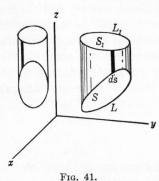

single valued, continuous functions of x, y, z which admit continuous first derivatives. It will be assumed also that in this region $\overline{R}$ there exists a portion of a surface S which has two sides and which is bounded by a closed line L. One side of the surface will be regarded as positive, the other as negative. Let α, β, γ be the direction cosines of the normal erected on the positive side of the surface at the surface element $d\omega$.

Fig. 41.

It will be shown that

$$\int_L P\,dx = \int_S \left(\beta \frac{\partial P}{\partial z} - \gamma \frac{\partial P}{\partial y} \right) d\omega,$$

where the integral in the right member is taken over the portion of the surface S which is bounded by L, and the left member is the line integral taken around the boundary L in the counter-clockwise direction as seen from the positive side of S.

It will be assumed, at first, that both P and γ preserve their signs throughout S. This restriction will be removed later.

At each point m of S draw a line mm_1 parallel to the z-axis and equal in length to the magnitude of P at m. The locus of the point m_1 thus defined is a surface S_1 bounded by a closed contour L_1 (Fig. 41). The straight lines which join the points of L to the corresponding points of L_1 form a cylindrical surface C. Since S, C, and S_1 taken together form a closed surface, the projection of this surface upon any plane is zero. This fact will be formulated for the projection upon the xz-plane.

Let ds be an element of the contour L cut out by two infinitely close generators of the cylindrical surface. The distance between the projections of these two generators upon the xz-plane is dx. Hence the area of the projection of that portion of the cylindrical surface which is included between the two generators above mentioned is Pdx and the area of the projection of the entire cylindrical surface upon the xz-plane is

$$\int_L Pdx.$$

Consider now an element $d\omega$ of the surface S. The tangent plane at this element makes the same angle with the xz-plane as the normal at this element makes with the y-axis, that is, the angle whose cosine is β. Hence the projection of $d\omega$ upon the xz-plane is $\beta d\omega$, and the entire projection of S is

$$\int_S \beta d\omega.$$

Using a corresponding notation for the S_1 plane, it is evident that the projection of S_1 upon the xz-plane is

$$\int_{S_1} \beta_1 d\omega_1.$$

The sum of these three projections is zero. Therefore

$$\int_L Pdx + \int_S \beta d\omega + \int_{S_1} \beta_1 d\omega_1 = 0. \tag{1}$$

Let the element $d\omega_1$ correspond to the element $d\omega$ in the sense that $d\omega$ and $d\omega_1$ are cut out of S and S_1 by the same infinitesimal cylinder parallel to the z-axis. Since this infinitesimal cylinder is closed, its projection upon the xy-plane also is zero, and since the projection of the cylindrical surface upon the xy-plane is zero by itself, there remains

$$\gamma d\omega + \gamma_1 d\omega_1 = 0,$$

and therefore

$$dω_1 = -\frac{\gamma}{\gamma_1}dω.$$

The substitution of this value in Eq. (1) gives

$$\int_L P dx + \int_S \frac{\beta\gamma_1 - \gamma\beta_1}{\gamma_1} dω = 0. \tag{2}$$

Let the equation of the surface S be $z = f(x, y)$, then

$$\varphi(x, y, z) \equiv f(x, y) - z = 0. \tag{3}$$

The direction cosines of the normal to this surface α, β, γ are proportional to

$$\frac{\partial\varphi}{\partial x}, \quad \frac{\partial\varphi}{\partial y}, \quad \frac{\partial\varphi}{\partial z};$$

or if

$$p = \frac{\partial z}{\partial x}, \quad q = \frac{\partial z}{\partial y},$$

the equations

$$\frac{\alpha}{p} = \frac{\beta}{q} = \frac{\gamma}{-1} \tag{4}$$

hold. Similarly on the surface S_1,

$$\frac{\alpha_1}{p_1} = \frac{\beta_1}{q_1} = \frac{\gamma_1}{-1}. \tag{5}$$

From Eqs. (4) and (5), it follows that

$$q = -\frac{\beta}{\gamma}, \quad q_1 = -\frac{\beta_1}{\gamma_1}. \tag{6}$$

For the surface $S_1(x_1, y_1, z_1)$, it is evident that

$$x_1 = x, \quad y_1 = y, \quad z_1 = z + P(x, y, z).$$

Therefore

$$\frac{\partial z_1}{\partial x_1} = p_1 = p + \frac{\partial P}{\partial x} + p\frac{\partial P}{\partial z},$$

$$\frac{\partial z_1}{\partial y_1} = q_1 = q + \frac{\partial P}{\partial y} + q\frac{\partial P}{\partial z}.$$

If the values of q and q_1 are substituted from Eq. (6) into the second of these equations, there results

$$\frac{\beta\gamma_1 - \gamma\beta_1}{\gamma_1} = \gamma\frac{\partial P}{\partial y} - \beta\frac{\partial P}{\partial z}$$

which shows that Eq. (2) can be written

$$\int_L P dx = \int_S \left(\beta\frac{\partial P}{\partial z} - \gamma\frac{\partial P}{\partial y}\right)dω, \tag{7}$$

and this is the formula it was desired to establish.

The restriction that P and γ shall preserve their signs is now easily removed. If this condition is not satisfied of itself, S can be divided up by auxiliary curves in such a way that in each portion P and γ do preserve their signs unchanged. Equation (7) holds for each of these portions separately. The sum of the portions is S, and the sum of the contours is L, since the auxiliary curves have been described twice, but in opposite directions, while the contour L has been described but once. Hence, Eq. (7) holds in general. The restriction serves merely to make the geometric interpretation clear.

80. Stokes' Theorem.—From Eq. (79.7) two analogous equations are obtained by permuting the letters. These three equations are

$$\left.\begin{aligned}
\int_L P\,dx &= \int_S \left(\beta\frac{\partial P}{\partial z} - \gamma\frac{\partial P}{\partial y}\right)d\omega, \\
\int_L Q\,dy &= \int_S \left(\gamma\frac{\partial Q}{\partial x} - \alpha\frac{\partial Q}{\partial z}\right)d\omega, \\
\int_L R\,dz &= \int_S \left(\alpha\frac{\partial R}{\partial y} - \beta\frac{\partial R}{\partial x}\right)d\omega.
\end{aligned}\right\} \tag{1}$$

On taking the sum of these three equations, there results

$$\int_L (P\,dx + Q\,dy + R\,dz) =$$

$$\int_S \left[\alpha\left(\frac{\partial R}{\partial y} - \frac{\partial Q}{\partial z}\right) + \beta\left(\frac{\partial P}{\partial z} - \frac{\partial R}{\partial x}\right) + \gamma\left(\frac{\partial Q}{\partial x} - \frac{\partial P}{\partial y}\right)\right]d\omega, \quad (2)$$

which is Stokes' theorem.

The functions P, Q, R are the components of a vector K which is defined at each point of S. Let A be a point of this contour, and let K_t be the component of K which is tangent to the contour at A. K_t is positive if it has the direction of a positive motion of the point A along the contour, otherwise negative. Let ds be

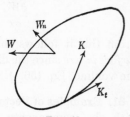

FIG. 42.

a positive infinitesimal displacement of the point A along the contour with the components dx, dy, dz. If the vector K is regarded as a force, it is evident that

$$P\,dx + Q\,dy + R\,dz = K_t\,ds$$

is the element of work done in this small displacement, and

$$\int_L (Pdx + Qdy + Rdz) = \int_L K_t ds$$

is the amount of work done in completing an entire circuit.

It can also be supposed, that there exists a second field of vectors W in the region R, and that the components of W are

$$W_x = \frac{\partial R}{\partial y} - \frac{\partial Q}{\partial z}, \qquad W_y = \frac{\partial P}{\partial z} - \frac{\partial R}{\partial x}, \qquad W_z = \frac{\partial Q}{\partial x} - \frac{\partial P}{\partial y}. \quad (3)$$

This vector W, which is evidently related to K, is called the *curl* of the vector K. Furthermore

$$\alpha W_x + \beta W_y + \gamma W_z = W_n$$

is the component of W which is normal to the surface S. Equation (2) can, therefore, be written

$$\int_L K_t ds = \int_S W_n \, d\omega,$$

and can be expressed in words as follows:

Stokes' Theorem.—The work which is done by a vector acting on a point which describes a closed circuit is equal to the flux of the curl of this vector across any continuous surface which is bounded by the circuit.

This form of statement shows that the theorem does not depend upon any choice of axes.

It will be observed that the divergence (Sec. 56) of the curl of any vector vanishes identically, since

$$\frac{\partial W_x}{\partial x} + \frac{\partial W_y}{\partial y} + \frac{\partial W_z}{\partial z} \equiv 0.$$

From this it follows that *the flux of the curl across any closed surface is zero* since the divergence of the curl vanishes throughout the volume, Eq. (56.4).

81. Examples of Vector Curls.—Suppose V is a constant vector with the components X, Y, Z, and K is the moment of V with respect to the point x_0, y_0, z_0. If V is acting at the point x, y, z, the components of K are

$$P = (y - y_0)Z - (z - z_0)Y,$$
$$Q = (z - z_0)X - (x - x_0)Z,$$
$$R = (x - x_0)Y - (y - y_0)X.$$

The components of the curl of K are readily found to be $-2X$, $-2Y$, $-2Z$. That is $W = -2V$.

As a second illustration, consider the velocity of any point of a rigid body which is moving in any manner in space. Imagine a set of rectangular axes rigidly attached to the body with the origin at the point O, and let $m(x, y, z)$ be any point of the body.

As is well known, the motion of the body can be resolved into a pure translation, which is equal to that of the point O, and a pure rotation ω about some axis which passes through the point O. Let the components of the translation with respect to a set of axes which are fixed in space, but which instantaneously are parallel to the set of axes which are fixed in the body, be X_0, Y_0, Z_0, and let the components of the rotation ω with respect to these same axes be ω_x, ω_y, ω_z. Then the components of the velocity K of the point m with respect to the set of axes which are fixed in space are

$$P = X_0 + z\omega_y - y\omega_z,$$
$$Q = Y_0 + x\omega_z - z\omega_x,$$
$$R = Z_0 + y\omega_x - x\omega_y.$$

The components of the translation, X_0, Y_0, Z_0, and of the rotation, ω_x, ω_y, ω_z, are evidently independent of the coordinates of the point m. Hence the components of the curl W of the velocity vector K are $2\omega_x$, $2\omega_y$ and $2\omega_z$. That is the curl of the velocity of the point m is twice the angular velocity of the point m about the instantaneous axis of rotation. It was this fact which gave rise to the term *curl* which is due to Maxwell. Clifford called it the *spin*.

82. The Vector and Its Curl Are Orthogonal.—The moment of a vector is perpendicular to the vector itself, and the velocity of a particle of a rigid body, in so far as that velocity is due to spin, is perpendicular to the instantaneous axis of rotation. If, however, the translation of the body is taken into account, the velocity of a particle and its curl are not mutually perpendicular in general.

The orthogonality of a vector and its curl has an important interpretation in analysis which can be stated as follows:

Theorem.—A necessary and sufficient condition that the expression $Pdx + Qdy + Rdz$ admits an integrating factor is that the vector K (P, Q, R) and its curl W are mutually perpendicular to each other.

The analytic condition for the orthogonality of a vector K, which has the components P, Q, and R, and its curl W, Eq. (80.3), is

$$P\left(\frac{\partial R}{\partial y} - \frac{\partial Q}{\partial z}\right) + Q\left(\frac{\partial P}{\partial z} - \frac{\partial R}{\partial x}\right) + R\left(\frac{\partial Q}{\partial x} - \frac{\partial P}{\partial y}\right) = 0. \qquad (1)$$

If the differential expression $Pdx + Qdy + Rdz$ admits an integrating factor $\psi(x, y, z)$, so that

$$\psi(Pdx + Qdy + Rdz) = dU, \qquad (2)$$

and therefore

$$\psi P = \frac{\partial U}{\partial x}, \qquad \psi Q = \frac{\partial U}{\partial y}, \qquad \psi R = \frac{\partial U}{\partial z}, \qquad (3)$$

the function ψ must satisfy certain differential equations. If the first of Eqs. (3) is differentiated with respect to y and the second with respect to x, the two right members are equal, and therefore the two left members are equal. In this way, and by cyclical permutations of the letters, it is found that ψ must satisfy the three equations

$$\left.\begin{aligned} P\frac{\partial \psi}{\partial y} - Q\frac{\partial \psi}{\partial x} &= -\psi\left(\frac{\partial P}{\partial y} - \frac{\partial Q}{\partial x}\right), \\ Q\frac{\partial \psi}{\partial z} - R\frac{\partial \psi}{\partial y} &= -\psi\left(\frac{\partial Q}{\partial z} - \frac{\partial R}{\partial y}\right), \\ R\frac{\partial \psi}{\partial x} - P\frac{\partial \psi}{\partial z} &= -\psi\left(\frac{\partial R}{\partial x} - \frac{\partial P}{\partial z}\right). \end{aligned}\right\} \qquad (4)$$

If the first of Eqs. (4) is multiplied by R, the second by P, and the third by Q, and the three equations are then added, Eq. (1) results. Hence, the orthogonality of the vector K and its curl W is a necessary condition for the existence of an integrating factor. In order to show that it is also sufficient it is necessary to show that if Eq. (1) holds, Eqs. (4) admit a solution.

Without diminishing the generality of the proof it can be assumed that R is equal to -1, if it is not zero identically; for Eq. (2) can equally well be written

$$(-\psi R)\left(\frac{P}{-R}dx + \frac{Q}{-R}dy - dz\right) = dU,$$

and then by obvious changes in the notation R would be equal to -1. For this value of R, Eq. (1) becomes

$$Q\frac{\partial P}{\partial z} - P\frac{\partial Q}{\partial z} = \frac{\partial Q}{\partial x} - \frac{\partial P}{\partial y}, \qquad (5)$$

and Eqs. (4) reduces to the two independent equations

$$\frac{\partial \psi}{\partial x} + P\frac{\partial \psi}{\partial z} + \psi\frac{\partial P}{\partial z} = 0,$$

$$\frac{\partial \psi}{\partial y} + Q\frac{\partial \psi}{\partial z} + \psi\frac{\partial Q}{\partial z} = 0.$$

By changing the variables and taking $d\psi/\psi = -d\varphi$, these equations are somewhat simplified and become

$$\left.\begin{aligned}\frac{\partial \varphi}{\partial x} + P\frac{\partial \varphi}{\partial z} &= \frac{\partial P}{\partial z}, \\ \frac{\partial \varphi}{\partial x} + Q\frac{\partial \varphi}{\partial z} &= \frac{\partial Q}{\partial z}.\end{aligned}\right\} \tag{6}$$

This is a system of two partial differential equations with three independent variables, and since, by virtue of Eq. (5),

$$\left(\frac{\partial}{\partial y} + Q\frac{\partial}{\partial z}\right)\left(\frac{\partial \varphi}{\partial x} + P\frac{\partial \varphi}{\partial z}\right) = \left(\frac{\partial}{\partial x} + P\frac{\partial}{\partial z}\right)\left(\frac{\partial \varphi}{\partial y} + Q\frac{\partial \varphi}{\partial z}\right)$$

the system is complete. Furthermore, since

$$\left(\frac{\partial}{\partial y} + Q\frac{\partial}{\partial z}\right)\left(\frac{\partial P}{\partial z}\right) = \left(\frac{\partial}{\partial x} + P\frac{\partial}{\partial z}\right)\left(\frac{\partial Q}{\partial z}\right)$$

the system is consistant. The solution of Eqs. (6), therefore, consists of a particular integral plus the general integral of the homogeneous equations.[1]

In the particular case in which

$$\frac{\partial P}{\partial z} = \frac{\partial Q}{\partial z} = 0, \tag{7}$$

Eq. (5) shows that

$$\frac{\partial Q}{\partial x} = \frac{\partial P}{\partial y}, \tag{8}$$

and the curl W vanishes identically. Equations (6) admit the obvious solution $\varphi = $ const., and the differential expression $Pdx + Qdy + Rdz = dU$ is exact. Conversely, if it is exact, φ is a constant, Eqs. (7) and (8) are satisfied, and the curl vanishes. Hence the additional theorem:

Theorem.—A necessary and sufficient condition that the differential expression $Pdx + Qdy + Rdz$ be exact is that the curl of the vector K shall vanish identically.

[1] GOURSAT, E., "Leçons sur l'intégration des équations aux dérivées partielles du premier ordre," p. 68.

83. Condition That a Line Integral Shall be Independent of the Path of Integration.—Let A and B be any two points in the region R in which the vector K and its first derivatives are continuous. Join the two points by any curve C_1 which lies wholly within R and let I_1 be the integral

$$I_1 = \int_A^B (Pdx + Qdy + Cdz) = \int_A^B K_t ds$$

taken along the curve C_1. Join the two points A and B by a second curve C_2, and let I_2 be the same integral from A to B taken along the curve C_2 (Fig. 43).

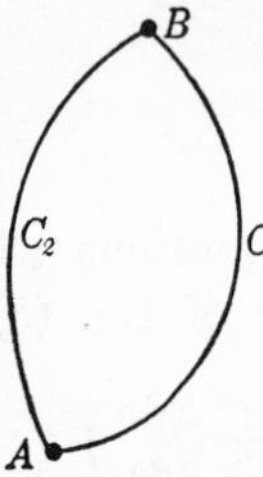

If the value of the integral is independent of the path, $I_1 = I_2$, and

$$I = I_1 - I_2 = \int_L (Pdx + Qdy + Rdz) = 0,$$

Fig. 43.

where L is the circuit from A to B along C_1 and back from B to A along C_2. If, further, the area S bounded by this circuit lies wholly within R, so that K and its first derivatives are everywhere continuous, Stokes' theorem (Eq. (80.2)) gives

$$I = \int_S \left[\alpha\left(\frac{\partial R}{\partial y} - \frac{\partial Q}{\partial z}\right) + \beta\left(\frac{\partial P}{\partial z} - \frac{\partial R}{\partial x}\right) + \gamma\left(\frac{\partial Q}{\partial x} - \frac{\partial P}{\partial y}\right) \right] d\omega = 0.$$

By hypothesis, A and B are any two points in R and therefore L is any closed circuit. Hence $I = 0$ on every surface S which is bounded by a closed circuit which lies wholly within R. Evidently then the coefficients of α, β, and γ in I must each be zero, for if they were not, and if, say, $\frac{\partial Q}{\partial x} - \frac{\partial P}{\partial y} \neq 0$, a plane surface S for which $\alpha = \beta = 0$, $\gamma = +1$ could be taken and a circuit L sufficiently small that $\frac{\partial Q}{\partial x} - \frac{\partial P}{\partial y}$ would everywhere have the same sign, and the integral I would not be zero. As this would contradict the hypothesis, it follows that

$$\frac{\partial R}{\partial y} - \frac{\partial Q}{\partial z} = 0, \qquad \frac{\partial P}{\partial z} - \frac{\partial R}{\partial x} = 0, \qquad \frac{\partial Q}{\partial x} - \frac{\partial P}{\partial y} = 0,$$

everywhere within R, and therefore the curl of the vector K vanishes identically. This is merely another way of saying that

$$Pdx + Qdy + Rdz = dU$$

is an exact differential (Sec. 82).

84. Condition That a Surface Integral Shall Depend upon the Contour Only.—A question which is analogous to that of the preceeding section is the following: Under what conditions is a surface integral dependent upon the bounding contour only and not at all dependent upon the particular surface which passes through the contour?

Suppose there is given a vector W with the components F, G, and H, which together with their first derivatives are continuous within a certain domain R. Let L be any closed contour lying wholly within R, and S any continuous surface which passes through and is bounded by L. If α, β, γ are the direction cosines of the normal to S, the integral

$$I = \int_S (\alpha F + \beta G + \gamma H) d\omega = \int_S W_n d\omega$$

is the flux of W across S. The question is: What condition must be satisfied by W in order that the flux across S shall depend upon L but shall be the same for every S which is bounded by L.

Let S_1 and S_2 be two such surfaces across which the flux is the same. If a positive direction along the contour is defined, the positive sides of these surfaces also are defined and the normals are assumed to be directed from the positive side of the surfaces. Let I_1 be the flux across S_1 and I_2 be the flux across S_2. So that $I_1 = I_2$. The surfaces S_1 and S_2 bound a certain volume. Let the normals on one of the surfaces be reversed, thus reversing the sign of the flux across that surface, so that the normals are everywhere directed outward from the enclosed volume. The condition $I_1 = I_2$ then becomes

$$I_3 = \int_{S_1+S_2} (\alpha F + \beta G + \gamma H) d\omega = \int_{S_1+S_2} W_n d\omega = 0, \quad (1)$$

and this condition holds by hypothesis for every contour L which lies within R. This is the same as saying that Eq. (1) holds for every closed surface in R.

By Eq. (56.2) the integral I_3 is the same as the integral

$$\int_V \left(\frac{\partial F}{\partial x} + \frac{\partial G}{\partial y} + \frac{\partial H}{\partial z} \right) d\tau = 0. \quad (2)$$

Since Eq. (2) holds for every bounded volume which lies wholly in R it is evident that

$$\frac{\partial F}{\partial x} + \frac{\partial G}{\partial y} + \frac{\partial H}{\partial z} = 0$$

everywhere in R. That is to say, the divergence of the vector W vanishes identically. Hence the theorem follows:

Theorem.—A necessary and sufficient condition that the integral

$$\int_S (\alpha F + \beta G + \gamma H)d\omega \tag{3}$$

taken over any bounded portion of a surface shall depend only upon the bounding contour is that the divergence of the vector W shall vanish identically.

If the integral Eq. (3) depends only on the contour L it should be possible to reduce the surface integral to a line integral. In order to show how this is done, the following theorem is useful:

Theorem.—If the divergence of a given vector $W(F, G, H)$ is zero, there exist infinitely many vectors $K(P, Q, R)$ for which W is the curl.

That is to say, if the three functions F, G, and H are given, and if

$$\frac{\partial F}{\partial x} + \frac{\partial G}{\partial y} + \frac{\partial H}{\partial z} = 0, \tag{4}$$

there exist infinitely many triples of functions P, Q, and R such that

$$\left(\frac{\partial R}{\partial y} - \frac{\partial Q}{\partial z}\right) = F, \quad \left(\frac{\partial P}{\partial z} - \frac{\partial R}{\partial x}\right) = G, \quad \left(\frac{\partial Q}{\partial x} - \frac{\partial P}{\partial y}\right) = H. \tag{5}$$

It will be shown first that there exist solutions of Eqs. (5) for which $R \equiv 0$. Assuming that R is zero identically, Eqs. (5) become

$$\frac{\partial Q}{\partial z} = -F, \quad \frac{\partial P}{\partial z} = G, \quad \frac{\partial Q}{\partial x} - \frac{\partial P}{\partial y} = H. \tag{6}$$

The second of Eqs. (6) gives

$$P = \int_{z_0}^{z} G(x, y, z)dz,$$

and the first gives

$$Q = -\int_{z_0}^{z} F(x, y, z)dz + f(x, y),$$

where f is, at the moment, an arbitrary function of x and y. The third of Eqs. (6) now requires that

$$\frac{\partial f}{\partial x} - \int_{z_0}^{z}\left(\frac{\partial F}{\partial x} + \frac{\partial G}{\partial y}\right)dz = H;$$

or, in view of Eq. (4),

$$\frac{\partial f}{\partial x} + \int_{z_0}^{z} \frac{\partial H}{\partial z} dz = H,$$

which is the same as

$$\frac{\partial f}{\partial x} = H(x, y, z_0),$$

and therefore

$$f = \int_{x_0}^{x} H(x, y, z_0) dx.$$

Eqs. (5) therefore, are satisfied by the functions

$$P_1 = \int_{z_0}^{z} G(x, y, z) dz, \quad Q = \int_{x_0}^{x} H(x, y, z_0) - \int_{z_0}^{z} F(x, y, z) dz, \quad R_1 \equiv 0.$$

Now let P, Q, and R be any triple of functions which satisfies Eqs. (5), and let

$$P_2 = P - P_1, \qquad Q_2 = Q - Q_1, \qquad R_2 = R - R_1.$$

The substitution of these expressions in Eqs. (5) gives

$$\frac{\partial R_2}{\partial y} - \frac{\partial Q_2}{\partial z} = 0, \qquad \frac{\partial P_2}{\partial z} - \frac{\partial R_2}{\partial x} = 0, \qquad \frac{\partial Q_2}{\partial x} - \frac{\partial P_2}{\partial y} = 0;$$

therefore, if $U(x, y, z)$ is an arbitrary function of x, y, and z,

$$P_2 = \frac{\partial U}{\partial x}, \qquad Q_2 = \frac{\partial U}{\partial y}, \qquad R_2 = \frac{\partial U}{\partial z}.$$

Hence, any solution of Eqs. (5) can be written

$$P = P_1 + \frac{\partial U}{\partial x}, \qquad Q = Q_1 + \frac{\partial U}{\partial y}, \qquad R = R_1 + \frac{\partial U}{\partial z},$$

where U is some function of x, y, and z, and this establishes the theorem.

The integral

$$\int_{S} (\alpha F + \beta G + \gamma H) d\omega$$

can now be written

$$\int_{S} \left[\alpha \left(\frac{\partial R}{\partial y} - \frac{\partial Q}{\partial z} \right) + \beta \left(\frac{\partial P}{\partial z} - \frac{\partial R}{\partial x} \right) + \gamma \left(\frac{\partial Q}{\partial x} - \frac{\partial P}{\partial y} \right) \right] d\omega,$$

and, by Stokes' theorem, this is equal to the line integral

$$\int_{L} (P dx + Q dy + R dz)$$

taken around the bounding contour L.

It is easy to see that this integral is independent of U, since

$$\int_L \left(\frac{\partial U}{\partial x} dx + \frac{\partial U}{\partial y} dy + \frac{\partial U}{\partial z} dz \right) = 0.$$

Problems

1. If $r = \sqrt{x^2 + y^2 + z^2}$ is measured from a point O, which may be either inside or outside of a closed surface S, the volume which is enclosed by S is given by the formula

$$\text{vol.} = \frac{1}{6} \int_S \frac{\partial r^2}{\partial n} d\omega.$$

2. Show that the exhaustion of potential energy of a homogeneous oblate spheroid for which a is the equatorial radius and e the eccentricity of a meridian section, is

$$W = \frac{3}{5} k^2 \frac{M^2}{a} \frac{\sin^{-1} e}{e}.$$

3. If M is the maximum value of the harmonic function V on the closed surface S, and m is its minimum, show that within S

$$m \leqq V \leqq M.$$

4. Starting with Laplace's equations in rectangular coordinates, derive the corresponding equation for polar coordinates.

CHAPTER IV

THE ATTRACTIONS OF SURFACES AND LINES

85. The Occasion for Their Study.—In the domain of electricity it is found that an electrically charged conductor in electrical equilibrium acts as though the surface were covered with an infinitely thin layer of electricity which attracts or repels according to the law of the inverse squares, and this leads to a consideration of the properties of such surfaces. By the term *electrical density* of such a surface is meant the amount of electricity per unit area. In the sense of volumes the density is infinite since the thickness is taken to be zero.

But quite apart from the occurrence of such surfaces in nature, the concept is very useful even as a mathematical fiction, as was seen in the discussion of Sec. 61.

It is evident from the definition that the potential function exists at all points which are not in the given surface, and the derivatives of the potential functions at all such points represent the components of the attracting or repelling force. It is further evident that the potential function and its derivatives are continuous at all points which do not lie in the surface. It is proposed to study, in the present chapter, the values of the potential and its derivatives in the neighborhood of the surface itself. It will be found that the potential of the attracted point is continuous along a line that pierces the surface, but that the normal component of the attraction has an abrupt discontinuity of $4\pi\sigma$ as the attracted point passes through the surface at an ordinary point, σ being the density of the surface at the point where it is pierced.

ATTRACTION OF SURFACES

86. A Uniform Disk.—In Sec. 30 it was found that the potential of a uniform disk of radius a and density σ at any point p on the axis of the disk (which will be taken as the z-axis of a coordinate system), and the z-component of the attraction at the point p are given by the formulas

$$V = 2\pi\sigma[\sqrt{a^2 + z^2} - \sqrt{z^2}], \qquad Z = 2\pi\sigma\left[\frac{z}{\sqrt{a^2 + z^2}} - \frac{z}{\sqrt{z^2}}\right].$$

The potential is continuous along the normal, but Z is discontinuous as the point p passes through the disk.

It will be interesting to examine the component of attraction which lies in the plane of the disk. The natural reply to such an enquiry is that this component is zero from symmetry, but the enquiry is worthy of a closer examination. In Fig. 44, let C_3 with its center at O_1 be a uniform disk of density σ. With any other point O_4 as a center, draw a circle C_4 tangent externally to C_3. Then draw any small circle C_1 with O_1 as a center, and

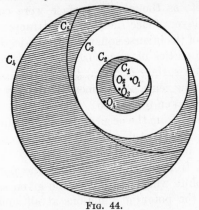

Fig. 44.

a last circle C_2 tangent externally to C_1 with the radius r_2, such that the proportion

$$\frac{r_2}{r_4} = \frac{r_1}{r_3} = \alpha.$$

holds, where r_1 is the radius of the circle C_1. The circles C_2 and C_4 are in perspective with respect to the point O_1; for, if any straight line be drawn through the point O_1 and the distances from O_1 to the points of intersections of this line with the circles C_2 and C_4 are ρ_2 and ρ_4, then it is true that

$$\frac{\rho_2}{\rho_4} = \frac{r_2}{r_4} = \alpha.$$

Since the circles C_1 and C_3 are concentric, it is evident that they also are in perspective with the same ratio of perspectivity α. If C_3 and C_4 be kept fixed but α is diminished, the circles C_1 and C_2 diminish in size and for $\alpha = 0$ reduce to the point O_1 itself. The perspectivity relationship holds, however small α may be.

Now imagine the disk, which is bounded by the Circle C_2, is removed from the disk C_3. The attraction of the remaining portion of the disk C_3 upon the point O_1, which will be denoted by $A_{c_3-c_2}$, is well defined, since O_1 is not a point of the attracting surface. If the attraction of the entire disk C_3 upon the point O_1, which is a point of C_3, is to have a meaning, then, this attraction will be the limit of $A_{c_3-c_2}$ as α diminishes. That is

Now
$$A_{c_3} = \lim A_{c_3-c_2}.$$

and
$$A_{c_3-c_2} = A_{c_3-c_1} - A_{c_2-c_1},$$

$$A_{c_3-c_1} = 0,$$

by virtue of symmetry. Hence
$$A_{c_3-c_2} = -A_{c_2-c_1}.$$

Since the crescent-moon shaped figures $C_4 - C_3$ and $C_2 - C_1$ are in perspective with respect to the point O_1, their attractions on the point O_1 are equal (Theorem II, Sec. 10). Therefore
$$A_{c_3-c_2} = -A_{c_4-c_3}.$$

But the attraction of $C_4 - C_3$ is independent of α and remains constant as α diminishes. Hence
$$\lim A_{c_3-c_2} = A_{c_3} = -A_{c_4-c_3}.$$

The attraction of $C_4 - C_3$ on O_1 is not zero, for a circle C_5 of the same radius as C_4 can be drawn which divides the area $C_4 - C_3$ into two portions, one of which is symmetrical with respect to the point O_1 and the other lies entirely on one side of a line through O_1.

Since the radius of C_4 is entirely arbitrary, and the direction of its center also, it follows that $A_{c_4-c_3}$ is arbitrary both as to magnitude and direction. Consequently, the *attraction of a uniform disk upon its center* does not have a definite sense.

87. An Infinite Homogeneous Universe.—An analogous situation arises with respect to the resultant attraction of an infinite homogeneous universe upon one of its own particles.

In Fig. 45, let P be any particle, and O any point chosen arbitrarily. About O as a center describe a sphere of radius OP. If this sphere is filled with matter of density σ, the gravitational force acting at the point P toward the point O is (Sec. 13),

$$F = \frac{4}{3}\pi\sigma\overline{PO}.$$

Now let a larger sphere of radius OQ be described about the
point O and the shell PQ be filled with matter of density σ.   The
resultant attraction of this shell upon the point P is zero (Sec. 11).
Hence the resultant attraction of the sphere Q upon the point P
is proportional to $\overline{PO}$, however large OQ may be.   Passing to the
limit, the attraction of an infinite homogeneous universe upon
the point P is

$$F = \frac{4}{3}\pi\sigma\overline{PO}.$$

But PO is arbitrary, both as to magnitude and direction.

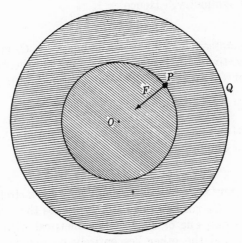

Fig. 45.

Neumann concluded from this that the postulate that the
universe is infinite and essentially homogeneous is in conflict
with the law of gravitation, but it is clear that this conclusion
rests upon still another postulate, namely, that every *physical*
situation is uniquely defined, or that nature is never ambiguous—
a postulate that, doubtless, will readily be granted.   Quite
likely, the law of gravitation is only a remarkably close approximation and that it fails at sufficiently great distances.

The same remark can be made with respect to a distribution
of electricity upon the surface of a conductor.   In a domain which
is of the order of magnitude of the electrons, it is not legitimate
to regard the distribution as a surface distribution.   The approximation fails in a domain sufficiently small.

88. Proper and Improper Integrals.—If $f(x)$ is a function of x which is continuous in the interval $a \leqq x \leqq b$, the integral

$$\int_a^b f(x)dx \tag{1}$$

has a perfectly definite sense, and is called a proper integral. If, however, $f(x)$ is infinite at one or more points of the interval, the integral considered as the limit of a sum does not immediately have a sense. Suppose, for example, $f(a)$ is infinite, but that elsewhere in the interval $f(x)$ is continuous. If ϵ is any small positive quantity, the integral

$$\int_{a+\epsilon}^b f(x)dx \tag{2}$$

has a sense, however small ϵ may be. If the limit of Eq. (2) as ϵ tends towards zero is finite, this limiting value is defined to be the meaning of Eq. (1), and the integral is said to be *improper*. In analogy with the theory of infinite series it is convenient to say that the integral Eq. (1) is *convergent* if the limit of Eq. (2) exists, and that it is *divergent* if the limit of Eq. (2) does not exist, as will be the case when the value of Eq. (2) increases indefinitely as ϵ decreases, or even oscillates indefinitely between finite limits.

Simple Integrals.—Suppose there exists a number ξ such that if $a \leqq x \leqq \xi$

$$|f(x)| < \frac{M}{(x-a)^\alpha},$$

where M and α are two fixed positive numbers. Then

$$\int_a^b f(x)dx = \int_a^\xi f(x)dx + \int_\xi^b f(x)dx,$$

and

$$\int_a^b |f(x)|dx < \int_a^\xi \frac{M}{(x-a)^\alpha}dx + \int_\xi^b |f(x)|dx.$$

The last integral is a proper integral and has a finite value L. Hence

$$\left| \int_{a+\epsilon}^b f(x)dx \right| \leqq \int_{a+\epsilon}^b \left| f(x) \right| dx < M \left[\frac{(\xi-a)^{1-\alpha}}{1-\alpha} - \frac{\epsilon^{1-\alpha}}{1-\alpha} \right] + L.$$

If $\alpha < 1$, it is evident that

$$\lim_{\epsilon=0} \left| \int_{a+\epsilon}^b f(x)dx \right| < M \frac{(\xi-a)^{1-\alpha}}{1-\alpha} + L,$$

and the given integral is convergent.

If, on the other hand, in the same interval, $a \leqq x \leqq \xi$,

$$|f(x)| > \frac{N}{(x-a)^\beta}$$

where N and β are two fixed positive numbers, the integral

$$\left|\int_{a+\epsilon}^{\xi} f(x)dx\right| = \int_{a+\epsilon}^{\xi} \left|f(x)\right|dx > \int_{a+\epsilon}^{\xi} \frac{N}{(x-a)^\beta}dx,$$

and therefore

$$\left|\int_{a+\epsilon}^{\xi} f(x)dx\right| > N\left[\frac{(\xi-a)^{1-\beta}}{1-\beta} - \frac{\epsilon^{1-\beta}}{1-\beta}\right].$$

If $\beta > 1$, it is evident that no limit exists and the integral is divergent.

Double Integrals.—Suppose $f(x, y)$ is a continuous function of x and y in and on the boundary of a certain area S. The integral

$$\int\int_S f(x, y)dxdy$$

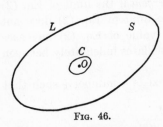

FIG. 46.

has a definite sense and is a proper integral. But if at some point O of the area $f(x, y)$ becomes infinite the integral has no sense directly; it is necessary to give it one.

In Fig. 46, let S, the area of integration, be bounded by the closed curve L, and let O be a point at which $f(x, y)$ becomes infinite. For simplicity it will be assumed that there is but one such point. Around the point O describe a small closed curve C, and let the symbol $\int\int_{L-C}$ indicate the double integral over the area which lies between the curves L and C. Then the integral

$$\int\int_{L-C} f(x, y)dxdy \tag{3}$$

is a proper integral, and it has a certain value V. If V has a definite finite limit when the curve C shrinks down upon the point O, independent of the shape of the curves through which C shrinks, then the limit of V is defined to be the value of the integral Eq. (3), and the integral is convergent. If, however, no limit exists the integral is divergent.

Suppose, at first, that it is possible to draw a fixed circle C_1 of radius r_1 with the point O as a center (Fig. 47) inside of which $f(x, y)$ is everywhere of the same sign, say positive; and that there exist two positive numbers M and α such that everywhere inside of C_1

$$f(x, y) < \frac{M}{r^\alpha},$$

where r is the distance of the point x, y, from O. Draw a second circle C_2 with O as a center and radius $r_2 < r_1$. Then, if the integral over S has any sense, it is

$$\iint_S f(x, y)dxdy = \iint_{L-C_1} f(x, y)\,dxdy$$
$$+ \lim \iint_{C_1-C_2} f(x, y)dxdy. \quad (4)$$

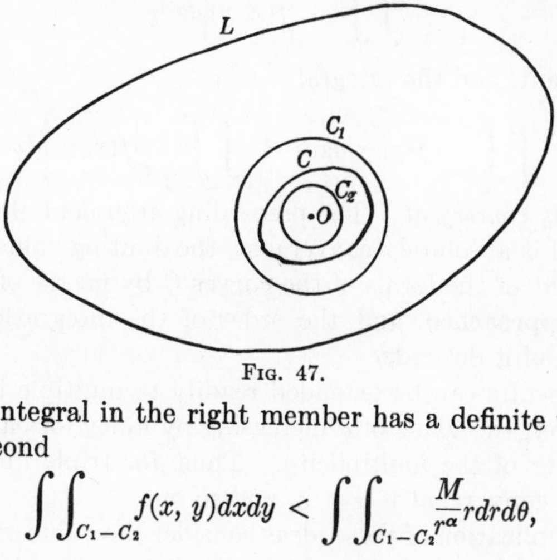

Fig. 47.

The first integral in the right member has a definite value. As for the second

$$\iint_{C_1-C_2} f(x, y)dxdy < \iint_{C_1-C_2} \frac{M}{r^\alpha}rdrd\theta,$$

or

$$\iint_{C_1-C_2} f(x, y)dxdy < \frac{2\pi M}{2-\alpha}\Big[r_1{}^{2-\alpha} - r_2{}^{2-\alpha}\Big].$$

If $\alpha < 2$, this expression has a finite limiting value. Any other contour C can be enclosed between two circles C_1' and C_2' (not drawn in the figure) with centers at O. Then

$$\iint_{C_1-C_1'} < \iint_{C_1-C} < \iint_{C_1-C_2'},$$

and since the two extreme integrals have the same limit the central one has the same limit also. It follows, therefore, that if $\alpha < 2$, the integral Eq. (4) is convergent.

In a similar manner, it is proved that if $f(x, y)$ is positive everywhere within C_1, if there exist two positive numbers M and β such that

$$f(x, y) > \frac{M}{r^\beta},$$

and if $\beta > 2$, then the integral Eq. (4) is divergent.

If there does not exist a circle C_1 with O as a center inside of which $f(x, y)$ has everywhere the same sign, it may still be true that there exists a circle C_1 and two positive numbers M and α ($\alpha < 2$) such that everywhere inside of C_1

$$|f(x, y)| < \frac{M}{r^\alpha}.$$

If these conditions are satisfied, the integral

$$\int\int_{C_1-C} \left| f(x, y) \right| dxdy$$

is convergent, and the integral

$$\int\int_{C_1-C} f(x, y) dxdy < \int\int_{C_1-C} \left| f(x, y) \right| dx$$

is *absolutely convergent*. The preceeding argument shows that if an integral is absolutely convergent, the limiting value is entirely independent of the forms of the curves C by means of which the limit is approached, and the order of the integrations can be interchanged if desired.

These results can be extended readily to multiple integrals of higher order, the value of α increasing by unity for each increase in the order of the multiplicity. Thus, for triple integrals, the integral is convergent if $\alpha < 3$, and so on.

As an application of these ideas consider the value of the potential of a plane area S, for which the density function is σ, at a point O of the area itself. Let O be taken as the origin of a system of coordinates. Then

$$V = \int\int_S \frac{\sigma}{r} dxdy.$$

If σ is continuous throughout S, a small circle can be drawn about the origin inside of which the maximum value of $|\sigma| < M$. The value of α is 1, and, since this is less than 2, the integral is convergent. The potential, therefore, has a definite value at each point of the area S.

Consider a component of attraction at a point inside the attracting volume. If the point under consideration is taken as the origin,

$$X = -\int\int\int \frac{\sigma x}{r^3} dx dy dz.$$

If, in a small sphere of radius ρ about the origin, the maximum value of $|\sigma|$ is M, then, since $|x| < r$ and

$$\left|\frac{\sigma x}{r^3}\right| < \frac{M}{r^2},$$

the integral is convergent, for $\alpha = 2$, which is less than three. The component of attraction has a definite value.

89. Semi-convergent Integrals.—A series of numbers may converge without being absolutely convergent. For example

$$1 - \frac{1}{2} + \frac{1}{3} - \frac{1}{4} + \frac{1}{5} - \frac{1}{6} + \cdots \tag{a}$$

converges, and its value is the log 2. But the series

$$1 + \frac{1}{2} + \frac{1}{3} + \frac{1}{4} + \frac{1}{5} + \frac{1}{6} + \cdots$$

diverges. Such a series (a) is *semi-convergent*, and the limit depends upon the order in which the terms are taken.

Example of a Simple Integral.—In a similar manner, an integral may be convergent without being absolutely convergent. For example, consider the integral

$$I = \int_{-1}^{+1} \frac{xdx}{(\sqrt{x^2})^3} = \lim\left[\int_{\epsilon_1}^{1}\frac{dx}{x^2} - \int_{\epsilon_2}^{1}\frac{dx}{x^2}\right],$$

where ϵ_1 and ϵ_2 are two small positive quantities which bound off the origin, and $\sqrt{x^2}$ is always positive. It is easily verified that

$$I = \lim\left(\frac{1}{\epsilon_1} - \frac{1}{\epsilon_2}\right),$$

and its value depends upon the manner in which the interval $\epsilon_1\epsilon_2$ shrinks to zero. Suppose λ is any given constant, and

$$\epsilon_1 = \frac{\epsilon_2}{1 + \epsilon_2\lambda};$$

then

$$\frac{1}{\epsilon_1} - \frac{1}{\epsilon_2} = \lambda,$$

for all values of ϵ_1. Therefore

$$I = \lambda,$$

which is arbitrary.

The integral of the modulus, however,

$$\int_{-1}^{+1}\frac{dx}{x^2} = \lim\left(\frac{1}{\epsilon_1} + \frac{1}{\epsilon_2}\right) = \infty,$$

diverges.

Double Integral.—Consider the double integral

$$\int_{\xi}^{a}\int_{\eta}^{b}\frac{y^2 - x^2}{(x^2 + y^2)^2}dxdy,$$

where

$$0 < \xi < a,$$
$$0 < \eta < b.$$

Since

$$\frac{\partial^2}{\partial x \partial y}\left(\tan^{-1}\frac{y}{x}\right) = \frac{y^2 - x^2}{(x^2 + y^2)^2},$$

the value of this integral is

$$\tan^{-1}\frac{b}{a} - \tan^{-1}\frac{b}{\xi} - \tan^{-1}\frac{\eta}{a} + \tan^{-1}\frac{\eta}{\xi},$$

which is perfectly definite if the values of the angle are limited to the first quadrant.

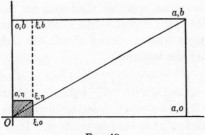

Fig. 48.

In order to evaluate the integral for both lower limits equal to zero, let the origin be bounded off by a small rectangle of sides ξ and η, Fig. 48. The integral over the remainder of the rectangle, of which the sides are a and b, is

$$\tan^{-1}\frac{b}{a} - \tan^{-1}\frac{\eta}{\xi}.$$

The limit of this expression as the point ξ, η approaches the origin, depends upon the direction of approach, for this expression represents the angle between the diagonal of the rectangle ab and the diagonal of the rectangle $\xi\eta$. The integral converges, but it is semi-convergent.

It will be observed that

$$\frac{|y^2 - x^2|}{(x^2 + y^2)^2} < \frac{1}{r^2},$$

so that $\alpha = 2$.

Triple Integral.—It is desired to compute the attraction of an infinite, homogeneous universe on a given point. Let the axes be chosen so that the given point is at the origin. With the point $(-\xi, 0, 0)$ as a center describe a sphere of radius $r > \xi$.

The center of this sphere is arbitrary, and therefore the series of bounding spheres (r increasing) is arbitrary. If the origin is moved to the center of the sphere and if the density is taken equal to unity, the integral is

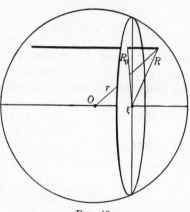

$$I = \iiint_V \frac{x - \xi}{\rho^3} dx\, dy\, dz.$$

If a plane is passed through the attracted point perpendicular to the x-axis it will separate the sphere into two parts,

Fig. 49. In the segment of the sphere to the right of this plane $x - \xi$ is positive; in the segment to the left it is negative. The integral will be taken over the two segments separately, the one to the right, for which $x - \xi > 0$, being taken first.

Since

$$\frac{x - \xi}{\rho^3} = -\frac{\partial}{\partial x}\left(\frac{1}{\rho}\right),$$

where

$$\rho^2 = (x - \xi)^2 + y^2 + z^2,$$

the integration with respect to x gives (Eq. (35.4))

$$I_1 = \iint \left[\frac{1}{R_0} - \frac{1}{R}\right] dy\, dz,$$

in which

$$R_0 = \sqrt{y^2 + z^2}, \qquad R = \sqrt{(\sqrt{r^2 - (y^2 + z^2)} - \xi)^2 + y^2 + z^2},$$

are the two values of ρ where the elementary column for which y and z are constants pierces the surface of the segment.

For the first integral,

$$\int\int\frac{dydz}{R_0} = \int_0^{\sqrt{r^2-\xi^2}}\int_0^{2\pi} dR_0 d\psi = 2\pi\sqrt{r^2-\xi^2},$$

as is found by setting

$$y = R_0 \cos\psi, \qquad z = R_0 \sin\psi.$$

The second integral also is easily evaluated by taking

$$y = \sqrt{r^2 - \frac{(r^2+\xi^2-R^2)^2}{4\xi^2}}\cos\psi,$$

$$z = \sqrt{r^2 - \frac{(r^2+\xi^2-R^2)^2}{4\xi^2}}\sin\psi,$$

in which R and ψ are the independent variables. The ratio between the differential products $dydz$ and $dRd\psi$ is the jacobian[1] of y and z with respect to R and ψ. That is

$$dydz = \begin{vmatrix} \dfrac{\partial y}{\partial R} & \dfrac{\partial y}{\partial \psi} \\ \dfrac{\partial z}{\partial R} & \dfrac{\partial z}{\partial \psi} \end{vmatrix} dRd\psi;$$

or

$$dydz = \frac{1}{2\xi^2}(r^2+\xi^2-R^2)RdRd\psi.$$

Hence

$$\int\int\frac{dydz}{R} = \frac{1}{2\xi^2}\int_{r-\xi}^{\sqrt{r^2-\xi^2}}\int_0^{2\pi}(r^2+\xi^2-R^2)dRd\psi$$

$$= \frac{2\pi}{3\xi^2}\{\sqrt{r^2-\xi^2}(r^2+2\xi^2)-(r^3-\xi^3)\};$$

and

$$I_1 = \int\int\frac{dydz}{R_0} - \int\int\frac{dydz}{R}$$

$$= \frac{2\pi}{3\xi^2}\left\{(r^3-\xi^3)-(r^2-\xi^2)^{\frac{3}{2}}\right\}.$$

The integral over the other segment is obtained from I_1 by changing ξ into $-\xi$ and then reversing the sign of the entire expression. That is

$$I_2 = \frac{2\pi}{3\xi^2}\left\{-(r^3+\xi^3)+(r^2-\xi^2)^{\frac{3}{2}}\right\}.$$

The sum of these two integrals is

$$I = I_1 + I_2 = -4\pi\xi,$$

which is arbitrary, since ξ is arbitrary, and it is independent of r.

[1] GOURSAT-HEDRICK, "Mathematical Analysis," p. 266.

From the manner in which the integration has been carried out, it is seen that

$$I_M = \int\!\!\int\!\!\int \frac{|x - \xi|}{\rho^3} dx\,dy\,dz = I_1 - I_2$$
$$= \frac{4\pi}{3\xi^2}\left\{r^3 - (r^2 - \xi^2)^{\frac{3}{2}}\right\} = \frac{4}{3}\pi \frac{2r^2 + r\sqrt{r^2 - \xi^2} - \xi^2}{r + \sqrt{r^2 - \xi^2}}.$$

For large values of r the value is approximately

$$I_M = 2\pi r,$$

which increases as r increases. The integral of the modulus, therefore, is divergent, and the integral I is semi-convergent.

90. The Potential at a Point of the Surface.—In Sec. 88, it was proved that the potential of a plane surface has a definite value at each point of the surface itself. It is desired to extend this result to curved surfaces.

Let O be an ordinary point on the surface S, that is a point at which the surface has a definite tangent plane. Draw the normal and the tangent plane at O, and then cut the surface S into two portions by a cylinder whose axis is the normal and whose radius is δ. Let S_1 be the small curved disk which is cut out of S and which contains the point O, and let S_2 be the remainder of the surface. The potential of S_2 on the point O is perfectly definite, since O is not a point of S_2. There remains for consideration only the disk S_1, the potential of which is

$$V_1 = \int_{S_1} \frac{\sigma}{\rho} d\omega,$$

where $d\omega$ is an element of the surface S_1 and σ, which is a continuous function of its position, is its density.

Let P_1 be the point of the surface at which $d\omega$ is located (Fig. 50), let φ be angle which the normal at P_1 makes with the normal at O, P be the pro-

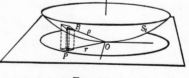

Fig. 50.

jection of P_1 on the tangent plane, and $r\,dr\,d\theta$ be the projection of the element $d\omega$ upon the tangent plane. Then

$$d\omega = r \sec \varphi \, dr\,d\theta,$$
$$OP = r, \qquad\qquad OP_1 = \rho, \qquad\qquad \rho = r \sec \psi,$$

if ψ is the angle between ρ and r. Hence V_1 can be written

$$V_1 = \int_0^\delta \int_0^{2\pi} \sigma \frac{\sec \varphi}{\sec \psi} dr d\theta. \qquad (1)$$

Since at the limit, $\varphi = \psi = 0$, the modulus of the ratio $\sec \varphi / \sec \psi$ has a maximum value M on S_1, and so also has σ a maxi-

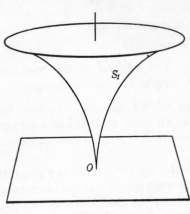

FIG. 51.

mum Σ, if δ is sufficiently small. Hence V_1 is a proper integral and its value is less than $2\pi M \Sigma \delta$.

Equation (1) still holds at a conical point of revolution of the surface provided the plane, instead of being tangent, is perpendicular to the axis of revolution at the conical point, φ is the angle which the normal makes with the axis of revolution, and ψ is the angle which ρ makes with the normal plane (Fig. 51). Suppose

the axis of revolution is taken as the z-axis, and the normal plane is taken as the xy-plane. Suppose further that the generating curve is sufficiently represented by the equation

$$z = \alpha r^{s+1}, \qquad -1 < s \leqq 0,$$

where

$$r = \sqrt{x^2 + y^2}.$$

Then

$$\sec \varphi = \sqrt{1 + \alpha^2(s+1)^2 r^{2s}}, \qquad \sec \psi = \sqrt{1 + \alpha^2 r^{2s}}.$$

Since s is negative, the limit of the ratio is

$$\lim \left| \frac{\sec \varphi}{\sec \psi} \right| = 1 + s < 1.$$

Therefore, if σ is continuous on S_1, the value of V_1 is perfectly well defined, no matter how sharp the conical point may be. If $s = 0$, the cone is an ordinary right circular cone.

91. The Potential is Continuous across the Surface.—Let S be the given surface, and O an ordinary point of S. Draw the normal and the tangent plane at O, and any line L which pierces the surface at O. Let O_1 be any point on L near O. It will be shown that the value of the potential of S at O_1 varies continuously as the point O_1 passes through the point O.

As in the preceding section, let the surface S be divided into two parts by a cylinder of radius δ, the axis of the cylinder coinciding with the normal at O. Let S_1 be the disk cut out of S by the cylinder, and let S_2 be the remainder of the surface. The value of the potential at O_1 due to the surface S_2 is continuous in the neighborhood of O, since O does not lie in S_2. That is to say, if $OO_1 = l$, if U_0 and U_1 are the potentials of S_2 at O and O_1 respectively and if ϵ is any positive number given in advance, the length l can be taken so small that

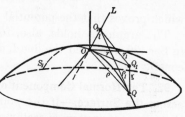

$$\left| U_0 - U_1 \right| < \frac{1}{2}\epsilon,$$

however small δ may be.

Let Fig. 52 represent S_1, and

Fig. 52.

let V_0 and V_1 be the values of the potential of S_1 at the points O and O_1 respectively. Then

$$V_0 = \int_{S_1} \frac{\sigma d\omega}{\rho}, \qquad V_1 = \int_{S_1} \frac{\sigma d\omega}{\rho_1}.$$

If r, θ, φ, and ψ have the same significance as in Sec. 90, these integrals can be written

$$V_0 = \int_0^\delta \int_0^{2\pi} \frac{\sec \varphi}{\sec \psi} \sigma dr d\theta, \qquad V_1 = \int_0^\delta \int_0^{2\pi} \frac{\rho}{\rho_1} \frac{\sec \varphi}{\sec \psi} \sigma dr d\theta,$$

and

$$V_0 < 2\pi M \Sigma \delta.$$

In the triangle QOO_1, let the angles at O and O_1 be denoted by α and α_1. Then, from the law of sines,

$$\frac{\rho}{\rho_1} = \frac{\sin \alpha_1}{\sin \alpha}.$$

If γ is the angle which L makes with the normal, the limiting value of the angle α as the point Q approaches the point O lies between $\frac{\pi}{2} - \gamma$ and $\frac{\pi}{2} + \gamma$, and the limiting value of $\sin \alpha$ is not zero. Let the maximum value of the modulus on S_1 be

$$\left| \frac{\sin \alpha_1}{\sin \alpha} \right|_{\max} = N.$$

This will exist if δ is not too large, however small l may be, and

$$V_1 < 2\pi MN\Sigma\delta.$$

Consequently δ can be taken so small that

$$\left|V_0 - V_1\right| < 2\pi M(N + 1)\Sigma\delta < \frac{1}{2}\epsilon.$$

From this it follows that if W_0 and W_1 are the values of the potential at O and O_1 respectively, due to the entire surface S

$$|W_0 - W_1| < |U_0 - U_1| + |V_0 - V_1| < \epsilon,$$

which proves that the potential is continuous across the surface.

The argument holds, also, for the conical points considered in Sec. 90, provided the line L does not coincide with axis of the cone.

92. The Normal Component of the Attraction is Discontinuous across the Surface.—If the point O of the surface S is taken as the origin of a system of rectangular coordinates with the tangential plane as the $\xi\eta$-plane. the equation of the surface can be written

$$\zeta = a_{20}\xi^2 + a_{02}\eta^2 + \cdots, \tag{1}$$

assuming that the surface is analytic. Or, if

$$\xi = r\cos\theta, \qquad \eta = r\sin\theta,$$

the equation is

$$\zeta = r^2(a_{20}\cos^2\theta + a_{02}\sin^2\theta) + r^3(\cdots),$$

the important point being that

$$\lim_{r=0}\left|\frac{\zeta}{r^2}\right|$$

is finite.

Since the point O is not a part of the surface S_2, the normal component of the attraction of S_2 is continuous at O, so that it is necessary to consider only the surface S_1. At the point $O_1(x, y, z)$ the z-component of the attraction is

$$Z = \int_{S_1}\frac{\zeta - z}{\rho_1{}^3}\sigma d\omega.$$

It will be shown that, if $\sigma \neq 0$ at O, the limit of this expression for $z = 0$ is not zero, assuming that the point O_1 moves along the line L, Fig. 52, and that the limit for z positive is different from the limit for z negative.

The expression for Z can be written as the difference of the two integrals

$$Z = \int_{S_1 \rho_1^3} \frac{\zeta}{\sigma} d\omega - \int_{S_1} \frac{z}{\rho_1^3} \sigma d\omega.$$

Consider the first integral Z_1, which can be written

$$Z_1 = \int_{S_1} \frac{\zeta}{\rho_1^2} \cdot \frac{\sigma d\omega}{\rho_1}$$

$$= \int_0^\delta \int_{O_1}^{2\pi} \frac{\zeta}{r^2 \sec^2 \psi} \left(\frac{\rho}{\rho_1}\right)^3 \frac{\sec \varphi}{\sec \psi} \sigma dr d\theta.$$

If the maximum values of the moduli of ζ/r^2 and ρ^3/ρ_1^3 on S_1 are A and R, then

$$|Z_1| < 2\pi A M \Sigma R \delta,$$

if the notation of Sec. 90 is preserved. As this expression vanishes with δ, the value of Z_1 is continuous across the surface.

There remains the integral

$$Z_2 = - \int_{S_1} \frac{z}{\rho_1^3} \sigma d\omega.$$

Let σ_0 be the value of σ at the point O, and consider the integral

$$Z_3 = \int_{S_1} \frac{z}{\rho_1^3} (\sigma - \sigma_0) d\omega = \int_{S_1} \frac{z}{r_1^3} \left(\frac{r_1^3}{\rho_1^3}\right) (\sigma - \sigma_0) d\omega.$$

The ratio

$$\frac{r_1^2}{\rho_1^2} = \frac{(\xi - x)^2 + (\eta - y)^2 + z^2}{(\xi - x)^2 + (\eta - y)^2 + (\zeta - z)^2},$$

for a given value of ζ, is a maximum or a minimum for all values of ξ and η, if $\xi = x$ and $\eta = y$, according as

$$\frac{z^2}{(\zeta - z)^2} \overset{>}{<} +1.$$

For, if the same quantity is added to the numerator and denominator of a fraction the value of the fraction is increased if its value is less than unity and decreased if it is greater than unity. Hence, wherever the point ξ, η, ζ may be on S_1, the value of the ratio r_1^2/ρ_1^2 lies between $+1$ and $z^2/(\zeta - z)^2$.

If the direction cosines of the line L are α, β, and γ, the values of the coordinates of the point O_1 are

$$x = l\alpha, \qquad y = l\beta, \qquad z = l\gamma;$$

also,
$$\xi = r \cos \theta, \qquad \eta = r \sin \theta,$$
$$\zeta = r^2 (a_{20} \cos^2 \theta + a_{02} \sin^2 \theta) + \cdots.$$

If $\xi = x$ and $\eta = y$, then $r^2 = l^2\kappa^2$, where $\kappa^2 = \alpha^2 + \beta^2 = 1 - \gamma^2$, and

$$\frac{z^2}{(\zeta - z)^2} = \frac{l^2\gamma^2}{[l\gamma - l^2\kappa^2(a_{02}\cos^2\theta + a_{20}\sin^2\theta) + \cdots]^2},$$

which has the limiting value $+1$ for $l = 0$. Hence, the ratio r_1^2/ρ_1^2 converges uniformly to $+1$ as the value of z diminishes. For z sufficiently small then, essentially,

$$Z_3 = \int_{S_1} \frac{z}{r_1^3}(\sigma - \sigma_0)d\omega.$$

If M is the maximum value of the derivative of σ with respect to r on S_1, then it is true that

$$|\sigma - \sigma_0| < Mr,$$

and

$$Z_3 \leqq \int_{S_1} \frac{Mzr}{r_1^3}d\omega = Mz \int_0^{2\pi} d\theta \int_0^\delta \frac{r^2 dr}{r_1^3},$$

where

$$\left. \begin{array}{l} r_1^2 = z^2 + r^2 - 2l\kappa r \cos(\theta - \theta_0) + l^2\kappa^2 \\ = l^2 - 2l\kappa r \cos(\theta - \theta_0) + r^2, \end{array} \right\} \tag{2}$$

and θ_0 is the angle between the ξ-axis and the projection of L on the $\xi\eta$-plane. Since it makes no difference in the result and it simplifies the notation, $\theta - \theta_0$ will be replaced by θ. The integration with respect to r then gives

$$Z_3 \leqq Ml\gamma \int_0^{2\pi} \left\{ \frac{(2\kappa^2\cos^2\theta - 1)\delta - l\kappa\cos\theta}{(1 - \kappa^2\cos^2\theta)\sqrt{l^2 - 2l\kappa\delta\cos\theta + \delta^2}} \right.$$
$$+ \frac{\kappa\cos\theta}{1 - \kappa^2\cos^2\theta}$$
$$\left. + \log\frac{\sqrt{l^2 - 2l\kappa\delta\cos\theta + \delta^2} + \delta - l\kappa\cos\theta}{1 - \kappa\cos\theta} - \log l \right\} d\theta.$$

The terms in the integrand which depend upon θ are finite for all values of θ and in numerical value are less than

$$M_1 = \frac{(2\kappa^2 + 1)\delta + l\kappa}{(1 - \kappa^2)\sqrt{l^2 - 2\kappa l\delta + \delta^2}} + \frac{\kappa}{1 - \kappa^2}$$
$$- \log\frac{\sqrt{l^2 - 2\kappa l\delta + \delta^2} + \delta - l\kappa}{1 + \kappa}.$$

Therefore

$$Z_3 < 2\pi MM_1\gamma l - 2\pi M\gamma l \log l,$$

which vanishes with l. It follows then that the integral Z_3 is continuous across the surface.

There remains, finally, for consideration the integral

$$Z_4 = -z\sigma_0 \int_{S_1} \frac{d\omega}{r_1^3} = -\sigma_0 \int_0^{2\pi} d\theta \int_0^\delta \frac{zr\,dr}{r_1^3}.$$

On replacing the value of $z = \pm l\sqrt{1 - \kappa^2}$ and performing the integration with respect to r, it is found that

$$Z_4 = \pm\sigma_0\sqrt{1 - \kappa^2} \int_0^{2\pi} \left[\frac{\delta\kappa\cos\theta - l}{(1 - \kappa^2\cos^2\theta)\sqrt{l^2 - 2\kappa l\delta\cos\theta + \delta^2}} + \frac{1}{1 - \kappa^2\cos^2\theta} \right] d\theta,$$

and it is the limit of this integral for $l = 0$ that is desired. For fixed values of κ and δ, however, this is a proper integral, and therefore the limit of the integral is the integral of the limit of the integrand; that is the order of the processes can be changed. Hence

$$\lim_{l=0} Z_4 = \pm\sigma_0\sqrt{1 - \kappa^2} \int_0^{2\pi} \frac{1 + \kappa\cos\theta}{1 - \kappa^2\cos^2\theta} d\theta$$

$$= \pm\sigma_0\sqrt{1 - \kappa^2} \int_0^{2\pi} \frac{d\theta}{1 - \kappa\cos\theta} = \pm 2\pi\sigma_0,$$

the positive or negative sign to be taken according as the approach to the surface is made from the negative or from the positive side.

The discontinuity in the normal component of the attraction as the attracted point passes through the surface is the difference between these two limiting values, or $4\pi\sigma_0$, where σ_0 is the value of the density at the point of passage.

93. The Tangential Components of the Attraction Are Continuous.—The x-component of the attraction of the surface S_1, which is the only part of the surface that need be considered, is

$$X = \int_{S_1} \frac{\xi - x}{\rho_1^3} \sigma d\omega = \int_{S_1} \frac{\xi - x}{r_1^3} \left(\frac{r_1}{\rho_1}\right)^3 \sigma d\omega.$$

As in Sec. 92, the ratio r_1^3/ρ_1^3 converges uniformly to $+1$ as the point O_1 approaches the point O along the line L. Hence, for a given δ, there exists an ϵ, which vanishes with l, such that

$$\int_{S_1} \frac{\xi - x}{\rho_1^3} \sigma d\omega = (1 + \epsilon) \int_{S_1} \frac{\xi - x}{r_1^3} \sigma d\omega,$$

provided this last integral is finite, and therefore

$$\lim_{l=0} X = \lim_{l=0} \int_{S_1} \frac{\xi - x}{r_1^3} \sigma d\omega.$$

The integral $\int \frac{\xi - x}{r_1^3} \sigma d\omega$ represents the attraction of a plane disk upon the point O_1, the density upon the plane disk being the same at the point ξ, η as upon the surface S_1 at the point ξ, η, ζ. The disk is, therefore, non-homogeneous. It is assumed however, that the density is continuous and that there exists a positive number M such that, on S_1

$$|\sigma - \sigma_0| < Mr.$$

Consider first the difference between the attractions of the non-homogeneous disk and the homogeneous disk of density σ_0 (the density at the point O), the two disks having the same radius δ. Let

$$X_1 = \int_{S_1} \frac{\xi - x}{r_1^3} (\sigma - \sigma_0) d\omega$$

$$= \int_0^{2\pi} \int_0^\delta \frac{\xi - x}{r_1^3} (\sigma - \sigma_0) r dr d\theta.$$

It will be shown that this integral is continuous along the line L in the neighborhood of the point

Since

$$r_1^2 = (\xi - x)^2 + (\eta - y)^2 + z^2,$$

it is evident that

$$\left| \frac{\xi - x}{r_1} \right| \leq 1.$$

Hence

$$|X_1| < \int_0^{2\pi} \int_0^\delta \frac{1}{r_1^2} |\sigma - \sigma_0| r dr d\theta$$

$$< M \int_0^{2\pi} d\theta \int_0^\delta \frac{r^2 dr}{r_1^2}.$$

On substituting, Eq. (92.2),

$$r_1^2 = l^2 - 2l\kappa r \cos \theta + r^2,$$

and then integrating with respect to r, it is found that

$$|X_1| < M \int_0^{2\pi} \Big\{ \delta + l\kappa \cos\theta \log (l^2 - 2l\kappa\delta \cos\theta + \delta^2) -$$

$$2l\kappa \cos\theta \log l + \frac{l(2\kappa \cos\theta - 1)}{\sqrt{1 - \kappa^2 \cos^2\theta}} \left[\tan^{-1} \frac{\delta - l\kappa \cos\theta}{l\sqrt{1 - \kappa^2 \cos^2\theta}} + \right.$$

$$\left. \tan^{-1} \frac{\kappa \cos\theta}{\sqrt{1 - \kappa^2 \cos^2\theta}} \right] \Big\} \, d\theta.$$

This is a proper integral, and remains so even for $l = 0$. The limit of the integral for $l = 0$ is therefore the same as the integral of the limit of the integrand for $l = 0$. Therefore

$$|X_1| < 2\pi M \delta,$$

and X_1 is continuous.

There remains still for consideration the limit of the x-component of the attraction of the homogeneous disk on the point O_1 as l tends towards zero; that is

$$X_2 = \lim_{l=0} \sigma_0 \int_{S_1} \frac{\xi - x}{r_1^3} d\omega.$$

In Fig. 53, let C_1 be the circle of radius δ and center at O which bounds the homogeneous disk. Let O_1 on the line L be the

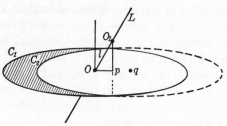

Fig. 53.

attracted point. Drop a perpendicular from O_1 to the plane of the disk, intersecting the disk at the point p. Let the point q lie in the line Op and the distance Oq be twice the distance $Op = l\kappa$. With q as a center and a radius δ draw a circle C_2. The portion of the circle C_1 which is cut out by the circle C_2 is symmetric with respect to the point p. Therefore the x-component of the attraction of this portion of the circle is zero, by symmetry. The area A of the remainder of the disk (shaded in the diagram) is equal to the diameter 2δ of the circle C_1 multiplied by the distance Oq, or $2l\kappa$. Hence the area is

$$A = 4\kappa\delta l.$$

With these preliminaries disposed of, it is easily seen that

$$X_2 = \lim_{l=0} \sigma_0 \int_A \frac{\xi - x}{r_1{}^3} d\omega,$$

and

$$|X_2| \leq \lim_{l=0} \sigma_0 \int_A \frac{d\omega}{(\delta - l\kappa)^2}$$
$$\leq \lim_{l=0} \frac{4\sigma_0\kappa\delta l}{(\delta - l\kappa)^2}$$
$$= 0.$$

Hence, the limit of the x-component of the attraction of the homogeneous disk upon the point O_1, as the point O_1 approaches the point O, is zero, and for the original surface S_1, therefore, this component of the attraction is continuous. The same argument holds for the y-component which, also, is continuous. It follows, therefore, that the tangential component of the attraction of the original surface S upon the point O_1 is continuous as the point O_1 passes through the surface.

The results of Sec. 86 show that at the point O of the surface the tangential component of the attraction does not have a definite meaning.

94. Discontinuities in the Derivatives of Surface Potentials.— Suppose there is given a surface S, on which there is a given distribution of matter σ, for which the potential is $V(x, y, z)$. Suppose further that the straight line L pierces the surface S at the point O at which the density is σ_0, and that O_1 is a point on L near O. If A and B are the tangential components of the attraction and C is the normal component, the X-, Y-, and Z-components of the attraction are

$$\frac{\partial V}{\partial x} = X = \alpha_2 A + \alpha_1 B + \alpha C,$$

$$\frac{\partial V}{\partial y} = Y = \beta_2 A + \beta_1 B + \beta C,$$

$$\frac{\partial V}{\partial z} = Z = \gamma_2 A + \gamma_1 B + \gamma C,$$

where α, β, γ are the direction cosines of the normal to S at O, and α_1, β_1, γ_1; α_2, β_2, γ_2 are the direction cosines for the two tangents at O.

As the point O_1 passes through the point O the components A and B vary in a continuous manner, but the component C has a discontinuity of $4\pi\sigma_0$, and therefore the derivatives of the potential also have discontinuities. The numerical values of these discontinuities are

$$\frac{\partial V}{\partial x} = 4\pi\sigma_0\alpha, \qquad \frac{\partial V}{\partial y} = 4\pi\sigma_0\beta, \qquad \frac{\partial V}{\partial z} = 4\pi\sigma_0\gamma, \qquad (1)$$

where, as already stated, α, β, γ are the direction cosines of the normal at the point O.

If the line L makes an angle φ with the normal and l is the distance OO_1, the discontinuity in the directional derivative $\partial V/\partial l$ is evidently

$$\frac{\partial V}{\partial l} = 4\pi\sigma_0 \cos \varphi.$$

Discontinuities in the Second Derivatives of a Volume Potential at the Surface.—Suppose B is a volume filled with matter of density $\sigma(\xi, \eta, \zeta)$ and bounded by a surface S. The volume density at the surface will be denoted by $\sigma_0(\xi, \eta, \zeta)$. In Sec. 61 it was shown that the first derivatives of the potential V can be expressed as the sum of two potentials, one of which is a volume potential for which the density is $\partial\sigma/\partial\xi$ and the other is a surface potential, the surface density being σ_0 multiplied by a direction cosine. Thus, Eq. (61.3),

$$\frac{\partial V}{\partial x} = \int_B \frac{\partial\sigma}{\partial\xi} \frac{d\tau}{\rho} - \int_S \frac{\alpha\sigma_0}{\rho}d\omega, \qquad (2)$$

the direction cosines of the normal being α, β, γ.

If it is assumed that the density σ admits second derivatives, Eq. (2) can be differentiated again. The first integral, being a volume potential, has first derivatives which are everywhere continuous. The second integral, however, is a surface potential. It has derivatives which are continuous everywhere except on the surface itself. For Eq. (2) the numerical value of the jump along the normal is $4\pi\alpha\sigma_0$, and for dx positive is $-4\pi\alpha\sigma_0$ (Sec. 15). Hence the finite jumps in the second derivatives of V, from Eq. (2) and similar equations for $\partial V/\partial y$ and $\partial V/\partial z$, are

$$\frac{\partial^2 V}{\partial x^2} = -4\pi\sigma_0\alpha^2, \qquad \frac{\partial^2 V}{\partial y\partial x} = -4\pi\sigma_0\beta\alpha, \qquad \frac{\partial^2 V}{\partial z\partial x} = -4\pi\sigma_0\gamma\alpha,$$

$$\frac{\partial^2 V}{\partial x\partial y} = -4\pi\sigma_0\alpha\beta, \qquad \frac{\partial^2 V}{\partial y^2} = -4\pi\sigma_0\beta^2, \qquad \frac{\partial^2 V}{\partial z\partial y} = -4\pi\sigma_0\gamma\beta,$$

$$\frac{\partial^2 V}{\partial x\partial z} = -4\pi\sigma_0\alpha\gamma, \qquad \frac{\partial^2 V}{\partial y\partial z} = -4\pi\sigma_0\beta\gamma, \qquad \frac{\partial^2 V}{\partial z^2} = -4\pi\sigma_0\gamma^2.$$

The discontinuity in the Laplacian is

$$\frac{\partial^2 V}{\partial x^2} + \frac{\partial^2 V}{\partial y^2} + \frac{\partial^2 V}{\partial z^2} = -4\pi\sigma_0,$$

which is Poisson's equation, although the proof here holds only for the discontinuities at regular points of the surface.

Discontinuities in the Logarithmic Potentials of Attracting Lines.—The results which have been obtained for attracting surfaces and the Newtonian potential are also true for attracting lines and the logarithmic potential. The change involves merely a reduction of unity in the dimensions.

The potential itself is continuous across the attracting line; the normal derivative has an abrupt discontinuity of $2\pi\sigma$, if σ is the linear density of the line at the point of crossing; and the tangential component is continuous.

95. Example.—A Non-homogeneous Disk.—The potential of a uniform oblate spheroid, Eq. (39.2), at an exterior point is

$$V = \frac{2\pi\sigma a^2 c}{\sqrt{a^2 - c^2}}\left(1 - \frac{x^2 + y^2 - 2z^2}{2(a^2 - c^2)}\right)\sin^{-1}\sqrt{\frac{a^2 - c^2}{a^2 + \kappa}}$$
$$+ \frac{\pi\sigma a^2 c}{a^2 - c^2}\left(\frac{\sqrt{c^2 + \kappa}}{a^2 + \kappa}(x^2 + y^2) - \frac{2z^2}{\sqrt{c^2 + \kappa}}\right), \qquad (1)$$

where κ satisfies the relation

$$\frac{x^2 + y^2}{a^2 + \kappa} + \frac{z^2}{c^2 + \kappa} = 1.$$

If the polar axis of the spheroid c is taken very small relative to the equatorial radius and at the same time the density σ is increased in such a way as to keep the product $c\sigma = \sigma_0$ constant, the spheroid is very nearly a disk with a surface density which is proportional to the thickness of the spheroid, namely

$$\sigma = 2\sigma_0\sqrt{1 - \frac{\rho^2}{a^2}}, \qquad (2)$$

where ρ is the distance from the center, and at the limit, for c equal to zero, it is exactly so. If $x^2 + y^2$ is replaced by r^2, the potential of a plane disk with the surface density (2) is the limit of Eq. (1) for $\sigma c = \sigma_0$ and $c = 0$, namely

$$V = 2\pi\sigma_0 a\left(1 - \frac{r^2 - 2z^2}{2a^2}\right)\sin^{-1}\frac{a}{\sqrt{a^2 + \kappa}} + \pi\sigma_0\left(\frac{r^2\sqrt{\kappa}}{a^2 + \kappa} - \frac{2z^2}{\sqrt{\kappa}}\right), \quad (3)$$

where κ is defined by the relation

$$\frac{r^2}{a^2 + \kappa} + \frac{z^2}{\kappa} = 1. \tag{4}$$

The derivatives of V with respect to r is the component of the attraction which is parallel to the plane of the disk, and the derivative with respect to z is the component which is normal to it. Since differentiation with respect to κ is not necessary (Sec. 39), it is readily found that

$$\left. \begin{aligned} \frac{\partial V}{\partial r} &= 2\pi\sigma_0 r\left(\frac{\sqrt{\kappa}}{a^2 + \kappa} - \frac{1}{a}\sin^{-1}\frac{a}{\sqrt{a^2 + \kappa}}\right), \\ \frac{\partial V}{\partial z} &= 4\pi\sigma_0 z\left(\frac{1}{a}\sin^{-1}\frac{a}{\sqrt{a^2 + \kappa}} - \frac{1}{\sqrt{\kappa}}\right). \end{aligned} \right\} \tag{5}$$

Now imagine that the attracted point approaches the disk along a line L which pierces the disk at the point x_0, y_0 at a distance ρ from the center, Fig. 54. For simplicity, let the x-axis also pass through this point. Then the parametric equations of L are

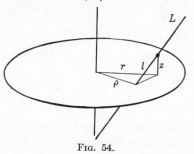

Fig. 54.

$$x = \rho + l\alpha, \qquad y = l\beta, \qquad z = l\gamma;$$

and

$$r^2 = \rho^2 + 2l\rho\alpha + l^2(\alpha^2 + \beta^2).$$

The derivative of V with respect to l is

$$\begin{aligned} \frac{\partial V}{\partial l} &= \frac{\partial V}{\partial r}\frac{\partial r}{\partial l} + \frac{\partial V}{\partial z}\frac{\partial z}{\partial l} \\ &= \frac{\partial V}{\partial r}\frac{\rho\alpha + l(\alpha^2 + \beta^2)}{r} + \frac{\partial V}{\partial z}\gamma. \end{aligned}$$

As l tends towards zero, r tends towards ρ, and the coefficient of $\partial V/\partial r$ tends towards α. Hence

$$\lim_{l=0}\frac{\partial V}{\partial l} = \lim_{l=0}\left[\alpha\frac{\partial V}{\partial r} + \gamma\frac{\partial V}{\partial z}\right].$$

As for κ, it is the positive root of Eq. (4). If $\rho < a$ and z tends towards zero, κ also tends towards zero in such a way that

$$\lim_{z=0}\frac{z}{\sqrt{\kappa}} = \pm\sqrt{1 - \frac{\rho^2}{a^2}}; \tag{6}$$

but if $\rho > a$ and z tends towards zero, κ tends towards $\rho^2 - a^2$. In order that L may pierce the disk, it is necessary that ρ should be less than a, and therefore the limit of $z/\sqrt{\kappa}$ is given by Eq. (6).

Since the limit of κ is zero, it is seen from Eq. (5) that

$$\lim_{l=0} \frac{\partial V}{\partial r} = -\pi^2 \sigma_0 \frac{r}{a};$$

and from Eq. (6), that

$$\lim_{l=0} \frac{\partial V}{\partial z} = \mp 4\pi\sigma_0 \sqrt{1 - \frac{\rho^2}{a^2}}. \tag{7}$$

But, since the surface density σ is given by the formula

$$\sigma = 2\sigma_0 \sqrt{1 - \frac{\rho^2}{a^2}}$$

Eq. (7) can be written

$$\lim_{l=0} \frac{\partial V}{\partial z} = \mp 2\pi\sigma,$$

and therefore

$$\lim_{l=0} \frac{\partial V}{\partial l} = -\pi^2 \sigma_0 \frac{r}{a} \alpha \mp 2\pi\sigma\gamma.$$

The discontinuity is $4\pi\sigma\gamma$, which vanishes at the edge of the disk, since the density σ vanishes there.

For a similar reason if the attracted point approaches the disk from the outside, say along the x-axis, the attraction remains finite. The explicit formula is

$$X = 2\pi\sigma_0 x \left[\frac{\sqrt{x^2 - a^2}}{x^2} - \frac{1}{a} \sin^{-1} \frac{a}{\sqrt{x^2}} \right],$$

since for points on the x-axis, $\kappa = x^2 - a^2$. The limit of this expression, for positive values of x, as x tends towards a is $-\pi^2\sigma_0$, which is remarkable in that it is independent of the radius of the disk.

96. Discontinuities in the Second Derivatives of Surface Potentials.—It will be found in Chap. VI that the discontinuities in the first derivatives of the potentials of two-layer surfaces depend upon the discontinuities of the second derivatives of the potentials of simple layers. It is necessary, therefore, to examine these discontinuities. The analysis which is set forth here follows rather closely the argument given by Poincaré in the sixth chapter of his "Théorie du Potentiel Newtonien."

The Potential of a Plane Surface.—Suppose the given surface S is plane and that it is bounded by a closed contour C. The potential at any point $P(x, y, z)$ is then

$$V(x, y, z) = \int_S \frac{\sigma}{\rho} d\xi d\eta,$$

where σ is the surface density and

$$\rho = \sqrt{(x - \xi)^2 + (y - \eta)^2 + (z - \zeta)^2}.$$

It is assumed that σ and its first derivatives are continuous on S, and that the second derivatives are finite. This potential is an even function of the argument z; that is

$$V(x, y, +z) = V(x, y, -z).$$

The first derivative of V with respect to z is an odd function of z; that is

$$\frac{\partial V(x, y, +z)}{\partial z} = - \frac{\partial V(x, y, -z)}{\partial z};$$

and the second derivative is again an even function. This means that if $P(+z)$ and $P(-z)$ tend towards coincidence at some point of S, the potential V and its second derivative $\partial^2 V/\partial z^2$, having the same values always at the two points $P(+z)$ and $P(-z)$, tend toward the same limit, if a limit exists, and are continuous across S. The first derivative $\partial V/\partial z$, however, has opposite signs, although numerically equal, at these two points. The limits at the surface are, therefore, different, in general, and the first derivative has a discontinuity in crossing the surface. According to Sec. 92, this discontinuity is equal to $4\pi\sigma$, where σ is the density at the point of crossing.

The tangential derivatives, however, are continuous. For example

$$\frac{\partial V}{\partial x} = \int_S \frac{\partial}{\partial x}\left(\frac{1}{\rho}\right) \cdot \sigma d\xi d\eta$$

$$= - \int_S \frac{\partial}{\partial \xi}\left(\frac{1}{\rho}\right) \cdot \sigma d\xi d\eta,$$

which gives, on integrating by parts,

$$\frac{\partial V}{\partial x} = - \int_C \frac{\sigma}{\rho} d\eta + \int_S \frac{\partial \sigma}{\partial \xi} \frac{d\xi d\eta}{\rho}.$$

The first of these integrals is the potential of a mass distribution of linear density σ on the contour C. It is evidently continuous everywhere except, perhaps, on the contour itself. The second integral is the potential of a mass distribution on S for which the surface density is $\partial\sigma/\partial\xi$, and this, too, is continuous across the surface, by Sec. 91. Since the same argument holds for $\partial V/\partial y$, it is evident that the tangential derivative in any direction is continuous everywhere except, perhaps, on the contour.

Since the integral $\int_C$ is the potential of an attracting line, all of its derivatives are continuous everywhere except on the line C itself. There is no need to examine it further for discontinuities across S. But the derivative with respect to z of the surface potential

$$\int_S \frac{\partial\sigma}{\partial\xi}\frac{d\xi d\eta}{\rho}$$

has a discontinuity equal to $-4\pi\partial\sigma/\partial\xi$, while its derivatives with respect to x and y are continuous across S. Hence

$$\left.\begin{aligned}
&\frac{\partial^2 V}{\partial x \partial z} \text{ has the discontinuity } -4\pi\frac{\partial\sigma}{\partial\xi} \text{ across } S, \\
\text{likewise,}\quad & \\
&\frac{\partial^2 V}{\partial y \partial z} \text{ has the discontinuity } -4\pi\frac{\partial\sigma}{\partial\eta} \text{ across } S;
\end{aligned}\right\} \quad (1)$$

while the derivatives

$$\frac{\partial^2 V}{\partial x^2}, \qquad \frac{\partial^2 V}{\partial y^2}, \qquad \frac{\partial^2 V}{\partial z^2}, \qquad \frac{\partial^2 V}{\partial x \partial y}$$

are continuous across S. Since $\partial^2 V/\partial x^2$ and $\partial^2 V/\partial y^2$ are continuous across S, and

$$\Delta V = 0$$

at all points not on S, it is evident that

$$\frac{\partial^2 V}{\partial z^2} = \Delta V - \left(\frac{\partial^2 V}{\partial x^2} + \frac{\partial^2 V}{\partial y^2}\right)$$

also is continuous across S.

It is worthy of note that these discontinuities do not vanish even when the density at the point of crossing is zero unless the derivatives of the density also are zero.

Certain Properties of the Potential of a General Surface.— Returning to the notation of Sec. 91, let O be an ordinary point of the general surface S. Let the tangent plane at O be taken as the $\xi\eta$-plane so that the normal at O is the ζ-axis. Let L

be any straight line which pierces S at the point O, and let O_1, of which the coordinates are x, y, z, be any point on L near O.

Let the surface S be divided into two parts by a cylinder of radius δ, the axis of the cylinder coinciding with the ζ-axis. Let S_1, Fig. 52, be the disk cut out of S by the cylinder, and let S_2 be the remainder of the surface. Let the surface element $d\omega$ be located at

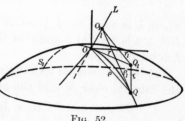

Fig. 52.

the point Q, and let Q_1 be the projection of Q on the $\xi\eta$-plane, so that $\overline{Q_1Q}$ is ζ. Finally let

$$\overline{OO_1} = l, \qquad \overline{OQ} = \rho, \qquad \overline{O_1Q} = \rho_1, \qquad OQ_1 = r, \qquad O_1Q_1 = r_1,$$

so that

$$\rho_1{}^2 = (x - \xi)^2 + (y - \eta)^2 + (z - \zeta)^2,$$
$$r_1{}^2 = (x - \xi)^2 + (y - \eta)^2 + z^2,$$
$$\rho^2 = \xi^2 + \eta^2 + \zeta^2, \qquad r^2 = \xi^2 + \eta^2.$$

If the projection of the surface element $d\omega$ upon the $\xi\eta$-plane is $d\xi d\eta$ and if α, β, γ are the direction cosines of the normal at $d\omega$, the potential of S at the point O_1 is

$$U = \int_S \frac{\sigma}{\rho_1} d\omega = \int_\Sigma \frac{\sigma}{\gamma \rho_1} d\xi d\eta, \tag{2}$$

Σ being the area into which the surface S projects upon the $\xi\eta$-plane.

Let this plane area be covered with matter of density σ/γ. The potential of this plane surface at the point O_1 is then

$$V = \int_\Sigma \frac{\sigma}{\gamma r_1} d\xi d\eta. \tag{3}$$

The difference between these two potentials will be denoted by the letter W, so that

$$W = U - V = \int_\Sigma \left(\frac{1}{\rho_1} - \frac{1}{r_1} \right) \frac{\sigma}{\gamma} d\xi d\eta. \tag{4}$$

Let DW be any derivative of W, and therefore of the form

$$DW = \int_\Sigma \varphi(\xi, \eta) \, d\xi d\eta,$$

where φ is some function of ξ and η. Suppose that over S_1

$$|\varphi| < \frac{k}{r},$$

where k is some fixed, positive number. It will be shown that DW tends toward a limit as the point O_1 moves along the line L toward the point O.

Let W be separated into two parts, one of which corresponds to the integral over S_1 and the other the integral over S_2. Thus

$$W = W_1 + W_2,$$

and

$$DW = DW_1 + DW_2.$$

since, by hypothesis,

$$|DW_1| < \int_{\Sigma_1} \frac{k \, d\xi \, d\eta}{r},$$

it is found readily by integrating, that

$$|DW_1| < 2\pi k \delta.$$

It is evident also, since $|\varphi| < k/r$, that DW has a definite value at the point O, which, separated into two parts, as before, can be written

$$DW^{(0)} = DW_1^{(0)} + DW_2^{(0)}.$$

On forming the difference, there is obtained

$$DW - DW^{(0)} = DW_1 - DW_1^{(0)} + DW_2 - DW_2^{(0)},$$

and therefore

$$|DW - DW^{(0)}| < |DW_1 - DW_1^{(0)}| + |DW_2 - DW_2^{(0)}|.$$

It will be shown that

$$\lim |DW - DW^{(0)}| = 0;$$

that is, given a positive number ϵ, as small as desired, the radius δ and the distance l can be taken so small that

$$|DW - DW^{(0)}| < \epsilon.$$

Obviously δ can be chosen so small that

$$|DW_1| < \frac{1}{3}\epsilon, \qquad \text{and also,} \qquad |DW_1^{(0)}| < \frac{1}{3}\epsilon,$$

so that

$$|DW_1 - DW_1^{(0)}| < \frac{2}{3}\epsilon.$$

Furthermore, since DW_2 is continuous in the neighborhood of the point O, the distance l can be chosen so small that

$$|DW_2 - DW_2{}^{(0)}| < \frac{1}{3}\epsilon.$$

For such positions of the point O_1 it is evident that

$$|DW - DW^{(0)}| < \epsilon.$$

Hence the limiting value of DW is $DW^{(0)}$, and the function DW is continuous across the surface.

If the function φ satisfies the inequality

$$|\varphi| < \frac{k}{r^n},$$

for δ sufficiently small, the function φ is said to be of the order n. Thus the functions $1/\rho_1$ and $1/r_1$ are each of the order 1. The ratio ρ_1/r_1 is of the order zero; likewise

$$\frac{x - \xi}{\rho_1}, \qquad \frac{y - \eta}{\rho_1}, \qquad \frac{z - \zeta}{\rho_1}$$

are of the order zero. It is seen from Eq. (92.1) that ζ is of the order -2; and $\rho_1 - r_1$ also is of the order -2, since

$$|\rho_1 - r_1| < \zeta.$$

The First Derivatives of W are Continuous across S.—The first derivatives of W are

$$\frac{\partial W}{\partial x} = -\int (x - \xi)\left(\frac{1}{\rho_1{}^3} - \frac{1}{r_1{}^3}\right)\frac{\sigma}{\gamma}d\xi d\eta,$$

$$\frac{\partial W}{\partial y} = -\int (y - \eta)\left(\frac{1}{\rho_1{}^3} - \frac{1}{r_1{}^3}\right)\frac{\sigma}{\gamma}d\xi d\eta,$$

$$\frac{\partial W}{\partial z} = -\int \left(\frac{z - \zeta}{\rho_1{}^3} - \frac{z}{r_1{}^3}\right)\frac{\sigma}{\gamma}d\xi d\eta.$$

For the derivative with respect to x,

$$\varphi = \frac{\sigma}{\gamma}(x - \xi)\left(\frac{1}{\rho_1{}^3} - \frac{1}{r_1{}^3}\right).$$

If δ is small, γ is very near unity; and if the density does not vanish, σ/γ is of the order zero. The remaining factors of φ can be written

$$\frac{(x - \xi)}{\rho_1}\left(\frac{1}{\rho_1{}^2 r_1} + \frac{1}{\rho_1 r_1{}^2} + \frac{1}{r_1{}^3}\right)(r_1 - \rho_1).$$

The first factor of this expression is of the order zero; the second factor is of the order $+3$; and the third factor is of the order -2. Hence φ is of the order $+1$, and $\partial W/\partial x$ is continuous across S.

The same analysis, without essential change, applies also to the other two derivatives. Hence all of the first derivatives of W are continuous across S.

The Second Derivatives of W at a Point Where the Density Vanishes.—The six second derivatives of W are

$$\frac{\partial^2 W}{\partial x^2} = \int \left[3(x - \xi)^2 \left(\frac{1}{\rho_1{}^5} - \frac{1}{r_1{}^5} \right) - \left(\frac{1}{\rho_1{}^3} - \frac{1}{r_1{}^3} \right) \right]_\gamma^\sigma d\xi d\eta,$$

$$\frac{\partial^2 W}{\partial y^2} = \int \left[3(y - \eta)^2 \left(\frac{1}{\rho_1{}^5} - \frac{1}{r_1{}^5} \right) - \left(\frac{1}{\rho_1{}^3} - \frac{1}{r_1{}^3} \right) \right]_\gamma^\sigma d\xi d\eta,$$

$$\frac{\partial^2 W}{\partial z^2} = \int \left[\frac{3(z - \zeta)^2}{\rho_1{}^5} - \frac{3z^2}{r_1{}^5} - \left(\frac{1}{\rho_1{}^3} - \frac{1}{r_1{}^3} \right) \right]_\gamma^\sigma d\xi d\eta,$$

$$\frac{\partial^2 W}{\partial x \partial y} = \int \left[3(x - \xi)(y - \eta) \left(\frac{1}{\rho_1{}^5} - \frac{1}{r_1{}^5} \right) \right]_\gamma^\sigma d\xi d\eta,$$

$$\frac{\partial^2 W}{\partial y \partial z} = \int \left[3(y - \eta) \left(\frac{z - \zeta}{\rho_1{}^5} - \frac{z}{r_1{}^5} \right) \right]_\gamma^\sigma d\xi d\eta,$$

$$\frac{\partial^2 W}{\partial z \partial x} = \int \left[3(x - \xi) \left(\frac{z - \zeta}{\rho_1{}^5} - \frac{z}{r_1{}^5} \right) \right]_\gamma^\sigma d\xi d\eta.$$

Suppose now that σ vanishes at the point O, but that its first derivatives do not vanish. Then σ/γ is of the order -1. Consider any one of the six second derivatives, say $\partial^2 W/\partial x^2$. The function φ can be written

$$\varphi = \frac{\sigma}{\gamma} \left\{ \frac{3(x - \xi)^2}{\rho_1{}^2} \cdot \frac{\rho_1}{r_1} \cdot (r_1 - \rho_1) \left(\frac{1}{\rho_1{}^4} + \frac{1}{\rho_1{}^3 r_1} + \frac{1}{\rho_1{}^2 r_1{}^2} + \frac{1}{\rho_1 r_1{}^3} + \frac{1}{r_1{}^4} \right) \right.$$
$$\left. - (r_1 - \rho_1) \left(\frac{1}{\rho_1{}^3 r_1} + \frac{1}{\rho_1{}^2 r_1{}^2} + \frac{1}{\rho_1 r_1{}^3} \right) \right\},$$

which, it is readily verified, is of the order $+1$. Therefore $\partial^2 W/\partial x^2$ is continuous across S at the point O. It is the same also for the other five derivatives.

Now the potential of S at O_1 is, Eq. (4)

$$U = W + V,$$

where V, Eq. (3), is the potential of a plane area tangent to S at O_1. Since all of the second derivatives of W are continuous across S at O, the discontinuities in the second derivatives of U are the same as the discontinuities in the second derivatives of V. By Eq. (1) these discontinuities are

$$-4\pi\frac{\partial}{\partial\xi}\left(\frac{\sigma}{\gamma}\right) \quad\text{in}\quad \frac{\partial^2 U}{\partial x\partial z},$$

$$-4\pi\frac{\partial}{\partial\eta}\left(\frac{\sigma}{\gamma}\right) \quad\text{in}\quad \frac{\partial^2 U}{\partial y\partial z};$$

the remaining derivatives

$$\frac{\partial^2 U}{\partial x^2}, \quad \frac{\partial^2 U}{\partial y^2}, \quad \frac{\partial^2 U}{\partial z^2}, \quad \frac{\partial^2 U}{\partial x\partial y}$$

being continuous. Since γ is equal to $+1$ at O and has a maximum there, the discontinuities can also be written

$$\left.\begin{array}{ll}
-4\pi\dfrac{\partial\sigma}{\partial\xi} \quad\text{in}\quad \dfrac{\partial^2 U}{\partial x\partial z}, \\[2mm]
-4\pi\dfrac{\partial\sigma}{\partial\eta} \quad\text{in}\quad \dfrac{\partial^2 U}{\partial y\partial z}.
\end{array}\right\} \tag{5}$$

The Density at the Point O is Not Zero.—If the ξ- and η-axes are chosen so as to coincide with the tangents of the lines of curvature at the point O, the equation of the surface S in the neighborhood of the point O is

$$\zeta = a_{20}\xi^2 + a_{02}\eta^2 + \text{terms of higher degree.} \tag{6}$$

Let

$$\frac{\partial\zeta}{\partial\xi} = p_1, \qquad \frac{\partial\zeta}{\partial\eta} = q_1,$$

$$\frac{\partial^2\zeta}{\partial\xi^2} = p_2, \qquad \frac{\partial^2\zeta}{\partial\xi\partial\eta} = s_2, \qquad \frac{\partial^2\zeta}{\partial\eta^2} = q_2.$$

It is evident then that at the point O

$$p_1 = q_1 = s_2 = 0.$$

It will be sufficient to study the potential of the disk of radius δ about the point O, for the potential of the remainder of the surface and all of its derivatives are continuous at O. The potential U then can be written

$$U = \int_{S_1}\frac{\sigma d\omega}{\rho_1} = \int_{\Sigma_1}\frac{\sigma}{\gamma}\frac{d\xi d\eta}{\rho_1},$$

Σ_1 being a plane circular area with O as its center.

It is evident that

$$\frac{\partial U}{\partial x} = \int_{\Sigma_1}\frac{\partial}{\partial x}\left(\frac{1}{\rho_1}\right)\cdot\frac{\sigma}{\gamma}d\xi d\eta,$$

where

$$\rho_1{}^2 = (x - \xi)^2 + (y - \eta)^2 + (z - \zeta)^2.$$

No

$$\frac{\partial}{\partial x}\left(\frac{1}{\rho_1}\right) = -\frac{x - \xi}{\rho_1{}^3},$$

and, bearing in mind that ζ is a function of ξ and η through the relation Eq. (6),

$$\frac{\partial}{\partial \xi}\left(\frac{1}{\rho_1}\right) = +\frac{x - \xi}{\rho_1{}^3} + \frac{z - \zeta}{\rho_1{}^3} \cdot p_1,$$

and therefore

$$\frac{\partial}{\partial \xi}\left(\frac{1}{\rho_1}\right) = -\frac{\partial}{\partial x}\left(\frac{1}{\rho_1}\right) - \frac{\partial}{\partial z}\left(\frac{1}{\rho_1}\right)p_1,$$

or,

$$\frac{\partial}{\partial x}\left(\frac{1}{\rho_1}\right) = -\frac{\partial}{\partial \xi}\left(\frac{1}{\rho_1}\right) - \frac{\partial}{\partial z}\left(\frac{1}{\rho_1}\right)p_1.$$

Therefore

$$\left.\begin{array}{l} \dfrac{\partial U}{\partial x} = -\displaystyle\int \dfrac{\partial}{\partial \xi}\left(\dfrac{1}{\rho_1}\right)\dfrac{\sigma}{\gamma}d\xi d\eta - \displaystyle\int \dfrac{\partial}{\partial z}\left(\dfrac{1}{\rho_1}\right)p_1\dfrac{\sigma}{\gamma}d\xi d\eta \\[2mm] \hphantom{\dfrac{\partial U}{\partial x}} = J_1 + J_2, \end{array}\right\} \qquad (7)$$

where

$$J_1 = -\int \frac{\partial}{\partial \xi}\left(\frac{1}{\rho_1}\right)\frac{\sigma}{\gamma}d\xi d\eta, \qquad J_2 = -\int \frac{\partial}{\partial z}\left(\frac{1}{\rho_1}\right)p_1\frac{\sigma}{\gamma}d\xi d\eta.$$

The first integral J_1 can be integrated by parts, giving

$$J_1 = -\int \frac{\sigma}{\gamma} \cdot \frac{d\eta}{\rho_1} + \int \frac{\partial}{\partial \xi}\left(\frac{\sigma}{\gamma}\right) \cdot \frac{d\xi d\eta}{\rho_1}; \qquad (8)$$

or, if ds is an element of the edge of the disk and β_1 is the cosine of the angle between ds and the η-axis,

$$J_1 = -\int_C \frac{\sigma\beta_1}{\gamma} \cdot \frac{ds}{\rho_1} + \int_{\Sigma_1} \frac{\partial}{\partial \xi}\left(\frac{\sigma}{\gamma}\right) \cdot \frac{d\xi d\eta}{\rho_1}. \qquad (9)$$

Thus J_1 is expressed as the sum of two potentials, the first of which is the potential of an attracting line, coinciding with the edge of the disk, on which the linear density is $-\sigma\beta_1/\gamma$. This potential and all of its derivatives are continuous at the point O, since O is not on the line C. The second,

$$\int_{S_1} \frac{\partial}{\partial \xi}\left(\frac{\sigma}{\gamma}\right)\frac{\gamma d\omega}{\rho_1},$$

is the potential of a distribution of matter of density

$$\gamma\frac{\partial}{\partial\xi}\left(\frac{\sigma}{\gamma}\right)$$

distributed over the surface S_1. This potential, and its tangential derivatives also, are continuous across S. Therefore J_1 and its tangential derivatives are continuous across S and, from Eq. (7), the discontinuities in $\partial U/\partial x$ and its tangenital derivatives

$$\frac{\partial^2 U}{\partial x^2} \qquad \text{and} \qquad \frac{\partial^2 U}{\partial x \partial y}$$

are the same as the discontinuities in J_2 and its tangential derivatives.

If a function $F(x, y, z)$ is defined by the relation

$$F = -\int_{S_1}\frac{\sigma p_1}{\rho_1}d\omega, \qquad (10)$$

it is seen that

$$J_2 = \frac{\partial F}{\partial z}, \qquad \frac{\partial J_2}{\partial x} = \frac{\partial^2 F}{\partial x \partial z}, \qquad \frac{\partial J_2}{\partial y} = \frac{\partial^2 F}{\partial y \partial z}.$$

The function F is the potential of a surface on which the density is σp_1. This density vanishes at the point O, since p_1 vanishes at O. Hence, by the preceeding case, $J_2 = \partial F/\partial z$, is continuous across S, while

$$\frac{\partial J_2}{\partial x} = \frac{\partial^2 F}{\partial x \partial z} \qquad \text{has the discontinuity} \qquad 4\pi\frac{\partial}{\partial\xi}\left(\frac{\sigma p_1}{\gamma}\right),$$

and

$$\frac{\partial J_2}{\partial y} = \frac{\partial^2 F}{\partial y \partial z} \qquad \text{has the discontinuity} \qquad 4\pi\frac{\partial}{\partial\eta}\left(\frac{\sigma p_1}{\gamma}\right).$$

Since p_1 is zero and γ is equal to $+1$ with a maximum at O, these expressions can be simplified, so that

$$4\pi\frac{\partial}{\partial\xi}\left(\frac{\sigma p_1}{\gamma}\right) = 4\pi\sigma\frac{\partial p_1}{\partial\xi} = 4\pi\sigma p_2,$$

$$4\pi\frac{\partial}{\partial\eta}\left(\frac{\sigma p_1}{\gamma}\right) = 4\pi\sigma\frac{\partial p_1}{\partial\eta} = 4\pi\sigma s_2 = 0.$$

Since J_1 and J_2 are continuous across S, it follows that $\partial U/\partial x$ is continuous across S, a result, of course, already known. Since the discontinuities of $\dfrac{\partial^2 U}{\partial x^2}$ and $\dfrac{\partial^2 U}{\partial x \partial y}$ are the same as the discontinuities of $\dfrac{\partial J_2}{\partial x}$ and $\dfrac{\partial J_2}{\partial y}$ it follows that the discontinuity in

$\partial^2 U / \partial x^2$ is $4\pi\sigma p_2$, and that $\partial^2 U / \partial x \partial y$ is continuous.

By an argument entirely similar (or, by symmetry if one prefers) it is found that the discontinuity in $\partial^2 U / \partial y^2$ is $4\pi\sigma q_2$. Since the Laplacian is zero everywhere not on S,

$$\frac{\partial^2 U}{\partial z^2} = -\left(\frac{\partial^2 U}{\partial x^2} + \frac{\partial^2 U}{\partial y^2}\right),$$

and the discontinuities in $\partial^2 U / \partial z^2$ are therefore $-4\pi\sigma(p_2 + q_2)$.

In order to find the discontinuities in

$$\frac{\partial^2 U}{\partial x \partial z} \qquad \text{and} \qquad \frac{\partial^2 U}{\partial y \partial z},$$

it is found from the equation

$$\frac{\partial U}{\partial x} = J_1 + J_2$$

that

$$\frac{\partial U}{\partial x \partial z} = \frac{\partial J_1}{\partial z} + \frac{\partial J_2}{\partial z}.$$

Since

$$\frac{\partial J_2}{\partial z} = \frac{\partial^2 F}{\partial z^2},$$

and since in Eq. (10) the density vanishes at the point O, it follows that $\partial^2 F / \partial z^2$ is continuous across S. It is seen from Eq. (8) that J_1 is the sum of two potentials, the first is a line potential which, together with all of its derivatives is continuous across S at the point O; the second is a surface potential for which the density is

$$\gamma \frac{\partial}{\partial \xi}\left(\frac{\sigma}{\gamma}\right).$$

Hence the normal derivative (derivative with respect to z) of J_1 has the discontinuity

$$-4\pi\gamma \frac{\partial}{\partial \xi}\left(\frac{\sigma}{\gamma}\right) = -4\pi \frac{\partial \sigma}{\partial \xi} \quad \text{at the point } O,$$

and this is therefore the discontinuity in $\dfrac{\partial^2 U}{\partial x \partial z}$.

A similar argument shows that the discontinuity in $\dfrac{\partial^2 U}{\partial y \partial z}$ is

$$- 4\pi \frac{\partial \sigma}{\eta}.$$

Let R_1 and R_2 be the principal radii of curvature at O. Then, since the ξ and η axes coincide with the tangents to the lines of curvature of S at O,

$$p_2 = \frac{1}{R_1} \quad \text{and} \quad q_2 = \frac{1}{R_2}.$$

Collected together and expressed in terms of the principal radii of curvature, the density and its derivatives, the discontinuities in the six second derivatives

$$\frac{\partial^2 U}{\partial x^2}, \qquad \frac{\partial^2 U}{\partial y^2}, \qquad \frac{\partial^2 U}{\partial z^2}, \qquad \frac{\partial^2 U}{\partial x \partial y}, \qquad \frac{\partial^2 U}{y \partial z}, \qquad \frac{\partial^2 U}{\partial z\, x}$$

are respectively

$$\frac{4\pi\sigma}{R_1}, \qquad \frac{4\pi\sigma}{R_2}, \qquad -4\pi\sigma\left(\frac{1}{R_1} + \frac{1}{R_2}\right), \qquad 0, \qquad -4\pi\frac{\partial\sigma}{\partial\xi}, \qquad -4\pi\frac{\partial\sigma}{\partial\eta}.$$

$$(11)$$

97. Singular Points of the Surface.—In the discussion of the attraction of surfaces in the neighborhood of points of the surface it was assumed that the point O under con- 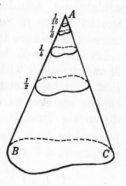 sideration was a regular point of the surface in the sense that the surface had a definite tangent plane at O, that over a circle of radius δ about O as a center the coordinate ζ of the surface was continuous and less than Br^2, where B is a fixed number, and that the density was continuous with $|\sigma| < \sigma_0 + Mr$, where M also is a fixed number. That these restrictions were necessary can be seen by considering the attraction of a cone upon its apex and the attraction of a homogeneous rectangle upon a point of its edge.

Fig. 55.

Attraction of a Cone upon Its Apex.—In Fig. 55, let A be the apex of a cone and BC be its base, which will be assumed to lie in a plane. Pass other planes through the cone parallel to the base which divide the perpendicular from the apex to the base in the ratios $1/2$, $1/4$, $1/8$, $1/16$, $\cdots$. There are infinitely many of these planes. The zones of the cone between the consecutive planes are in perspective with respect to the point A. By Theorem II, Sec. 10, these zones attract the point of perspectivity equally. The attraction of each is finite (not zero) and since there are infinitely many of them the attraction of the surface of the cone upon its apex is infinite.

Attraction of a Plane upon an Edge.—In Fig. 56 let P be a point on an edge of the homogeneous rectangle R. Draw a

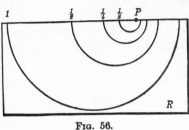

series of semicircles which are in perspective with respect to the point P, the radii of which are in the ratios 1, 1/2, 1/4, 1/8, $\cdots$. The areas between consecutive semicircles are in perspective with respect to the point P, and attract the point P equally. Since the attrac-

FIG. 56.

tion of each is finite and there are infinitely many of them, the total attraction of the rectangle on the point P is infinite.

ATTRACTION OF LINES

98. A Straight Rod.—The attraction and potential of a straight rod, considered as a line with the line density σ, was treated briefly in Sec. 31, but it will be of interest to examine the subject more closely.

Let AB, Fig. 57, be a straight line of length $2l$ and density σ with its center at O, and let $P(x, y, z)$ be an attracted point. Let $dm = \sigma d\zeta$ be an element of mass of the line at a distance ζ from O, ρ the length of the line joining dm to P, and $r = \sqrt{x^2 + y^2}$. Then the potential V is

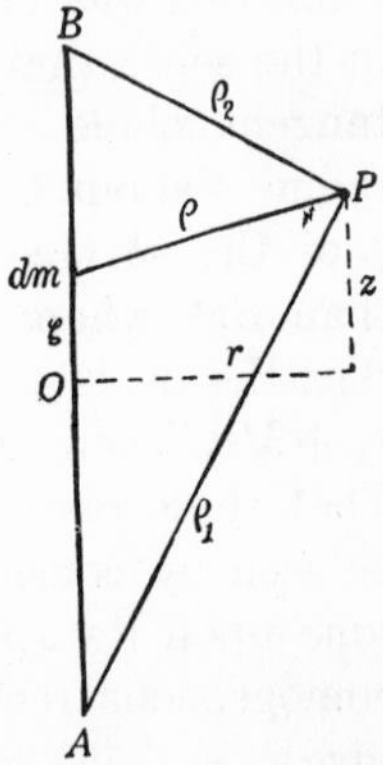

$$V = \sigma \int_{-l}^{+l} \frac{d\zeta}{\sqrt{r^2 + (\zeta - z)^2}}.$$

If ρ_2 is the value of ρ at the point B and ρ_1 the value at the point A, so that

$$\rho_1{}^2 = r^2 + (z + l)^2, \qquad \rho_2{}^2 = r^2 + (z - l)^2, \tag{1}$$

it is found by direct integration that

$$V = \sigma \log \frac{\rho_2 - z + l}{\rho_1 - z - l}.$$

From Eqs. (1) it is found that

$$4lz = \rho_1{}^2 - \rho_2{}^2, \tag{2}$$

FIG. 57.

and therefore

$$l + z = \frac{\rho_1{}^2 - \rho_2{}^2 + 4l^2}{4l}, \qquad l - z = \frac{4l^2 - \rho_1{}^2 + \rho_2{}^2}{4l};$$

so that

$$\left.\begin{aligned}
V &= \sigma \log \frac{4l\rho_2 + \rho_2{}^2 + 4l^2 - \rho_1{}^2}{4l\rho_1 - \rho_1{}^2 + \rho_2{}^2 - 4l^2} \\
&= \sigma \log \frac{(\rho_1 + \rho_2 + 2l)(\rho_2 - \rho_1 + 2l)}{(\rho_2 + \rho_1 - 2l)(\rho_2 - \rho_1 + 2l)} \\
&= \sigma \log \frac{\rho_1 + \rho_2 + 2l}{\rho_1 + \rho_2 - 2l}.
\end{aligned}\right\} \qquad (3)$$

From this expression for V, it is seen that the level surfaces, $V = $ const., are defined by the relation

$$\rho_1 + \rho_2 = 2a,$$

where a is a constant. The level surfaces are, therefore, prolate spheroids with the major axis $2a$ and foci at the ends of the rod. If e is the eccentricity of a meridian section of the level surface, it is evident that

$$l = ae.$$

Therefore, the expression for the potential, Eq. (3), becomes

$$V = \sigma \log \frac{1+e}{1-e} = 2\sigma \tanh^{-1} e.$$

For points which are remote from the rod a is large and therefore e is small. The equipotential surfaces are very nearly spheres. For points on the rod itself

$$\rho_1 + \rho_2 = 2l = 2a,$$

so that e is equal to unity and V is infinite. At points in the neighborhood of the line e is less than unity and V is very large. At large distances e and V both tend towards zero.

99. The Components of Attraction.—Let R be the component of attraction in a plane perpendicular to the rod and Z the component parallel to the rod. Then

$$R = \frac{\partial V}{\partial e}\frac{\partial e}{\partial r}, \qquad Z = \frac{\partial V}{\partial e}\frac{\partial e}{\partial z}.$$

where

$$e = \frac{2l}{\rho_1 + \rho_2}, \qquad \begin{aligned} \rho_1{}^2 &= r^2 + (z + l)^2, \\ \rho_2{}^2 &= r^2 + (z - l)^2. \end{aligned}$$

Now

$$\frac{\partial V}{\partial e} = \frac{2\sigma}{1 - e^2}, \qquad \frac{\partial e}{\partial \rho_1} = \frac{\partial e}{\partial \rho_2} = -\frac{2l}{(\rho_1 + \rho_2)^2} = -\frac{e}{2a},$$

and

$$\frac{\partial \rho_1}{\partial r} = \frac{r}{\rho_1}, \qquad \frac{\partial \rho_2}{\partial r} = \frac{r}{\rho_2},$$

$$\frac{\partial \rho_1}{\partial z} = \frac{z + l}{\rho_1}, \qquad \frac{\partial \rho_2}{\partial z} = \frac{z - l}{\rho_2},$$

so that

$$R = \frac{-\sigma e}{a(1 - e^2)}\left(\frac{r}{\rho_1} + \frac{r}{\rho_2}\right), \qquad Z = \frac{-\sigma e}{a(1 - e^2)}\left(\frac{z + l}{\rho_1} + \frac{z - l}{\rho_2}\right).$$

From Eq. (98.2) it is found that

$$Z = \frac{1}{4l}(\rho_1{}^2 - \rho_2{}^2) = \frac{a}{2l}(\rho_1 - \rho_2), \qquad \rho_1 + \rho_2 = 2a, \qquad l = ae.$$

Hence

$$\rho_1 = a + ez, \qquad \rho_2 = a - ez,$$

and

$$R = \frac{-\sigma}{1 - e^2} \cdot \frac{2er}{a^2 - e^2 z^2}, \qquad Z = -\frac{2\sigma e z}{a^2 - e^2 z^2}. \tag{1}$$

Or, if r is eliminated by means of the equation of the ellipse

$$\frac{r^2}{a^2(1 - e^2)} + \frac{z^2}{a^2} = 1,$$

there results

$$R = \mp \frac{2\sigma e^3}{\sqrt{1 - e^2}} \frac{\sqrt{l^2 - e^2 z^2}}{l^2 - e^4 z^2}, \qquad Z = -\frac{2\sigma e^3 z}{l^2 - e^4 z^2}, \tag{2}$$

which contain only two variables, e and z.

If the attracted point moves along a level surface for which the semi-axes are a and b, R and Z have maximum numerical values, namely

$$R_{\max} = \frac{2\sigma e}{a\sqrt{1 - e^2}}, \qquad Z_{\max} = \frac{2\sigma e}{a(1 - e^2)},$$

and, since

$$b = a\sqrt{1 - e^2},$$

it is seen that

$$\frac{Z_{\max}}{a} = \frac{R_{\max}}{b}.$$

Suppose the value of z is kept fixed with $|z| < l$, and e tends toward unity. In this event, the attracted point moves towards the attracting rod along a perpendicular line. The limits of the components of attraction are

$$\lim_{e=1} Z = -\frac{2\sigma z}{l^2 - z^2}, \qquad \lim_{e=1} R = \mp \infty .$$

as the attracted point crosses the attracting line the Z-component varies continuously, but the R-component has an infinite discontinuity. It will be remembered that the potential at the attracted point also tends towards infinity as the point approaches the attracting line.

100. Attraction in the Line Is Not Well Defined.—Consider the attraction of a homogeneous line upon any one of its own points. Let L (Fig. 58) be the given line and O any one of its

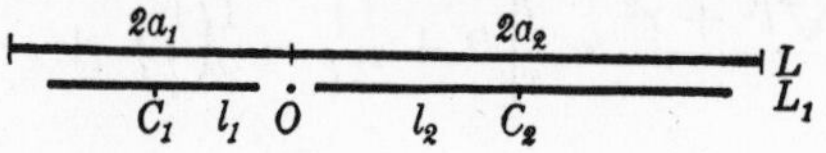

FIG. 58.

points. Let $2a_1$ and $2a_2$ be the distances of the point O from the ends of the line, and let C_1 and C_2 be the middle points so that $C_1O = a_1$ and $C_2O = a_2$. Let a gap be cut in the line L about the point O and let the ends of the line also be cut off in such a way that the points C_1 and C_2 still remain the center points of their respective portions, as indicated in the line L_1. If $2l_1$ and $2l_2$ are the lengths of these portions, the attraction of the line L upon the point O will be understood to mean the limit of the attraction of L_1 upon the point O for $l_1 = a_1$ and $l_2 = a_2$.

Using the second formula of Eqs. (99.1)

$$Z = -\frac{2\sigma e z}{a^2 - e^2 z^2}$$

for the attraction of each portion of the line, it is seen that, since $z = a$ and $ez = l$,

$$A = 2\sigma\left(\frac{l_2}{a_2{}^2 - l_2{}^2} - \frac{l_1}{a_1{}^2 - l_1{}^2}\right),$$

where A is the resultant attraction.

Now let λ be any real quantity, positive or negative, and let l_2 be related to l_1 in such a way that

$$\frac{l_2}{a_2{}^2 - l_2{}^2} = \frac{l_1}{a_1{}^2 - l_1{}^2} + \lambda.$$

As l_1 tends towards a_1 so also does l_2 tend towards a_2, and the limit of L_1 is L. But the limit of A is

$$\lim_{l_1=a_1} A = 2\sigma\lambda,$$

which is anything whatever, since λ is entirely arbitrary. It follows that the "attraction of a line upon one of its own points" does not have a definite meaning.

101. Asymptotic Expression for the Potential.—For points lying in the xy-plane, which bisects the rod perpendicularly, the expression for the potential is

$$V = 2\sigma \int_0^l \frac{d\zeta}{\sqrt{\zeta^2 + r^2}} = 2\sigma \log \frac{l + \sqrt{l^2 + r^2}}{r}. \tag{1}$$

Since

$$\frac{l + \sqrt{l^2 + r^2}}{r} = \frac{l}{r}\left[2 + \frac{1}{2}\frac{r}{l} - \frac{1}{8}\left(\frac{r}{l}\right) + \cdots\right],$$

and

$$\log\left[1 + \frac{1}{4}\left(\frac{r}{l}\right) - \frac{1}{16}\left(\frac{r}{l}\right)^2 + \cdots\right] = \frac{1}{4}\left(\frac{r}{l}\right) - \frac{3}{32}\left(\frac{r}{l}\right)^2 + \cdots,$$

it follows that for values of r less than l

$$V = 2\sigma \log \frac{2l}{r} + 2\sigma\left[\frac{1}{4}\left(\frac{r}{l}\right)^2 - \frac{3}{32}\left(\frac{r}{l}\right)^2 + \cdots\right]. \tag{2}$$

and for very small values of r the expression

$$V = 2\sigma \log \frac{2l}{r} \tag{3}$$

is a good approximation.

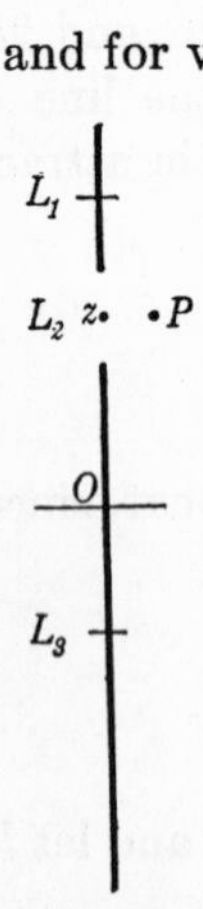

FIG. 59.

Suppose now that the attracted point P lies near the rod, not at the middle point but at a distance z from the middle point. Let the rod be divided into three parts L_1, L_2, and L_3 of lengths $2l_1$, $2l_2$, and $2l_3$ with the center of L_2 at the distance z from the center of the rod, Fig. 59. Then

$$l = 2l_1 + l_2 + z = 2l_3 + l_2 - z.$$

The values of the potentials of L_1 and L_3 at the point z as given by Eq. (98.3) are

$$V_1 = \sigma \log \frac{l - z}{l_2}, \qquad V_3 = \sigma \log \frac{l + z}{l_2};$$

and therefore

$$V_1 + V_3 = 2\sigma \log \frac{\sqrt{(l-z)(l+z)}}{l_2}.$$

At the point P the sum of these potentials is the value at z plus a power series in r which vanishes with r, since the point z is not a point of L_1 nor of L_3. By Eq. (3) the potential of L_2 at P is

$$V_2 = 2\sigma \log \frac{2l_2}{r} + \text{P.S.},$$

where P.S. is to be understood as meaning a power series in r which vanishes with r. Hence the potential of the entire rod L at the point P is

$$V_1 + V_2 + V_3 = V = 2\sigma \log \frac{2\sqrt{(l-z)(l+z)}}{r} + \text{P.S.} \quad (4)$$

102. The Potential of a Uniform Hoop.—In Fig. 60, let H be a uniform hoop which will be regarded as a circumference

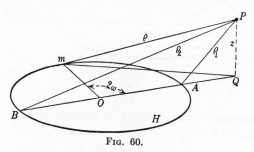

FIG. 60.

of a circle of radius a with constant linear density σ. Let P be any point in space not in H. From P drop the perpendicular $PQ = z$ to the plane of the hoop. Draw the diameter of the circle BOA which, extended, passes through Q. Let m be any point on the circle, and draw

$$Pm = \rho, \qquad PA = \rho_1, \qquad PB = \rho_2.$$

Evidently ρ_1 and ρ_2 are the minimum and maximum values of ρ as the point m runs around the circle.

If the angle mOA is represented by 2ω, the arc element is $ds = 2ad\omega$, and the expression for the potential is

$$V = 2a\sigma \int_0^\pi \frac{d\omega}{\rho}. \quad (1)$$

If the length OQ is represented by r, then

$$\rho_1{}^2 = (r - a)^2 + z^2, \quad \overline{mQ}^2 = r^2 + a^2 - 2ar \cos 2\omega,$$
$$\rho_2{}^2 = (r + a)^2 + z^2, \quad \rho^2 = r^2 + a^2 + z^2 - 2ar \cos 2\omega.$$

The expression for ρ^2 can also be written

$$\begin{aligned}
\rho^2 &= (r^2 + a^2 + z^2)(\cos^2 \omega + \sin^2 \omega) - 2ar(\cos^2 \omega - \sin^2 \omega) \\
&= [(r - a)^2 + z^2] \cos^2 \omega + [(r + a)^2 + z^2] \sin^2 \omega \\
&= \rho_1{}^2 \cos^2 \omega + \rho_2{}^2 \sin^2 \omega.
\end{aligned}$$

If $M = 2\pi a\sigma$ is the mass of the hoop, the expression for the potential, Eq. (1), becomes

$$V = \frac{2M}{\pi} \int_0^{\frac{\pi}{2}} \frac{d\omega}{\sqrt{\rho_1{}^2 \cos^2 \omega + \rho_2{}^2 \sin^2 \omega}}. \tag{2}$$

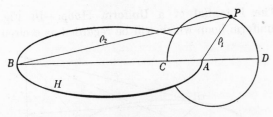

FIG. 61.

This expression shows that V is symmetric in ρ_1 and ρ_2, for if ω is replaced by $\pi/2 - \psi$ it becomes

$$V = \frac{2M}{\pi} \int_0^{\frac{\pi}{2}} \frac{d\psi}{\sqrt{\rho_1{}^2 \sin^2 \psi + \rho_2{}^2 \cos^2 \psi}}, \tag{3}$$

and therefore

$$V(\rho_1, \rho_2) = V(\rho_2, \rho_1).$$

Along the axis of the hoop $\rho_1 = \rho_2$, and if ρ_a is their common value, it is seen at once that the value of the potential along this axis V_a is

$$V_a = \frac{M}{\rho_a}.$$

The function $V(\rho_1, \rho_2)$, Eq. (2), is homogeneous of degree -1 in ρ_1 and ρ_2. Therefore, $\rho_1 V$ is homogeneous of degree zero and depends only upon the ratio ρ_2/ρ_1. In a plane which passes through the axis of the hoop, the curve

$$\frac{\rho_1}{\rho_2} = c, \tag{4}$$

where c is constant, is a circle, for Eq. (4) is the equation of a circle in bipolar coordinates; and this circle, Fig. 61, divides the line $BCAD$ harmonically, since by Eq. (4)

$$\frac{AC}{BC} = \frac{AD}{BD} = c.$$

If K is the complete elliptic integral of the first kind for the modulus $k^2 = 1 - c^2 < 1$, it is seen from Eq. (3) that along this circle

$$\left.\begin{aligned}
V &= \frac{2c}{\pi} K \frac{M}{\rho_1} \\
&= \frac{M}{\rho_2}\left[1 + \left(\frac{1}{2}\right)^2 k^2 + \left(\frac{1 \cdot 3}{2 \cdot 4}\right)^2 k^4 + \left(\frac{1 \cdot 3 \cdot 5}{2 \cdot 4 \cdot 6}\right)^2 k^6 + \cdots \right].
\end{aligned}\right\} \tag{5}$$

103. Evaluation of the Potential According to Gauss.— Equation (102.5) shows that if the value of the potential were known at the point C, Fig. 61, it would also be known at all points along the circle which passes through C. It is, therefore, sufficient to know the value of the potential at all points in the plane of the hoop which lie inside of the hoop itself, and Gauss devised a very ingenious method by which this can be found.

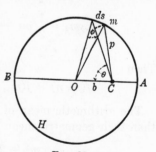

Let the circle in Fig. 62 represent the hoop and $BOCA$ represent the same diameter as in Figs. 60 and 61. Let the arc element at the point m of the hoop be ds and ρ the length of the line joining C to the point m. It is evident from the diagram that in the

FIG. 62.

infinitesimal right triangle of which ds is the hypothenuse $ds \cos \varphi = \rho d\theta$, and therefore

$$\frac{ds}{\rho} = \frac{d\theta}{\cos \varphi}.$$

Let the distance $OC = b$. Then from the triangle OmC it is seen that

$$\frac{\sin \varphi}{b} = \frac{\sin \theta}{a}.$$

Hence

$$V_C = \sigma \int \frac{ds}{\rho} = \sigma a \int_0^{2\pi} \frac{d\theta}{\sqrt{a^2 - b^2 \sin^2 \theta}}$$

$$= M \frac{2}{\pi} \int_0^{\frac{\pi}{2}} \frac{d\theta}{\sqrt{a^2 \cos^2 \theta + (a^2 - b^2) \sin^2 \theta}}$$

$$= M \cdot f(a, \sqrt{a^2 - b^2}).$$

But it is already known from Eq. (102.3) that, when the point P of Fig. 61 coincides with the point C,

$$V_C = M \cdot f(a + b, a - b). \tag{4}$$

Hence

$$f(a + b, a - b) = f(a, \sqrt{a^2 - b^2}). \tag{5}$$

Or, since a is the arithmetic mean of $a + b$ and $a - b$, and $\sqrt{a^2 - b^2}$ is their geometric mean, for any two numbers m and n the function f has the property that

$$f(m, n) = f\left(\frac{m + n}{2}, \sqrt{mn}\right).$$

Now let

$$m_1 = \frac{1}{2}(m + n), \qquad n_1 = \sqrt{mn},$$

$$m_2 = \frac{1}{2}(m_1 + n_1), \qquad n_2 = \sqrt{m_1 n_1}$$

$$\cdots \cdots \cdots , \qquad \cdots \cdots \cdots .$$

Then

$$f(m, n) = f(m_1, n_1) = f(m_2, n_2) = \cdots .$$

The arithmetic mean of any two positive numbers is greater than their geometric mean. Since $(m - n)^2 > 0$, it follows that

$$m^2 + 2mn + n^2 > 4mn,$$

and therefore

$$\frac{1}{2}(m + n) > \sqrt{mn}.$$

Suppose, for definiteness, $m > n$. Then the arithmetic mean is less than m and the geometric mean is greater than n. Hence

$$m > m_1 > m_2 \cdots , \qquad n < n_1 < n_2 \cdots ,$$

$$m > n, \qquad m_1 > n_1, \qquad m_2 > n_2 \cdots .$$

Consider the difference $m_{i+1} - n_{i+1}$. Since $n_{i+1} > n_i$, it is evident that

$$m_{i+1} - n_{i+1} < m_{i+1} - n_i,$$
$$< \frac{1}{2}(m_i + n_i) - n_i.$$
$$< \frac{1}{2}(m_i - n_i),$$

and therefore

$$m_i - n_i < \frac{1}{2^i}(m - n).$$

Thus the sequence of numbers $m, m_1, m_2, m_3 \cdots$ converges to a limit, and the sequence $n, n_1, n_2, n_3, \cdots$ also converges to a limit, and these two limits are the same. Gauss, to whom this analysis is due, called this common limit the arithmetic-geometric mean of the two quantities m and n. The sequence converges rapidly as seen from the example $m = 1$, $n = 1/4$, for which

$$m_1 = .625 \qquad n_1 = .5$$
$$m_2 = .5625 \qquad n_2 = .55901700$$
$$m_3 = .56075850 \qquad n_3 = .56075580$$
$$m_4 = .56075715 \qquad n_4 = .56075715.$$

Returning now to Eq. (4), let g be the arithmetic-geometric mean of the numbers $a + b$ and $a - b$. Then

$$\left. \begin{aligned} V_C &= Mf(a + b, a - b) = Mf(g, g) \\ &= \frac{M}{g}, \end{aligned} \right\} \tag{6}$$

and the value of the potential at any point along the circle which passes through C is

$$V = \frac{M(a - b)}{g\rho_1}. \tag{7}$$

If the values of ρ_1 and c (Eq. (102.4)),

$$c = \frac{\rho_1}{\rho_2} = \frac{a - b}{a + b}, \qquad \rho_1 = a - b,$$

are substituted in Eq. (102.5) and the result is then compared with Eq. (6), it is seen that if γ is the arithmetic-geometric mean of 1 and $\sqrt{1 - k^2}$, then $g = (a + b)\gamma$, and

$$\frac{a + b}{g} = \frac{1}{\gamma} = 1 + \left(\frac{1}{2}\right)^2 k^2 + \left(\frac{1 \cdot 3}{2 \cdot 4}\right)^2 k^4 + \left(\frac{1 \cdot 3 \cdot 5}{2 \cdot 4 \cdot 6}\right)^2 k^6 + \cdots.$$

For the numerical example given above

$$a + b = 1, \qquad a - b = c = \frac{1}{4}, \qquad k^2 = \frac{15}{16},$$

this series converges very slowly, and at least three hundred terms would be required to give the same approximation as that given by m_4 and n_4.

104. Asymptotic Expression for the Potential.—If the point C approaches the circumference, $a - b$ tends towards zero and so also does g while the value of the potential tends towards infinity. It will be of interest to examine the nature of this singularity.

Let the circumference be separated into two parts, one of length $2l$ with the point A as a center, and the remainder of the circumference of length $2\pi a - 2l$. The potential of the main part of the hoop is an analytic function of the position of the point C. If the point C moves along the radius to the point A, its distance from A being denoted by the letter r, the potential is expansible as a power series in r reducing to a certain value at the point A which will be denoted by the symbol V_h. If θ_0 is the angle which the arc of length

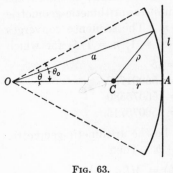

Fig. 63.

l subtends at the center, it is readily found from Eq. (102.2) that

$$\left. \begin{array}{c} V_h = \sigma \displaystyle\int_{\theta_0}^{\pi} \dfrac{d\theta}{\sin \frac{1}{2}\theta} = -2\sigma \log \tan \dfrac{\theta_0}{4} \\[2mm] = +2\sigma \log \dfrac{4a}{l} + \text{P} \cdot \text{S} \cdot \left(\dfrac{l}{a}\right). \end{array} \right\} \tag{1}$$

Let V_a be the potential of the arc of length $2l$ at the point C. Then (Fig. 63)

$$\left. \begin{array}{c} V_a = 2\sigma \displaystyle\int_0^{\frac{l}{a}} \dfrac{a\,d\theta}{\sqrt{a^2 - 2a(a - r)\cos\theta + (a - r)^2}} \\[2mm] = 2\sigma \displaystyle\int_0^{\frac{l}{a}} \dfrac{a\,d\theta}{\sqrt{4a(a - r)\sin^2 \frac{1}{2}\theta + r^2}}. \end{array} \right\} \tag{2}$$

If l is very small in comparison with the radius a, the potential of the arc of length $2l$ differs very little from the potential of a straight line of length $2l$ which is tangent at A. Let V_l be the potential of the straight line at the point C. Then, using the same coordinates,

$$\left. \begin{aligned} V_l &= 2\sigma \int_0^{\tan^{-1}\frac{l}{a}} \frac{a \sec^2 \theta d\theta}{\sqrt{a^2 \sec^2 \theta - 2a(a-r) + (a-r)^2}} \\ &= 2\sigma \int_0^{\tan^{-1}\frac{l}{a}} \frac{a \sec^2 \theta d\theta}{\sqrt{a^2 \tan^2 \theta + r^2}}. \end{aligned} \right\} \quad (3)$$

On changing the variable of integration by the substitution,

$$a\theta = \lambda,$$

these two integrals, Eqs. (2) and (3), take the form

$$V_a = 2\sigma \int_0^l \frac{d\lambda}{\sqrt{4a(a-r)\sin^2\dfrac{\lambda}{2a} + r^2}},$$

$$V_l = 2\sigma \int_0^{a\tan^{-1}\frac{l}{a}} \frac{\sec^2\dfrac{\lambda}{2a} d\lambda}{\sqrt{a^2 \tan^2\dfrac{\lambda}{a} + r^2}}. \quad (4)$$

The potential of the straight line, however, is independent of the radius of the circle, a, and by taking $a = +\infty$ these integrals reduce to the form

$$V_a = V_l = 2\sigma \int_0^l \frac{d\lambda}{\sqrt{\lambda^2 + r^2}},$$

which is the form given in Eq. (101.1) for the straight line. That these two integrals have the same limiting form was to be expected, since the limit of the arc is the straight line.

Expanded in powers of $1/a$

$$4a(a-r)\sin^2\frac{\lambda}{2a} + r^2 = (\lambda^2 + r^2) - \frac{r\lambda^2}{a} - \frac{\lambda^2}{12a^2} + \frac{r\lambda^4}{12a^3}$$

$$+ \cdots,$$

is a series which is convergent for all positive values of a and all values of λ.   Hence

$$\frac{1}{\sqrt{4a(a - r)\sin^2\dfrac{\lambda}{2a} + r^2}} = \frac{1}{\sqrt{r^2 + \lambda^2}} + \frac{r^2\lambda^2}{(r^2 + \lambda^2)^{\frac{3}{2}}} \cdot \frac{1}{2a}$$
$$+ \cdots, \tag{5}$$

converges as long as

$$\left| \frac{4a(a - r)\sin^2\dfrac{\lambda}{2a} - \lambda^2}{r^2 + \lambda^2} \right| < 1.$$

If $|\lambda| < 2\pi a$, the numerator of this fraction is negative, and the series is convergent if

$$\lambda^2 - 4a(a - r)\sin^2\frac{\lambda}{2a} < r^2 + \lambda^2$$

which is certainly satisfied if $r < a$.   Equation (5) can, therefore, be integrated term by term, and, using the results of Sec. 101,

$$V_a = 2\sigma \log\frac{2l}{r} + \cdots, \tag{6}$$

the terms not written vanishing with r and $1/a$.

This analysis has assumed that r and l were fixed while a increases; but since, in the units of length, V_a is homogeneous of degree zero, the result is the same as though r and l diminished, with $r < l$, and a is kept fixed.

Finally, on adding Eqs. (1) and (6), it is found that

$$\left.\begin{aligned} V = V_h + V_a &= 2\sigma \log\frac{4a}{l} + 2\sigma \log\frac{2l}{r} + \cdots \\ &= 2\sigma \log\frac{8a}{r} + \cdots, \end{aligned}\right\} \tag{7}$$

the terms not written vanishing with r and l.   From the symmetry of the circumference it is evident that the potential is entirely independent of l, and therefore the terms in l vanish identically. The remaining terms vanish with r alone.

If Eq. (7) is compared with Eq. (102.5) and r/a is expressed in terms of k^2, it is found without difficulty that asymptotically,

$$\frac{1}{\gamma} = 1 + \left(\frac{1}{2}\right)^2 k^2 + \left(\frac{1 \cdot 3}{2 \cdot 4}\right)^2 k^4 + \left(\frac{1 \cdot 3 \cdot 5}{2 \cdot 4 \cdot 6}\right)^2 k^6 + \cdots$$
$$\doteq \frac{2}{\pi} \log\frac{4}{\sqrt{1 - k^2}}$$
$$\doteq 1.465871 \log_{10}\frac{4}{\sqrt{1 - k^2}};$$

and the approximation gives the first seven significant figures accurately for $\sqrt{1 - k^2} = .001$. The asymptotic expression for the complete elliptic integral of the first kind is accordingly

$$K(k) \doteq \log_e \frac{4}{\sqrt{1 - k^2}}.$$

In his *"Exercises de calcul integral,"* t. I, p. 68, Legendre gives the formulas

$$\int_0^{\frac{\pi}{2}} \frac{d\varphi}{\sqrt{1 - k^2 \sin^2 \varphi}} = \left[1 + \frac{1}{4}k_1{}^2 + \frac{9}{64}k_1{}^4 + \cdots \right] \log \frac{4}{k_1}$$
$$- \left[\frac{1}{4}k_1{}^2 + \frac{21}{128}k_1{}^4 + \cdots \right],$$

$$\int_0^{\frac{\pi}{2}} \sqrt{1 - k^2 \sin^2 \varphi}\, d\varphi = \left[\frac{1}{2}k_1{}^2 + \frac{3}{16}k_1{}^4 + \cdots \right] \log \frac{4}{k_1}$$
$$+ \left[1 - \frac{1}{4}k_1{}^2 - \frac{13}{64}k_1{}^4 - \cdots \right],$$

where $k_1{}^2 = 1 - k^2$.

CHAPTER V

SURFACE DISTRIBUTIONS OF MATTER

105. Transformation by Reciprocal Radii.—Suppose there is given a sphere S of radius a with its center at the origin of a rectangular system of axes. If the point $P(x, y, z)$ lies within the sphere at a distance $r = \sqrt{x^2 + y^2 + z^2}$ from the origin

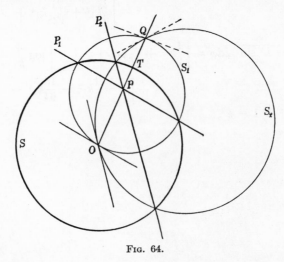

Fig. 64.

O (Fig. 64) and the point $Q(\xi, \eta, \zeta)$ lies on the line OP extended at a distance $\rho = \sqrt{\xi^2 + \eta^2 + \zeta^2}$ from the origin, and if

$$\frac{r}{a} = \frac{a}{\rho}, \tag{1}$$

each of the points P and Q is the transform of the other by reciprocal radii with respect to the sphere S. This transformation sets up a one to one correspondence between the points interior to the sphere and the points exterior to it, the points in the neighborhood of the origin in the interior corresponding to points in the neighborhood of infinity in the exterior. Points on the surface are unaltered, and therefore, the sphere is said to be transformed into itself.

If the direction cosines of the line OPQ are λ, μ, and ν, it is evident that

$$x = r\lambda, \qquad \xi = \rho\lambda,$$
$$y = r\mu, \qquad \eta = \rho\mu,$$
$$z = r\nu, \qquad \zeta = \rho\nu,$$

and therefore, since $\rho r = a^2$,

$$\left. \begin{array}{lll} \xi = \dfrac{a^2}{r^2}x, & \eta = \dfrac{a^2}{r^2}y, & \zeta = \dfrac{a^2}{r^2}z, \\[2mm] x = \dfrac{a^2}{\rho^2}\xi, & y = \dfrac{a^2}{\rho^2}\eta, & z = \dfrac{a^2}{\rho^2}\zeta. \end{array} \right\} \tag{2}$$

Provided q is not zero, the plane P_1, (Fig. 64),

$$lx + my + nz + q = 0,$$

is transformed into the sphere S_1,

$$\xi^2 + \eta^2 + \zeta^2 + \frac{la^2}{q}\xi + \frac{ma^2}{q}\eta + \frac{na^2}{q}\zeta = 0,$$

which passes through the origin. Conversely, the sphere S_1 through the origin is transformed into the plane P_1; but the sphere S_1, Fig. 66,

$$x^2 + y^2 + z^2 + lx + my + nz + q = 0,$$

which does not pass through the origin ($q \neq 0$), is transformed into another sphere S_2,

$$\xi^2 + \eta^2 + \zeta^2 + \frac{la^2}{q}\xi + \frac{ma^2}{q}\eta + \frac{na^2}{q}\zeta + \frac{a^4}{q} = 0,$$

which does not pass through the origin.

If R_1 and R_2 are the radii of the spheres S_1 and S_2, and if L_1 and L_2 are the distances of their centers from the origin, then the centers of the two spheres lie on the same straight line through the origin and

$$L_2 = \frac{a^2 L_1}{L_1^2 - R_1^2}, \qquad R_2 = \pm \frac{a^2 R_1}{L_1^2 - R_1^2},$$

the sign in the last expression to be chosen so that R_2 is positive.

If P_1 and P_2 are two planes which are transformed into the spheres S_1 and S_2, Fig. 64, the tangent planes to the spheres at their points of intersection make the same angle with each other as do the planes P_1 and P_2. Indeed, it is evident from the diagram that the plane tangent to S_1 at O is parallel to P_1, and the plane tangent to S_2 at O is parallel to P_2. Hence the tangent planes make the same angle as P_1 and P_2 do. But the mutual inclination of the two tangent planes of two spheres is independent of the particular point of intersection chosen. Hence the two tangent planes at Q, which is the transform of P, also form the same angle as do the two planes at P.

A transformation is said to be *conform* if every pair of two intersecting lines is transformed into another pair of two intersecting lines in such a way that the angles of intersection are preserved. It is clear that the transformation by reciprocal radii possesses this property.

An infinitesimal length $ds = \sqrt{dx^2 + dy^2 + dz^2}$ is transformed into another infinitesimal length $d\sigma = \sqrt{d\xi^2 + d\eta^2 + d\zeta^2}$. Since

$$dx = \frac{a^2}{\rho^2}\left(1 - 2\frac{\xi^2}{\rho^2}\right)d\xi - \frac{a^2}{\rho^2}\left(2\frac{\xi\eta}{\rho^2}\right)d\eta - \frac{a^2}{\rho^2}\left(2\frac{\xi\zeta}{\rho^2}\right)d\zeta,$$

$$dy = -\frac{a^2}{\rho^2}\left(2\frac{\xi\eta}{\rho^2}\right)d\xi + \frac{a^2}{\rho^2}\left(1 - 2\frac{\eta^2}{\rho^2}\right)d\eta - \frac{a^2}{\rho^2}\left(2\frac{\eta\zeta}{\rho^2}\right)d\zeta,$$

$$dz = -\frac{a^2}{\rho^2}\left(2\frac{\xi\zeta}{\rho^2}\right)d\xi - \frac{a^2}{\rho^2}\left(2\frac{\eta\zeta}{\rho^2}\right)d\eta + \frac{a^2}{\rho^2}\left(1 - 2\frac{\zeta^2}{\rho^2}\right)d\zeta,$$

it is verified readily that

$$ds = \frac{a^2}{\rho^2}d\sigma.$$

If da is an infinitesimal area, its transform $d\alpha$ is a similar infinitesimal area, since the angles are preserved. Similar areas are proportional to the squares of their homologous lines. Hence

$$da = \frac{a^4}{\rho^4}d\alpha.$$

If dt is an infinitesimal volume, its transform $d\tau$ is a similar infinitesimal volume, and therefore,

$$dt = \frac{a^6}{\rho^6}d\tau,$$

a formula which can be verified directly by forming the Jacobian of the transformation. That is

$$dxdydz = \frac{d(x, y, z)}{d(\xi, \eta, \zeta)}d\xi d\eta d\zeta.$$

106. Application of the Transformation to Potentials.—In Fig. 65, suppose P_2 is the transform of P_1, and M_2 is the transform of M_1. That is

$$\frac{\rho_1}{a} = \frac{a}{\rho_2}, \qquad \frac{r_1}{a} = \frac{a}{r_2}.$$

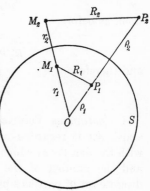

Let the distance M_1P_1 be denoted by R_1 and M_2P_2 by R_2. Let particles of mass m_1 and m_2 be placed at the points M_1 and M_2 respectively. Then the potentials of m_1 at the point P_1 and of m_2 at the point P_2 are respectively,

$$V_1 = \frac{m_1}{R_1}, \qquad V_2 = \frac{m_2}{R_2}.$$

Since the triangles M_1OP_1 and P_2OM_2 are similar, it follows that

Fig. 65.

$$\frac{\rho_1}{r_2} = \frac{r_1}{\rho_2} = \frac{R_1}{R_2}.$$

Suppose also that the masses m_1 and m_2 are related, so that

$$\frac{m_1}{m_2} = \frac{r_1}{a} = \frac{a}{r_2},$$

then

$$\frac{V_1}{V_2} = \frac{m_1}{m_2}\frac{R_2}{R_1} = \frac{\rho_2}{a} = \frac{a}{\rho_1}.$$

Hence

$$V_2 = \frac{\rho_1}{a}V_1 = \frac{a}{\rho_2}V_1,$$

and the coefficient ρ_1/a depends only upon the position of P_1 and is independent of the position of M_1.

A Discrete Set of Points.—If there are many points $M_1{}^{(i)}$ at which are located masses $m_1{}^{(i)}$, the potential of this set at the point P_1 is

$$V_1 = \Sigma\frac{m_1{}^{(i)}}{R_1{}^{(i)}}.$$

The transform of this set of points is $M_2{}^{(i)}$ at which are placed particles of mass $m_2{}^{(i)}$, and the potential of the transformed set at the point P_2 is

$$V_2 = \Sigma\frac{m_2{}^{(i)}}{R_2{}^{(i)}}.$$

If the masses $m_1{}^{(i)}$ and $m_2{}^{(i)}$ are related, so that

$$\frac{m_1{}^{(i)}}{m_2{}^{(i)}} = \frac{r_1{}^{(i)}}{a} = \frac{a}{r_2{}^{(i)}},$$

then, as before,

$$\frac{m_2{}^{(i)}}{R_2{}^{(i)}} = \frac{\rho_1}{a}\frac{m_1{}^{(i)}}{R_1{}^{(i)}}$$

and therefore

$$V_2 = \frac{\rho_1}{a}V_1 = \frac{a}{\rho_2}V_1.$$

A Continuous Volume Distribution.—If each particle of the above set is regarded as occupying an element of volume $d\tau_1$ with the density σ_1 which may, of course, be a function of x, y, z, and the number of the particles is increased indefinitely, the discrete set of particles passes over into a continuous mass which occupies a certain volume, and its potential at P_1 is

$$V_1 = \int \frac{\sigma_1 d\tau_1}{R_1}.$$

The potential of the mass, transformed by reciprocal radii, upon the point P_2 is

$$V_2 = \int \frac{\sigma_2 d\tau_2}{R_2}.$$

If

$$\frac{dm_1}{dm_2} = \frac{\sigma_1 d\tau_1}{\sigma_2 d\tau_2} = \frac{r_1}{a_2} = \frac{a}{r_2}, \qquad (1)$$

it is still true that

$$V_2 = \frac{\rho_1}{a}V_1 = \frac{a}{\rho_2}V_1 \qquad (2)$$

By Sec. 105,

$$\frac{d\tau_1}{d\tau_2} = \left(\frac{r_1}{a}\right)^6;$$

and this relation combined with Eq. (1) gives

$$\sigma_2 = \left(\frac{r_1}{a}\right)^5 \sigma_1.$$

Hence, the ratio of the densities at corresponding points is directly proportional to the fifth power of the distance of the original point from the center of inversion O.

Linear and Surface Distributions.—In case the distribution of matter is continuous but is either linear or over a surface, the argument proceeds just as for volumes, and the same conclusion is reached, *viz.*,

$$V_2 = \frac{\rho_1}{a} V_1; \tag{3}$$

but, if the distribution is over a surface, the density is directly proportional to the third power of r_1/a, and in case the distribution is along a line the density is directly proportional to the first power of r_1/a.

Owing to the fact that the transformation by reciprocal radii is of great value in the theory of electrical attraction, Lord Kelvin, to whom the use of this method is due, called the mass M_2 the *electric image* of M_1 in the sphere S.

107. The Potential of a Uniform Distribution of Matter on a Sphere.—In Sec. 29 it was found that if a quantity of matter M is distributed uniformly over the surface of a sphere of radius a the potential is constant inside of the surface, and its value is $V_1 = M/a$. If the distribution of matter is transformed by Lord Kelvin's principle (Sec. 106) with the center of the sphere O as the center of inversion, the distribution is unaltered since the sphere is transformed into itself.

If P_1 is any point within the spherical surface at a distance ρ_1 from O, and P_2 is its tra sform Eq. (105.1) at a distance ρ_2 from O, then by Eq. (106.2) the potential at P_2 is

$$V_2 = \frac{a}{\rho_2} V_1 = \frac{a}{\rho_2} \frac{M}{a} = \frac{M}{\rho_2},$$

which is the same as the result found in Sec. 29 by other methods.

108. A Non-uniform Spherical Distribution.—Suppose S_1 (Fig. 66) is a sphere of radius a_1 which does not pass through the center of inversion O. If there is a uniform distribution of matter on S_1 of amount M_1, its potential at a point P_1, exterior to it, is M_1/R_1. If the sphere S_2 is the electric image of S_1 in the sphere S, and if P_2 and O_2 are the transforms by reciprocal radii of P_1 and O_1, then by Kelvin's principle the potential of S_2 at the point P_2 is

$$V_2 = \frac{\rho_1}{a} V_1 = \frac{\rho_1}{a} \frac{M_1}{R_1} = \frac{r_2}{a} \frac{M_1}{R_2} = \frac{a}{r_1} \frac{M_1}{R_2}.$$

The ratio a/r_1 is independent of the point P_1 or P_2. Hence the sphere S_2 attracts particles exterior to it just as though a mass

$$M_2 = \frac{a}{r_1} M_1$$

were concentrated at the point O_2.

If, however, the point P_1 lies inside of S_1, where the potential V_1 is constant, P_2 lies inside of S_2 and the potential at P_2 is

$$V_2 = \frac{\rho_1}{a} V_1 = \frac{a}{\rho_2} \cdot \frac{M_1}{a_1} = \frac{a}{a_1} \frac{M_1}{\rho_2},$$

and the attraction at the point P_2 is just the same as though a mass

$$M_2 = \frac{a}{a_1} M_1$$

were concentrated at the point O.

The density on the sphere S_2, however, is not uniform. According to Sec. 106, it varies inversely as the cube of the distance from the point of inversion O. In the diagram the center of inversion lies outside the sphere S_1. Hence if P_1 lies inside of S_1, P_2 lies inside of S_2; and if P_1 lies outside of S_1, P_2 lies outside of

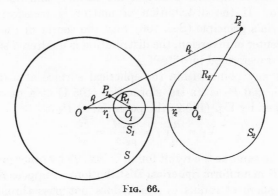

Fig. 66.

S_2. But if the center of inversion O lies inside of S_1, then P_2 will be outside of S_2 if P_1 is inside of S_1, and will be inside of S_2 if P_1 is outside of S_1. The results arrived at above, however, hold whether O lies inside of S_1, or outside.

If S_1 is a uniform, solid sphere of mass M, S_2 also is a solid sphere, but its density varies inversely as the fifth power of the distance from O. If P_1 lies outside of S_1 and P_2 outside of S_2, then

$$V_2 = \frac{a}{r_1} \frac{M}{R_2},$$

and P_2 is attracted just as though all of the mass of S_2, which is equal to Ma/r_1, were concentrated at the point O_2, which is also the center of gravity of S_2.

109. Inversion of a Homogeneous Ellipsoidal Shell.—Suppose there is given a homogeneous ellipsoidal shell E (Fig. 67) which is bounded by two similar, co-axial, ellipsoidal surfaces and a sphere of inversion S which has its center at O in the hollow of the shell. The shell E is the electric image of a certain other shell I which is obtained by inverting E with respect to S, and which is bounded by surfaces which are of the fourth order. In this inversion, it will be observed that the inner surface of E becomes the outer surface of I, and that any point P_1 within E is transformed into a point P_2 which lies outside of I.

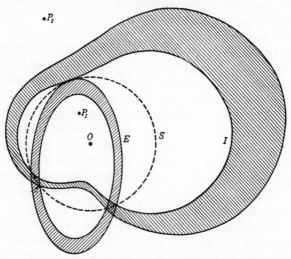

Fig. 67.

In Sec. 11 it was found that a homogeneous shell such as E, attracts a particle anywhere in its interior equally in all directions. The potential of E in its interior, V_1, is therefore constant (Sec. 34). If ρ_2 is the distance of P_2 from the center of inversion O, and a is the radius of the sphere S, the potential of I, the density of which varies inversely as the fifth power of the distance from O, at the point P_2, is by Sec. 106,

$$V_2 = \frac{a}{\rho_2} V_1,$$

and therefore, the shell I attracts any particle which is exterior to it just as though a mass equal to aV_1 were concentrated at the point O.

Since the potential of E at points *exterior* to it is a complicated function of the position of the attracted point (Sec. 36), the same is true, also, of the potential of I at points which are *interior* to it.

110. Centrobaric Bodies.—That a sphere which is homogeneous in concentric layers should attract exterior particles just as though all of its mass were concentrated at its center does not seem surprising, on account of its symmetry; but it certainly does seem surprising that such an unsymmetrical distribution of matter as that which is exhibited by I in Fig. 67, also should possess this property. The illustrations which have been given above are examples of a class of bodies which are called *centrobaric*. If the resultant attraction of the earth, or any other mass, upon a rigid body is equivalent to a single force which always passes through a fixed point relatively to the body, irrespective of orientation and distance, the body is said to be centrobaric.

If a body B is centrobaric with respect to a given body A, Lord Kelvin has shown that it is centrobaric with respect to all bodies. Imagine a rod attached rigidly to the body A, and the rod pivoted at a point O sufficiently far from B that the sphere which can be described by A does not contain B. In every position which is possible to A by this constraint, the resultant attraction passes through a fixed point G of B. Let A take n (very great) different positions distributed as nearly uniformly as possible over the sphere. If an nth part of A were left in each position the resulting distribution of A would be very nearly a distribution homogeneous in concentric layers over the spherical shell, and the resultant attraction of this shell would pass through G. The greater n is, the more nearly can such a distribution be made uniform, and the limit for n infinite is a shell homogeneous in concentric layers, which attracts B with a force which passes through G. But the shell attracts B as would a particle at the point O. Hence, B is centrobaric with respect to a particle, and therefore, centrobaric with respect to all bodies.

With respect to a particle the lines of force are always directed through the point G. They are, therefore, straight lines and the level surfaces are spheres. By the theorem of Sec. 74, the average value of the potential of any distribution of matter over any spherical surface which contains all of the attracting matter in its interior is just the same as though all of the matter were concentrated at its center. Hence, if the total mass of B is M, its potential at all points which lie outside of the smallest sphere which has its center at G and wholly contains B, is

$$V = \frac{M}{\rho},$$

and this formula holds evidently for all points outside of B.

111. The Center of Gravity of Centrobaric Bodies.—If a body is centrobaric with respect to a point G which is fixed relatively to the body, the point G is its center of mass. In order to prove this, imagine the body placed in the gravitational field of a very massive particle at a great distance, such as the gravitational field of the earth. In this case, the center of gravity coincides with the center of mass, and since both points are fixed relatively to the body, they must always coincide.

If a body is centrobaric with respect to points which lie outside of the body, its center of gravity (or center of mass) must lie inside of the body in the sense that every path from the center of gravity to infinity passes through attracting matter. For example, the center of gravity of an anchor ring does not lie within the body in this sense, but the center of gravity of a uniform spherical shell does lie within the body. For outside points the potential of a centrobaric body is $V = M/\rho$. If it were possible to reach the center of gravity without passing through attracting matter, all along this path the potential would be M/ρ. The average value of the potential over a sphere about the center of gravity, so small that no matter lies within it, is M/r, where r is the radius of the sphere, and by Sec. 74 this is the value at the center. But M/ρ is infinite at the center. Hence, the center of gravity cannot be reached by an open path from infinity, and bodies whose center of gravity can be reached by open paths from infinity cannot be centrobaric.

The example of Sec. 108 shows that a shell of matter can be centrobaric with respect to points outside of the shell, and also centrobaric with a different center, with respect to points lying within the shell. But if a shell is centrobaric for points lying within its empty interior, the center of attraction must lie outside of this interior, since the potential function is everywhere finite. An analytic function which represents a potential function in a certain domain A of empty space will continue to represent the potential function in every region of empty space which can be reached from A by paths which pass through empty space only. In different regions, which are closed by attracting matter, the potential function will be represented by different analytic functions, and the points at which the analytic functions become infinite must certainly lie outside of the regions in which they represent the potential function, since the potential function is everywhere continuous.

112. The Central Ellipsoid of Inertia.—The moment of inertia of a body with respect to an axis is

$$\int_B p^2 dm,$$

where p is the perpendicular distance of the element of mass dm from the given axis. Thus, the moments of inertia of a body with respect to the x-, y-, and z-axes are

$$\int_B (y^2 + z^2)dm, \qquad \int_B (z^2 + x^2)dm, \qquad \int_B (x^2 + y^2)dm.$$

Suppose the given body B is centrobaric and that its center of gravity is at the origin. Let V be its potential function, which, analytically, is different in different regions. Describe a sphere S around the origin, large enough to contain B wholly within its interior, and let U be any function which is harmonic within S and which vanishes at the origin. Then by Green's theorem, Eq. (57.4),

$$\int (U\Delta V - V\Delta U)d\tau = \int \left(U\frac{\partial V}{\partial n} - V\frac{\partial U}{\partial n}\right)d\omega, \qquad (1)$$

the integral on the left being taken over the volume of the sphere, and the integral on the right taken over its surface. Since V is a potential and U is harmonic,

$$\Delta V = -4\pi\sigma, \qquad \Delta U = 0,$$

σ representing the density inside of S. On the surface S

$$V = \frac{M}{\rho}, \qquad \frac{\partial V}{\partial n} = -\frac{M}{\rho^2},$$

both of which are constant. Hence, Eq. (1) becomes

$$4\pi \int U\sigma d\tau = \frac{M}{\rho}\int \frac{\partial U}{\partial n}d\omega + \frac{M}{\rho^2}\int U d\omega.$$

By Eqs. (62.2) and (74.3)

$$\int \frac{\partial U}{\partial n}d\omega = 0, \qquad \int U d\omega = 0,$$

the last integral holding since U vanishes at the center of the sphere, by hypothesis. It follows, then, that

$$\int_B U\sigma d\tau = \int_B U dm = 0. \tag{2}$$

The volume integral can be reduced from the sphere to the body, since σ vanishes outside of the body.

Suppose now that

$$U = (x^2 + y^2) - (z^2 + x^2)$$

which satisfies both conditions, namely, that U is harmonic and that it vanishes at the origin. Then

$$\int_B (x^2 + y^2) dm = \int_B (z^2 + x^2) dm;$$

that is, the moment of inertia with respect to the z-axis is equal to the moment of inertia with respect to the y-axis. As nothing has been said about the orientation of the body B with respect to the coordinate system, this conclusion holds for every orientation; therefore, the moment of inertia is the same for every axis through the origin. From this, it follows that the central ellipsoid of inertia is a sphere for every body which is centrobaric with respect to exterior points.

113. A System of Detached Masses Cannot Be Centrobaric.— Suppose a body consisted of two detached portions, such as M_1 and M_2 in Fig. 68, and suppose further that this body were centrobaric. According to Sec. 111, the center of gravity G must lie inside of one of the masses, which will here be taken to be M_1, and the potential of the body is

$$V = \frac{M_1 + M_2}{\rho},$$

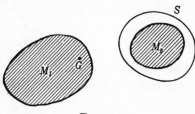

Fig. 68.

where ρ is measured from G.

Describe a closed surface S about the mass M_2, and take the surface integral of the normal derivative of V over S. By Eq. (66.1)

$$\int_S \frac{\partial V}{\partial n} d\omega = (M_1 + M_2) \int_S \frac{\partial}{\partial n}\left(\frac{1}{\rho}\right) d\omega = 0,$$

since G lies outside of S. But by Gauss' theorem, Eq. (68.3),

$$\int \frac{\partial V}{\partial n} d\omega = -4\pi M_2.$$

It follows, therefore, that M_2 is zero and that all of the mass is in M_1. A centrobaric body, therefore, consists of a single mass which is bounded externally by a single closed surface. It may be in the form of a shell which is bounded by two closed surfaces, but it cannot consist of two or more masses which are wholly detached.

114. Theorems Relating to Electric Images.—The following theorems relating to electric images will be of interest.

Theorem I.—*If a body is centrobaric for exterior particles, its electric image in any sphere whose center lies outside of the body also is centrobaric for exterior particles.*

Suppose B_1 is centrobaric and that M_1 is its mass and O_1 its center of gravity. Let B_2 be its electric image in the sphere S, of radius a, and center at O which is outside of B_1. Let P_1 be any point exterior to B_1, and P_2 its transform by reciprocal

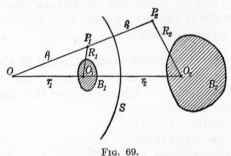

Fig. 69.

radii with respect to S; also, let O_2 be the transform of O_1. Then from the diagram, Fig. 69,

$$\frac{r_1}{\rho_2} = \frac{\rho_1}{r_2} = \frac{R_1}{R_2}. \tag{1}$$

The potential of B_1 at P_1 is

$$V_1 = \frac{M_1}{R_1}; \tag{2}$$

therefore, the potential of B_2 at P_2 is

$$V_2 = \frac{a}{\rho_2} V_1 = \frac{a}{\rho_2} \frac{M_1}{R_1} = \frac{a}{r_1} \frac{M_1}{R_2}; \tag{3}$$

or

$$V_2 = \frac{M_2}{R_2},$$ (4)

where

$$M_2 = \frac{a}{r_1} M_1,$$

obviously, is the mass of B_2, since the formula,

$$\lim_{R = \infty} RV = M,$$

holds for any mass, centrobaric or otherwise. Equation (4) shows that B_2 also is centrobaric.

Theorem II.—If the body B_1 is a shell which is centrobaric for exterior particles, its electric image, in any sphere whose center O lies in the hollow interior of the shell, Fig. 70, is again a shell which is centrobaric for interior particles.

Let the center of mass of B_1 be at the interior point O_1, and let P_1 be an exterior point. If O_2 and P_2 are the transforms

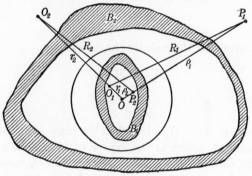

Fig. 70.

of O_1 and P_1, the point O_2 will lie outside of B_2, and P_2 will lie inside. The same notation as before can be used, and Eqs. (1), (2), and (3) hold unaltered. Particles in the interior of B_2 are attracted toward the exterior point O_2 just as though a mass M_1a/r_1 were located there and the body B_2 did not exist. The point O_2, obviously, is not the center of mass of the body B_2.

If B_1, of Fig. 70, is an infinitely thin shell of mass M_1, then B_2 also will be an infinitely thin shell of mass M_2, where, Eq. (106.1),

$$M_2 = \int_{B_2} dm_2 = a \int_{B_1} \frac{dm_1}{r} = aV_0,$$

in which r is the distance from the point O to the element dm_1, and V_0 is the potential of B_1 at the point O. Points in the interior of B_2 are attracted toward the point O_2 just as though a mass

$$M = M_1 \frac{a}{r_1}$$

were placed at the point O_2. Since B_1 is centrobaric with respect to the point O_1 for exterior particles, its exterior potential is M_1/R_1. Let its interior potential be V. Then, at all interior points, R_1 being measured from the point O_1

$$\frac{M_1}{R_1} - V > 0.$$

On the surface B_1 this expression vanishes, since the potential is continuous across B_1. Describe a small sphere Σ about the point O_1. If the radius of this sphere is sufficiently small, $M_1/R_1 - V$ is certainly positive on Σ. Since it is harmonic in the region between Σ and B_1 and vanishes on B_1, it is positive everywhere in this region. Therefore, at the point O,

$$V_0 < \frac{M_1}{r_1}.$$

Also, on multiplying through by the constant a,

$$aV_0 < M_1 \frac{a}{r_1};$$

so that

$$M_2 < M;$$

that is, the mass M_2 on B_2 is less than the mass M at the point O_2.

If the point O, which is the center of inversion, approaches the point O_1, the center of mass of B_1, the point O_2 recedes toward infinity, and the range of the variation of the potential within the hollow of B_2 diminishes, so that if O_2 is very remote the potential within B_2 is very nearly constant. If the center of inversion is at O_1 the point O_2 does not exist and the potential within B_2 is constant. This is readily seen from Eqs. (1) and (3), for

$$V_2 = \frac{aM_1}{r_1 R_2} = \frac{aM_1}{\rho_2 R_1},$$

and as the point O approaches the point O_1 the length ρ_1 approaches the length R_1, so that

$$V_2 \rightarrow \frac{aM_1}{\rho_2 \rho_1} = \frac{M_1}{a},$$

which is constant. Hence the theorem:

Theorem III.—If a closed shell of matter is centrobaric with its center of mass G in its hollow interior, its electric image in any sphere which has G as its center is a shell of matter for which the interior potential is constant.

The converse of this theorem also follows readily, namely,

Theorem IV.—If the potential of a shell is constant throughout its interior, its electrical image in any sphere whose center lies in the interior is centrobaric for exterior particles, and the center of mass of the electric image is at the center of inversion. If the center of inversion O lies outside the shell, the electric image is centrobaric with respect to the point O for particles in the interior of the shell.

115. Level Layers.—Suppose there is given a system of masses which has the potential V. Suppose $V = C$ is an equipotential surface that entirely surrounds all of the attracting matter, or only part of it. Imagine that matter is distributed over this equipotential surface in such a way that at each point of it

$$\sigma = \frac{1}{4\pi}\frac{\partial V}{\partial n_i};\qquad (0)$$

that is, the surface density at each point is equal to the *interior* normal derivative of V divided by 4π. Since the interior normal derivative of V is the magnitude of the attracting force F, this can be written also

$$\sigma = \frac{1}{4\pi}F.\qquad (1)$$

With this distribution of matter upon it, the level surface becomes a *level layer*.

Let $P(x,\ y,\ z)$ be a point exterior to the level layer S. The potential at P due to the matter in the level layer is

$$V_L = \int_S \frac{\sigma}{\rho}d\omega = \frac{1}{4\pi}\int_S \frac{1}{\rho}\frac{\partial V}{\partial n_i}d\omega.$$

where ρ is the distance measured from the point P. The function $1/\rho$ is harmonic inside of S. Therefore, Eq. (71.2) gives

$$\int_S \frac{1}{\rho}\frac{\partial V}{\partial n_i}d\omega = \int_S V\frac{\partial}{\partial n_i}\left(\frac{1}{\rho}\right)d\omega + 4\pi\int_B \frac{dm}{\rho},$$

where, in the last integral, B represents the volume enclosed by S and dm is an element of the mass enclosed by S. Since V

is constant on S, and $1/\rho$ is harmonic in side of S, the first integral in the right member is zero, Eq. (66.1). Hence

$$V_L = \frac{1}{4\pi} \int_S \frac{1}{\rho} \frac{\partial V}{\partial n_i} d\omega = \int_B \frac{dm}{\rho}. \tag{2}$$

This result can be stated in the following theorem:

Theorem.—*The potential of a level layer at any point outside of it is the same as the potential of the matter which is enclosed by it.*

From this it follows that, so far as the attraction at outside points is concerned, the matter inside of a level layer can be replaced by the level layer. Since the attraction of the level layer is the same as that of the enclosed mass at remote points, it follows that the total mass of the level layer is equal to the total mass which is enclosed by it.

In empty space the potential function can have neither a maximum nor a minimum; and, since the potential is constant on S, it must have the same constant value everywhere inside of S. Hence the attraction of a level layer at interior points vanishes.

It is interesting to note that if an equipotential surface which encloses the entire mass were covered with *negative* matter so as to form a negative level layer, the sum of the two potentials $V + V_L$ would vanish everywhere outside of S, and the level layer would act as a screen to the attraction of the matter within it. The sum of the two masses also would be zero. In the interior of S the screen would have no action and the original masses would continue to attract just as though the screen did not exist.

Reduction to Two Dimensions.—Suppose there is given a system of masses in a plane for which the logarithmic potential is V. Suppose $V = c$ is an equipotential contour that encloses all, or only part, of the attracting matter. Suppose that matter is distributed over this equipotential contour in such a way that at each point of it the linear density is

$$\sigma = \frac{1}{2\pi} \frac{\partial V}{\partial n_i} = \frac{1}{2\pi} F. \tag{3}$$

With this distribution of matter upon it the equipotential contour becomes a *level thread.*

A repetition of the preceeding argument for the logarithmic potential gives the analogous theorem:

Theorem.—*The potential of a level thread at any point outside of it is the same as the potential of the matter which is enclosed by it.*

Since the potential can have neither a maximum nor a minimum in empty space and since the potential is constant along the level thread, it has the same constant value everywhere inside of it.

116. Families of Level Layers.—Suppose q_1, q_2, q_3 is a triply orthogonal system of coordinates and that the level surfaces in empty space are $q_3 = \text{const.}$ Expressed in terms of these coordinates $V(q_3)$ is a function of q_3 alone. Using the notation of Eq. (56.5)

$$\frac{\partial V}{\partial n} = \frac{1}{R_3} \frac{\partial V}{\partial q_3}.$$

The element of area on this surface is

$$d\omega_3 = R_1 R_2 dq_1 dq_2.$$

Hence, the element of mass in the level layer on the surface $q_3 = \text{const.}$ is

$$dm = \frac{1}{4\pi} \frac{R_1 R_2}{R_3} \frac{\partial V}{\partial q_3} dq_1 dq_2. \tag{3}$$

Since V is a potential function, $\Delta V = 0$ in empty space, and therefore, by Eq. (56.8),

$$\frac{\partial}{\partial q_1}\left(\frac{R_2 R_3}{R_1} \frac{\partial V}{\partial q_1}\right) + \frac{\partial}{\partial q_2}\left(\frac{R_3 R_1}{R_2} \frac{\partial V}{\partial q_2}\right) + \frac{\partial}{\partial q_3}\left(\frac{R_1 R_2}{R_3} \frac{\partial V}{\partial q_3}\right) = 0; \tag{4}$$

Since V does not contain q_1 and q_2, the first and second terms of Eq. (4) vanish by themselves. Therefore

$$\frac{\partial}{\partial q_3}\left(\frac{R_1 R_2}{R_3} \frac{\partial V}{\partial q_3}\right) = 0, \tag{5}$$

which shows that the element of mass in Eq. (3) is independent of q_3. From this it follows that:

Theorem.—*If $f(q_1, q_2, a) = 0$ is any closed curve on the level surface $q_3 = a$, and if $f(q_1, q_2, b) = 0$ is the corresponding closed curve on the level surface $q_3 = b$, the amount of matter enclosed by the curve in the level layer $q_3 = a$ is the same as the amount of matter enclosed by the corresponding curve in the level layer $q_3 = b$.*

The theorem is true for the corresponding elements of the two areas; therefore, it is true for the entire areas.

It follows also from Eq. (5), by integration, that

$$\frac{R_1 R_2}{R_3} \frac{\partial V}{\partial q_3} = f(q_1, q_2)$$

where f is a function of q_1 and q_2 only; and since $\partial V/\partial q_3$ is a function of q_3 alone, say

$$\frac{\partial V}{\partial q_3} = g(q_3), \qquad (6)$$

it is evident that

$$\frac{R_1 R_2}{R_3} = \frac{f(q_1, q_2)}{g(q_3)}; \qquad (7)$$

that is, $R_1 R_2/R_3$ is factorable, one factor containing q_3 alone and the other independent of q_3. Equation (3) then becomes

$$dm = \frac{1}{4\pi} f(q_1, q_2) dq_1 q_2. \qquad (8)$$

Conversely, suppose a triply orthogonal system of surfaces is given and that $R_1 R_2/R_3$ is factorable in the form of Eq. (7). A function V can be determined from Eq. (6) merely by a quadrature, the constant of integration being chosen so that V vanishes at infinity. The function V so determined is harmonic, vanishes at infinity, and is constant on the surface $q_3 =$ const. Hence, V is the potential of a distribution of matter on this surface for which

$$\sigma = \frac{1}{4\pi R_3} \frac{\partial V}{\partial q_3}.$$

Theorem.—A necessary and sufficient condition that one family, $q_3 = $ const., of a triply orthogonal system of surfaces may also be a family of level surfaces is that $R_1 R_2/R_3$ is factorable in the form of Eq. (7), and that there exists a constant C such that

$$\int g(q_3) dq_3 + C$$

vanishes at infinity.

117. Level Layer on an Arbitrarily Given Surface.—If it were known that every closed surface is an equipotential surface for some distribution of matter that lies wholly within or on the surface, the results of the preceeding sections would prove that there exists a distribution of any given quantity of matter M on any given closed surface S for which the potential is constant on S; or, in other words, for which S itself is an equi-potential surface. Quite likely, if S is properly restricted, there are infinitely many volume distributions for which S is an equipotential surface, although there is no proof to this effect; but it is true that there exists one, and only one, surface distribution on S of a given quantity of matter M for which S itself is an equipotential surface, a theorem which is due to Gauss, although his argument is not sufficient to prove the proposition.

Suppose the mass M is placed upon S at random and suppose also that the particles of M repel each other instead of attract. This last hypothesis does not affect the potential V, but it does change the sign of the potential energy of the distribution which, by Eq. (76.1), is

$$W = \frac{1}{2}\int_S V\sigma d\omega, \qquad (1)$$

where V and σ are the values of the potential and the density at the surface element $d\omega$.

Let R be the maximum distance between any two points on S.   Then

$$V = \int \frac{dm}{\rho} \geqq \frac{M}{R},$$

and

$$W \geqq \frac{M^2}{2R},$$

which shows that, whatever the distribution may be, the potential energy, which is necessarily positive, has a limit below which it cannot sink.   It does not prove that W has a minimum, for, conceivably, the lower limit might be approached by many distributions and be attained by none.

For any infinitesimal variation of the distribution (that is, a variation in σ) the change in the potential energy is

$$\delta W = \frac{1}{2}\int_S (\sigma \delta V + V \delta \sigma)d\omega;$$

and, since the total amount of matter is constant,

$$\delta M = \int_S \delta \sigma \cdot d\omega = 0. \qquad (2)$$

The change in the value of V at any given point is

$$\delta V = \int_S \frac{\delta \sigma}{\rho}d\omega. \qquad (3)$$

Hence

$$\left.\begin{aligned}
\delta W &= \frac{1}{2}\int_S \left[\sigma \int_S \frac{\delta\sigma}{\rho}d\omega + \delta\sigma \int_S \frac{\sigma}{\rho}d\omega\right]d\omega \\
&= \int_S V \cdot \delta\sigma \cdot d\omega,
\end{aligned}\right\} \tag{4}$$

the order of integration being immaterial.

The potential due to the given distribution, if it is not already constant, varies from point to point of the surface. There exists a point, line, or area where the potential has a maximum value, and another point, line, or area where it has a minimum value. Since the potential function cannot have a maximum in empty space, matter is always present in the region of maximum potential. If a small portion of this matter is moved from the area of highest potential to the area of lowest potential, the potential energy of the distribution is decreased, for, in Eq. (4), $\delta\sigma$ is negative where V has its largest value, positive where it has its smallest value, and zero elsewhere. Therefore, δW is negative, and the potential energy is decreased.

Furthermore, Eq. (3) shows that the potential is decreased at the point from which the matter is removed and increased at the point where the matter was deposited. Let V_h and ρ_h be the functions at the point of highest potential. Then in the expression

$$\delta V_h = \int_S \frac{\delta\sigma}{\rho_h}d\omega,$$

$\delta\sigma$ is negative where $1/\rho_h$ has its largest values, positive where it has smaller values, and zero elsewhere. Hence, δV_h is negative and the potential at the highest point is decreased. In a similar manner, it is shown that the minimum value of the potential is increased.

The process of removing matter from the areas of highest potential to areas of lowest potential results in a continued diminution of the potential energy and in a continued approach of the extreme values of the potential toward equality. The process is always possible as long as differences of potential exist. It is exactly like the levelling of a piece of rough ground. If infinite density at isolated points and along isolated lines is admitted, it would seem that the limiting distribution, for which

V is constant over the surface, necessarily exists, if the singularities of S are sufficiently restricted.

Suppose

$$f(\varphi, \theta) = \sum_{i=0}^{\infty} \sum_{j=0}^{\infty} \frac{\lambda^i \mu^i}{i - j \cos^2 \varphi \cos^2 \theta},$$

where $|\lambda| < 1, |\mu|, < |$, and $i + j \neq 0$. This function[1] is definitely infinite if the product $\cos^2 \varphi \cos^2 \theta$ is a rational number. The series is absolutely convergent if $\cos^2 \varphi \cos^2 \theta$ is a Liouville irrational number of Class I, and therefore the function f is finite. Liouville's Class I of irrational numbers includes all of those irrational numbers which are roots of algebraic equations with coefficients which are rational numbers, and also certain transcendental irrationals, *e.g.*, $e, e^k, \cdots$. All other irrationals belong to Liouville's Class II. It is not known whether the above series converges for Class II, but, for definiteness, $f(\varphi, \theta)$ will be defined to be infinite for this class.

The surface

$$r = r_0 + \frac{1}{1 + |f(\varphi, \theta)|}$$

might be called a hairy or fuzzy sphere, since $r = r_0$, if $\cos^2 \varphi \cos^2 \theta$ is rational, or of Liouville's Class II; and $r > r_0$, if $\cos^2\varphi \cos^2\theta$ is irrational of Liouville's Class I.

A surface element $d\omega$ and surface density σ cannot be defined on such a surface. Consequently the concept *potential* cannot be applied, and the problem under consideration disappears altogether; even Green's theorem, and other theorems of a similar character, cease to have any meaning for a fuzzy surface.

Rigorous proofs of the existence of surface distributions, which produce a constant potential on the surface itself, are given in Chap. VI for certain classes of surfaces. These proofs are due to Neumann and to Poincaré.

For a minimum of W, if a minimum exists, the variation, Eq. (4), vanishes, and since $\int \delta\sigma d\omega$ is always zero, it is evident that $V = $ const. satisfies the condition.

---

[1]See MacMillan, Convergence of the Series $\displaystyle\sum_{i=0}^{\infty} \sum_{j=0}^{\infty} \frac{x^i y^i}{i - j\gamma}$, Bull. Am. Math. Soc'y, Vol. XXII, p. 29 (1915).

In order to make sure that there is no other solution, let V_0 be the average value of V on S for the assumed solution. The variation of W can also be written

$$\delta W = \int (V - V_0)\delta\sigma d\omega, \tag{5}$$

and this must vanish for every set of $\delta\sigma$ which satisfies Eq. (2). Let P be the portion of the surface S on which $V - V_0$ is positive, and N the portion on which it is negative. Let the variations of σ in the region P be negative and in the region N be positive, but of such values that $\int \delta\sigma d\omega$ is zero. Then evidently the variation of W in Eq. (5) is negative and not zero, since the integrand is decreased everywhere. Hence $V = $ const. is the only solution.

There cannot be two different distributions of the same amount of matter on S for which the potential is constant on S. Suppose there are two different distributions which have constant potentials on S. Let V_1 and V_2 be the external potentials of these two distributions, and $V_1{}^{(0)}$ and $V_2{}^{(0)}$ their values on S. Then

$$V_2{}^{(0)} = \mu V_1{}^{(0)}$$

where μ is some constant. Consider the difference

$$V = V_2 - \mu V_1.$$

The function V is a potential function which vanishes on S and at infinity. It is, therefore, zero everywhere (Sec. 75), and

$$V_2 = \mu V_1.$$

But, since the total quantity of matter is the same in the two distributions, the limit of the ratio V_2/V_1 at infinity is unity. Therefore

$$\mu = 1, \quad \text{and} \quad V_2{}^{(0)} = V_1{}^{(0)}.$$

There cannot be two different constant values, but conceivably there might be two different distributions which have the same constant potential on S, but this also is impossible. Since the density on the surface is (Sec. 115)

$$\sigma = \frac{1}{4\pi}\frac{\partial V}{\partial n_i},$$

and since $V_2 = V_1$, the normal derivatives are everywhere the same and, therefore, the densities in the two distributions are identical.

There cannot be more than one distribution of a given quantity of matter on S for which the potential is constant on S.

It should be observed that in this distribution of matter on S, every portion of the surface is covered with matter, if S is a closed surface. If it were not so, there would be a path from the interior of S, where the potential is constant, to the exterior, where it is not constant, which did not pass through attracting matter. By Theorem III, Sec. 75, this is impossible and the surface must everywhere be covered, with the possible exception of isolated points and lines at which the density might vanish.

The theorem that the distribution which makes the potential energy a minimum also makes the potential constant in the interior and on the surface is a particular case of a somewhat more general theorem which is due to Gauss.

Reduction to Two Dimensions.—The above argument, without any essential modification, indicates, also, that there can exist but one distribution of a given quantity of matter on any plane contour C for which the contour becomes a level thread; that is, for which the logarithmic potential of the distribution is constant everywhere on C, and therefore within C, if C is closed.

118. Robin's Integral Equation.

—If V_e and V_i are the external and the internal potentials of a closed level layer, then

$$\lim \frac{1}{4\pi} \frac{\partial V_e}{\partial n_e} = -\sigma, \qquad \lim \frac{1}{4\pi} \frac{\partial V_i}{\partial n_e} = 0.$$

This is the familiar discontinuity in the normal derivative of the potential of a surface distribution of matter. If m is a point of the surface, the normal derivative of the potential at m does not have a definite sense.

Suppose m_i is an interior point on the normal through m and infinitely near m, and m_e is an exterior point on the same normal also infinitely near m. If ρ_i and ρ_e are measured from m_i and m_e respectively and φ is the angle between the direction of ρ and the direction of the exterior normal, then (Sec. 66)

$$\frac{\partial V_e}{\partial n_e} = \int_S \frac{\cos \varphi}{\rho_e^2} \sigma d\omega, \qquad \frac{\partial V_i}{\partial n_e} = \int_S \frac{\cos \varphi}{\rho_i^2} \sigma d\omega.$$

Hence

$$\sigma_m = \lim \frac{1}{4\pi} \int_S \frac{\cos \varphi}{\rho_e^2} \sigma d\omega, \qquad 0 = \lim \frac{1}{4\pi} \int_S \frac{\cos \varphi}{\rho_i^2} \sigma d\omega.$$

If ρ_m is measured from the point m itself, the integral

$$I = \int_S \frac{\cos \varphi}{\rho_m^2} \sigma d\omega,$$

which represents the normal component of the attraction of S on m, has a perfectly definite sense and can be evaluated.

Let a plane perpendicular to the normal at m, which is assumed to be a regular point of the surface, be passed through the point m_i. This plane divides the surface S into two parts, an infinitesimal disk s with its center at m, and the rest of the surface Σ. The normal components of the attraction of Σ at the points m and m_i differ infinitely little, since the two points m and m_i differ infinitely little in position. The limit of the normal component of the attraction of s on m_i as m_i approaches m is $2\pi\sigma$ directed towards the exterior, since the limit of the solid angle subtended by s at m_i is 2π (Sec. 8). Hence, the limit of the normal component of the attraction of Σ on m_i also is $2\pi\sigma$ directed toward the interior, since the total attraction on m_i is zero.

The limit of the normal component of the attraction of s at the point m is zero, since the limit of s is a plane disk in which m lies. Therefore the normal component of the attraction of S on m is the limit of the normal component of Σ on m, that is $2\pi\sigma_m$. Hence

$$\left. \begin{aligned} 2\pi\sigma_m &= \int_S \frac{\cos \varphi}{\rho_m^2} \sigma d\omega, \\[2mm] \text{or} \qquad \sigma_m &= \frac{1}{2\pi} \int_S \frac{\cos \varphi}{\rho_m^2} \sigma d\omega, \end{aligned} \right\} \tag{1}$$

which is Robin's integral equation.

If the total mass on S is M, then

$$M = \int_S \sigma d\omega, \tag{2}$$

and the distribution of matter on S is completely defined by Eqs. (1) and (2).

119. Picard's Solution of Robin's Equation.—Combining the general line of thought of Neumann in his method of the arithmetic mean with his own method of successive approxima-

tions, Picard has given the following solution of Robin's equation[1] for a surface which is everywhere convex,

$$\sigma(x, y, z) = \frac{1}{2\pi} \int_S \frac{\cos \varphi}{\rho^2} \sigma(\xi, \eta, \zeta) d\omega,$$

where the σ in the left member is the density of the distribution at the point from which ρ is measured, and in the right member is the density at the surface element $d\omega$.

Let f be any function whatever that is continuous on S. A series of functions, $f_1, f_2, \ldots$ is defined by the relations

$$f_1 = \frac{1}{2\pi} \int \frac{\cos \varphi}{\rho^2} f d\omega,$$

$$f_2 = \frac{1}{2\pi} \int_S \frac{\cos \varphi}{\rho^2} f_1 d\omega,$$

$$\cdots \cdots \cdots \cdots \cdots,$$

$$f_n = \frac{1}{2\pi} \int_S \frac{\cos \varphi}{\rho^2} f_{n-1} d\omega,$$

$$\cdots \cdots \cdots \cdots \cdots$$

It will be shown that, aside from a constant factor, f_n tends toward the function σ which represents the density of the distribution in a level layer.

The first of these equations can be written

$$f_1 = \frac{1}{2\pi} \int_S \frac{f}{\sigma} \frac{\sigma \cos \varphi}{\rho^2} d\omega.$$

Since σ does not vanish on S, let A be the maximum value of the ratio f/σ and B be the minimum; so that $(A + B)/2$ is the mean value. Let α be that portion of the surface for which the ratio f/σ is greater than the mean, and β the portion for which it is less than the mean. Then

$$2\pi f_1 \leqq A \int_\alpha \frac{\sigma \cos \varphi}{\rho^2} d\omega + \frac{A + B}{2} \int_\beta \frac{\sigma \cos \varphi}{\rho^2} d\omega,$$

and

$$2\pi f_1 \geqq \frac{A + B}{2} \int_\alpha \frac{\sigma \cos \varphi}{\rho^2} d\omega + B \int_\beta \frac{\sigma \cos \varphi}{\rho^2} d\omega.$$

[1] PICARD, É., "Traité D'Analyse," Vol. I, p. 203.

These equations can be rearranged so as to read

$$2\pi f_1 \leqq A \int_S \frac{\sigma \cos \varphi}{\rho^2} d\omega - \frac{A - B}{2} \int_\beta \frac{\sigma \cos \varphi}{\rho^2} d\omega,$$

$$2\pi f_1 \geqq B \int_S \frac{\sigma \cos \varphi}{\rho^2} d\omega + \frac{A - B}{2} \int_\alpha \frac{\sigma \cos \varphi}{\rho^2} d\omega.$$

The integral over the entire surface is $2\pi\sigma$. For the other integrals, let

$$2\pi\theta_\alpha = \int_\alpha \frac{\sigma \cos \varphi}{\rho^2} d\omega, \qquad 2\pi\theta_\beta = \int_\beta \frac{\sigma \cos \varphi}{\rho^2} d\omega,$$

so that θ_α and θ_β are each less than σ (the integrand being everywhere positive). With this notation, the above inequalities become

$$\frac{f_1}{\sigma} \leqq A - \frac{A - B}{2} \frac{\theta_\beta}{\sigma},$$

$$\frac{f_1}{\sigma} \geqq B + \frac{A - B}{2} \frac{\theta_\alpha}{\sigma},$$

for any point on the surface.

If two different points are taken and are distinguished by the subscripts 1 and 2, these inequalities give

$$\frac{f_{11}}{\sigma_1} \leqq A - \frac{A - B}{2} \frac{\theta_{1\beta}}{\sigma_1}, \qquad \frac{f_{11}}{\sigma_1} \geqq B + \frac{A - B}{2} \frac{\theta_{1\alpha}}{\sigma_1},$$

$$\frac{f_{12}}{\sigma_2} \leqq A - \frac{A - B}{2} \frac{\theta_{2\beta}}{\sigma_2}, \qquad \frac{f_{12}}{\sigma_2} \geqq B + \frac{A - B}{2} \frac{\theta_{2\alpha}}{\sigma_2}.$$

Hence

$$\frac{f_{11}}{\sigma_1} - \frac{f_{12}}{\sigma_2} \leqq (A - B) - \frac{A - B}{2}\left(\frac{\theta_{1\beta}}{\sigma_1} + \frac{\theta_{2\alpha}}{\sigma_2}\right),$$

$$\frac{f_{11}}{\sigma_1} - \frac{f_{12}}{\sigma_2} \geqq (B - A) + \frac{A - B}{2}\left(\frac{\theta_{1\alpha}}{\sigma_1} + \frac{\theta_{2\beta}}{\sigma_2}\right).$$

The coefficients of $(A - B)/2$ in the right members of these equations are each less than 2; therefore

$$\left|\frac{f_{11}}{\sigma_1} - \frac{f_{12}}{\sigma_2}\right| < \mu(A - B),$$

where μ is some positive number less than 1. Since this inequality holds for any two points on S, it follows that if A_1 is the maximum value of f_1/σ and B_1 is its minimum value

$$(A_1 - B_1) < \mu(A - B).$$

In a similar manner, it is shown that

$$(A_n - B_n) < \mu^n(A - B),$$

where A_n and B_n are the maximum and minimum values of the ratio f_n/σ. Consequently, if f_n tends toward a limit at every point of S, the ratio f_n/σ tends toward a constant value, since the difference between its maximum and minimum values tends toward zero.

Now

$$f_n = \frac{1}{2\pi} \int_S \frac{\bar{f}_{n-1}}{\bar{\sigma}} \frac{\bar{\sigma} \cos \bar{\varphi}}{\bar{\rho}^2} d\omega,$$

and

$$1 = \frac{1}{2\pi\sigma} \int_S \frac{\bar{\sigma} \cos \bar{\varphi}}{\bar{\rho}^2} d\omega,$$

the dashes on the letters indicating the value of the function at the surface element $d\omega$. On multiplying the second equation by f_{n-1} and subtracting from the first, there results

$$f_n - f_{n-1} = \frac{1}{2\pi} \int_S \left(\frac{\bar{f}_{n-1}}{\bar{\sigma}} - \frac{f_{n-1}}{\sigma} \right) \frac{\bar{\sigma} \cos \bar{\varphi}}{\bar{\rho}^2} d\omega;$$

and since

$$\left| \frac{\bar{f}_{n-1}}{\bar{\sigma}} - \frac{f_{n-1}}{\sigma} \right| < \mu^{n-1}(A - B),$$

it follows that

$$|f_n - f_{n-1}| < \mu^{n-1}(A - B)\sigma < \mu^{n-1}(A - B)\sigma_0,$$

where σ_0 is the maximum value of σ.

By writing

$$f_n = f_0 + (f_1 - f_0) + (f_2 - f_1) + \cdots + (f_n - f_{n-1}),$$

it is seen that f_n can be regarded as a sum of terms which decrease like the terms of a geometric progression. It has, therefore, a definite limit, and if C is some constant.

$$\lim_{n=\infty} f_n = C\sigma.$$

120. Example of a Level Layer.—Suppose two particles, each of unit mass, are placed at the points O_1 and O_2 (Fig. 71), the distance between the points being $2l$. If the distances of the point P from O_1 and O_2 are ρ_1 and ρ_2, the expression for the potential at P is

$$V = \frac{1}{\rho_1} + \frac{1}{\rho_2},$$

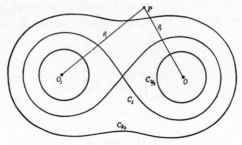

Fig. 71.

and along an equipotential surface V is constant. If the value of this constant is $2a/l$ the equation of the surface is

$$\frac{1}{\rho_1} + \frac{1}{\rho_2} = \frac{2a}{l}. \tag{1}$$

The force F which is acting at P is the resultant of two forces $1/\rho_1{}^2$ and $1/\rho_2{}^2$ directed toward O_1 and O_2 respectively. Its magnitude as given by the parallelogram law is

$$F = \left[\left(\frac{1}{\rho_1} + \frac{1}{\rho_2} \right) \left(\frac{1}{\rho_1{}^3} + \frac{1}{\rho_2{}^3} \right) - \frac{4l^2}{\rho_1{}^3 \rho_2{}^3} \right]^{\frac{1}{2}}.$$

Hence, a level layer can be constructed by distributing matter over the level surface, Eq. (1), in such a way that the density is

$$\sigma = \frac{1}{4\pi} \left[\left(\frac{1}{\rho_1} + \frac{1}{\rho_2} \right) \left(\frac{1}{\rho_1{}^3} + \frac{1}{\rho_2{}^3} \right) - \frac{4l^2}{\rho_1{}^3 \rho_2{}^3} \right]^{\frac{1}{2}}, \tag{2}$$

and this level layer attracts points outside of it just as the particles at O_1 and O_2 do. For $a = 3/4$, the level layer is a single closed surface of revolution which contains both of the attracting particles. For $a = 1$, the level layer has the shape of an hour glass, at the point midway of which the force F vanishes and therefore, the density σ also. For $a = 3/2$, the surface consists of two ovals each of which contains one of the particles, and therefore (Sec. 115) each oval of the level layer, for particles outside of it, is equivalent to the particle which is contained within it. If the particle at O_1 is left undisturbed, but the particle at O_2 is replaced by a level layer which is a single oval, the system is equivalent to the two particles at O_1 and O_2 for particles outside of the oval. The potential inside of the oval is constant; therefore, the attraction of the oval on an interior point is equal and opposite to the attraction of the particle at O_1. The level layer surrounding O_2, taken by itself, is centrobaric for outside particles, and attracts inside particles just as though all of its mass were negative (repellant) and were concentrated at the point O_1.

121. Level Layers on Prolate Spheroids.—The equipotential surfaces of a homogeneous straight rod are prolate spheroids (Sec. 98). If ρ_1 and ρ_2 are distances measured from the ends of the rod, the equation of these surfaces in bi-polar coordinates is

$$\rho_1 + \rho_2 = 2a,$$

where a is the polar semi-axis.

Let λ and μ be parameters defined by the relations

$$\rho_1 + \rho_2 = 2\lambda, \qquad \rho_1 - \rho_2 = 2\mu,$$

and let θ be the longitude with respect to a polar axis, which coincides with the rod. The surface $\lambda = \text{const.}$ is an ellipsoid; the surface $\mu = \text{const.}$ is one of the sheets of a two-sheeted hyperboloid of revolution; and $\theta = \text{const.}$ is a plane. These three surfaces are confocal and intersect each other orthogonally. If the length of the rod is $2l$, the equations of transformation for rectangular coordinates are

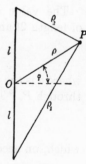

Fig. 72.

$$x = \frac{1}{l}\sqrt{(\lambda^2 - l^2)(l^2 - \mu^2)} \cos \theta,$$
$$y = \frac{1}{l}\sqrt{(\lambda^2 - l^2)(l^2 - \mu^2)} \sin \theta, \qquad (0)$$
$$z = \frac{\lambda\mu}{l},$$

the coordinates λ, μ, θ being restricted to the intervals

$$\lambda \geqq l, \qquad -l \leqq \mu \leqq +l, \qquad 0 \leqq \theta \leqq 2\pi.$$

The λ-direction is normal to the ellipsoid, the μ-direction is normal to the hyperboloid, and the θ-direction is normal to the plane in the sense of longitude increasing.

If $P(x, y, z)$ is a point on an ellipsoid for which $\lambda = a$, the *normal* displacement of the point p due to an infinitesimal change in the coordinates is

$$dn = \sqrt{\left(\frac{\partial x}{\partial \lambda}\right)^2 + \left(\frac{\partial y}{\partial \lambda}\right)^2 + \left(\frac{\partial z}{\partial \lambda}\right)^2} d\lambda = \sqrt{\frac{\lambda^2 - \mu^2}{\lambda^2 - l^2}} d\lambda, \qquad (1)$$

for the value $\lambda = a$. Similarly the displacements along a meridian and along a circle of latitude on the ellipsoid are respectively,

$$\sqrt{\left(\frac{\partial x}{\partial \mu}\right)^2 + \left(\frac{\partial y}{\partial \mu}\right)^2 + \left(\frac{\partial z}{\partial \mu}\right)^2} d\mu = \sqrt{\frac{\lambda^2 - \mu^2}{l^2 - \mu^2}} d\mu, \qquad (2)$$

and

$$\sqrt{\left(\frac{\partial x}{\partial \theta}\right)^2 + \left(\frac{\partial y}{\partial \theta}\right)^2 + \left(\frac{\partial z}{\partial \theta}\right)^2} d\theta = \frac{1}{l}\sqrt{(\lambda^2 - l^2)(l^2 - \mu)} d\theta, \quad (3)$$

also for the value $\lambda = a$.

The value of the potential of a homogeneous straight rod of length $2l$ and mass unity at a given point P is

$$V = \frac{1}{2l} \log \frac{a + l}{a - l}, \qquad (4)$$

where a is the polar semi-axis of the prolate spheroid which passes through P. The normal derivative of V is

$$\frac{\partial V}{\partial n} = \frac{\partial V}{\partial a} \frac{\partial a}{\partial n},$$

which, on account of Eqs. (1) and (4), becomes

$$\frac{\partial V}{\partial n} = \frac{-1}{\sqrt{(a^2 - l^2)(a^2 - \mu^2)}}. \qquad (5)$$

Hence, the density of the level layer on this spheroid is

$$\sigma = -\frac{1}{4\pi} \frac{\partial V}{\partial n} = \frac{1}{4\pi\sqrt{(a^2 - l^2)(a^2 - \mu^2)}}.$$

The element of area on the spheroid is the area of the rectangle of which the sides are given in Eqs. (2) and (3). That is,

$$d\omega = \frac{1}{l}\sqrt{(a^2 - l^2)(a^2 - \mu^2)} d\mu d\theta;$$

and the element of mass is $\sigma d\omega$, or

$$dm = \frac{1}{4\pi l} d\mu d\theta.$$

If dm_c is the element of mass in a collar of width $d\mu$, the integration of this equation gives

$$dm_c = \frac{d\mu}{2l}, \tag{6}$$

and the integration with respect to μ from $-l$ to $+l$ gives the total mass $+1$, as of course it should. The simplicity of Eq. (6), however, shows a simple distribution of the mass in latitude. The distribution is uniform with respect to μ, and therefore, uniform with respect to z, also; that is the mass included between any two planes which intersect the spheroid and which are parallel to the equatorial plane is proportional to the distance between the planes. As a varies, the mass included between any two hyperboloids remains constant.

If the rod is regarded merely as an auxiliary concept the spheroidal level layers being the principal one, it is evident from Eq. (4) that there are infinitely many spheroids, for a given mass, for which V has a fixed value, say unity. On taking $l = ae$, where e is the eccentricity of a meridian section, Eq. (4),

$$2l = \log\frac{1 + e}{1 - e},$$

defines the relation between l and e. The potential energy of a unit mass distributed as a level layer on each of these surfaces is the same. No work is required in passing from one of these distributions to another. It is interesting to note that of all of these spheroids, which vary in shape from the sphere with a radius unity to a straight line of infinite length, the sphere is the one which encloses a minimum volume.

122. Level Layers on Ellipsoids.—It was proved in Sec. 11 that a homogeneous ellipsoidal homoeoid attracts an interior particle equally in all directions, so that the resulting attraction is everywhere zero. This means, of course, that the potential is constant inside the homoeoid, and that if the shell is infinitely thin the surface is an equipotential surface. If the distribution of matter is a surface distribution, the density is proportional to the thickness of an infinitely thin homoeoid. That is

$$h_1 dn.$$

where h_1 is a factor of proportionality.

If $f(x, y, z) = 0$ is the surface, and

$$R = \sqrt{\left(\frac{\partial f}{\partial x}\right)^2 + \left(\frac{\partial f}{\partial y}\right)^2 + \left(\frac{\partial f}{\partial z}\right)^2},$$

then, Eq. (54.4),

$$\frac{\partial f}{\partial n} = R, \quad \text{and} \quad dn = \frac{1}{R}df.$$

Since df is constant over the surface,

$$\sigma = \frac{h_2}{R},$$

where h_2 is a constant factor of proportionality.

The equation

$$f(x, y, z) = \frac{x^2}{a^2 - q} + \frac{y^2}{b^2 - q} + \frac{z^2}{-q} - 1 = 0, \qquad a^2 > b^2, \qquad (1)$$

represents a family of confocal conicoids, if q is regarded as a parameter. The three roots of this equation, when regarded as a cubic in q, are the elliptic coordinates of the point x, y, z; thus[1]

$$\left. \begin{aligned} x^2 &= \frac{(a^2 - q_1)(a^2 - q_2)(a^2 - q_3)}{a^2(a^2 - b^2)}, \\ y^2 &= \frac{(q_1 - b^2)(b^2 - q_2)(b^2 - q_3)}{b^2(a^2 - b^2)}, \\ z^2 &= -\frac{q_1 q_2 q_3}{a^2 b^2}. \end{aligned} \right\} \qquad (2)$$

The order of the magnitude of the roots is

$$a^2 > q_1 > b^2 > q_2 > 0 > q_3.$$

and $q = q_3$ in Eq. (1) is an e'lipsoid.

If[2]

$$R_1^2 = \frac{(q_1 - q_2)(q_1 - q_3)}{4(a^2 - q_1)(q_1 - b^2)q_1} = \frac{1}{4}\frac{\partial f}{\partial q}\bigg|_{q = q_1},$$

$$R_2^2 = \frac{(q_1 - q_2)(q_2 - q_3)}{4(a^2 - q_2)(b^2 - q_2)q_2} = \frac{1}{4}\frac{\partial f}{\partial q}\bigg|_{q = q_2},$$

$$R_3^2 = \frac{-(q_1 - q_3)(q_2 - q_3)}{4(a^2 - q_3)(b^2 - q_3)q_3} = \frac{1}{4}\frac{\partial f}{\partial q}\bigg|_{q = q_3},$$

the components of the displacement of the point x, y, z due to an infinitesimal change in the elliptic coordinates are $R_1 dq_1$, $R_2 dq_2$, and $R_3 dq_3$. These three components are mutually

---

[1] "Statics and the Dynamics of a Particle," p. 355.

[2] Ibid., p. 359.

orthogonal, the first two lying in the plane tangent to the ellipsoid, and the third being normal to the ellipsoid.

It follows at once from Eq. (1) that

$$\left(\frac{\partial f}{\partial x}\right)^2 + \left(\frac{\partial f}{\partial y}\right)^2 + \left(\frac{\partial f}{\partial z}\right)^2 = 4\frac{\partial f}{\partial q}\bigg|_{q\,=\,q_3},$$

and therefore

$$R^2 = 4R_3{}^2.$$

The density in the level layer on the ellipsoid is then

$$\sigma = \frac{h_2}{2}\sqrt{\frac{-q_3(a^2 - q_3)(b^2 - q_3)}{(q_1 - q_3)(q_2 - q_3)}};$$

or, since q_3 is constant on the ellipsoid, the constant factors can all be included in a single factor of proportionality, and then

$$\sigma = \frac{h}{\sqrt{(q_1 - q_3)(q_2 - q_3)}}.$$

The element of area on the ellipsoid evidently is

$$d\omega = R_1 R_2 dq_1 dq_2,$$

or

$$d\omega = \frac{(q_1 - q_2)\sqrt{(q_1 - q_3)(q_2 - q_3)}}{4\sqrt{(a^2 - q_1)(q_1 - b^2)q_1(a^2 - q_2)(b^2 - q_2)q_2}}dq_1 dq_2;$$

and the element of mass, $dm = \sigma d\omega$, is

$$dm = \frac{h(q_1 - q_2)dq_1 dq_2}{4\sqrt{(a^2 - q_1)(q_1 - b^2)q_1 \cdot (a^2 - q_2)(b^2 - q_2)q_2}}. \tag{3}$$

This expression for the element of mass is independent of q_3, and therefore, it holds for each member of the family of confocal ellipsoids. The constant h can be determined by the condition that the mass of the level layer is equal to unity. Hence, on integrating over an octant of the ellipsoid,

$$\frac{1}{2h} = \int_{b^2}^{a^2}\int_0^{b^2} \frac{(q_1 - q_2)dq_1 dq_2}{\sqrt{(a^2 - q_1)(q_1 - b^2)q_1 \cdot (a^2 - q_2)(b^2 - q_2)q_2}}$$

$$= \int_{b^2}^{a^2} \frac{(q_1 - b^2)dq_1}{\sqrt{(a^2 - q_1)(q_1 - b^2)q_1}}\int_0^{b^2} \frac{dq_2}{\sqrt{(a^2 - q_2)(b^2 - q_2)q_2}}$$

$$+ \int_{b^2}^{a^2} \frac{dq_1}{\sqrt{(a^2 - q_1)(q_1 - b^2)q_1}}\int_0^{b^2} \frac{(b^2 - q_2)dq_2}{\sqrt{(a^2 - q_2)(b^2 - q_2)q_2}}.$$

The substitutions $\sqrt{a^2 - q_1} = \sqrt{a^2 - b^2}\sin\varphi$ in the first and third integrals, and $\sqrt{q_2} = b\sin\varphi$ in the second and fourth integrals, effect the reductions to Legendre's normal forms, and it is readily found that

$$\frac{1}{2h} = 4(EK_1 + E_1K - KK_1),$$

where K and E are Legendre's complete elliptic integrals of the first and second kind, for the modulus

$$k^2 = \frac{a^2 - b^2}{a^2},$$

and K_1 and E_1 are the same quantities for the complementary modulus $k_1^2 = 1 - k^2$. But, as Legendre proved,

$$EK_1 + E_1K - KK_1 = \frac{\pi}{2},$$

whatever value k^2 may have. Hence, for a level layer of unit mass

$$h = \frac{1}{4\pi}, \quad \text{and} \quad \sigma = \frac{1}{4\pi\sqrt{(q_1 - q_3)(q_2 - q_3)}}. \quad (4)$$

For $q_3 = 0$, the ellipsoid is a plane double elliptical sheet. Therefore, a single plane ellipse will be a level layer of mass unity if the density on it is

$$\sigma = \frac{1}{2\pi\sqrt{q_1 q_2}}.$$

It is found from Eq. (2) that, for $q_3 = 0$,

$$\frac{x^2}{a^2} + \frac{y^2}{b^2} = 1 - \frac{q_1 q_2}{a^2 b^2}.$$

Hence, the lines of constant density are ellipses which are *similar* to the given ellipse. The density at the edge ($q_2 = 0$) is infinite, and at the center, where $q_1 = a^2$ and $q_2 = b^2$, it is

$$\sigma_0 = \frac{1}{2\pi ab}.$$

The average density is twice the density at the center.

It will be shown in the next section that the equipotential surfaces of this elliptical disk are the confocal ellipsoids. Equation (3) shows that if the double elliptical disk should expand through the series of confocal ellipsoids, retaining always the constant mass unity, the same element of mass would be found in the tube defined by q_1, $q_1 + dq_1$, q_2, $q_2 + dq_2$, each constant. The density would vary from one surface to another, but the element of mass would remain the same.

123. The Potential of Ellipsoidal Level Layers.—The direct computation of the potential of an ellipsoidal level layer involves very difficult integrations which, probably, have never been carried out. But the potentials can be obtained without difficulty from the expressions for the potential of a homogeneous solid ellipsoid simply by differentiation.

The potential of a homogeneous, solid ellipsoid at an exterior point x, y, z, is Eq. (36.1)

$$U = \pi\sigma\alpha\beta\gamma \int_{\kappa}^{\infty} \left(1 - \frac{x^2}{\alpha^2 + s} - \frac{y^2}{\beta^2 + s} - \frac{z^2}{\gamma^2 + s}\right) \frac{ds}{\sqrt{(\alpha^2 + s)(\beta^2 + s)(\gamma^2 + s)}},$$

where α, β, γ, are the semi-axes of the ellipsoid and κ is the positive root of the equation

$$\frac{x^2}{\alpha^2 + \kappa} + \frac{y^2}{\beta^2 + \kappa} + \frac{z^2}{\gamma^2 + \kappa} = 1.$$

The potential of the similar ellipsoid whose axes are $(1 + \lambda)\alpha$, $(1 + \lambda)\beta$, and $(1 + \lambda)\gamma$ at the same point x, y, z is

$$W = \pi\sigma\alpha\beta\gamma \int_{\kappa_2}^{\infty} \left((1 + \lambda)^2 - \frac{x^2}{\alpha^2 + s} - \frac{y^2}{\beta^2 + s} - \frac{z^2}{\gamma^2 + s}\right) \frac{ds}{\sqrt{(\alpha^2 + s)(\beta^2 + s)(\gamma^2 + s)}},$$

where κ_2 is the positive root of the equation

$$\frac{x^2}{\alpha^2 + \kappa_2} + \frac{y^2}{\beta^2 + \kappa_2} + \frac{z^2}{\gamma^2 + \kappa_2} = (1 + \lambda)^2.$$

The potential of the shell which has been added is, therefore,

$$V = W - U;$$

and for λ very small

$$V = \frac{\partial W}{\partial \lambda}\bigg|_{\lambda = 0} d\lambda.$$

The lower limit of the integral, κ_2, is, of course, a function of λ, but this fact can be ignored in the differentiation, since the function within the parenthesis vanishes for $s = \kappa_2$. On differentiating then with respect to λ so far as λ occurs explicitly and then setting λ equal to zero, there results

$$V = 2\pi\sigma\alpha\beta\gamma \cdot d\lambda \int_{\kappa}^{\infty} \frac{ds}{\sqrt{(\alpha^2 + s)(\beta^2 + s)(\gamma^2 + s)}}.$$

The mass of the ellipsoid is

$$M = \frac{4}{3}\pi\sigma\alpha\beta\gamma(1 + \lambda)^3,$$

and the mass of the infinitely thin shell is

$$dM = 4\pi\sigma\alpha\beta\gamma d\lambda.$$

Since the mass of this shell is unity it follows that

$$1 = 4\pi\sigma\alpha\beta\gamma d\lambda,$$

and therefore, the potential of the ellipsoidal level layer of unit mass is

$$V = \frac{1}{2}\int_\kappa^\infty \frac{ds}{\sqrt{(\alpha^2 + s)(\beta^2 + s)(\gamma^2 + s)}}.$$

At the surface $\kappa = 0$, and, since the potential is continuous across the surface and constant in the interior, the value of the potential at all interior points is

$$V = \frac{1}{2}\int_0^\infty \frac{ds}{\sqrt{(\alpha^2 + s)(\beta^2 + s)(\gamma^2 + s)}}$$

For the elliptical disk $\gamma^2 = 0$. The potential is constant over the surface for which κ is constant. That is, each member of the family of confocal ellipsoids is a level surface.

124. Layers of Finite Thickness.—If an infinitesimal amount of matter is distributed over a level surface in such a way, however, that the surface density is everywhere proportional to $\partial V/\partial n$, the potential due to the matter so distributed is constant within the surface, and it will remain constant if the matter expands so as to fill the volume between two infinitely close level surfaces, the amount of matter associated with each element of surface remaining proportional to $\partial V/\partial n$ just as before. The volume density in this new distribution, however, is proportional to $(\partial V/\partial n)^2$.

In order to show this, suppose the amount of matter distributed is mdl and that it is distributed in a shell of uniform thickness dl. The amount of matter associated with each element of surface is

$$\frac{1}{4\pi}\frac{\partial V}{\partial n}d\omega dl;$$

and this amount of matter is expanded to fill the element of volume $d\omega dn$, dn being the distance between the two level surfaces. If σ is the volume density

$$\sigma d\omega dn = \frac{1}{4\pi}\frac{\partial V}{\partial n}d\omega dl.$$

After removing the common factor $d\omega$ and then multiplying through by $\partial V/\partial n$, this expression becomes

$$\sigma dV = \frac{1}{4\pi}\left(\frac{\partial V}{\partial n}\right)^2 dl;$$

and, since dV and dl are constant over the surface, this equation can be written

$$\sigma = h\left(\frac{\partial V}{\partial n}\right)^2 = hF^2, \tag{1}$$

where h is constant over the surface, and F is the intensity of the force at the point under consideration. This distribution of matter leaves the level surfaces undisturbed. Infinitely many such layers can be built up into a shell of finite thickness for which the internal potential is constant, and the external equipotential surfaces are the same as for the original mass. If the total mass of the shell is M, its attraction on particles exterior to it is just the same as the attraction of the original mass. The factor of proportionality h in Eq. (1) may vary from layer to layer in any manner whatever, continuously or discretely, but in any given layer the volume density is proportional to the square of the resultant force at that point.

The electric image of any of these shells in any sphere whose center lies inside of the shell is a centrobaric body (Sec. 114) for exterior particles. Green's theory, therefore, shows how to construct an infinite variety of bodies which possess the interesting property of attracting outside particles just as though the body itself were a particle.

125. A Finite Shell Bounded by Confocal Spheroids.—In Sec. 121 a level layer was constructed on a prolate spheroid. As it is desired to extend these results to the construction of a shell of finite thickness bounded by two confocal prolate spheroids, the notation and formulas of that section will be useful in the present one.

For a homogeneous rod of length of length $2l$ it is convenient to transform to the coordinates λ, μ, θ which were defined in Eq. (121.0), namely:

$$x = \frac{1}{l}\sqrt{(\lambda^2 - l^2)(l^2 - \mu^2)} \cos \theta,$$

$$y = \frac{1}{l}\sqrt{(\lambda^2 - l^2)(l^2 - \mu^2)} \sin \theta,$$

$$z = \frac{\lambda\mu}{l}.$$

If the mass of the rod is unity, its potential at any point on the surface of the prolate spheroid which is confocal with the ends of the rod and for which λ is the polar semi-axis is, Eq. (121.4),

$$V = \frac{1}{2l} \log \frac{\lambda + l}{\lambda - l}. \tag{1}$$

The force acting at any point P of this surface is given by Eq. (121.5)

$$F = \frac{\partial V}{\partial n} = \frac{-1}{\sqrt{(\lambda^2 - l^2)(\lambda^2 - \mu^2)}},$$

and therefore, the volume density at P is

$$\sigma = h\left(\frac{\partial V}{\partial n}\right)^2 = \frac{h}{(\lambda^2 - l^2)(\lambda^2 - \mu^2)},$$

where h is constant over the surface of the spheroid, but can vary from one spheroid to another. That is, h can be a function of λ but not a function of μ or θ. Let this function be chosen so that in the plane of the equator, where $\mu = 0$, the density is constant and equal to σ_0. Then $h = \sigma_0\lambda^2(\lambda^2 - l^2)$, and

$$\sigma = \frac{\sigma_0\lambda^2}{\lambda^2 - \mu^2}. \tag{2}$$

Since the three displacements defined in Eqs. (121.1), (121.2) and (121.3) are mutually orthogonal, the element of volume is obtained by taking their product. That is

$$d\tau = \frac{\lambda^2 - \mu^2}{l}d\lambda d\mu d\theta;$$

and the element of mass, $dm = \sigma d\tau$, is

$$dm = \frac{\sigma_0}{l}\lambda^2 d\lambda d\mu d\theta.$$

Hence, if a is the polar semi-axis of the outer surface, and b that of the inner one, the total mass M is

$$M = \frac{\sigma_0}{l}\int_b^a \int_{-l}^{+l} \int_0^{2\pi} \lambda^2 d\lambda d\mu d\theta \left.\vphantom{\int}\right\}$$
$$= 4\pi\sigma_0 \int_b^a \lambda^2 d\lambda = \frac{4}{3}\pi\sigma_0(a^3 - b^3), \quad (3)$$

which is the same as that of a homogeneous spherical shell of which the bounding spheres have the radii a and b and the density of which is the equatorial density of the non-homogeneous spheroidal shell.

The surfaces of constant density are defined (Eq. (2)) by the relation $\mu^2/\lambda^2 =$ a constant. Since

$$\rho_1 + \rho_2 = 2\lambda, \qquad \rho_1 - \rho_2 = 2\mu,$$

it is evident that, if the ratio λ/μ is constant, so also is the ratio ρ_2/ρ_1 constant. The surfaces of constant density are, therefore, spheres which have their centers on the axis of the spheroid; furthermore these spheres divide the line of the half-rod externally and internally in the same ratio, as is indicated by the dotted lines in Fig. 73.

It is known from the theory

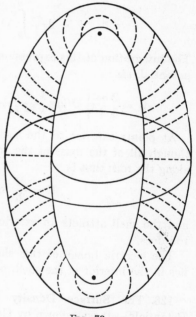

Fig. 73.

of Sec. 115 that this spheroidal shell possesses the property that its internal potential is constant. It is desired to ascertain the value of this constant.

If an infinitesimal amount of matter dM is distributed over a level surface in accordance with Eq. (2), its potential at external points and on the level surface itself is the same as though it were uniformly distributed over the line of length $2l$ which joins the two foci. Equation (1) then gives

$$dV = \frac{1}{2l}\log\frac{\lambda + l}{\lambda - l}dM;$$

and this is the value of the potential throughout the interior of a shell of infinitesimal thickness which is bounded by two level surfaces, the density of which is defined by Eq. (2). From Eq. (3), it is found that

$$dM = 4\pi\sigma_0\lambda^2 d\lambda.$$

Hence

$$dV = 2\pi\frac{\sigma_0}{l}\lambda^2 \log \frac{\lambda + l}{\lambda - l}d\lambda,$$

and for the shell of finite thickness

$$V = 2\pi\frac{\sigma_0}{l}\int_b^a \lambda^2 \log \frac{\lambda + l}{\lambda - l}d\lambda.$$

The integration of this expression gives the value of the interior potential, *viz.*:

$$V = \frac{2}{3}\frac{\sigma_0}{l}\pi\left[\lambda^3 \log \frac{\lambda + l}{\lambda - l} + l^3 \log (\lambda^2 - l^2) + \lambda^2 l\right]_b^a.$$

At points exterior to the shell the potential is the same as though all of the mass of the shell were uniformly distributed along the rod; that is

$$V = \frac{M}{2l} \log \frac{\lambda + l}{\lambda - l},$$

and the shell attracts an exterior particle just the same as the rod does.

The electric image of this shell in any sphere whose center lies in the interior of the shell, is, of course, a centrobaric body.

126. The Surface Density Necessary to Produce Given Potentials.—It was shown by Green as one of the earliest applications of his theory that if a closed surface S is given, if $V_i(x, y, z)$ is harmonic (Sec. 62) inside of S and $V_e(x, y, z)$ is harmonic outside of S, vanishing at infinity in the order of $1/r$, and if $V_i = V_e$ on S, there exists one and only one distribution of matter on S for which V_i is the internal potential and V_e is the external potential.

In order to prove this, let x, y, z be the coordinates of a point p inside of S and ξ, η, ζ the coordinates of any point on S. If the distance between these two points is

$$\rho = \sqrt{(\xi - x)^2 + (\eta - y)^2 + (\zeta - z)^2},$$

the value of V_i at the point p is given by the surface integral, Eq. (63.3),

$$V_i(x, y, z) = \frac{1}{4\pi} \int_S \left[\frac{1}{\rho} \frac{\partial V_i}{\partial n_e} - V_i \frac{\partial}{\partial n_e}\left(\frac{1}{\rho}\right) \right] d\omega, \tag{1}$$

the external normal derivatives being taken.

Outside of S the function $1/\rho$ is harmonic. The function V_e also is harmonic and vanishes at infinity in the order of $1/r$. Hence, as is proved in Sec. 63 for an exterior point,

$$0 = \frac{1}{4\pi} \int_S \left[\frac{1}{\rho} \frac{\partial V_e}{\partial n_i} - V_e \frac{\partial}{\partial n_i}\left(\frac{1}{\rho}\right) \right] d\omega. \tag{2}$$

In Eq. (1), the normal derivative is taken outward with respect to S, and in Eq. (2) it is taken inward. The inward normal derivative and the outward normal derivative of $1/\rho$ differ only in sign; on the surface S, $V_i = V_e$; hence, on taking the sum of Eqs. (1) and (2), it is found that

$$V_i(x, y, z) = \frac{1}{4\pi} \int_S \left[\frac{\partial V_i}{\partial n_e} + \frac{\partial V_e}{\partial n_i} \right] \frac{d\omega}{\rho}. \tag{3}$$

If the point p, at which the potential is evaluated, lies outside of S, it is necessary only to interchange the subscripts e and i in Eqs. (1) and (2), and therefore, also in Eq. (3); that is

$$V_e(x, y, z) = \frac{1}{4\pi} \int_S \left[\frac{\partial V_i}{\partial n_e} + \frac{\partial V_e}{\partial n_i} \right] \frac{d\omega}{\rho}; \tag{4}$$

the form of the right member remaining unaltered.

Now let a distribution of matter be made on S in such a way that the surface density is

$$\sigma = \frac{1}{4\pi} \left[\frac{\partial V_i}{\partial n_e} + \frac{\partial V_e}{\partial n_i} \right], \tag{5}$$

which is definite and unique since the normal derivatives of V_i and V_e are definite and unique. The potential due to this distribution of matter is

$$V = \int_S \sigma \frac{d\omega}{\rho}.$$

If the point at which V is evaluated lies inside of S, Eq. (3) shows that $V = V_i$, and if it lies outside of S, Eq. (4) shows that $V = V_e$. Hence, one and the same distribution of matter on S produces the potential V_i inside of S and the potential V_e outside of S.

127. Green's Problem.—The functions V_e and V_i are not as independent as the above proposition might lead one to infer. Indeed, if V_e, harmonic outside of S and vanishing at infinity, is given arbitrarily, there exists, at most, but one function V_i which is harmonic inside of S and equal to V_e on S. Suppose there are two such functions, and that the second function is $V_i + W$. Then W is harmonic inside of S and equal to zero on S. It is, therefore, (Theorem I, Sec. 75) equal to zero everywhere inside of S, and there can be but one function, if any at all, that is harmonic inside of S and equal to V_e on S.

Suppose the exterior potential is given, then Green's problem for the interior of a surface can be formulated as follows:

Green's Interior Problem.—*Given a closed surface S, does there exist a function $V(x, y, z)$, which is harmonic within S and which takes a given continuous set of values on S?*

The equation, Eq. (63.3),

$$V_i(x, y, z) = \frac{1}{4\pi} \int_S \left[\frac{1}{\rho} \frac{\partial V_i}{\partial n} - V_i \frac{\partial}{\partial n}\left(\frac{1}{\rho}\right) \right] d\omega \qquad (1)$$

requires a knowledge not only of the values of V_i but also of the values of $\partial V_i/\partial n$ on S. But since, if the function V_i exists at all, it is unique, V_i and $\partial V_i/\partial n$ are not independent, and Green's formula requires more information than the question pre-supposes.

Green himself observed that if there exists a function

$$G = \frac{1}{\rho} + H, \qquad (2)$$

in which H is harmonic inside of S, equal to $-1/\rho$ on S, so that G vanishes on S, and admits a finite well defined normal derivative on S, the value of V_i at any interior point is given by the equation

$$V_i(x, y, z) = -\frac{1}{4\pi} \int_S V_i \frac{\partial G}{\partial n} d\omega, \qquad (3)$$

an equation which is obtained from Corollary I in Sec. 63 by taking $\varphi = V_i$ and $\varphi_1 = G$, and remembering that $G = 0$ on S. The function G, which is known as Green's function, is associated with the surface S, and is entirely independent of the function V_t.

The problem, therefore, can be re-stated as follows: *Given a closed surface S and a point p within it at which ρ vanishes, does* *there exist a function* $G = \dfrac{1}{\rho} + H$, *in which H is harmonic inside of S and equal to* $-1/\rho$ *on S?*

Evidently a similar problem exists for the region exterior to the surface S. It can be stated as follows:

Green's Exterior Problem.—*Given a closed surface S, does there exist a function* $V_e(x, y, z)$, *which is harmonic outside of S, vanishes at infinity, and takes a given continuous set of values on S?*

The equivalent reduced problem is

Given a closed surface S and a point p outside of it at which ρ *vanishes, does there exist a function* $G = \dfrac{1}{\rho} + H$, *in which H is harmonic outside of S, vanishes at infinity and is equal to* $-1/\rho$ *on S?*

128. Certain Physical Considerations.—From certain physical considerations, Green was satisfied that the answer to these questions is in the affirmative. Suppose the surface S is a perfect conductor of electricity which is maintained at zero potential under all circumstances by a wire, which also is a perfect conductor, connected with the earth. If a unit particle of positive electricity is placed at a point p inside of S a certain charge of electricity is thereby induced upon S. The potential at any other point inside of S, due to both charges of electricity, is

$$G = \frac{1}{\rho} + H,$$

where $1/\rho$ is the potential due to the unit charge at p, and H is the potential due to the surface charge induced on S. Since H is a potential due to a surface distribution on S, it is harmonic inside of S; and since the surface S is grounded, its potential is always zero. Hence G vanishes on S, and H is the harmonic function in question.

A second example from the domain of physics is the following: Suppose the individual points of the surface of a body are maintained at constant temperatures, although the temperature may vary from point to point in any continuous manner over the surface. In the course of time, the interior of the body will reach a state of thermal equilibrium, in which the temperature at any given point remains constant. The function T which represents the temperature of the steady state is harmonic, for the equation $\Delta T = 0$ means that the heat received and discharged at each point is the same (Sec. 56). The temperature also takes prescribed values on the surface. Therefore, T satisfies the conditions required in Green's problem

129. The Existence of Green's Function.—Given any closed surface S and a point p either within it or without it. Let ρ be the distance measured from p to any point. If p is inside of S, it is required to find a function H which is harmonic inside of S, and equal to $-1/\rho$ on S. If p is outside of S, it is required to find a function which is harmonic outside of S, vanishes at infinity, and is equal to $-1/\rho$ on S.

Let a sphere Σ of radius a be described about the point p as a center, and let the surface S be transformed into the surface S^* by the method of reciprocal radii (Sec. 105) with respect to the sphere Σ. Let a quantity of matter Q be distributed upon the surface S^* in such a way that the the potential due to the distribution is constant within and on S^* (Sec. 117).

The electric image of S^* in the sphere Σ coincides with the given surface S, and the resulting distribution of matter on S is centrobaric with respect to the point p for points outside of S if p is inside, and for points inside of S, if p is outside (Theorem IV, Sec. 114).

If p lies inside of S, the quantity of matter Q can be chosen so that the mass of the distribution on S is unity, and the potential of this distribution at all outside points is $1/\rho$. If V_i is the interior potential of this distribution, V_i is harmonic inside of S and is equal to $1/\rho$ on S, since the potential function is continuous across S. Hence the function

$$H = -V_i$$

satisfies all the requirements of Green's interior problem.

If p lies outside of S, the quantity of matter Q can be chosen so that the potential of the distribution on S is $1/\rho$ at all interior points. If V_e is the exterior potential of this distribution of matter on S, the function V_e is harmonic outside of S, vanishes at infinity and is equal to $1/\rho$ on S. Hence

$$H = -V_e$$

is a function which satisfies all of the requirements of Green's exterior problem.

The existence of a solution of Green's problem for any closed surface S is thus made to depend upon Gauss' theorem that there exists one, and only one, distribution of a given quantity of matter upon a given closed surface S for which the potential is constant on S. Indeed, Gauss' problem is equivalent to Green's problem.

130. Miscellaneous Properties of Green's Function.

(a) Green's interior function, which is always relative to a closed surface S and a fixed point p, is the potential of a certain distribution of matter; namely, a particle of positive matter of unit mass located at the point p and a centrobaric distribution of negative matter relative to the point p on the surface S, of which the total mass is -1. The potential of such a distribution is zero on S and everywhere outside of S, for the negative matter repels an exterior particle with the same intensity and in the same straight line as the positive particle attracts. Hence, G is zero on S and everywhere outside of S.

(b) The exterior and interior potentials of the surface distribution on S having been determined, namely,

$$V_e = -\frac{1}{\rho}, \qquad V_i = H,$$

the density on S which is necessary to produce these potentials is given by Eq. (126.5); namely,

$$\left. \begin{aligned} \sigma &= \frac{1}{4\pi}\left[\frac{\partial V_i}{\partial n_e} + \frac{\partial V_e}{\partial n_i}\right] \\ &= \frac{1}{4\pi}\frac{\partial G}{\partial n_e}. \end{aligned} \right\} \tag{1}$$

In view of this result, Eq. (127.3) becomes

$$V_i(x, y, z) = -\int_S V_i(\xi, \eta, \zeta)\sigma(x, y, z; \xi, \eta, \zeta)d\omega, \tag{2}$$

where x, y, z are the coordinates of an interior point p, and ξ, η, ζ the coordinates of a point on the surface. Therefore, if V_i is any function which is harmonic inside of S, and if its values are known on S, its value at any point p inside can be obtained by integrating the product $-\sigma V_i$ over the surface.

Let p_1 with the coordinates x_1, y_1, z_1 be the fixed point and p with the coordinates x, y, z be the variable point. Then Green's function relative to the fixed point p_1 is

$$G_1 = \frac{1}{\rho_1} + H_1(x_1, y_1, z_1; x, y, z),$$

where

$$\rho_1 = \sqrt{(x - x_1)^2 + (y - y_1)^2 + (z - z_1)^2},$$

and $G_1 = 0$, if the point p lies on S.

If the point p_1 is interior to the surface, G_1 is Green's interior function relative to the surface S and the point p_1; and if p_1 is outside of the surface, G_1 is Green's exterior function relative to the surface S and the point p_1.

(c) *The Interior Function is Positive Everywhere within S.*— Since

$$\rho_1 G_1 = 1 + \rho_1 H_1,$$

and H_1 is finite everywhere within S,

$$\lim_{\rho_1 = 0} \rho_1 G_1 = +1.$$

Hence, on a small sphere Σ with its center at the point p_1 the function G_1 is positive and very large. On S it vanishes; and in the region between Σ and S it is harmonic. It is, therefore, Sec. 75, positive everywhere inside of S.

(d) *The Exterior Function is Positive Everywhere outside of S.*— If it is borne in mind that, for the exterior function, H_1 vanishes at infinity, the same argument as above shows that the exterior function is everywhere positive outside of S.

(e) *In Their Respective Domains the Green Functions are Everywhere Less than $1/\rho$.*—Since $H_1 = -1/\rho_1$ on the surface and is harmonic in the domain of its validity, it is negative everywhere within that domain (except at infinity where it vanishes). Hence $G_1 < 1/\rho$ everywhere, save at infinity where G_1 vanishes.

FIG. 74.

(f) *The Same Point but Different Surfaces.*— Suppose the fixed point p_1 lies within the surface S_1, and that the surface S_1 is wholly enclosed by the surface S_2 (Fig. 74). Let $G_1^{(1)}$ be the Green function relative to p_1 and S_1, and $G_1^{(2)}$ be the Green function relative to p_1 and S_2, so that

$$G_1^{(1)} = \frac{1}{\rho_1} + H_1^{(1)}(x_1, y_1, z_1; x, y, z),$$

$$G_1^{(2)} = \frac{1}{\rho_1} + H_1^{(2)}(x_1, y_1, z_1; x, y, z),$$

Within and on the surface S_1, it is evident that

$$G_1^{(2)} - G_1^{(1)} = H_1^{(2)} - H_1^{(1)}$$

On S_1, the function $G_1^{(2)} > 0$, by (c), so that $\dfrac{1}{\rho_1} + H_1^{(2)} > 0$.
Also

$$H_1^{(2)} > -\frac{1}{\rho_1} \text{ on } S_1.$$

$$-H_1^{(1)} = +\frac{1}{\rho_1} \text{ on } S_1.$$

Hence

$$H_1^{(2)} - H_1^{(1)} > 0 \text{ on } S_1.$$

Since $H_1^{(2)} - H_1^{(1)}$ is harmonic inside of S_1 and positive on the surface, it is positive everywhere inside of S_1, and therefore

$$G_1^{(2)} > G_1^{(1)} \text{ everywhere within } S_1. \tag{1}$$

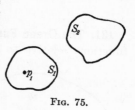

This proposition is still true, if the surface S_1 lies wholly outside of S_2 (Fig. 75), and if the symbols have the same significance as before, so that $G_1^{(2)}$ is the exterior Green function for the surface S_2 relative to the point p_1. The argument is similar. Since $G_1^{(2)} > 0$ at all point outside of S_2, and $G_1^{(1)} = 0$ on S_1,

FIG. 75.

$$G_1^{(2)} - G_1^{(1)} = H_1^{(2)} - H_1^{(1)} > 0 \text{ on } S_1,$$

and, since it is harmonic, it is positive everywhere inside of S_1. Therefore $G_1^{(2)} > G_1^{(1)}$ everywhere inside and on S_1.

(g) Surfaces on Which Green's Function is Constant.—Let S be a closed surface, and G the Green function relative to the interior point p. Then G vanishes on S, is positive everywhere within S, and becomes infinite at p. If G_0 is a positive constant, the surface S_0, on which $G = G_0$, lies everywhere within S, and if G_0 is

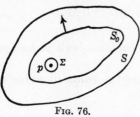

very large the surface $G = G_0$ differs but little from the small sphere

$$\rho = \frac{1}{G_0},$$

since H is continuous in S (Fig. 76). For very small values of G_0, the surface differs but little from the surface S.

FIG. 76.

Let G_0 be given. Then describe a small sphere Σ about the point p. In the space between Σ and the surface S_0, the function

G is harmonic. Its maximum values are on Σ and its minimum value is on S_0. In the volume between S and S_0, G is everywhere less than G_0. It has derivatives of all orders, since it is a potential function in empty space. It is evident, therefore, that at all points of the surface S_0 the external normal derivative of G is negative.

Consider now the surface integral of the normal derivative

$$\int_{S_0} \frac{\partial G}{\partial n} d\omega = \int_{S_0} \frac{\partial}{\partial n}\left(\frac{1}{\rho}\right) d\omega + \int_{S_0} \frac{\partial H}{\partial n} d\omega.$$

By Gauss' theorem, Eq. (68.1), the first integral in the right member is equal to -4π; and since H is harmonic inside of S the second integral is zero (Eq. (62.2)). Hence

$$\int_{S_0} \frac{\partial G}{\partial n} d\omega = -4\pi.$$

131. The Green Function is Symmetric.—Consider the Green functions relative to a surface S and the two interior points p_1 and p_2. Let $G(p_1,\ p)$ be the Green function relative to the point p_1, and $G(p_2,\ p)$ be the Green function relative to the point p_2 (Fig. 77), the point p being the variable point. It will be shown that

FIG. 77.

$$G(p_1,\ p_2) = G(p_2,\ p_1).$$

For simplicity of notation, the functions $G(p_1,\ p)$ and $G(p_2,\ p)$ will be denoted by $G_1(p)$ and $G_2(p)$.

From Corollary II, Sec. 63, it is seen that if S_1 is the surface on which the Green function has the constant value $G_1 = \epsilon_1$

$$\frac{1}{4\pi} \int_{S_1} \left(G_1 \frac{\partial G_2}{\partial n} - G_2 \frac{\partial G_1}{\partial n}\right) d\omega = G_1(p_2) - G_2(p_1),$$

which is independent of ϵ_1 provided S_1 contains both p_1 and p_2 in its interior.

On the surface S_1 the function G_1 has the constant value ϵ_1 which can be as small as desired. Hence

$$\frac{1}{4\pi} \int_{S_1} G_1 \frac{\partial G_2}{\partial n} d\omega = \frac{\epsilon_1}{4\pi} \int \frac{\partial G_2}{\partial n} d\omega = -\epsilon_1.$$

The function G_2 is not constant on S_1, but it is everywhere positive. If ϵ_2 is its maximum value, then, since $\partial G_1/\partial n$ is everywhere negative,

$$-\frac{1}{4\pi}\int_{S_1} G_2 \frac{\partial G_1}{\partial n}d\omega < -\frac{\epsilon_2}{4\pi}\int_{S_1}\frac{\partial G_1}{\partial n} = \epsilon_2.$$

Therefore

$$\frac{1}{4\pi}\int_{S_1}\left(G_1\frac{\partial G_2}{\partial n} - G_2\frac{\partial G_1}{\partial n}\right)d\omega < \epsilon_1 + \epsilon_2,$$

which vanishes for $\epsilon_1 = 0$, since ϵ_2 also vanishes with ϵ_1. Hence

$$G_1(p_2) - G_2(p_1) = 0$$

rigorously, since it is independent of ϵ_1, and the Green function

$$G(p_1,\, p_2) = G(p_2,\, p_1)$$

is symmetric.

It will be observed that this proof does not assume that the normal derivative of H exists and is well defined on S, as would be the case if the integration had been taken over the surface S directly.

132. The Normal Derivative of the Green Function is Harmonic.—Assuming that derivatives of the first three orders exist and are well defined on S, it is easy to show that the normal derivative of $G(p_1, p)$ on S is an harmonic function of the point p_1.

Let λ, μ, ν be the direction cosines of the exterior normal to S at the point $p(x, y, z)$. Then (Eq. (54.2))

$$\frac{\partial G}{\partial n} = \lambda\frac{\partial G}{\partial x} + \mu\frac{\partial G}{\partial y} + \nu\frac{\partial G}{\partial z}.$$

The partial derivatives in the right members are functions of the coordinates of both p and p_1; that is, they are functions of x, y, z; x_1, y_1, z_1. The direction cosines λ, μ, ν are functions of x, y, z, but not functions of x_1, y_1, z_1. Let

$$\Delta_1 = \frac{\partial^2}{\partial x_1^2} + \frac{\partial^2}{\partial y_1^2} + \frac{\partial^2}{\partial z_1^2}.$$

Then

$$\Delta_1\frac{\partial G}{\partial n} = \lambda\Delta_1\frac{\partial G}{\partial x} + \mu\Delta_1\frac{\partial G}{\partial y} + \nu\Delta_1\frac{\partial G}{\partial z},$$

$$= \lambda\frac{\partial}{\partial x}(\Delta_1 G) + \mu\frac{\partial}{\partial y}(\Delta_1 G) + \nu\frac{\partial}{\partial z}(\Delta_1 G).$$

The function G satisfies the equation of Laplace in the letters x, y, z by hypothesis, and since it is symmetric in the coordinates of the points p and p_1, it follows that,

$$\Delta_1 G \equiv 0,$$

and therefore

$$\Delta_1 \frac{\partial G}{\partial n} = 0.$$

133. The Green Function for the Sphere.—Let S_2, Fig. 78, with the radius a_2 and center at C be the given sphere; and

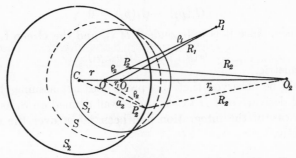

Fig. 78.

let O be the point inside of S_2 with respect to which the Green function is to be determined. Describe any sphere S of radius a about O as a center, and let S_1 of radius a_1 and center O_1 be the inverse of S_2 with respect to S. If $CO = r$ and $OO_1 = r_1$, the following relations are obtained from Eq. (105.3):

$$r_1 = \frac{a^2 r}{a_2{}^2 - r^2}, \qquad a_1 = \frac{a^2 a_2}{a_2{}^2 - r^2}. \tag{1}$$

If the point O_2 is the inverse of O with respect to the sphere S_2, and $\overline{OO_2}$ is denoted by r_2, then

$$\frac{r}{a_2} = \frac{a_2}{r + r_2}.$$

From this equation and the first of Eqs. (1) it is found that

$$\frac{r_1}{a} = \frac{a}{r_2}, \tag{2}$$

which shows that the point O_2 is also the inverse of the point O_1 with respect to the sphere S. This fact permits the location of the point O_1 graphically by the usual method.

Now let S_1 be covered uniformly with a layer of mass M_1, and let S_2 be the electric image of S_1 in the sphere S. Let P_1 be any point outside of S_1, and P_2 its inverse with respect to S; also let $O_1P_1 = R_1$, $O_2P_2 = R_2$.

Since the center of S lies *inside* of S_1, the point P_2 lies *inside* of S_2. The potential of S_1 at P_1 is

$$V_{1e} = \frac{M_1}{R_1}.$$

Therefore, by Lord Kelvin's principle, the potential of S_2 at P_2 is (Sec. 108)

$$V_{2i} = \frac{a}{r_1} \frac{M_1}{R_2},$$

the subscripts e and i denoting external and internal respectively.

Also, the potential of S_1 at the internal point P_2 is

$$V_{1i} = \frac{M_1}{a_1};$$

therefore the potential of S_2 at the external point P_1 is

$$V_{2e} = \frac{a}{a_1} \frac{M_1}{\rho_1}.$$

In order that the mass on S_2 shall be equal to unity (Sec. 129), it is necessary that the coefficient of $1/\rho_1$ in V_{2e} shall equal unity. Therefore

$$M_1 = \frac{a_1}{a} = \frac{aa_2}{a_2{}^2 - r^2} \qquad \text{(by Eq. (1))};$$

and the density on S_1 is

$$\sigma_1 = \frac{1}{4\pi a a_1}. \tag{3}$$

This value of M_1 makes

$$V_{2e} = \frac{1}{\rho_1}, \qquad V_{2i} = \frac{a_2}{rR_2}.$$

Green's function, then, is the difference between these two potentials, both taken at the point P_2, namely

$$G = \frac{1}{\rho_2} - \frac{a_2}{rR_2}. \tag{4}$$

It is evident from this expression that Green's function for the sphere can be regarded as the potential of two particles: The first of mass $+1$ located at the point O_1, and the second of mass $-a_2/r$ located at the point O_2.

Equation (4) remains unaltered even though the point P_2 lies outside of S_2. It represents, therefore, either the interior function or the exterior function. It is a simple matter to show directly that G vanishes if the point P_2 lies on the surface of the sphere S_2.

The Green Function is Symmetric.—Referring to Fig. 79, the Green function relative to the sphere S and the point O_1 at the point Q_1 is

$$G = \frac{1}{\rho} - \frac{a}{rR},$$

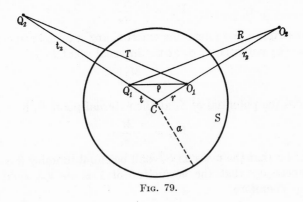

Fig. 79.

and the Green function relative to the point Q_1 at the point O_1 is

$$G = \frac{1}{\rho} - \frac{a}{tT},$$

where Q_2 is the inverse of Q_1 and O_2 is the inverse of the point O_1. It is proposed to show that these two expressions are equal.

The triangles CO_1Q_2 and CQ_1O_2 are similar, for

$$rr_2 = a^2, \qquad tt_2 = a^2,$$

and the angle at C is common. Since two sides are proportional and the included angle is the same, all three sides are proportional. That is,

$$\frac{r_2}{t_2} = \frac{t}{r} = \frac{R}{T}.$$

From this it follows that

$$rR = tT,$$

and the two expressions for G are equal. To put the symmetry in evidence, it is a simple matter to show that

$$rR = tT = \sqrt{(a^2 - r^2)(a^2 - t^2) + a^2\rho^2}.$$

134. The Normal Derivative on the Sphere.—Taking Green's function in the form

$$G = \frac{1}{\rho} - \frac{a}{rR},$$

the normal derivative of G is

$$\frac{\partial G}{\partial n} = -\frac{1}{\rho^2} \cos \widehat{n\rho} + \frac{a}{rR^2} \cos \widehat{nR}; \tag{1}$$

for, according to Eq. (66.1),

$$\frac{\partial \rho}{\partial n} = \cos \widehat{n\rho}, \qquad \frac{\partial R}{\partial n} = \cos \widehat{nR}.$$

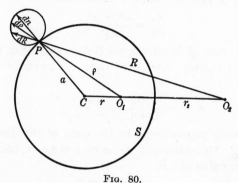

Fig. 80.

It is easily proved directly however. Since

$$\rho^2 = r^2 + a^2 - 2ar \cos \widehat{ar},$$

there results, on varying a and ρ, the distance r and the angle $\widehat{ar}$ remaining constant,

$$\frac{\partial \rho}{\partial n} = \frac{\partial \rho}{\partial a} = \frac{a - r \cos \widehat{ar}}{\rho} = \cos \widehat{n\rho};$$

and similarly for R.

From the triangle (Fig. 80) CPO_2, there is obtained

$$r_2^2 = a^2 + R^2 - 2aR \cos \widehat{nR}. \tag{2}$$

Since G vanishes on the surface, and $rr_2 = a^2$ always,

$$R = \frac{a}{r}\rho, \qquad r_2 = \frac{a^2}{r}.$$

On making these substitutions in Eq. (2) and then multiplying through by r^2/a^2, there is obtained

$$a^2 = r^2 + \rho^2 - 2r\rho \cos \widehat{nR}.$$

Likewise

$$r^2 = a^2 + \rho^2 - 2a\rho \cos \widehat{n\rho}$$

is obtained directly from the triangle CPO_1. The difference between these two equations gives

$$a^2 - r^2 = \rho(a \cos \widehat{n\rho} - r \cos \widehat{nR}).$$

If this equation is divided through by $a\rho^3$ and the coefficient $r/(a\rho^2)$ is replaced by its equal $a/(rR^2)$, there results

$$\frac{a^2 - r^2}{a\rho^3} = \frac{\cos \widehat{n\rho}}{\rho^2} - \frac{a \cos \widehat{nR}}{rR^2}. \tag{3}$$

A comparison of Eqs. (1) and (3) shows that

$$\frac{\partial G}{\partial n} = \frac{r^2 - a^2}{a\rho^3}. \tag{4}$$

The Distribution of Matter on the Sphere.—By Eq. (130.1) the density of the matter distributed over the sphere, taken positively, is

$$\sigma = -\frac{1}{4\pi} \frac{\partial G}{\partial n} = \frac{1}{4\pi} \frac{a^2 - r^2}{a\rho^3},$$

that is, inversely proportional to the cube of the distance from the point O_1. The minimum value of ρ is $a - r$, and therefore, the maximum value of σ is

$$\sigma_{\max} = \frac{1}{4\pi a} \frac{a + r}{(a - r)^2}.$$

This expression shows that the maximum density tends toward infinity as the point of inversion (the pole of Green's function) approaches the surface of the sphere. Diametrically opposite, the density tends towards zero. The matter shows a strong tendency to gather about the point of inversion. The dotted lines in Figs. 81 and 82 show the distribution for $r/a = .8$ and .9 respectively.

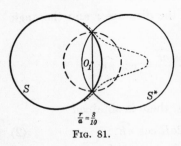

$\dfrac{r}{a} = \dfrac{8}{10}$

Fig. 81.

If R is the radius of the sphere of inversion and

$$a - r \leqq R \leqq a + r,$$

it is easily shown that the amount of matter which lies on the spherical cap which is inside the sphere of inversion is

$$m = \frac{a + r}{2r} - \frac{a^2 - r^2}{2rR}.$$

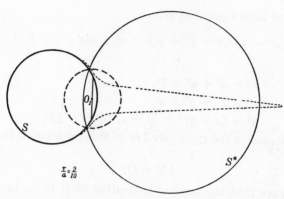

$$\frac{r}{a} = \frac{2}{10}$$

Fig. 82.

The limit of this expression as $r \to a$ is $+1$ for every R. At the limit all of the matter on the sphere lies inside of the sphere of inversion, however small that sphere may be. The rest of the sphere is bare.

The Normal Derivative Is Harmonic.—Let the coordinates of the point O_1 be x, y, z, and the coordinates of the point P, which lies on the surface of the sphere, be ξ, η, ζ, so that $\xi^2 + \eta^2 + \zeta^2 = a^2$. Let

$$a\frac{\partial G}{\partial n} = N = \frac{x^2 + y^2 + z^2 - a^2}{[(x - \xi)^2 + (y - \eta)^2 + (z - \zeta)^2]^{\frac{3}{2}}}.$$

It will be shown by a direct computation that N is harmonic with respect to the variables x, y, z.

The first differentiation with respect to x gives

$$\frac{\partial N}{\partial x} = \frac{2x}{\rho^3} - \frac{3(x - \xi)(x^2 + y^2 + z^2 - a^2)}{\rho^5};$$

and the second differentiation with respect to x gives

$$\frac{\partial^2 N}{\partial x^2} = \frac{2}{\rho^3} - \frac{12x(x - \xi)}{\rho^5} - \frac{3(r^2 - a^2)}{\rho^5} + \frac{15(x - \xi)^2(r^2 - a^2)}{\rho^7}.$$

Hence, also,

$$\frac{\partial^2 N}{\partial y^2} = \frac{2}{\rho^3} - \frac{12y(y - \eta)}{\rho^5} - \frac{3(r^2 - a^2)}{\rho^5} + \frac{15(y - \eta)^2(r^2 - a^2)}{\rho^7},$$

$$\frac{\partial^2 N}{\partial y^2} = \frac{2}{\rho^3} - \frac{12z(z - \zeta)}{\rho^5} - \frac{3(r^2 - a^2)}{\rho^5} + \frac{15(z - \zeta)(r^2 - a^2)}{\rho^7}.$$

The sum of these equations gives

$$\Delta N = \frac{6}{\rho^5}[\rho^2 - 2\{x(x - \xi) + y(y - \eta) + z(z - \zeta)\} + r^2 - a^2].$$

If

$$a^2 = \xi^2 + \eta^2 + \zeta^2,$$
$$r^2 = x^2 + y^2 + z^2,$$
$$\rho^2 = (x - \xi)^2 + (y - \eta)^2 + (z - \zeta)^2,$$

are substituted in the right member of this equation, it is found that

$$\Delta N = O;$$

which shows that the normal derivative of G is an harmonic function of the coordinates of the point O_1.

135. Green's Equation for the Sphere.—It was proved in Sec. 127 for any closed surface S that if V is harmonic inside of S and if its values are known on S, its value at any interior point $p(x, y, z)$ is given by the equation

$$V(x, y, z) = -\frac{1}{4\pi} \int \frac{\partial G}{\partial n} V(\xi, \eta, \zeta) d\omega.$$

For the sphere this equation becomes

$$V(x, y, z) = \frac{1}{4\pi a} \int \frac{a^2 - r^2}{\rho^3} V(\xi, \eta, \zeta) d\omega, \qquad (1)$$

where

$$r^2 = x^2 + y^2 + z^2, \qquad \rho^2 = (x - \xi)^2 + (y - \eta)^2 + (z - \zeta)^2.$$

In spherical coordinates, a point on the surface is

$$\xi = a \sin \varphi_1 \cos \theta_1, \qquad \eta = a \sin \varphi_1 \sin \theta_1, \qquad \zeta = a \cos \varphi_1;$$

and the coordinates of the interior point p are

$$x = r \sin \varphi_0 \cos \theta_0, \qquad y = r \sin \varphi_0 \sin \theta_0, \qquad z = r \cos \varphi_0.$$

In this system, the north pole of latitude lies on the z-axis and the zero of longitude on the x-axis. The argument φ is the distance from the north pole.

Take a new system of rectangular axes X, Y, Z, with the same origin but with the Z-axis passing through the point p, the X-axis lying in the xy-plane and the positive end of the Y-axis lying always in the northern hemisphere. The equations of transformation are

$$x = \alpha_1 X + \alpha_2 Y + \alpha_3 Z,$$
$$y = \beta_1 X + \beta_2 Y + \beta_3 Z,$$
$$z = \gamma_1 X + \gamma_2 Y + \gamma_3 Z,$$

where the α, β, γ,'s are the direction cosines of the new axes with respect to old ones. The values of these direction cosines are[1]

$$\alpha_1 = -\sin\theta_0, \qquad \alpha_2 = -\cos\varphi_0\cos\theta_0, \qquad \alpha_3 = \sin\alpha_0\cos\theta_0;$$
$$\beta_1 = +\cos\theta_0, \qquad \beta_2 = -\cos\alpha_0\sin\theta_0, \qquad \beta_3 = \sin\alpha_0\sin\theta_0;$$
$$\gamma_1 = 0, \qquad \gamma_2 = +\sin\varphi_0, \qquad \gamma_3 = \cos\varphi_0.$$

If φ is the polar distance and θ is the longitude with respect to the X, Y, Z-system, then for points on the surface of the sphere the polar distances and the longitudes in the two systems are related by the following equations:

$$\sin\varphi_1\cos\theta_1 = \alpha_1\sin\varphi\cos\theta + \alpha_2\sin\varphi\sin\theta + \alpha_3\cos\varphi,$$
$$\sin\varphi_1\sin\theta_1 = \beta_1\sin\varphi\cos\theta + \beta_2\sin\varphi\sin\theta + \beta_3\cos\varphi,$$
$$\cos\varphi_1 = \gamma_1\sin\varphi\cos\theta + \gamma_2\sin\varphi\sin\theta + \gamma_3\cos\varphi.$$

In the coordinates of the new system

$$d\omega = a^2\sin\varphi d\varphi d\theta,$$
$$\rho^2 = a^2 + r^2 - 2ar\cos\varphi,$$

and, since ρ is independent of the longitude, Green's equation (Eq. (1)) can be written

$$V(x, y, z) = \frac{a}{4\pi}\int_0^\pi \frac{a^2 - r^2}{\rho^3}\sin\varphi d\varphi \int_0^{2\pi} V(\varphi, \theta)d\theta, \qquad (2)$$

the integration with respect to θ depending only upon the function $V(\varphi, \theta)$. The integration of this equation by means of spherical harmonics is given in Sec. 208.

136. A Generalization for the Sphere.—Green's equation was derived upon the assumption that V is harmonic inside of S and that its values are given on S. Suppose the values of

[1] "Statics and the Dynamics of a Particle," p. 367.

V are given on the surface, continuous but otherwise arbitrary, without any statement as to the nature of V elsewhere.

Green's equation,

$$W(x, y, z) = \frac{1}{4\pi a}\int \frac{a^2 - r^2}{\rho^3}V(\xi, \eta, \zeta)d\omega, \tag{1}$$

certainly defines some function of x, y, z in the interior of S. It is the purpose of the present section to show that the function so defined is necessarily harmonic inside of S, and that the limit of W as the point p approaches the surface is the value of V at the point of approach.

The Function W Is Harmonic.—Any function F can be expressed in rectangular or in polar coordinates, where

$$x = r \cos \varphi \cos \theta, \qquad y = r \cos \varphi \sin \theta, \qquad z = r \sin \varphi.$$

Consequently

$$\delta F = \frac{\partial F}{\partial x}\delta x + \frac{\partial F}{\partial y}\delta y + \frac{\partial F}{\partial z}\delta z = \frac{\partial F}{\partial r}\delta r + \frac{\partial F}{\partial \varphi}\delta\varphi + \frac{\partial F}{\partial \theta}\delta\theta \tag{2}$$

for any set of variations. If the variations are taken radially, $\delta\varphi = \delta\theta = 0$, and the relation between the other variations are

$$\frac{\delta x}{x} = \frac{\delta y}{y} = \frac{\delta z}{z} = \frac{\delta r}{r}.$$

Hence Eq. (2) becomes

$$r\frac{\partial F}{\partial r} = x\frac{\partial F}{\partial x} + y\frac{\partial F}{\partial y} + z\frac{\partial F}{\partial z}. \tag{3}$$

Returning to Eq. (1), take

$$\frac{1}{4\pi a}V(\xi, \eta, \zeta) = \sigma, \tag{4}$$

and therefore

$$W = \int_S \frac{a^2 - r^2}{\rho^3}\sigma d\omega.$$

Now let

$$U = \int_S \frac{\sigma}{\rho}d\omega,$$

so that U is a Newtonian potential for the density σ. Then

$$r\frac{\partial U}{\partial r} = r\int_S \frac{\partial}{\partial r}\left(\frac{1}{\rho}\right)\sigma d\omega,$$

and, since

$$\rho^2 = r^2 + a^2 - 2ar \sin \varphi,$$

it follows that

$$2r\frac{\partial}{\partial r}\left(\frac{1}{\rho}\right) = -\frac{2}{\rho^3}(r^2 - ar\sin\varphi)$$

$$= -\frac{1}{\rho^3}(r^2 - a^2 + \rho^2).$$

Therefore

$$2r\frac{\partial U}{\partial r} = -\int_S \frac{\sigma}{\rho}d\omega + \int_S \frac{a^2 - r^2}{\rho^3}\sigma d\omega$$

$$= W - U.$$

Hence

$$W = U + 2r\frac{\partial U}{\partial r}$$

$$= U + 2\left(x\frac{\partial U}{\partial x} + y\frac{\partial U}{\partial y} + z\frac{\partial U}{\partial z}\right)$$

By differentiating twice with respect to x, y, z there is obtained

$$\frac{\partial^2 W}{\partial x^2} = 5\frac{\partial^2 U}{\partial x^2} + 2\left(x\frac{\partial^3 U}{\partial x^3} + y\frac{\partial^3 U}{\partial y\partial x^2} + z\frac{\partial^3 U}{\partial z\partial x^2}\right),$$

$$\frac{\partial^2 W}{\partial y^2} = 5\frac{\partial^2 U}{\partial y^2} + 2\left(x\frac{\partial^3 U}{\partial x\partial y^2} + y\frac{\partial^3 U}{\partial y^3} + z\frac{\partial^3 U}{\partial z\partial y^2}\right),$$

$$\frac{\partial^2 W}{\partial z^2} = 5\frac{\partial^2 U}{\partial z^2} + 2\left(x\frac{\partial^3 U}{\partial x\partial z^2} + y\frac{\partial^3 U}{\partial y\partial z^2} + z\frac{\partial^3 U}{\partial z^3}\right).$$

The sum of these expressions is

$$\Delta W = 5\Delta U + 2\left(x\frac{\partial}{\partial x} + y\frac{\partial}{\partial y} + z\frac{\partial}{\partial z}\right)\Delta U \equiv 0.$$

Hence W is harmonic, since, evidently, it is continuous.

$W = V$ *on the Surface of the Sphere.*—It still remains to be shown that, if the point p approaches the point P on the surface along any line whatever, the limit of $W(p)$ is $V(P)$.

Suppose p approaches P along a line which makes an angle λ with the normal, and that

$$W(p) = (a^2 - r^2)\int_S \frac{\sigma}{\rho^3}d\omega.$$

Imagine P as the origin of a set of rectangular axes, x, y, z, with the z-axis directed toward the center of the sphere, and therefore coinciding with the line PC, Fig. 83.   The coordinates of p in this system are x, y, z and

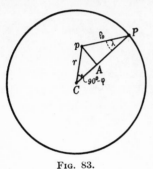

$$PA = z = \rho_0 \cos \lambda.$$

Since z is a constant in the process of integration, the expression for W can be written

$$W = \frac{a^2 - r^2}{\rho_0 \cos \lambda} \int_S \frac{z}{\rho^3} \sigma d\omega.$$

Since

$$a^2 - r^2 = 2a\rho_0 \cos \lambda - \rho_0{}^2,$$

FIG. 83.

it is evident that

$$\lim_{\rho_0 = 0} \frac{a^2 - r^2}{\rho_0 \cos \lambda} = 2a.$$

The integral

$$\int_S \frac{z}{\rho^3} \sigma d\omega$$

is the normal component of the attraction of a surface with the density (Eq. (4))

$$\sigma = \frac{V}{4\pi a}.$$

It was proved in Sec. 92 that the limiting value of this attraction is $2\pi\sigma$.   Hence the limiting value of W is

$$\lim_{\rho_0 = 0} W(p) = 2a \cdot 2\pi \cdot \frac{V}{4\pi a} = V(P).$$

Hence Green's equation

$$V(x, y, z) = \frac{a^2 - r^2}{4\pi a} \int_S \frac{V(\xi, \eta, \zeta)}{\rho^3} d\omega \tag{2}$$

defines a function which is harmonic in the interior and takes the prescribed set of values on the surface.

The above proof, which is purely analytic in character, is given by Poincaré.   A proof which makes a stronger appeal to the intuition can be obtained from the results of Sec. 134. Green's equation can also be written, Eq. (130.2),

$$W(x, y, z) = +\int_S V(\xi, \eta, \zeta) \sigma d\omega, \tag{5}$$

if the negative matter in the distribution is replaced by positive matter.

Let the integral over the whole sphere be separated into the sum of two integrals, one of which, $\int_C$, is taken over the spherical cap described in Sec. 132, and the other, $\int_D$, is taken over the remainder of the sphere. If the pole of Green's function (x, y, z) is sufficiently close to the surface, the radius of the sphere of inversion can be taken so small that the value of $V(\xi, \eta, \zeta)$ is essentially constant over the cap. Hence

$$\int_C V(\xi, \eta, \zeta)\sigma d\omega \doteq V_C \int_C \sigma d\omega,$$

and

$$\int_D V(\xi, \eta, \zeta)\sigma d\omega \leqq V_{max.} \int_D \sigma d\omega,$$

where V_C is the value of V at the center of the cap and V_{max} is the modulus of the maximum value of V on S. Since

$$\lim \int_C \sigma d\omega = 1 \quad \text{and} \quad \lim \int_D \sigma d\omega = 0,$$

it is evident that

$$\lim W = \lim \int_C V \sigma d\omega = V_C.$$

137. Green's Equation for Any Surface.—Green's formula, Eq. (127.3),

$$V(x, y, z) = -\frac{1}{4\pi} \int_S V(\xi, \eta, \zeta) \frac{\partial}{\partial n} G(x, y, z; \xi, \eta, \zeta) d\omega, \quad (1)$$

where x, y, z are the coordinates of the pole of G and ξ, η, ζ are the coordinates of the surface element $d\omega$, was derived upon the assumption that V is harmonic inside of S and that its values on S are known.

If a continuous, but otherwise arbitrary, set of values is specified upon S, the right member of Eq. (1) defines a certain function of x, y, z which can be denoted by $W(x, y, z)$. Since the integrand is finite everywhere on S, it is evident that $W(x, y, z)$ is continuous and single valued everywhere within S. Derivatives of all orders exist, since they exist for G. Therefore

$$\Delta W = -\frac{1}{4\pi} \int_S V(\xi, \eta, \zeta) \Delta \left(\frac{\partial G}{\partial n}\right) d\omega = 0,$$

since the normal derivative of G is an harmonic function of x, y, z, (Sec. 132). The function W, therefore, is harmonic inside of S, since it is single valued, has derivatives of the first two orders, and satisfies the equation of Laplace.

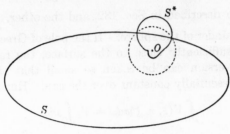

Fig. 84.

In the case of the sphere, it was shown in the preceeding section that as O, the pole of G, approaches the surface, the value of W tends toward the value of V at the point of approach. It is desired to show that the same property holds for any surface.

Let p, the point approached, be a regular point of the surface

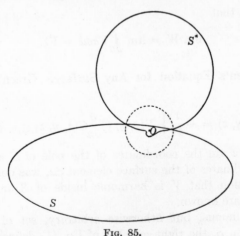

Fig. 85.

S in the sense that it has a definite tangent plane and two principal radii of curvature. It is then possible to describe two spheres S_1 and S_2 which are tangent to the surface at p, one of which has a radius equal to the minimum radius of curvature and the other the maximum. Let a third sphere be described about p as a center with a radius R. If R is sufficiently small, the portion of the surface intercepted by this sphere will lie wholly between S_1 and S_2 if the radii of curvature have the same sign, and outside of both of them if they have opposite signs.

Let O be the pole of Green's function. About O as a center describe a sphere Σ, the radius of which R is kept fixed as the point O approaches the point p. Let the surface S^* be the transform of S by reciprocal radii with respect to the sphere Σ, Fig. 84. The portion of S which lies inside of Σ is transformed into the portion of S^* which lies outside of Σ; and the portion of S which lies outside of Σ is transformed into the portion of S^*

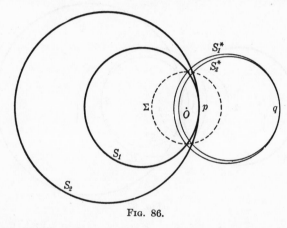

Fig. 86.

which lies inside of Σ. As the point O approaches the point p, the portion of S^* that lies outside of Σ expands and rapidly approaches the form of a sphere, Fig. 85, while the interior portion contracts. It is much as though the surface S were a film of soap solution, the portion lying within Σ being blown into a large bubble while the remainder of the surface contracts to an insignificant irregularity upon it.

That the bubble approaches the form of a sphere as it increases in size is seen from Fig. 86, if the two radii of curvature have the same sign. The portion of the surface S which lies inside the sphere of inversion Σ also lies between the two spheres S_1 and S_2 which is the region that is transformed into the volume between the two spheres S_1^* and S_2^*. The point p is transformed into the point q; and since S_1 and S_2 are tangent to each other at p, the spheres S_1^* and S_2^*, which are the transforms of S_1 and S_2, are mutually tangent at q. As the point of inversion

O approaches the point p, the point q recedes in such a way that the equation

$$\overline{Op} \cdot \overline{Oq} = R^2$$

is always satisfied.

If the two radii of curvature of S at p have different signs, the portion of S which lies inside of Σ lies outside of both S_1 and S_2. As is seen from Fig. 87, the region which is outside of S_1 and S_2 transforms into the volume which lies between S_1^* and S_2^*.

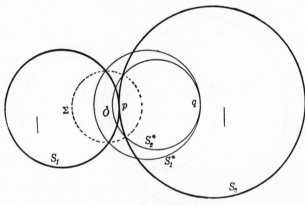

Fig. 87.

In either case the portion of the surface S which lies inside of Σ is transformed into a portion of S^* which lies between S_1^* and S_2^* and which passes through the point q. The portion of S which lies outside of Σ is transformed into a portion of S^* which lies inside of Σ. It is evident therefore that if Op is very small the surface S^* is essentially a very large sphere with a small irregularity near p. Consequently, in the distribution of a level layer on S^*, the density is very nearly constant, and inversely proportional to $\overline{pq}$, Sec. 133, and the limit of this density as $\overline{Op}$ diminishes is zero.

Consider now the electric image of S^*. It coincides geometrically with S, but nearly all of the mass lies on that portion of S which is inside of Σ. Let this portion of S be denoted by C and the remainder of the surface by D. Then

$$\int_S \sigma d\omega = 1 = \int_C \sigma d\omega + \int_D \sigma d\omega.$$

Since the limit of σ over D is zero it follows that the limit of the last integral is zero, whatever R may be. Hence

$$\lim \int_C \sigma d\omega = 1,$$

for every R which is sufficiently small.

Since $V(\xi, \eta, \zeta)$ is finite on S, it is evident also that

$$\int_D V \sigma d\omega \leqq |V|_{max}.\int_D \sigma d\omega,$$

which has the limit zero. Consequently

$$\lim W = \lim \int_C V \sigma d\omega,$$

for every R sufficiently small. But R can be taken so small that V is essentially constant over C and equal to the value which it has at p. Hence

$$\lim \int_C V \sigma d\omega = V(p)\int_C \sigma d\omega = V(p),$$

and

$$\lim W = V(p).$$

138. A General Theorem of Green's.—Given a closed surface S and a continuous set of values $V(\xi, \eta, \zeta)$ on S, Green's equation (Eq. (137.1)) defines a function $V_i(x, y, z)$ which is harmonic within S and equal to $V(\xi, \eta, \zeta)$ on S, provided G is Green's interior function. If G is Green's exterior function, the function $V_e(x, y, z)$ so defined is harmonic outside of S, is equal to $V(\xi, \eta, \zeta)$ on S, and vanishes at infinity.

It follows at once from the analysis of Sec. 126 that V_i and V_e are the interior and exterior potentials of a distribution of matter on S in which, Eq. (126.5),

$$\sigma = \frac{1}{4\pi}\left[\frac{\partial V_i}{\partial n_e} + \frac{\partial V_e}{\partial n_i}\right].$$

Hence, the general theorem due to Green and also to Gauss:

Theorem.—Given a closed surface S and a continuous set of values $V(\xi, \eta, \zeta)$ on S, there exists one and only one distribution of matter on S for which the potential on S itself is equal to V.

GREEN'S PROBLEM FOR THE LOGARITHMIC POTENTIAL

139. Statement of the Problem.—It is possible also to state Green's problem for an attracting line and the logarithmic potential. For the interior problem it is

Given a closed plane contour C, it is required to find a function which is harmonic inside of C and which takes a given continuous set of values on C.

For the exterior problem it is

Given a closed plane contour C, it is required to find a function which is harmonic in every closed region outside of C, and takes a given continuous set of values on C.

It will have been observed that practically all of the theorems relating to the Newtonian potential have their counterpart for the logarithmic potential. It would be expected, therefore, that the method which solves Green's problem for the Newtonian potential is also adaptable to the logarithmic potential. There is one step in the method, however, where there is a difference, and that is in the definition of electrical images.

140. Electric Images for the Logarithmic Potential.—In Sec. 106 (using the notation of that section) M_2 is said to be the electric image of M_1 if each element of volume of M_2 is the transform by reciprocal radii of the corresponding element of M_1, and if for the corresponding elements of mass

$$dm_2 = \frac{r_2}{a} dm_1.$$

For a logarithmic potential and a plane area, M_2 will be called the electric image of M_1 if each element of area (or line) of M_2 is the transform by reciprocal radii of the corresponding element of M_1, and if the corresponding elements of mass are equal; that is

$$dm_2 = dm_1.$$

Referring to Fig. 65, let S be the circle of inversion with radius a and center of inversion at O. Let a particle of mass m be located at M_1 and a second particle also of mass m located at M_2 which is the transform of M_1. Let P_1 be any other point and P_2 its transform. Let U_1 be the potential of the particle at M_1 at the point P_1, and U_2 the potential of the particle at M_2 at the point P_2. Then

$$U_1 = m \log \frac{R_0}{R_1}, \qquad U_2 = m \log \frac{R_0}{R_2},$$

where R_0 is an arbitrary constant; also, as in Sec. 106,

$$r_1 r_2 = \rho_1 \rho_2 = a^2, \qquad \frac{r_1}{\rho_2} = \frac{\rho_1}{r_2} = \frac{R_1}{R_2}. \tag{1}$$

The difference of the two potentials gives

$$U_2 = U_1 + m \log \frac{R_1}{R_2} = U_1 + m \log \frac{r_1}{\rho_2}$$

$$= U_1 - m \log \frac{R_0}{r_1} + m \log \frac{R_0}{\rho_2},$$

or

$$U_2 = U_1 - U_{10} + m \log \frac{R_0}{\rho_2}, \tag{2}$$

where U_{10} is the value of U_1 at the point O, and therefore independent of the position of P_1 or P_2.

Suppose there is a discrete set of particles M_1, and a corresponding discrete set M_2. There will be a corresponding set of Eq. (2). The sum of this set gives the relation between the potentials of the two sets at P_1 and P_2. Thus, if V_1 is the potential of the first set at P_1 and V_2 is the potential of the transformed set at P_2, so that

$$V_1 = \Sigma U_1, \qquad V_2 = \Sigma U_2, \qquad M = \Sigma m,$$

then

$$V_2 = V_1 - V_{10} + M \log \frac{R_0}{\rho_2}. \tag{3}$$

If the particles form a continuous aggregate, such as a line or area, Eq. (3), evidently, is still true. If σ_1 and σ_2 are the densities of such aggregates, it is easy to see, on account of the relationship $dm_1 = dm_2$, that

$$\left.\begin{array}{ll} \sigma_2 = \dfrac{a^2}{r_2{}^2}\sigma_1 & \text{(line densities),} \\[2ex] \sigma_2 = \dfrac{a^4}{r_4}\sigma_1 & \text{(areal densities).} \end{array}\right\} \tag{4}$$

141. Electric Images of Centrobaric Bodies.—It is now easy to prove theorems analogous to the four theorems of Sec. 114. The bodies referred to in these theorems are, of course mass distributions on plane areas, and the theorems hold only in the plane.

Theorem I.—If a body is centrobaric for exterior points, its electric image in any circle whose center lies outside of the body also is centrobaric for exterior particles.

Let M be the mass of the given body. Since it is centrobaric, its potential is (Fig. 69)

$$V_1 = M \log \frac{R_0}{R_1},$$

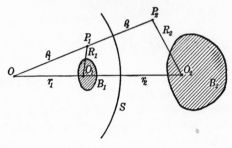

Fig. 69.

and the potential of its electric image is

$$V_2 = M \log \frac{R_0}{R_1} - M \log \frac{R_0}{r_1} + M \log \frac{R_0}{\rho_2}$$

$$= M \log \frac{R_0 r_1}{R_1 \rho_2},$$

which, by Eq. (1), becomes

$$V_2 = M \log \frac{R_0}{R_2};$$

that is, the electric image attracts exterior particles toward the point O_2 just as though all of its mass were a particle at O_2.

Theorem II.—If the body B_1 is a ring which is centrobaric for exterior particles, its electric image B_2 in any circle whose center O lies in the empty interior of the ring (Fig. 70) is a ring which is centrobaric for interior particles.

Since B_1 is centrobaric its potential for exterior particles is

$$V_1 = M \log \frac{R_0}{R_1},$$

the point O_1 being the center of attraction. Since P_1 lies outside of B_1, the point P_2 lies inside of B_2. Hence the potential of the electric image of B_1, that is B_2, at points interior to B_2 is

$$V_2 = M \log \frac{R_0}{R_1} - V_{10} + M \log \frac{R_0}{\rho_2}.$$

$$= M \log \frac{R_0{}^2}{R_1 P_2} - V_{10},$$

$$= M \log \frac{R_0{}^2}{R_2 r_1} - V_{10}$$

$$= M \log \frac{R_0}{R_2} + \left(M \log \frac{R_0}{r_1} - V_{10} \right).$$

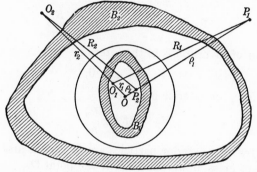

Fig. 70.

Since the point O is interior to B_1, the value of its potential at O is not known. Since it does not depend upon the position of the point P_1 or P_2, the expression within the parenthesis is some constant, the value of which is not known. Denoting by Q_0 a certain constant, the expression for V_2 can be written

$$V_2 = M \log \frac{Q_0}{R_2},$$

which shows that particles interior to B_2 are attracted towards O_2 just as though a particle of mass M were located there. That is, B_2 is centrobaric for interior particles.

As the point O tends toward O_1, the lines R_1 and ρ_1 tend toward equality, and the point O_2 recedes indefinitely. Hence the limit of V_2 as O approaches O_1 is

$$\lim V_2 = M \log \frac{R_0{}^2}{R_1 \rho_2} - V_{11} = M \log \frac{R_0{}^2}{\rho_1 \rho_2} - V_{11}$$

$$= M \log \frac{R_0{}^2}{a^2} - V_{11} = \text{const.},$$

V_{11} being the value of V_1 at the point O_1. Hence

Theorem III.—*If a closed ring of matter is centrobaric with its center of mass G in its hollow interior, its electric image in any circle which has G as its center is a ring of matter for which the interior potential is constant.*

Theorem IV.—*If the potential of a ring is constant in its interior (or if it is a level thread), its electrical image in any circle whose center lies in the interior is centrobaric for exterior particles, and the center of mass of the electrical image is at the center of inversion. If the center of inversion lies outside the ring the electric image is centrobaric with respect to the point O for particles in its interior.*

Since

$$V_2 = V_1 - V_{10} + M \log \frac{R_0}{\rho_2},$$

if the point of inversion is in the interior,

$$V_1 - V_{10} = 0,$$

and therefore, for exterior particles,

$$V_2 = M \log \frac{R_0}{\rho_2},$$

which states that exterior particles are attracted just as though a particle of mass M were located at the point O.

If the point of inversion O lies outside of the ring, V_1 is constant but not equal to V_{10}. For this case

$$V_2 = M \log \frac{R_0}{\rho_2} + \text{const.}$$

and the electric image is centrobaric for interior particles. They are attracted just as though a particle of mass M were located at the point O.

142. The Existence of Green's Function.—According to Corollary I, Sec. 64, if ρ is measured from a point inside of C; if

$$G = \log \frac{\rho_0}{\rho} + H,$$

where H is harmonic inside of C and equal to $- \log \frac{1}{\rho}$ on C;

and if U is any other function which is harmonic inside of C, then

$$U(x, y) = -\frac{1}{2\pi} \int_C U \frac{\partial G}{\partial n} d\lambda. \tag{1}$$

The same equation holds, by Corollary III, Sec. 64, if ρ is measured from a point outside of C; if

$$G = \log \frac{\rho_0}{\rho} + H,$$

where H is harmonic outside of C, is equal to $-\log \frac{\rho_0}{\rho}$ on C, and acts like a logarithmic potential at infinity, and if U is a logarithmic potential outside of C.

In either case, G is Green's function for the given contour. In order to establish the existence of Green's function, let p be the point from which ρ is measured. Describe a circle with any convenient radius a about p as a center. Let C^* be the transform of C by reciprocal radii with respect to this circle, and let a unit of matter be distributed along C^* in such a way as to make it a level thread, which is always possible for properly restricted contours, by Sec. 117. The electric image of this thread in the circle of inversion coincides with the given contour C, and the resulting distribution of matter on C is centrobaric with respect to the center of inversion—centrobaric for outside particles if p is inside of C, and centrobaric for interior particles if p lies outside of C (Theorem IV, Sec. 141).

Let V_i and V_e be the interior and exterior potentials of this centrobaric distribution. If the point p lies inside of C,

$$V_e = \log \frac{\rho_0}{\rho}.$$

The interior potential V_i is equal to $\log \rho_0/\rho$ on C, since the potential is continuous across C, Sec. 95, and it is harmonic inside of C since it is a potential function in empty space. Hence, Green's interior function is

$$G = \log \frac{\rho_0}{\rho} - V_i.$$

If the point p lies outside of C, the interior potential of the distribution on C is

$$V_i = \log \frac{\rho_0}{\rho} + K$$

where K has a certain constant value. The exterior potential V_e is equal to the interior potential on the surface. Hence the function

$$G = \log \frac{\rho_0}{\rho} - V_e + K$$

vanishes on the contour, and is the exterior Green function which was sought.

143. Green's Function for the Circle.—Given a circle C_2, Fig. 88, with a radius of a_2 and a point O at a distance r_2 from the center A of the given circle. Describe a circle C of radius a with the point O as a center. Let the transform of the circle C_2 with respect to the circle C be the circle C_1. If the center of C_1 is at O_1 at a distance r_1 from O and its radius is a_1, then, by Eq. (105.3)

$$r_1 = \frac{a^2 r_2}{a_2{}^2 - r_2{}^2}, \qquad a_1 = \frac{a^2 a_2}{a_2{}^2 - r_2{}^2}. \tag{1}$$

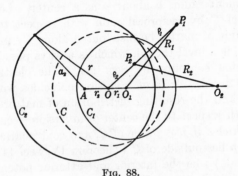

FIG. 88.

If a unit mass is placed upon C_1 in such a way as to make it a level thread, the density on C_1 is constant and is equal to

$$\sigma_1 = \frac{1}{2\pi a_1} = \frac{1}{2\pi} \frac{a_2{}^2 - r_2{}^2}{a^2 a_2}.$$

The electric image of this distribution on C_1 in the circle C is a distribution of matter on C_2 which is centrobaric with respect to the point O and for which the density is (Eq. (139.4)),

$$\sigma_2 = \frac{a^2}{r^2} \sigma_1 = \frac{1}{2\pi a_2} \frac{a_2{}^2 - r_2{}^2}{r^2},$$

where r is the distance from O to the element of mass dm_2 on the circumference of C_2. From this it is seen that the density on C_2 varies inversely as the square of the distance from the point O.

The potential of the distribution on C_1 at an exterior point P_1 is (Sec. 42)

$$V_1 = \log \frac{R_0}{R_1}$$

Hence, the potential of the distribution on C_2 at the interior point P_2, which is the transform of P_1 in the circle C, is, Eq. (139.3),

$$V_2 = V_1 - V_{10} + \log \frac{R_0}{P_2}.$$

The potential of C_1 at interior points is constant and equal to the value at the circumference; that is,

$$V_{10} = \log \frac{R_0}{a_1}.$$

Hence

$$V_2 = \log \frac{R_0}{R_1} - \log \frac{R_0}{a_1} + \log \frac{R_0}{\rho_2},$$

or

$$V_2 = \log \frac{R_0 a_1}{R_1 \rho_2};$$

and, since

$$\frac{r_1}{\rho_2} = \frac{\rho_1}{r_2} = \frac{R_1}{R_2}, \tag{2}$$

this becomes

$$V_2 = \log \frac{R_0 a_1}{R_2 r_1}.$$

Green's interior function, therefore, is

$$G = \log \frac{R_0}{\rho_2} - \log \frac{R_0 a_1}{R_2 r_1}$$

or,

$$G = \log \frac{R_2}{\rho_2} - \log \frac{a_1}{r_1} = \log \frac{R_2}{\rho_2} - \log \frac{a_2}{r_2}. \tag{3}$$

This expression vanishes if the point P_2 lies on C_2; for

$$\frac{R_2}{\rho_2} = \frac{R_1}{r_1}$$

by Eq. (2). If ρ_2 lies on C_2, P_1 lies on C_1 and then $R_1 = a_1$, so that on the circumference

$$\frac{R_2}{\rho_2} = \frac{a_1}{r_1}.$$

Equation (3) is also Green's exterior function if the point O lies outside of C_2.

144. The Principle of Dirichlet and Lord Kelvin.—The first efforts to give a mathematical proof of the existence of a solution of Green's problem were made by Lejeune-Dirichlet[1] and by Lord Kelvin,[2] and the assertion that a solution of Green's problem always exists has become known as *Dirichlet's principle.* Weierstrass pointed out that Dirichlet's conclusion did not follow from his argument, but inasmuch as the argument is simple and illuminating it will be given here.

The problem is: Given a closed surface S. Does there exist a function which is harmonic within S and takes a prescribed, continuous set of values on S?

It will be noted first that if the problem admits of any solution it admits but one. For, suppose V_1 is a solution and V_2 also is a solution. Then $V_2 - V_1$ is harmonic within S and vanishes at all points of S. Hence $V_2 - V_1$ vanishes everywhere within S, and V_2 does not differ from V_1.

Suppose the given surface is defined by the equation

$$f(x, y, z) = 0,$$

and that the prescribed set of values on S is $g(x, y, z)$. If $h(x, y, z)$ is any continuous function of its arguments, the function

$$g + f \cdot h, \tag{1}$$

which contains the arbitrary element h, also takes the prescribed set of values on S and satisfies the condition of continuity. There are infinitely many such functions. In this infinite set of functions there is one, V, which makes the volume integral

$$\int_B \left[\left(\frac{\partial V}{\partial x} \right)^2 + \left(\frac{\partial V}{\partial y} \right)^2 + \left(\frac{\partial V}{\partial z} \right)^2 \right] d\tau$$

a minimum. For the integrand is nowhere negative, and if

$$\frac{\partial V}{\partial x} = \frac{\partial V}{\partial y} = \frac{\partial V}{\partial z} = 0$$

throughout the volume, B, which is enclosed by S, the function V would be a constant and could not take a prescribed set of values on S.

Let U be any continuous function which vanishes on S. Then

$$V + tU,$$

---

[1] "Vorlesungen über die im umgekehrten Verhältniss des Quadrats der Entfernung Wirkenden Kräfte," p. 127.

[2] "Treatise on Natural Philosophy," Vol. I, p. 170.

where t is an arbitrary constant, belongs to the class of functions defined in Eq. (1); and the integral

$$J = \int_B \left[\left(\frac{\partial (V + tU)}{\partial x} \right)^2 + \left(\frac{\partial (V + tU)}{\partial y} \right)^2 + \left(\frac{\partial (V + tU)}{\partial z} \right)^2 \right] d\tau$$

is greater than the integral

$$I = \int_B \left[\left(\frac{\partial V}{\partial x} \right)^2 + \left(\frac{\partial V}{\partial y} \right)^2 + \left(\frac{\partial V}{\partial z} \right)^2 \right] d\tau,$$

since, by hypothesis, V makes the integral a minimum.

The integral J can be expanded in powers of t; viz.,

$$\left. \begin{array}{c} J = I + 2t \int_B \left[\dfrac{\partial V}{\partial x} \cdot \dfrac{\partial U}{\partial x} + \dfrac{\partial V}{\partial y} \cdot \dfrac{\partial U}{\partial y} + \dfrac{\partial V}{\partial z} \cdot \dfrac{\partial U}{\partial z} \right] d\tau \\ + t^2 \int_B \left[\left(\dfrac{\partial U}{\partial x} \right)^2 + \left(\dfrac{\partial U}{\partial y} \right)^2 + \left(\dfrac{\partial U}{\partial z} \right)^2 \right] d\tau. \end{array} \right\} \quad (2)$$

Suppose the integral which is the coefficient of $2t$ in the above expression were different from zero. It would then be possible to take t so small numerically and of such a sign that the sum of the last two terms in Eq. (2) would be negative and therefore $J < I$. As this contradicts the hypothesis that I is a minimum of this integral, it follows that for every continuous U which vanishes on S

$$\int_B \left[\frac{\partial V}{\partial x} \frac{\partial U}{\partial x} + \frac{\partial V}{\partial y} \frac{\partial U}{\partial y} + \frac{\partial V}{\partial z} \frac{\partial U}{\partial z} \right] d\tau = 0. \quad (3)$$

Now by Green's theorem in its first form, Eq. (57.3),

$$\int_B U \Delta V d\tau + \int_B \left[\frac{\partial V}{\partial x} \frac{\partial U}{\partial x} + \frac{\partial V}{\partial y} \frac{\partial U}{\partial y} + \frac{\partial V}{\partial z} \frac{\partial U}{\partial z} \right] d\tau = \int_S U \frac{\partial V}{\partial n} d\omega.$$

The right member of this equation vanishes, since U is everywhere zero on S. The second integral is zero, by Eq. (3); therefore, the first integral also is zero. Aside from the conditions that U is continuous and vanishes on S, the function U is arbitrary. If ΔV were not zero everywhere within S, the function U could be chosen in such a way that $U\Delta V$ was everywhere positive or zero, and therefore, the integral not zero. It follows that ΔV is zero everywhere, and the function V which makes the integral J a minimum is harmonic within S. As V takes the prescribed set of values on S, it is the function which was sought.

The criticism of Weierstrass was that this argument fails to distinguish between the existence of a *minimum* and the existence of a *lower limit*. The fact that the integral J has a lower limit does not justify the inference that there exists a function V which makes J a minimum.

Suppose, for example, from the totality of planes

$$\varphi(x,\, y,\, z) = ax + by + cz + d = 0,$$

that one is sought which renders the integral

$$J = \int \left[\left(\frac{\partial \varphi}{\partial x} \right)^2 + \left(\frac{\partial \varphi}{\partial y} \right)^2 + \left(\frac{\partial \varphi}{\partial z} \right)^2 \right] d\tau,$$

taken over a unit sphere at the origin, a minimum. The argument of Dirichlet would lead to the inference that such a plane existed. In this case, however, J is easily evaluated, and

$$J = \frac{4}{3}\pi(a^2 + b^2 + c^2).$$

The lower limit of J is zero, and there are infinitely many planes for which J is as small as may be desired; but a plane for which $J = 0$ does not exist.

It is true, however, that in very many cases the minimum does exist. Green, Lord Kelvin and Dirichlet were entirely correct in their conclusions that a solution of Green's problem exists for a very wide class of closed surfaces, notwithstanding the fact that their arguments are insufficient.

145. The Equivalent Problem of Poincaré.—A problem which is equivalent to Green's problem has been formulated by Poincaré.[1] It can be stated as follows:

Given a closed surface S, does there exist a function $V(x,\, y,\, z)$ which satisfies the following conditions:

1. *V and its first derivatives are continuous within S.*
2. *The second derivatives of V exist and are finite.*
3. *In the interior of S, the equation*

$$\Delta V = -4\pi\sigma$$

is satisfied, where σ is a given finite and integrable function.

4. *V vanishes on the surface S.*

[1] "Théorie du Potential Newtonian," p. 167.

In order to show the equivalence let it be assumed at first that a solution of Green's problem exists. Let the function U be defined by the relation

$$U = \int_B \sigma \frac{d\tau}{\rho},$$

the integral being taken over the volume enclosed by S. Since U, obviously, is a Newtonian potential, it satisfies the first three conditions of Poincaré's problem, but not the fourth.

Since a solution of Green's problem is always possible, there exists a function U_1 which satisfies the conditions.

$$\Delta U_1 = 0 \text{ within } S, \qquad \frac{1''}{2} U = -U_s \text{ on } S.$$

The function

$$V = U + U_1$$

then satisfies all four of the above conditions, and a solution of Poincaré's problem also exists.

Conversely, let it be assumed that a solution of Poincaré's problem always exists; it will be shown, as a consequence, that a solution of Green's problem always exists.

Let U be any function which is continuous, which has continuous first and second derivatives within S, and which is equal to U_S on S. There are, of course, infinitely many such functions. Let σ be defined by the relation

$$\sigma = \frac{1}{4\pi} \Delta U.$$

Let U_1 be the function which solves Poincaré's problem for this particular σ, so that

$$\Delta U_1 = -4\pi\sigma,$$

and

$$U_1 = 0 \quad \text{on } S.$$

Then, evidently,

$$V = U + U_1$$

satisfies the conditions of Green's problem, since $\Delta V = 0$, within S, and $V = U_s$ on S.

Since the existence of a solution of Green's problem implies the existence of a solution of Poincaré's problem, and conversely, the two problems are equivalent.

Problems.

1. Show by a limiting process from the sphere that the Green function relative to a point p for an infinite plane is

$$G = \frac{1}{\rho} - \frac{1}{\rho_1},$$

where ρ is measured from the point p and ρ_1 is measured from the optical image p_1 of p in the infinite plane.

2. If the point p is at a distance h from the plane, the distribution of matter on the plane necessary to make it centrobaric is

$$\sigma = \frac{h}{2\pi\rho^3}.$$

Particles on one side of the plane are attracted toward the point p_1 and on the other side toward the point p.

3. Let p_0 be a point in the first quadrant, p_1 the optical image of p_0 in the yz-plane, p_2 the optical image of p_1 in the xz-plane, p_3 the image of p_2 in the yz-plane, and therefore, also the image of p_0 in the xz-plane. If positive unit particles are placed at p_0 and p_2 and negative unit particles at p_1 and p_3, the potential due to the four particles vanishes on the yz-plane and also on the xz-plane, that is, these planes are level surfaces. It can also be imagined as vanishing on a spherical surface with origin at the center and radius R which is very great. Find the distribution of density on the closed surface which is bounded by the planes which pass through the positive x-axis and the z-axis, the positive y-axis and the z-axis, and the surface of the sphere, which makes this surface centrobaric.

4. Show that Problem 3 can be generalized, using the method of alternate reflections and alternately positive and negative masses, from the angle $\pi/2$ to the angle π/n, where n is an integer.

5. Using a triply infinite system of reflections, show how to construct Green's function for a rectangular parallelopiped.

6. Derive the potential of a level layer for an ellipsoid by the method of Sec. 116.

7. Show that, if $F(x, y, z)$ satisfies the equation of Laplace, the function

$$\frac{a}{\rho} F\left(\frac{a^2\xi}{\rho^2}, \frac{a^2\eta}{\rho^2}, \frac{a^2\zeta}{\rho^2}\right)$$

also satisfies it, where $\rho^2 = \xi^2 + \eta^2 + \zeta^2$.

CHAPTER VI

TWO-LAYER SURFACES

THE METHODS OF NEUMANN AND POINCARÉ

146. Various Types of Mass.—Up to the present point, it has been assumed that the force exerted by the given body upon a unit particle has been attractive. If the force is repellant, it is evident that it is sufficient merely to change the sign of the potential V or the sign of the mass of the particle, provided of course, that the force continues to vary inversely as the square of the distance. Gravitational, electric, and magnetic forces obey this law and the potentials for these forces differ from one another only in the constant factor of proportionality which is associated with the potential; this factor of proportionality depending upon the forces under consideration and the system of units which is employed.

It is possible to speak of gravitational mass, or electrical mass, or magnetic mass as the case may be, for, after all, it is the forces that are dealt with physically, and mass is a derived concept which is found to be convenient; and this concept is found to be convenient for all three types of force. In the case of gravitation, the forces are always forces of attraction, and there is but one kind of gravitational mass. This mass is always regarded as positive and its concentration is denoted by the term density. In the cases of electricity and magnetism both attractive and repellant forces occur, and therefore, in each case it is necessary to assume the existence of two kinds of mass; the one positive and the other negative. Two positive masses of electricity repel each other, and so also do two negative masses; but two masses of unlike sign, that is, one positive and one negative, attract each other. The same statements hold also for magnetic masses. The notion of density, mass per unit volume or mass per unit area, is likewise applicable.

147. The Magnetic Doublet.—Imagine two magnetic masses, $+\mu$ and $-\mu$, numerically equal but of opposite signs, placed

283

at the points N and S respectively, at a distance l apart (Fig. 89). Let there be placed at any point P in space a particle of magnetic mass equal to -1. Then the particles at N and P attract each other, while the particles at S and P repel each other. If

$$NP = \rho_1, \qquad SP = \rho_2,$$

the potentials at P due to the magnetic masses $+\mu$ and $-\mu$ respectively are

$$V_1 = +\frac{\mu}{\rho_1} \qquad V_2 = -\frac{\mu}{\rho_2}.$$

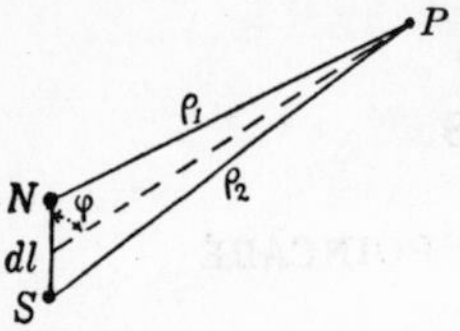

Fig. 89.

The potential at P due to both masses is simply the sum of these two potentials. That is,

$$V_1 + V_2 = V = \frac{\mu}{P_1} - \frac{\mu}{P_2}.$$

This expression can also be written

$$V = l\mu\frac{\left(\dfrac{1}{\rho_1} - \dfrac{1}{\rho_2}\right)}{l} = m\frac{\dfrac{1}{\rho_1} - \dfrac{1}{\rho_2}}{l},$$

where $m = l\mu$ is called the magnetic moment. Let the direction of l be taken from S toward N. If l is infinitely small dl the pair of magnetic masses $+\mu$ and $-\mu$ is said to form a *doublet*, or a magnetic element. For such a doublet

$$V = \mu dl \cdot \lim_{l=0} \frac{\dfrac{1}{\rho_1} - \dfrac{1}{\rho_2}}{l} = -\mu\frac{\partial}{\partial l}\left(\frac{1}{\rho}\right)dl,$$

where ρ is the line joining the doublet to the point P, and dl is the distance between the components of the doublet measured from S toward N.

By Sec. 54,

$$\frac{\partial}{\partial l}\left(\frac{1}{\rho}\right) = \frac{\partial}{\partial \rho}\left(\frac{1}{\rho}\right)\cos\widehat{l\rho} = -\frac{\cos\widehat{l\rho}}{\rho^2}.$$

If the angle $\widehat{l\rho}$ is denoted by φ, the expression for the potential becomes

$$V = +\mu dl\frac{\cos\varphi}{\rho^2} = +\frac{m\cos\varphi}{\rho^2}.$$

If the direction cosines of the doublet are α, β, γ, if x_0, y_0, z_0 are the coordinates of the doublet, and if x, y, z are the coordinates of the point P, then, (Sec. 54),

$$V = +m\left[\alpha\frac{\partial}{\partial x_0}\left(\frac{1}{\rho}\right) + \beta\frac{\partial}{\partial y_0}\left(\frac{1}{\rho}\right) + \gamma\frac{\partial}{\partial z_0}\left(\frac{1}{\rho}\right)\right],$$

or,

$$= -m\left[\alpha\frac{\partial}{\partial x}\left(\frac{1}{\rho}\right) + \beta\frac{\partial}{\partial y}\left(\frac{1}{\rho}\right) + \gamma\frac{\partial}{\partial z}\left(\frac{1}{\rho}\right)\right].$$

Since V is merely the difference between two Newtonian potentials, it is evident that V also is harmonic in every domain that does not contain the doublet itself.

148. The Bar Magnet.—Imagine a straight bar of length l built up of magnetic elements placed end to end. If the cross-section of the bar is infinitesimal, it is seen from Eq. (147.1) that the value of the potential of the bar at any exterior point P is

$$V = \mu\int_{-\frac{l}{2}}^{+\frac{l}{2}}\frac{\cos\varphi}{\rho^2}dl;$$

or, since

$$dl\cdot\cos\varphi = -d\rho,$$

$$V = -\mu\int_{\rho_2}^{\rho_1}\frac{d\rho}{\rho^2} = \mu\left(\frac{1}{\rho_1} - \frac{1}{\rho_2}\right).$$

That is, the bar magnet acts at exterior points just as though magnetic masses equal to $+\mu$ and $-\mu$ respectively were placed on the ends of the bar and there were no magnetic masses elsewhere. The north pole of the magnet is at the mass $+\mu$ and the south pole at $-\mu$.

149. Magnetic Sheets—Two-layer Surfaces.—It is possible also to imagine a sheet built up of magnetic elements placed side by side with the positive masses on one side of the sheet and the negative masses on the other, with the axes of the magnetic elements everywhere normal to the sheet. Since the thickness of the sheet is infinitesimal, it can be regarded as a surface made up of two layers—a two-layer surface—as contrasted with the single-layer surface which has been studied hitherto.

Let $d\omega$ be an element of area and σ its magnetic moment per unit area, or the density of its magnetic moment. Then $\sigma d\omega$ is the magnetic moment of the surface element $d\omega$. The potential of this element for a negative unit mass placed at an exterior point $P(x, y, z)$ is

$$\frac{\sigma \cos \varphi}{\rho^2} d\omega = -\sigma \frac{\partial}{\partial n}\left(\frac{1}{\rho}\right) d\omega,$$

and for a positive unit mass at the point P

$$-\frac{\sigma \cos \varphi}{P^2} d\omega = +\sigma \frac{\partial}{\partial n}\left(\frac{1}{\rho}\right) d\omega.$$

This expression is independent of the sense along the normal, for if n changes sign σ also changes sign. Regarding the mass at the point P as negative, the potential of the entire surface is

$$V = -\int_S \sigma \frac{\partial}{\partial n}\left(\frac{1}{\rho}\right) d\omega =$$
$$+ \int_S \sigma \left[\alpha \frac{\partial}{\partial x}\left(\frac{1}{\rho}\right) + \beta \frac{\partial}{\partial y}\left(\frac{1}{\rho}\right) + \gamma \frac{\partial}{\partial z}\left(\frac{1}{\rho}\right) \right] d\omega, \quad (1)$$

the integral being extended over the entire surface.

Let

$$\int_S \frac{\alpha\sigma}{\rho} d\omega = V_1 \qquad \int_S \frac{\beta\sigma}{\rho} d\omega = V_2, \qquad \int_S \frac{\gamma\sigma}{\rho} d\omega = V_3.$$

If, in these integrals, $\alpha\sigma$, $\beta\sigma$, and $\gamma\sigma$ are regarded as ordinary mass densities it is evident that V_1, V_2, and V_3 are the potentials of simple layers on S, and Eq. (1) can be written

$$V = -\left[\frac{\partial V_1}{\partial x} + \frac{\partial V_2}{\partial y} + \frac{\partial V_3}{\partial z} \right]. \quad (2)$$

Since the derivatives of simple layers have discontinuities in crossing the surface (Sec. 92), it is to be expected that discontinuities exist in the potential of double layers in crossing the surface.

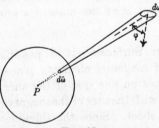

FIG. 90.

150. Closed, Uniform, Two-layer Surfaces.—Let $d\omega$ be an element of a two-layer surface, and let $d\bar{\omega}$ be the solid angle which is subtended by $d\omega$ at a given point P, so that $d\bar{\omega}$ is the area which this solid angle cuts out of a unit sphere described about P as a center, Fig. 90. Then, as was seen in Sec. 66,

$$d\bar{\omega} = \pm \frac{\cos \varphi}{\rho^2} d\omega.$$

The solid angle $d\tilde{\omega}$ will be regarded as positive when the positive side of $d\omega$ is turned toward P and negative when the negative side of $d\omega$ is turned toward P. If σ is the magnetic moment of the element $d\omega$, the potential of the surface at the point P is

$$V = \int_S \sigma \frac{\partial}{\partial n}\left(\frac{1}{\rho}\right)d\omega = \int_S \frac{\sigma \cos \varphi}{\rho^2}d\omega = \int_S \sigma d\tilde{\omega}.$$

If the surface S is closed and if σ is constant, that is, the magnetic moment is constant over the surface, then at an external point P the potential V is zero, since the solid angle pierces the surface an even number of times, and the elements

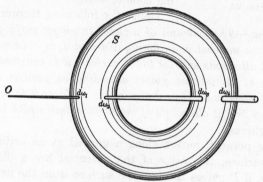

Fig. 91.

$d\omega_i$ which it cuts out of the surface present positive and negative sides alternately to the point P. (Fig. 91.)

If the point P is interior to the surface the solid angle pierces the surface an odd number of times. Hence, the potential has the value $\pm 4\pi\sigma$ at an interior point. It is $+4\pi\sigma$ if the positive magnetic mass is on the inside of the surface, and $-4\pi\sigma$ if the negative magnetic mass is on the inside of the surface.

Finally, if the point P is in the surface itself and if the surface has a definite tangent plane at this point, the value of the potential is $\pm 2\pi\sigma$ according as the positive or negative magnetic mass is on the inside of the surface. There are two possibilities in this case; one in which the surface lies entirely on one side of the tangent plane, and the other in which it does not. If the surface lies entirely on one side of the tangent plane, the integral $\int d\tilde{\omega}$ is evidently 2π since the solid angle $d\tilde{\omega}$ pierces the surface an odd number of times on one side of the tangent plane and not at all on the other.   If the surface does not lie entirely on one side of the tangent plane the solid angle $d\tilde{\omega}$ pierces the

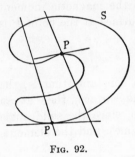

Fig. 92.

surface an odd number of times on one side of the tangent plane and an even number of times on the other (Fig. 92). The value of the integral is the same in both cases.

If the point P lies in the surface at a conical point or on an edge, the value of the potential at P is $\pm \sigma$ times the area cut out of the unit sphere by the enveloping cone or wedge.

Hence the following theorem:

Theorem.—The potential of a closed two-layer surface, on which the magnetic moment is uniformly distributed, is constant and equal to zero at all points exterior to the surface; it is constant and equal to $\pm 4\pi\sigma$ at all interior points according as positive or negative magnetic mass is on the interior of the surface; it is constant and equal to $\pm 2\pi\sigma$ at all points of the surface itself which have definite tangent planes.

As the point P moves along a normal at an ordinary point of the surface, the value of the potential has a discontinuity of $+4\pi\sigma$, if P passes through the surface from the negative side to the positive side, and $-4\pi\sigma$ if P passes from the positive side to the negative side.   If the point P is in the surface itself, the value of the potential is the arithmetic mean of the values on the two opposite sides of the surface at the point P.

If V_0 is the value of V at a point P_0 of the surface, and if V_{n0} and V_{p0} are the limits of V as the point P approaches the point P_0 from the negative and positive sides respectively, then

$$V_{p0} = V_0 + 2\pi\sigma,$$

$$V_{n0} = V_0 - 2\pi\sigma.$$

151. Uniform Surfaces Not Closed.—The discontinuity in the value of the potential, just mentioned, exists and has the same value even if the surface is not a closed one.   To show this let the given surface S be bounded by a closed contour C. Through the contour C pass another surface Σ, such that $S + \Sigma$ forms a closed surface, and let Σ be covered with a uniform two-layer material of the same moment as S.   If V is the potential due to S and U is the potential due to Σ, the potential of the entire closed surface is, evidently, $V + U$.

By Sec. 150, $U + V$ has a discontinuity of $\pm 4\pi\sigma$ if the point P crosses this closed surface at any point, say through the surface S. Since the points of S lie outside of Σ, the potential U due to Σ is continuous across S. Hence, the discontinuity of $U + V$ is due to the same discontinuity in V, since U is continuous.

If the surface is uniform, but not closed, and is of such shape that a straight line through P pierces it in but one point (Fig. 93), and if Ω is the solid angle which the surface subtends at P (that is, the apparent size), then

$$V = +\sigma\Omega,$$

if the positive side of S is turned toward P, and

$$V = -\sigma\Omega,$$

if the negative side of S is turned toward P.

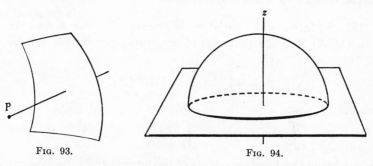

Fig. 93.   Fig. 94.

If one sheet of the surface, as seen from P, projects upon another sheet of opposite sign the two sheets in such projection contribute nothing to the potential. Consider, for example, an open hemisphere of radius a with its positive side outward resting on an xy-plane with the z-axis as the axis of symmetry. At any point in the xy-plane, outside of the circle which forms the base of the hemisphere, the value of the potential is zero, since the positive sheet of the hemisphere projects exactly upon the negative sheet. At all points situated above the xy-plane, but outside of the hemisphere, the potential is equal to $+\sigma$ times the apparent size of the base of the hemisphere; and at all points situated below the xy-plane the potential is equal to $-\sigma$ times the apparent size of the base. Along the z-axis

$$V = V_1 = -2\pi\sigma\left(1 + \frac{z}{\sqrt{a^2 + z^2}}\right), \quad \text{if } z < +a,$$

and

$$V = V_2 = +2\pi\sigma\left(1 - \frac{z}{\sqrt{a^2 + z^2}}\right), \quad \text{if } z > +a.$$

The limiting value of V_1 for $z = a$ is $-2\pi\sigma\left(1 + \frac{1}{\sqrt{2}}\right)$ and

the limiting value of V_2 for $z = a$ is $+2\pi\sigma\left(1 - \frac{1}{\sqrt{2}}\right)$. The

discontinuity is

$$\lim_{z=a} V_2 - \lim_{z=a} V_2 = 4\pi\sigma.$$

The value of V for $z = a$ is

$$\frac{1}{2}\left[\lim_{z=a} V_1 + \lim_{z=a} V_2\right] = \frac{2\pi\sigma}{\sqrt{2}},$$

as can be seen by a direct integration.

152. Surfaces with Variable Moments.—It was shown in
Eq. (149.2) that the potential of any two-layer surface can be
written

$$V = -\left[\frac{\partial V_1}{\partial x} + \frac{\partial V_2}{\partial y} + \frac{\partial V_3}{\partial z}\right],$$

where

$$V_1 = \int_S \frac{\alpha\sigma}{\rho}d\omega, \qquad V_2 = \int_S \frac{\beta\sigma}{\rho}d\omega, \qquad V_3 = \int_S \frac{\gamma\sigma}{\rho}d\omega,$$

α, β, γ being the direction cosines of the normal and σ the moment
at the element $d\omega$. Hence V_1, V_2, and V_3 can be regarded as
potentials of simple layers for which the surface densities are
$\alpha\sigma$, $\beta\sigma$, and $\gamma\sigma$. The potentials of *simple* layers are continuous
across the surface (Sec. 91), but the first derivatives in general
are discontinuous. According to Eq. (94.1), the discontinuities
are

$$\text{for} \quad \frac{\partial V_1}{\partial x}, \quad -4\pi\alpha\sigma \cdot \alpha = -4\pi\sigma\alpha^2,$$

$$\text{for} \quad \frac{\partial V_2}{\partial y}, \quad -4\pi\beta\sigma \cdot \beta = -4\pi\sigma\beta^2,$$

$$\text{for} \quad \frac{\partial V_3}{\partial z}, \quad -4\pi\gamma\sigma \cdot \gamma = -4\pi\sigma\gamma^2.$$

Hence, the discontinuity in V in crossing the surface is

$$4\pi\sigma(\alpha^2 + \beta^2 + \gamma^2) = 4\pi\sigma, \tag{1}$$

the sign, of course, depending upon the direction of crossing. The potential is continuous across any point at which σ vanishes.

Suppose that P_0 is a fixed point of the surface S and that V_0 is the value of the potential at P_0. If V_n is the value of the potential at a variable point P near P_0 on the negative side of the surface and V_p is the value of the potential for a point on the positive side of the surface near P, and if V_{n0} and V_{p0} are the limits of V_n and V_p as the points P approach P_0, it is desired to show that V_0 is the arithmetic mean of V_{n0} and V_{p0}, and therefore,

$$\left.\begin{matrix} V_{n0} = V_0 - 2\pi\sigma_0, \\ V_{p0} = V_0 + 2\pi\sigma_0, \end{matrix}\right\} \tag{2}$$

σ_0 being the density of moments at the point P_0.

The potential at any point can be written

$$V = \int_S \frac{\sigma_0 \cos\varphi}{\rho^2}d\omega + \int_S \frac{(\sigma - \sigma_0)\cos\varphi}{\rho^2}d\omega.$$

or, by setting

$$W = \int_S \frac{\sigma_0 \cos\varphi}{\rho^2}d\omega, \qquad U = \int_S \frac{(\sigma - \sigma_0)\cos\varphi}{\rho^2}d\omega,$$

the potential can be written

$$V = W + U.$$

It was shown in Secs. 150 and 151 that equations similar to Eqs. (2) hold for the potential W, which is the potential of a double layer of constant moment density. It will be sufficient, therefore, to show that the function U is continuous across the surface at the point P_0. But this is evident from Eq. (1), for U is the potential of a two-layer surface for which the density of moments $(\sigma - \sigma_0)$ vanishes at P_0. It is, therefore, continuous across the surface at P_0 and Eqs. (2) is established.

It might be remarked that in Green's formula, Eq. (63.4),

$$4\pi\Phi(x, y, z) = \int_S \frac{\partial}{\partial n}\left(\frac{1}{\rho}\right)\Phi d\omega - \int_S \frac{1}{\rho}\frac{\partial\Phi}{\partial n}d\omega,$$

the function Φ is represented as the difference between the potential of a two-layer surface, for which the moment density is

Φ, and the potential of a simple layer for which the mass density is $\partial\Phi/\partial n$.

153. Discontinuities in the First Derivatives.—The potential of a two-layer surface with variable moment density can be written

$$V = -\left(\frac{\partial V_1}{\partial x} + \frac{\partial V_2}{\partial y} + \frac{\partial V_3}{\partial z}\right),$$

where

$$V_1 = \int_S \frac{\alpha\sigma}{\rho}d\omega, \qquad V_2 = \int_S \frac{\beta\sigma}{\rho}d\omega, \qquad V_3 = \int_S \frac{\gamma\sigma}{\rho}d\omega,$$

α, β, γ are the direction cosines of the normal, and σ is the moment density at the element $d\omega$. The functions V_1, V_2, and V_3 are the potentials of certain simple layers on S.

It is evident that the first derivatives of the potentials of double layers are related to the second derivatives of the potentials of certain simple layers on the same surface. For example,

$$\frac{\partial V}{\partial x} = -\left(\frac{\partial^2 V_1}{\partial x^2} + \frac{\partial^2 V_2}{\partial x\partial y} + \frac{\partial^2 V_3}{\partial x\partial z}\right).$$

The discontinuities in the second derivatives of the potentials of simple layers were studied in Sec. 96. From the results of that section, it is found that the discontinuities of

$$\frac{\partial V_1}{\partial x^2}, \qquad \frac{\partial^2 V_2}{\partial x\partial y}, \qquad \frac{\partial^2 V_2}{\partial x\partial z},$$

under the assumption that the x, y-axes are parallel to the tangents of the lines of curvature at the point of crossing O of the surface, are

$$4\pi\alpha\sigma p_2, \qquad 0, \qquad -4\pi\gamma\frac{\partial\sigma}{\partial\xi};$$

or, since α is zero and γ is $+1$ at the point O, the discontinuities are

$$0, \qquad 0 \qquad -4\pi\frac{\partial\sigma}{\partial\xi}.$$

Hence, the discontinuity in $\frac{\partial V}{\partial x}$ is $+4\pi\frac{\partial\sigma}{\partial\xi}$; and in a similar manner it is found that the discontinuity in $\frac{\partial V}{\partial y}$ is $+4\pi\frac{\partial\sigma}{\partial\eta}$.

For the derivative with respect to z,

$$\frac{\partial V}{\partial z} = -\left(\frac{\partial^2 V_1}{\partial x \partial z} + \frac{\partial^2 V_2}{\partial y \partial z} + \frac{\partial^2 V_3}{\partial z^2}\right),$$

the discontinuities are

$$-4\pi\gamma\frac{\partial}{\partial \xi}\left(\frac{\alpha\sigma}{\gamma}\right), \qquad -4\pi\gamma\frac{\partial}{\partial \eta}\left(\frac{\beta\sigma}{\gamma}\right), \qquad -4\pi\sigma(p_2 + q_2).$$

Since,

$$\alpha = \beta = 0, \qquad \gamma = 1,$$

at the point O, these discontinuities are expressed more simply by

$$-4\pi\sigma\frac{\partial \alpha}{\partial \xi}, \qquad -4\pi\sigma\frac{\partial \beta}{\partial \eta}, \qquad -4\pi\sigma(p_2 + q_2).$$

The total discontinuity of $\partial V/\partial z$ is, therefore,

$$-4\pi\sigma\left(p_2 + q_2 + \frac{\partial \alpha}{\partial \xi} + \frac{\partial \beta}{\partial \eta}\right).$$

Now

$$\alpha = \frac{-p_1}{\sqrt{1 + p_1^2 + q_1^2}}, \qquad \beta = \frac{-q_1}{\sqrt{1 + p_1^2 + q_1^2}},$$

$$p_2 = \frac{\partial p_1}{\partial \xi}, \qquad\qquad q_2 = \frac{\partial q_1}{\partial \eta}.$$

At the point O,

$$p_1 = q_1 = \frac{\partial p_1}{\partial \eta} = \frac{\partial q_1}{\partial \xi} = 0,$$

from which it is found that

$$p_2 + q_2 + \frac{\partial \alpha}{\partial \xi} + \frac{\partial \beta}{\partial \eta}$$

also is zero at the point O. Hence, there is no discontinuity in $\partial V/\partial z$ in crossing the surface at the point O.

These results can be stated as follows: *The normal derivative of the potential of a two layer surface is continuous across the surface; the tangential derivatives, however, have the discontinuities*

$$4\pi\frac{\partial \sigma}{\partial \xi} \qquad and \qquad 4\pi\frac{\partial \sigma}{\partial \eta}. \tag{1}$$

154. The Configuration Constant of a Closed Surface.—
Suppose a given closed surface S is divided into two parts.

This division may be as simple as the division of the earth's surface into a northern and a southern hemisphere, or it may be as complicated as the division into the land and water areas of the earth's surface. Let these two parts be denoted by α and β, so that

$$S = \alpha + \beta.$$

Assume further that the surface S is everywhere convex, so that any given straight line pierces it not more than twice, and $\cos \varphi$ is never negative. Let the integral

$$\int_{\alpha,1} \frac{\cos \varphi}{\rho^2} d\omega = \int_{\alpha,1} d\tilde{\omega} \tag{1}$$

denote the total solid angle subtended by the area α at a fixed point of the surface denoted by the subscript 1. Likewise, the integral

$$\int_{\beta,2} d\tilde{\omega}$$

denotes the solid angle subtended by the area β at another fixed point of the surface denoted by the subscript 2. Under the hypothesis of convexity, the solid angle subtended by the entire surface at any point whatever of the surface is less than or at most equal to 2π. Hence

$$0 \leqq \int_{\alpha,1} d\tilde{\omega} \leqq 2\pi, \qquad 0 \leqq \int_{\beta,2} d\tilde{\omega} \leqq 2\pi,$$

and therefore,

$$0 \leqq \frac{1}{4\pi}\left[\int_{\alpha,1} d\tilde{\omega} + \int_{\beta,2} d\tilde{\omega} \right] \leqq 1. \tag{2}$$

In order that the lower limit of Eq. (2) be attained, it is necessary that every element $d\omega$ of the area α should be edgewise as seen from the point 1, and every element of the area β should be seen edgewise from the point 2. Thus, if the point 1 is the apex of a right circular cone (area α) and the point 2 is the apex of a second right circular cone (area β), the bases of the two cones having the same diameter, the surface formed by putting the two cones

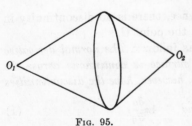

FIG. 95.

together base to base (Fig. 95) would be a surface for which the lower limit could be attained. The $\cos \varphi$ in Eq. (1) vanishes everywhere. Such surfaces were called double stars by Neumann, and are excluded from consideration. Single starred surfaces do not exist in the class of closed surfaces.

For a given surface S and a given manner of division of the surface, there exists a constant $\zeta > 0$, whatever the pair of fixed points may be, such that

$$\zeta \leq \frac{1}{4\pi}\left[\int_{\alpha,1} d\tilde{\omega} + \int_{\beta,2} d\tilde{\omega}\right] \leq 1,$$

for all possible divisions of the surface; and for all possible selections of the fixed points, ζ has a minimum which will be denoted by $1 - \lambda$. Hence for a given surface there exists a constant λ, which is independent of the mode of division of the surface, and independent of the choice of the two points, such that

$$0 \leq 1 - \frac{1}{4\pi}\left[\int_{\alpha,1} d\tilde{\omega} + \int_{\beta,2} d\tilde{\omega}\right] \leq \lambda < 1. \tag{3}$$

Neumann called λ the configuration constant of the surface.

155. The Spread of Values of the Potential on a Closed, Convex Surface.—Let the potential of a double layer on S, evaluated for some particular point of S, be denoted by $2\pi V_1$. Then

$$V_1 = \frac{1}{2\pi}\int_S \sigma \frac{\cos \varphi}{\rho^2} d\omega = \frac{1}{2\pi}\int_S \sigma d\tilde{\omega}. \tag{1}$$

Let M be the maximum value of σ on S, and m its minimum value. Draw the lines on S for which $\sigma = (M + m)/2$, which is possible since σ is assumed to be continuous. Let the area for which $\sigma > (M + m)/2$ be denoted by α and the area for which $\sigma < (M + m)/2$ be denoted by β. Since σ and $\cos \varphi$ are everywhere positive, it is evident from Eq. (1) that

$$V_1 \leq \frac{M}{2\pi}\int_{\alpha,1} d\tilde{\omega} + \frac{M + m}{4\pi}\int_{\beta,1} d\tilde{\omega},$$

and

$$V_1 \geq \frac{M + m}{4\pi}\int_{\alpha,1} d\tilde{\omega} + \frac{m}{2\pi}\int_{\beta,1} d\tilde{\omega}.$$

By virtue of the relation

$$\int_{\alpha,1} d\tilde{\omega} + \int_{\beta,1} d\tilde{\omega} = 2\pi,$$

these equations can also be written

$$\left.\begin{aligned}
V_1 &\leqq M - \frac{M - m}{4\pi} \int_{\beta,1} d\tilde{\omega}, \\
V_1 &\geqq m + \frac{M - m}{4\pi} \int_{\alpha,1} d\tilde{\omega}.
\end{aligned}\right\} \tag{2}$$

In a like manner, for a second fixed point on S,

$$\left.\begin{aligned}
V_2 &\leqq M - \frac{M - m}{4\pi} \int_{\beta,2} d\tilde{\omega}, \\
V_2 &\geqq m + \frac{M - m}{4\pi} \int_{\alpha,2} d\tilde{\omega}.
\end{aligned}\right\} \tag{3}$$

Equations (2) or (3) show that the maximum value of V on S is definitely less than M and its minimum definitely greater than m, unless σ is a constant, in which case $V = M = m$. On subtracting the second of Eqs. (2) from the first of Eqs. (3), there results

$$V_2 - V_1 \leqq (M - m)\left(1 - \frac{1}{4\pi}\left[\int_{\alpha,1} d\tilde{\omega} + \int_{\beta,2} d\tilde{\omega}\right]\right);$$

and therefore, by Eq. (154.3),

$$\left.\begin{aligned}
V_2 - V_1 &\leqq (M - m)\lambda, \\
0 &< \lambda < 1,
\end{aligned}\right\} \tag{4}$$

wherever the two fixed points on S, at which the potential was evaluated, may be. Hence, the maximum difference between the values of the potential at any two points on S does not exceed the maximum difference of the densities multiplied by λ, the configuration constant of the surface. This important theorem is due to Neumann.

156. Neumann's Proof of Dirichlet's Principle.—The first rigorous proof of the existence of a solution of Green's problem was given by C. Neumann.[1] His proof is limited to closed surfaces which are generally convex, although they may have

---

[1] Neumann, Dr. C., "Untersuchungen über das Logarithmische und Newton'sche Potential," 1877. Leipzig.

corners and edges, but excluding surfaces which he called double stars (Sec. 154).

It will be recalled that in Green's problem, it is required to find a function that is harmonic inside of a given closed surface S (interior problem), or harmonic on the outside and vanishing at infinity (exterior problem), and that takes a prescribed continuous set of values on S.

Neumann's *method of the arithmetic mean* shows how to build a double layer on S whose external, or internal, potential will have the required properties. Suppose the function which is given on S is $f(\xi, \eta, \zeta)$. Form the potential of a double layer on S whose moment density is $f/2\pi$, namely,

$$W_1 = \frac{1}{2\pi}\int_S f\frac{\cos \varphi}{\rho^2}d\omega = \frac{1}{2\pi}\int_S f d\tilde{\omega}. \tag{0}$$

If ρ is measured from a point on the outside of S, the function W_1 is the external potential; if ρ is measured from an inside point, W_1 is the internal potential; if ρ is measured from a point on S, the function W_1 is the value of the potential on the surface, and this fact will be denoted by the superscript zero.

If f is everywhere positive and the positive magnetic mass is on the inside of S, so that $d\tilde{\omega}$ is positive, it is evident that $W_1^{(0)}$ is positive. Since $W_1^{(0)}$ is continuous on S, $W_1^{(0)}/2\pi$ can be taken as the density for a second potential W_2, thus:

and, sequentially

$$\left.\begin{aligned} W_2 &= \frac{1}{2\pi}\int_S W_1^{(0)}d\tilde{\omega}; \\ W_3 &= \frac{1}{2\pi}\int_S W_2^{(0)}d\tilde{\omega}, \\ &\cdot\cdot\cdot\cdot\cdot\cdot\cdot\cdot\cdot\cdot \\ W_n &= \frac{1}{2\pi}\int_S W^{(0)}_{n-1}d\tilde{\omega}, \\ &\cdot\cdot\cdot\cdot\cdot\cdot\cdot\cdot\cdot\cdot \end{aligned}\right\} \tag{1}$$

Suppose M is the maximum value of f on S, and m is the minimum value. If S_1 is the spread of $W_1^{(0)}$ on S, that is, the difference between its maximum and minimum values, then, by Eq. (155.4),

$$S_1 \leqq (M - m)\lambda, \tag{2}$$

where λ is the configuration constant of the surface. In general, if S_n is the spread of $W_n^{(0)}$ on S, then

$$\left.\begin{array}{r} S_n \leqq S_{n-1}\lambda \\ \leqq S_{n-2}\lambda^2 \\ \leqq (M-m)\lambda^n. \end{array}\right\} \tag{3}$$

Since λ is a fixed constant less than unity for each surface of the class considered, it is evident that the limit of S_n as n increases is zero. That is, the successive double layers tend toward constant density on S.

If M_i and m_i are the maximum and minimum values of $W_i^{(0)}$, it follows from Eq. (155.3) that

$$\left.\begin{array}{l} M > M_1 > M_2 > \cdots > M_{n-1} > M_n > \cdots, \\ m < m_1 < m_2 < \cdots < m_{n-1} < m_n < \cdots. \end{array}\right\} \tag{4}$$

That is, the sequence of maxima is a decreasing sequence, while the sequence of minima is an increasing sequence. Since the spread tends toward zero, it follows that the limit of the maxima is the same as the limit of the minima, and the functions $W_n^{(0)}$ tend toward a definite constant value, or

$$W_\infty^{(0)} = C. \tag{5}$$

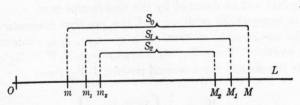

Fig. 96.

On the straight line L (Fig. 96), let points be marked at distances m and M from the point O. The interval mM, which will be denoted by S_0, is the spread of σ on S. That is

$$m \leqq \sigma \leqq M.$$

at all points of the surface. Similarly, mark the points m_1, m_2, $\ldots$; M_1, M_2, $\ldots$. Then

$$m_1 \leqq W_1^{(0)} \leqq M_1, \qquad m_2 \leqq W_2^{(0)} \leqq M_2, \qquad \cdots,$$

at all points of the surface. Since $W_1^{(0)}$ and σ both lie in the interval mM, it follows that

$$|W_1^{(0)} - \sigma| \leqq S_0,$$

even though the value of $W_1^{(0)}$ is taken at one point of the surface and the value of σ is taken at another. That is, this inequality holds for every pair of points on S. In a similar manner,

$$|W_2^{(0)} - W_1^{(0)}| \leqq S_1,$$

$$|W_3^{(0)} - W_2^{(0)}| \leqq S_2,$$

$$\cdot\;\cdot\;\cdot\;\cdot\;\cdot\;\cdot\;\cdot\;\cdot\;\cdot\;\cdot\;\cdot$$

$$|W_{n+1}^{(0)} - W_n^{(0)}| \leqq S_n,$$

$$\cdot\;\cdot\;\cdot\;\cdot\;\cdot\;\cdot\;\cdot\;\cdot\;\cdot\;\cdot$$

Indeed, since $W_{n+p}^{(0)}$ lies between m_n and M_n for every point on S, and for every p, it follows that

$$|W_{n+p}^{(0)} - W_n^{(0)}| \leqq S_n,$$

and therefore, by Eq. (3),

$$|W_{n+p}^{(0)} - W_n^{(0)}| \leqq S_0 \lambda^n. \tag{6}$$

The limit of $W^{(0)}_{n+p}$ for p infinite is, Eq. (5),

$$W_\infty^{(0)} = C.$$

Therefore

$$|C - W_n^{(0)}| \leqq S_0 \lambda^n,$$

and

$$C - S_0 \lambda^n \leqq W_n^{(0)} \leqq C + S_0 \lambda^n. \tag{7}$$

157. The Limiting Values of the Potentials W_n on S.—The limiting values of the potentials W_n, as the point at which the potential is evaluated approaches the surface from the inside or from the outside (internal or external limits), will be denoted by $W_n^{(i)}$ and $W_n^{(e)}$. If the positive magnetic mass is on the inside of S, and if $W_1^{(0)}$ is the value of W_1 at the point of the surface which is approached, then it is seen from Eqs. (152.2) and (156.0) that

$$W_1^{(e)} = W_1^{(0)} - f, \qquad W_1^{(i)} = W_1^{(0)} + f; \tag{1}$$

and similarly, from Eqs. (156.1),

$$\left.\begin{array}{ll} W_2^{(e)} = W_2^{(0)} - W_1^{(0)}, & W_2^{(i)} = W_2^{(0)} + W_1^{(0)}, \\ W_3^{(e)} = W_3^{(0)} - W_2^{(0)}, & W_3^{(i)} = W_3^{(0)} + W_2^{(0)}, \\ \cdot\;\cdot\;\cdot\;\cdot\;\cdot\;\cdot\;\cdot & \cdot\;\cdot\;\cdot\;\cdot\;\cdot\;\cdot\;\cdot \\ W_n^{(e)} = W_n^{(0)} - W_{n-1}^{(0)}, & W_n^{(i)} = W_n^{(0)} + W_{n-1}^{(0)}, \\ \cdot\;\cdot\;\cdot\;\cdot\;\cdot\;\cdot\;\cdot, & \cdot\;\cdot\;\cdot\;\cdot\;\cdot\;\cdot\;\cdot \end{array}\right\} \tag{2}$$

From these equations and Eq. (156.6) it follows at once that

$$|W_n^{(e)}| = |W_n^{(0)} - W_{n-1}^{(0)}| \leqq S_0 \lambda^n; \tag{3}$$

and therefore

$$\lim_{n=\infty} |W_n^{(e)}| = 0.$$

The expressions for the internal potentials can be written

$$2C - W_{n+1}^{(i)} = (C - W_{n+1}^{(0)}) + (C - W_n^{(0)});$$

and therefore

$$|2C - W^{(i)}_{n+1}| \leqq 2S_0\lambda^n, \tag{4}$$

from which it follows that

$$\lim_{n=\infty} |W_n^{(i)}| = 2C.$$

It is evident, therefore, that the functions $W_n^{(e)}$, $W_n^{(0)}$, and $W_n^{(i)}$ have the limiting values, for n equal to infinity, 0, C, and $2C$, in agreement with the theorem of Sec. 150 for uniform two-layer surfaces.

158. Harnack's Theorem for Harmonic Functions.—It is desirable to turn aside from the main line of Neumann's argument, for a moment, in order to prove that the limit of the sum of a sequence of harmonic functions is itself harmonic. Suppose

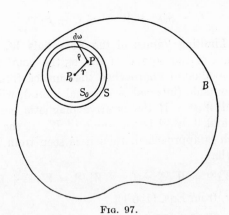

Fig. 97.

U_1, U_2, U_3, $\cdots$, is a sequence of functions of x, y, z which have the following properties:

(a) Each of the functions U_κ is positive everywhere within a certain domain B.

(b) Each of the functions U_κ is harmonic within the domain B.

(c) There exists a positive number M, which is independent of n and of the position of the point x, y, z, provided it remains within B, such that

$$U_1 + U_2 + U_3 + \cdots + U_n < M.$$

The sum

$$U = U_1 + U_2 + U_3 + \cdots + U_n + \cdots$$

evidently converges at every point of B and represents a certain function of x, y, z. It will be shown that U is harmonic within B.

Let P_0 be any point within B (Fig. 97). With P_0 as a center describe a sphere S which lies wholly in the interior of B, and a second sphere S_0 which lies inside of S. Let the radii of these two spheres be a and a_0 respectively. Let $d\omega$ be an element of the surface of the sphere S, and $P(x, y, z)$ be any point lying within the sphere S_0. Also let

$$\overline{P_0P} = r, \qquad \overline{Pd\omega} = \rho.$$

Since U_κ is harmonic, by Eq. (135.1),

$$U_\kappa(x, y, z) = \int_S \frac{a^2 - r^2}{4\pi a\rho^3} U_\kappa(\xi, \eta, \zeta) d\omega, \tag{1}$$

where $U_\kappa(x, y, z)$ is the value of U_κ at the point P, and $U_\kappa(\xi, \eta, \zeta)$ is the value of U_κ at the surface element $d\omega$. If

$$A_\kappa = \int_S U_\kappa(\xi, \eta, \zeta) d\omega,$$

it is evident that

$$\sum_{\kappa=1}^n A_\kappa = \int_S \sum U_\kappa(\xi, \eta, \zeta) d\omega;$$

and therefore

$$\sum_{\kappa=1}^n A_\kappa < 4\pi a^2 M.$$

Hence the series

$$A_1 + A_2 + A_3 + \cdots + A_n + \cdots,$$

all of whose terms are positive, is convergent.

Now let

$$\frac{a^2 - r^2}{4\pi a\rho^3} = \varphi(x, y, z).$$

If the point P remains inside of S_0, it is clear that ρ cannot vanish, since it is never less than $a - a_0$. Therefore, φ and all of its derivatives are finite inside of the sphere S_0, and therefore, have maximum values.

Let

$$|\varphi| < G_0,$$

$$\left|\frac{\partial \varphi}{\partial x}\right| < G_1, \qquad \left|\frac{\partial \varphi}{\partial y}\right| < G_1, \qquad \left|\frac{\partial \varphi}{\partial z}\right| < G_1,$$

$$\left|\frac{\partial^2 \varphi}{\partial x^2}\right| < G_2, \qquad \left|\frac{\partial^2 \varphi}{\partial y^2}\right| < G_2, \qquad \left|\frac{\partial^2 \varphi}{\partial z^2}\right| < G_2,$$

$$\text{etc.}$$

Then

$$U_\kappa = \int_S U_\kappa \varphi d\omega < G_0 A_\kappa,$$

$$\frac{\partial U_\kappa}{\partial x} = \int_S U_\kappa \frac{\partial \varphi}{\partial x} d\omega < G_1 A_\kappa,$$

$$\frac{\partial^2 U_\kappa}{\partial x^2} = \int_S U_\kappa \frac{\partial^2 \varphi}{\partial x^2} d\omega < G_2 A_\kappa,$$

$$\cdots \cdots \cdots$$

Hence, the series

$$U_1 + U_2 + U_3 + \cdots < G_0 \sum A_\kappa < 4\pi a^2 M G_0,$$

$$\frac{\partial U_1}{\partial x} + \frac{\partial U_2}{\partial x} + \frac{\partial U_3}{\partial x} + \cdots < G_1 \sum A_\kappa < 4\pi a^2 M G_1,$$

$$\frac{\partial^2 U_1}{\partial x^2} + \frac{\partial^2 U_2}{\partial x^2} + \frac{\partial^2 U_3}{\partial x^2} + \cdots < G_2 \sum A_\kappa < 4\pi a^2 M G_2,$$

$$\cdots \cdots \cdots \qquad \cdots \cdots \cdots$$

are absolutely and uniformly convergent within the sphere S_0, and they represent respectively.

$$U, \qquad \frac{\partial U}{\partial x}, \qquad \frac{\partial^2 U}{\partial x^2}, \qquad \cdots$$

From this it follows that

$$\Delta U = \sum_{\kappa=1}^{\infty} \Delta U_\kappa,$$

and since

$$\Delta U_\kappa = 0, \qquad \kappa = 1, 2, \cdots, \infty,$$

there results finally
$$\Delta U = 0;$$
that is, U is harmonic inside of S_0, since it is evidently continuous and has continuous derivatives of the first two orders; and therefore, harmonic within the entire domain B.

It is possible to go further and show that if the series
$$U_1 + U_2 + U_3 + \cdots + U_n + \cdots$$
is convergent at any point p whatever within the sphere S, the series
$$\sum_{\kappa=1}^{\infty} \int_S U_\kappa(\xi, \eta, \zeta)d\omega$$
is still convergent, and therefore, the function U is harmonic.

Let x, y, z be the coördinates of the point p; then Eq. (1) becomes
$$U_\kappa(p) = \int_S \frac{a^2 - r^2}{4\pi a P^3} U_k(\xi, \eta, \zeta)d\omega.$$
From Fig. 97 it is evident that
$$P \leqq a + r,$$
a being the radius of the sphere. Hence,
$$U_\kappa(p) > \frac{a - r}{4\pi a(a + r)^2} \int_S U_\kappa(\xi, \eta, \zeta)d\omega;$$
and
$$\int_S U(\xi, \eta, \zeta)d\omega > N U_\kappa(p)$$
where
$$N = \frac{4\pi a(a + r)^2}{a - r}$$
is a constant which is independent of κ. From this it follows that
$$\sum_{\kappa=1}^{\infty} \int_S U_\kappa(\xi, \eta, \zeta)d\omega < N \sum_{\kappa=1}^{\infty} U_\kappa(p).$$
But since
$$\sum_{\kappa=1}^{\infty} U_\kappa(p)$$
is convergent by hypothesis, it follows that the series
$$\sum_{\kappa=1}^{\infty} \int_S U_\kappa(\xi, \eta, \zeta)d\omega$$
also is convergent.

Suppose p_1 is any other point within the sphere.   Then

$$U_\kappa(p_1) = \int_S \frac{a^2 - r_1{}^2}{4\pi a \rho_1{}^3} U_\kappa(\xi, \eta, \zeta) d\omega;$$

but since

$$\rho_1 \geqq a - r_1,$$

it is evident that

$$U_\kappa(p_1) < \frac{a + r_1}{4\pi a(a - r_1)^2} \int_S U_k(\xi, \eta, \zeta) d\omega;$$

or,

$$U_\kappa(p_1) < M \int_S U_\kappa(\xi, \eta, \zeta) d\omega,$$

where

$$M = \frac{a + r_1}{4\pi a(a - r_1)^2}$$

is a constant which is independent of κ.   Hence, the series

$$\sum U_\kappa(p_1) < M \sum \int_S U_\kappa(\xi, \eta, \zeta) d\omega$$

also is convergent.   That is to say, if the functions U_κ, for $\kappa = 1, \ldots, \infty$, are each positive and harmonic within a given domain B, and if the series

$$U = \sum_{\kappa=1}^\infty U_\kappa$$

converges at any point within a sphere which lies wholly within B, the series will converge at every point which lies within the sphere.

It is a simple matter now to show that this series converges at every point of the domain B, assuming, of course, that the domain B is connected.   Suppose B (Fig. 98) is such a domain and that the series converges at the point P_0.   It is desired to show that the series converges at the point P.   Construct a sphere S_1 which contains the point P_0, and then a series of overlapping spheres, the last of which contains the point P.   In the regions which overlap mark the points $P_1, P_2, P_3, \cdots$.   Since the point P_1 lies in the sphere S_1, the series converges at P_1, since, by hypothesis, it converges at P_0.   But P_1 lies also in the sphere S_2; therefore, the series U converges at the point P_2, which also lies in S_2; therefore, it converges at P_3; and so on, until after a finite number of steps the conclusion is reached that U converges at the point P.

It follows also from Sec. 158 that U is harmonic in the entire domain B.

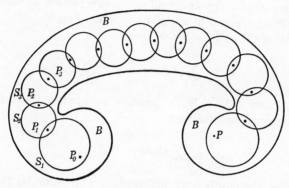

Fig. 98.

159. Case I.—The Constant C is Zero.—(A) *The Exterior Function.*—If the equations in the first column of Eqs. (157.1) and (157.2) are added, and the result is multiplied by -1, it is found that

$$-W_1^{(e)} - W_2^{(e)} - W_3^{(e)} - \cdots - W_n^{(e)} = f - W_n^{(0)}. \quad (0)$$

By hypothesis, the limit of $W_n^{(e)}$ as n increases, which is the constant C, is zero. Hence

$$-\sum_{\kappa=1}^{\infty} W_\kappa^{(e)} = f, \quad (1)$$

and since, Eq. (156.3),

$$|W_n^{(e)}| \leqq S_0\lambda^n, \quad (2)$$

the left member of Eq. (1) converges like a geometric series.

The function W_n is the exterior potential of a certain magnetic layer distributed over the given surface S. It is therefore harmonic everywhere outside of S, and it has the limiting value $W_n^{(e)}$ as the point at which it is evaluated approaches the surface S. Since it is harmonic, its maximum and minimum values occurs on S; that is, its maximum and minimum values are the maximum and minimum values of $W_n^{(e)}$; and since the sum of these maximum values converges, by Eq. (2), it follows that the function

$$W = - \sum_{\kappa = 1}^{\infty} W_{\kappa} \tag{3}$$

converges absolutely and uniformly everywhere outside of S, and its limit is equal to the given function f on S.

Equation (3) can also be written

$$W = \sum_{\kappa = 1}^{\infty} (S_0 \lambda^{\kappa} - W_{\kappa}) - \sum_{\kappa = 1}^{\infty} S_0 \lambda^{\kappa}.$$

The function $S_0 \lambda^{\kappa} - W_{\kappa}$ is positive everywhere outside of S, it is harmonic, and the sum

$$\sum_{\kappa = 1}^{\infty} (S_0 \lambda^{\kappa} - W_{\kappa})$$

converges absolutely and uniformly. This sum is, therefore, an harmonic function, by Harnack's theorem. Furthermore, the term

$$\sum_{\kappa = 1}^{\infty} S_0 \lambda^{n}$$

also is harmonic, since it is merely a constant.

Consequently

$$W = - \sum_{k = 1}^{\infty} W_{\kappa} \tag{4}$$

is the exterior function which was sought, for it is harmonic outside of S, vanishes at infinity, and takes the prescribed set of values f on S.

(B) *The Interior Function.*—If the equations in the second column of Eqs. (157.1) and (157.2) are taken alternately positive and negative and then added, it is found that

$$W_1^{(i)} - W_2^{(i)} + W_3^{(i)} - \cdots - (-1)^n W_n^{(i)}$$
$$= f - (-1)^n W_n^{(i)};$$

and since,

$$\lim_{n = \infty} W_n^{(i)} = 2C = 0,$$

it is evident that

$$W_1^{(i)} - W_2^{(i)} + W_3^{(i)} - W_4^{(i)} + \cdots = f,$$

the left member converging like a geometric series, Eq. (157.4). The function W_κ this time is the potential at an interior point of a certain magnetic mass distributed over S, and $W_\kappa^{(i)}$ is the limit of W_κ as the point P, at which the potential is evaluated, approaches S from the inside. Since W_κ is harmonic inside of S, its maximum and minimum values are the maximum and minimum values of $W_\kappa^{(i)}$, and since

$$| W_\kappa^{(i)} | < 2S_0\lambda^{\kappa-1}$$

for every point of the surface S (Eq. (156.4)), it follows that the function

$$W = W_1 - W_2 + W_3 - W_4 + \cdots \tag{5}$$

converges absolutely and uniformly everywhere inside of S, and takes the limit f on S.

This expression for W can also be written

$$W = \sum_{\kappa=1}^{\infty} (2S_0\lambda^{\kappa-1} + (-1)^\kappa W_\kappa) - \sum_{\kappa=1}^{\infty} 2S_0\lambda^{\kappa-1}.$$

The functions

$$2S_0\lambda^{\kappa-1} + (-1)^\kappa W_\kappa \qquad \kappa = 1, 2, \ldots, \infty,$$

are harmonic and everywhere positive inside of S, and their sum converges absolutely and uniformly. Therefore,

$$\sum_{\kappa=1}^{\infty} (2S_0\lambda^{\kappa-1} + (-1)^\kappa W_\kappa)$$

is harmonic, by Harnack's theorem. The constant term $\Sigma 2S_0\lambda^{\kappa-1}$ also is harmonic.

It follows, therefore, that W (Eq. (5)), is the interior function sought, for it is harmonic inside of S, and takes the prescribed set of values on S.

Dirichlet's principle is, therefore, established rigorously for the case $C = 0$.

160. The Interior and Exterior Functions as Potentials of the Same Simple Layer.—In order to distinguish between functions interior and functions exterior, the exterior function W, Eq. (159.4), will be denoted by W_E, and the interior function W, Eq. (159.5) will be denoted by W_I. Also if ρ is measured from an exterior point it will be denoted by ρ_e, and if it is measured from an interior point it will be denoted by ρ_i. Hence,

$$d\tilde{\omega} = \frac{\partial}{\partial n}\left(\frac{1}{\rho_e}\right)d\omega \quad \text{or} \quad d\tilde{\omega} = \frac{\partial}{\partial n}\left(\frac{1}{\rho_i}\right)d\omega,$$

according as the exterior or interior function is under consideration.

If the values of W_κ, in Eq. (159.4), are replaced by their values from Eqs. (156.1), it is seen that

$$W_E = -\frac{1}{2\pi}\int_S (f + W_1^{(0)} + W_2^{(0)} + W_3^{(0)} + \cdots)\frac{\partial}{\partial n}\left(\frac{1}{\rho_e}\right)d\omega,$$

and similarly from Eq. (159.5),

$$W_I = \frac{1}{2\pi}\int_S [(f - W_1^{(0)}) + (W_2^{(0)} - W_3^{(0)}) + \cdots]\frac{\partial}{\partial n}\left(\frac{1}{\rho_i}\right)d\omega.$$

Now by Eq. (157.2),

$$W_\kappa^{(0)} + W_{\kappa-1}^{(0)} = W_\kappa^{(i)}, \qquad W_\kappa^{(0)} - W_{\kappa-1}^{(0)} = W_\kappa^{(e)}.$$

Hence the expressions for W_E and W_I can also be written

$$\left.\begin{array}{l}W_E = -\dfrac{1}{2\pi}\displaystyle\int_S (W_1^{(i)} + W_3^{(i)} + W_5^{(i)} + \cdots)\dfrac{\partial}{\partial n}\left(\dfrac{1}{\rho_e}\right)d\omega, \\[2mm] W_I = -\dfrac{1}{2\pi}\displaystyle\int_S (W_1^{(e)} + W_3^{(e)} + W_5^{(e)} + \cdots)\dfrac{\partial}{\partial n}\left(\dfrac{1}{\rho_i}\right)d\omega, \end{array}\right\} \quad (1)$$

so that W_E and W_i are represented as the potentials of certain double layers on S.

The functions $W_\kappa^{(e)}$ and $W_\kappa^{(i)}$ are the surface values of the external and internal potentials of a certain double layer on S. These potentials are harmonic in their respective domains. Furthermore, $1/\rho_i$ is harmonic outside of S and $1/\rho_e$ is harmonic inside of S. Hence, by Green's theorem, Eq. (57.4),

$$\int_S\left[W_\kappa^{(i)}\frac{\partial}{\partial n}\left(\frac{1}{\rho_e}\right) - \frac{1}{\rho_e}\frac{\partial W_\kappa^{(i)}}{\partial n}\right]d\omega = 0,$$

$$\int_S\left[W_\kappa^{(e)}\frac{\partial}{\partial n}\left(\frac{1}{\rho_i}\right) - \frac{1}{\rho_i}\frac{\partial W_\kappa^{(e)}}{\partial n}\right]d\omega = 0.$$

That is

$$\int_S W_\kappa^{(i)}\frac{\partial}{\partial n}\left(\frac{1}{\rho_e}\right)d\omega = \int_S \frac{\partial W_\kappa^{(i)}}{\partial n}\cdot\frac{d\omega}{\rho_e},$$

$$\int_S W_\kappa^{(e)}\frac{\partial}{\partial n}\left(\frac{1}{\rho_i}\right)d\omega = \int_S \frac{\partial W_\kappa^{(e)}}{\partial n}\cdot\frac{d\omega}{\rho_i};$$

so that Eqs. (1) can also be written

$$
\left.
\begin{aligned}
W_E &= -\frac{1}{2\pi}\int_S \frac{\partial}{\partial n}(W_1{}^{(i)} + W_3{}^{(i)} + W_5{}^{(i)} + \cdots)\frac{d\omega}{\rho_e}, \\
W_I &= -\frac{1}{2\pi}\int_S \frac{\partial}{\partial n}(W_1{}^{(e)} + W_3{}^{(e)} + W_5{}^{(e)} + \cdots)\frac{d\omega}{\rho_i}.
\end{aligned}
\right\} \quad (2)
$$

Since the normal derivative of the potential of a two-layer surface is continuous across the surface, Eq. (153.1), it follows that

$$
\frac{\partial W_\kappa{}^{(i)}}{\partial n} = \frac{\partial W_\kappa{}^{(e)}}{\partial n}, \qquad \kappa = 1, 2, 3, \cdots .
$$

If therefore the common value of

$$
\frac{\partial}{\partial n}(W_1{}^{(i)} + W_3{}^{(i)} + \cdots) = \frac{\partial}{\partial n}(W_1{}^{(e)} + W_3{}^{(e)} + \cdots)
$$

be denoted by $-2\pi\sigma$, it is seen that

$$
W_E = \int_S \frac{\sigma}{\rho_e}d\omega, \qquad W_I = \int_S \frac{\sigma}{\rho_i}d\omega,
$$

and *the functions W_E and W_I are the external and internal potentials of the same simple layer σ on S.*

161. The Constant C is Not Zero.—If the constant C is different from zero, its value can be supposed known as the limit of the sequence of functions $W_\kappa{}^{(0)}$.

Let

$$
\varphi = f - C,
$$

and let the functions V_κ, analogous to the functions W_κ, be defined by relations similar to Eqs. (156.0) and (156.1):

$$
V_1 = \frac{1}{2\pi}\int_S \varphi \, d\tilde\omega, \qquad \cdots, \qquad V_\kappa = \frac{1}{2\pi}\int_S V_{\kappa-1}{}^{(0)}d\tilde\omega, \qquad \cdots .
$$

It is evident that

$$
V_1{}^{(0)} = \frac{1}{2\pi}\int (f - C)d\omega = W_1{}^{(0)} - C,
$$

and, in general,

$$
V_\kappa{}^{(0)} = W_\kappa{}^{(0)} - C
$$

Since

$$
W_\infty{}^{(0)} = C,
$$

it is evident that $V_\infty{}^{(0)}$ is zero, and the theory of the preceding case is applicable.

The function, Eq. (159.4),

$$V_E = - \sum_{\kappa=1}^{\infty} V_\kappa$$

is harmonic outside of S, vanishes at infinity, and is equal to φ on S. The function $V_E + C$ is harmonic outside of S, and is equal to

$$\varphi + C = f$$

on S, but it does not vanish at infinity, since it is equal to C at infinity. It is not, therefore, the exterior function which is sought.

The function, Eq. (159.5)

$$V_I = V_1 - V_2 + V_3 - V_4 + \cdots$$

is harmonic inside S, and is equal to φ on S. Hence the function

$$V_I + C$$

is harmonic inside of S, since C is merely a constant, and is equal to f on S. Since there is only one function that can satisfy these conditions, $V_I + C$ is the interior function sought. Since C can be regarded as the interior potential of a double layer of constant moment, $C/2$, on S, it is clear that the interior function can always be regarded as the potential of a double layer on S.

The exterior function, however, cannot be expressed as the potential of a double layer on S in the case that the constant C is not zero. For the total mass in a double layer is always zero, and therefore, if V is the potential,

$$\lim_{\rho = \infty} \rho V = 0,$$

for every potential of a two layer surface. For a Newtonian potential in which the mass M is not zero

$$\lim_{\rho = \infty} \rho V = M \neq 0.$$

It is clear therefore that exterior Newtonian potential cannot be represented as the potential of a double layer.

Suppose however a simple layer is distributed on S in such a way that it is also a level layer. If the potential of this level layer V_0 is equal to C on S, it will be equal to C everywhere within S, and will vanish at infinity. Consequently the function

$$V_E + V_0$$

is harmonic outside of S, vanishes at infinity and is equal to f on S; and the function

$$V_I + V_0$$

is harmonic within S and is equal to f on S. Therefore, if the constant C is not zero, both the exterior and interior functions can be represented as the potentials of a combination of a double layer and a simple level layer on S.

But, just as in Sec. 160, the potentials of the double layer, V_E and V_I can be represented as the potentials of a simple layer of which the total mass is zero. The equations analogous to Eqs. (160.2) are

$$V_E = -\frac{1}{2\pi} \int_S \frac{\partial}{\partial n}(V_1^{(i)} + V_3^{(i)} + V_5^{(i)} + \cdots)\frac{d\omega}{\rho_e},$$

$$V_i = -\frac{1}{2\pi} \int_S \frac{\partial}{\partial n}(V_1^{(e)} + V_3^{(e)} + V_5^{(e)} + \cdots)\frac{d\omega}{\rho_i}.$$

Just as before

$$\frac{\partial}{\partial n}(V_1^{(i)} + V_3^{(i)} + \cdots) = \frac{\partial}{\partial n}(V_1^{(e)} + V_3^{(e)} + \cdots);$$

and if the common value of these two normal derivatives is denoted by $-2\pi\sigma$, the above expressions for V_E and V_i become simply

$$V_E = \int_S \frac{\sigma}{\rho_e}d\omega, \qquad V_i = \int_S \frac{\sigma}{\rho_i}d\omega.$$

That is V_E and V_i are the exterior and interior potentials of the same simple layer on S.

Hence the functions which solve the exterior and interior Green problems can be represented always as the potentials of the same simple layer on S.

It remains to be shown how the level layer above mentioned can be constructed for the class of surfaces considered by Neumann.

162. The Construction of a Simple, Level Layer on S.— Suppose O is any point within S and ρ_0 is measured from the point O. Starting with, Sec. 156,

$$f = \frac{1}{\rho_0},$$

build up the series of exterior potentials W_1, W_2, W_3, $\cdots$, and $W_1^{(0)}$, $W_2^{(0)}$, $W_3^{(0)}$, $\cdots$. The limit of the functions $W_n^{(0)}$ as n increases is a certain constant which will be denoted by Γ;

$$W_\infty^{(0)} = \Gamma.$$

Form the function

$$U = -W_1 - W_2 - W_3 \cdots,$$

which is the exterior potential of a certain double layer on S, and therefore, vanishes at infinity. Its limiting value on S is, Eq. (159.0)

$$U_S = -W_1^{(e)} - W_2^{(e)} - W_1^{(e)} \cdots,$$

$$= \frac{1}{\rho_{0S}} - \Gamma,$$

where ρ_{0S} is the value of ρ_0 on S.

Now, consider the function

$$V_0 = \frac{1}{\rho_0} - U. \tag{1}$$

It is harmonic everywhere outside of S, and it vanishes at infinity. Therefore, since

$$\lim_{\rho_0 = \infty} \rho_0 V_0 = +1,$$

it is the Newtonian potential of some distribution of a unit amount of matter. Since

$$V_0 = \Gamma \qquad \text{on } S,$$

S is an equipotential surface of the distribution. Therefore, by Sec. 115, it is possible to distribute a unit amount of matter on S in such a way that S becomes a level layer. The density in this distribution is, Eq. (115.0),

$$\sigma = \frac{1}{4\pi} \int_S \frac{\partial V_0}{\partial n_i} d\omega.$$

The constant Γ is not zero. If it were, the function V_0 would vanish on S and at infinity. Since it is harmonic, it would vanish identically outside of S, and

$$U \equiv \frac{1}{\rho_0}.$$

This is impossible, however, since U is the potential of a double layer and $1/\rho_0$ is a Newtonian potential of a unit mass (Sec. 161).

If it is desired to have the potential of the level layer equal to C on S, it is necessary, merely, to take

$$V_0 = \frac{C}{\Gamma}\left(\frac{1}{\rho_0} - U\right),$$

and therefore, the total mass of the level layer is

$$M = \frac{C}{\Gamma}.$$

POINCARÉ'S MÉTHODE DU BALAYAGE

163. The Balayage of a Sphere.—The balayage of a volume consists in replacing the matter within the volume by an equivalent layer upon the surface: equivalent in the sense that the potential of the layer is the same as the potential of the volume at points which lie outside of the surface. In Secs. 108, 133, and 134, it was shown that if a unit particle is placed at a point O_1 within a sphere, its potential at points exterior to the sphere is just the same as the potential of a unit mass spread over the surface in such a way that the density on the surface is inversely proportional to the cube of the distance from the point O_1.

If there are two particles of masses m_1 and m_2 within the sphere, each particle can be replaced by an equal and equivalent mass distributed over the surface, and the surface distribution $m_1 + m_2$ will have the same potential at all points exterior to the sphere as the individual particles m_1 and m_2. This result, evidently, can be extended to any number of particles, and therefore any distribution of matter within the sphere can be replaced by an equivalent distribution of the same amount of matter upon the surface of the sphere. It is always possible, therefore, to balaye a sphere.

It will be observed that in this process negative masses are never introduced, and that the potential at outside points is unaltered. At all interior points, however, the potential is diminished. In order to prove this, let U be the interior potential of the equivalent surface distribution for a particle for which the exterior potential is $1/\rho$. Green's function is

$$G = \frac{1}{\rho} - U;$$

that is, it is the difference between the potential of the interior particle and the interior potential of the equivalent distribution on the surface. But, by Sec. 130, the Green function is always positive. Hence at every point of the interior

$$U < \frac{1}{\rho};$$

and in the process of balaying the sphere the potential at any interior point is diminished whenever a particle is replaced by an equivalent surface layer. It is therefore diminished for the final result whatever the distribution of matter within the sphere may have been.

164. Existence of a Level Layer on a Given Surface.—Suppose there is given a closed surface S which may have a finite number of

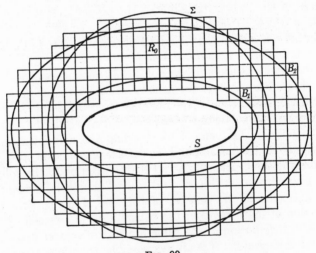

FIG. 99.

conical points and edges, but which at other points of the surface admits a definite tangent plane and two definite principal radii of curvature. It will be shown that there exists a function $V(x, y, z)$ which is equal to $+1$ at all points of the surface S, is continuous outside of S, except possibly along the edges, which vanishes at infinity, and which satisfies the equation of Laplace.

Let the surface S be surrounded by a region R_0 in the form of a shell bounded by two surfaces, B_1 and B_2, Fig. 99, and let the minimum distance between the surface S and the surface B_1 be δ_0. Imagine an infinity of such regions

$$\cdots, R_{-3}, R_{-2}, R_{-1}, R_0, R_1, R_2, R_3, \cdots$$

with the corresponding minimal distances

$$\cdots, \delta_{-3}, \delta_{-2}, \delta_{-1}, \delta_0, \delta_1, \delta_2, \delta_3, \cdots,$$

where $\delta_{-n} < \delta_{-n+1}$ tends toward zero as n increases, and $\delta_n > \delta_{n-1}$ tends toward infinity as n increases; and let the successive regions over lap so that every point of space exterior to S lies in at least one region R. Let ϵ_κ be slightly smaller than δ_κ, for every integer κ.

Let the region R_κ be divided up into cubes by planes which are parallel to a given set of reference planes and at a distance $\epsilon_\kappa/\sqrt{3}$ apart; so that the diagonals of the cubes are equal to ϵ_κ. A cube will be regarded as belonging to the region R_κ if any part of the cube is contained in R_κ. Let a sphere be constructed about the center of each cube, the diameters of these spheres being equal to δ_κ. Then each of these spheres lies wholly outside of the surface S, and every point of the region R_κ lies within at least one of these spheres. Furthermore the number of such spheres for the region R_κ is finite.

If spheres are constructed for every region R in the manner just described, there will be constructed a definite, infinite set of spheres which has the following properties.

(a) Every sphere lies wholly outside of S.

(b) Every point outside of S lies inside of at least one sphere.

(c) The set of spheres is denumerably infinite; that is, the spheres can be put into a one to one correspondence with the positive integers. For example, the spheres in R_0 can be numbered, and the numbering continued into R_1, then into R_{-1}, then R_2, and R_{-2}, and so on.

It is the properties of this system of spheres that is important, and not at all the particular system which has been defined. Any other system of spheres which possesses these three properties will serve equally well; but it was necessary to show that there exists at least one such system.

Construct a sphere Σ of radius A which contains the surface S in its interior. Let the mass M be distributed uniformly on Σ. Then the interior potential of Σ is constant and equal to M/A, and if M is chosen equal to A the interior potential of M is equal to unity. In particular, it is equal to unity within and on S.

Assuming that the sphere Σ passes through the sphere S_1 which was numbered one, let the sphere S_1 be balayed; then let S_2 be balayed; then S_1 again, then S_2, then S_3; then S_1 a third time; and so on, the spheres being taken in the order

$$S_1, S_2; S_1, S_2, S_3; S_1, S_2, S_3, S_4; S_1, S_2, \cdots \qquad (1)$$

so that each sphere is balayed infinitely many times.

The matter which originally was uniformly distributed on Σ is redistributed, at least in part, in each operation; unless the sphere which was balayed was already empty, in which case no alteration of any kind occurs. At the beginning, the potential was

$$V = 1 \qquad \text{inside of } \Sigma,$$

$$V = \frac{A}{\rho} \qquad \text{outside of } \Sigma.$$

Whenever a sphere S_κ is balayed the potential at all points outside of S_κ remains unaltered, but at all inside points it is diminished. Hence the potential V is never increased at any point by any operation, but is decreased everywhere within one of the numbered spheres by each non-vacuous operation. Since negative masses are never introduced, necessarily V remains positive always. Hence, as a result of the operations indicated in Eq. (1), at any fixed point outside of S, V tends toward a limit. Within and on S, the potential V remains unaltered and equal to $+1$.

Let V_n be the value of V after the nth operation. Then at any point p outside of S

$$1 \geqq V \geqq V_n > 0.$$

As the point p recedes toward infinity, V, which is equal to A/ρ, tends toward 0, and therefore V_n tends toward zero at infinity.

At a fixed point p the potential V_n tends toward a limit, as a result of the operations indicated in Eq. (1). Suppose the point p lies in the sphere S_i. This sphere is balayed infinitely many times, the numbers for the operations on this sphere being $\alpha_1, \alpha_2, \alpha_3, \cdots$ Consequently the sequence of potentials $V_{\alpha_1}, V_{\alpha_2}, V_{\alpha_3}, \cdots$ tends toward the same limit which will be denoted by V_∞. Hence

$$V_\infty = V_{\alpha_1} + (V_{\alpha_2} - V_{\alpha_1}) + (V_{\alpha_3} - V_{\alpha_2}) + (V_{\alpha_4} - V_{\alpha_3}) + \cdots.$$

Each of the terms in this series is zero or negative except the first, and the sum converges to the limit V_∞. Since the sphere S_i contains only empty space after it has been balayed, it follows that V_{α_j}, $j = 1, 2, \cdots, \infty$, satisfies the equation of Laplace in the neighborhood of the point p. Therefore, each term of this series is harmonic. It follows then from Harnack's theorem (Sec. 158) that the series and all of its derivatives are uniformly convergent. Consequently V_∞ is continuous and satisfies the equation of Laplace inside of the sphere S_i; and since every point of space is inside of some sphere S_i, it follows that V_∞ is harmonic everywhere outside of S.

It remains only to prove that V_∞ is continuous across S. Inside of S the value of the potential has remained steadily at $+1$. Outside of S, V_∞ is harmonic; but it is conceivable that V_∞ might not tend toward $+1$ as the point p approached the surface S. It will be shown that this is not the case.

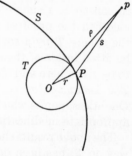

Fig. 100.

Let P, Fig. 100, be a point on S at which S has a definite tangent plane and two definite radii of curvature. It is possible, then, to construct a small sphere T of radius r with its center at O, which is tangent to S at P, and which lies wholly within S. Let p be any point outside of S, and let

$$Op = \rho, \qquad Pp = s.$$

The function r/ρ is harmonic outside of T, and is equal to $+1$ on T. The function V_n is the potential of positive masses which lie outside of S. It may, therefore, have maxima outside of S, but it cannot have minima (Theorems I and IV, Sec. 75). It is equal to $+1$ on S, and vanishes at infinity. The function

$$U = V_n - \frac{r}{\rho},$$

is the potential of positive masses outside of S and a negative mass equal to $-r$ at the center of T. Outside of S it can have maxima but not minima. It is equal to zero on S and at infinity.

It can, therefore, be positive or zero outside of S, but not negative. It follows therefore that

$$1 \geqq V_n \geqq \frac{r}{\rho}.$$

Now let the point p approach the point P along the line s, Fig. 100. It is evident then, that

$$1 \geqq V_\infty \geqq \frac{r}{\rho} \geqq \frac{r}{r+s},$$

and V_∞ tends toward unity as s tends toward zero. Hence, V_∞ is continuous across S at any ordinary point of the surface.

The proof as given above fails if the point P is at a corner or on an edge, because at a corner or on an edge it is not possible to construct a sphere T which lies wholly within S. Poincaré modified the proof so as to include conical points by replacing the sphere T by a surface which has a conical point which can be fitted inside of the conical point on S. The proof is too long to be given here and the reader is referred to Poincaré's paper in *The American Journal of Mathematics*, Vol. XII, p. 228, (1890). Doubtless, points which lie on edges also could be included by an appropriate modification of the surface T.

The above results show that part of the matter, which originally was on Σ, has been deposited upon S in such a way as to make S a level surface of potential $+1$, and part of it has been dispersed to infinity. The space outside of S is entirely empty. The proof for the existence of a solution of Green's problem follows at once from the existence proof for level layers by virtue of the relations given in Sec. 129, but a direct proof can be given by the method of balayage.[1]

165. Application of Harnack's Theorem.—Suppose there is given a closed surface S and a continuous function Φ which is defined on S. It is supposed, also, that

$$M > \Phi > m > 0,$$

on S, where M and m are two positive numbers.

Let Σ be a sphere which contains S wholly within its interior. Then it is always possible to find a sequence of polynomials P_n such that

$$0 < P_n < \epsilon_n$$

[1] POINCARÉ, "Theorie du Potentiel Newtonien," p. 283. (1899.)

within and on Σ, where ϵ_n is a sequence of positive numbers for which the series

$$\epsilon_1 + \epsilon_2 + \epsilon_3 + \cdots + \epsilon_n + \cdots$$

is convergent, and such that the function

$$U = P_1 + P_2 + P_3 + \cdots + P_n + \cdots$$

is equal to Φ on S.

Suppose that there exists, for every index n, a function V_n which is harmonic inside of S, and equal to P_n on S. Then, if $\delta_n^{(2)}$ and $\delta_n^{(1)}$ are the maximum and minimum values of P_n on S,

$$0 < \delta_n^{(1)} \leqq V_n \leqq \delta_n^{(2)} < \epsilon_n$$

within S, and the function

$$V = V_1 + V_2 + V_3 + \cdots + V_n + \cdots$$

is absolutely and uniformly convergent. Furthermore, it is equal to Φ on S, and by virtue of Harnack's theorem it is harmonic inside of S. A solution of Green's problem, therefore, exists if there always exists a function V_n which is harmonic within S and equal to a given polynomial P_n on S.

The restriction that Φ be positive and non-vanishing on S was necessary in order to apply Harnack's theorem, but this restriction can be removed. Suppose

$$|\Phi| < C,$$

where C is some positive number, on S. Then

$$\Phi = C - (C - \Phi),$$

and

$$C - \Phi > 0.$$

If W is a function which is harmonic within S and equal to $C - \Phi$ on S, the conditions of Harnack's theorem are satisfied. Then the function

$$V = C - W$$

is harmonic within S and is equal to Φ on S.

166. Construction of an Infinite System of Spheres within S.—
In order to show that there exists a function V which is harmonic within a given closed surface S and which is equal to a given polynomial P on S, let there be constructed first an infinite system of spheres which has the following properties:

(a) Every sphere of the system lies wholly within S.

(b) Every point inside of S lies in at least one of these spheres.

(c) The system of spheres is denumerably infinite.

These are the same conditions for the interior domain that were required in Sec. 164 for the exterior domain. In order to show that there exists at least one such system, let an interior region R_0 be defined as the region which lies in the interior of a closed surface which lies wholly within S and for which the minimum distance to the surface S is δ_0. Then construct an infinite series of overlapping shells

$$R_1, R_2, R_3, \cdots ,$$

for which the minimal distances to the surface S are

$$\delta_1, \delta_2, \delta_3, \cdots ,$$

of such magnitude that

$$\delta_n < \delta_{n-1},$$

and which have the limit zero as n increases, so that the outer boundary of the shell R_n tends toward coincidence with the surface S as n increases. Then every point in the interior of S lies in the interior of at least one domain R_κ.

Let ϵ_κ be slightly smaller than δ_κ for every κ, and let the region R_κ be divided up into cubes by planes which are parallel to a given set of reference planes and at a distance $\epsilon_\kappa / \sqrt{3}$ apart, so that the diagonals of the cubes are all equal to ϵ_κ. If a sphere of radius δ_κ is constructed about the center of each cube, there will be a finite number spheres each of which lies wholly within S, and every point of R_κ lies in at least one of these spheres.

If spheres are constructed in this manner for every region R_κ, the infinite system of spheres so constructed certainly satisfies conditions (a) and (b). It also satisfies condition (c) for, since the number of spheres in each region R_κ is finite, the spheres in R_0 can be numbered and the numbering continued into R_1, then into R_2, and so on. It will be assumed, hereafter, that the system of numbering has been carried, so that each sphere is definitely located in the sequence of spheres

$$S_1, S_2, S_3, \cdots , S_n, \cdots$$

167. The Existence of the Required Harmonic Function.—
Let P be the given polynomial. Form the Laplacian ΔP, and suppose, at first that

$$\Delta P < 0$$

everywhere within a sphere Σ which contains S wholly within its interior. Let

$$\Delta P = -4\pi\sigma,$$

where σ is positive, and let

$$W_0 = \int_\Sigma \frac{\sigma d\tau}{\rho},$$

so that W_0 is the potential of a volume distribution of positive masses and is, therefore, positive everywhere. Furthermore

$$\Delta W_0 = -4\pi\sigma = \Delta P$$

inside of Σ.

Regarding σ as the density of attracting matter, let the spheres S_κ inside of S be balayed in the order

$$S_1, S_2; S_1, S_2, S_3; S_1, S_2, S_3, S_4; \cdots,$$

so that each sphere is balayed infinitely many times. If W_n is the potential of the attracting matter after the nth operation, it is evident that

$$W_n > 0, \quad \text{and} \quad W_n \leqq W_{n-1}.$$

The sequence of potentials

$$W_1, W_2, W_3, \cdots,$$

therefore, has a limit which will be denoted by W. Inside of S

$$0 < W < W_0;$$

outside of S

$$W = W_0,$$

since the balayage of a sphere does not change the potential outside of the sphere.

The sphere S_κ has been balayed infinitely many times. If the numbers of these operations are, in order,

$$\alpha_1, \alpha_2, \alpha_3, \cdots,$$

then the functions

$$W_{\alpha_1}, W_{\alpha_2}, W_{\alpha_3}, \cdots$$

are harmonic inside of S_κ, since they represent the potentials of attracting matter in empty space; and they have the same limit W. Hence the series

$$W = W_{\alpha_1} + (W_{\alpha_2} - W_{\alpha_1}) + (W_{\alpha_3} - W_{\alpha_2}) + \cdots$$

is convergent. All of its terms, except the first, are negative or zero, and all of its terms are harmonic. Hence, by Harnack's theorem (Sec. 158), W is harmonic everywhere inside of S, since every point inside of S is also inside of some sphere S_κ. All of the matter which was within S has been deposited upon S by these operations, and the interior of S is empty.

In order to show that W is continuous across S at every point at which S has a definite tangent plane and two principal radii of curvature, let Q be a point of the surface at which these conditions are satisfied. Let S_0 be a small sphere outside of S and tangent to S at Q. Since the Green function for the sphere is known it is possible to effect a surface distribution of matter on S_0 for which the potential coincides with the values of W_0 on S_0. If U is the potential of this distribution of matter, U is harmonic outside of S_0, equal to W_0 on S_0, and vanishes at infinity.

The function $W - U$ can be regarded as the potential of a positive distribution of matter and a negative distribution on S_0. It can have maxima outside of S_0 but not minima. It vanishes at Q and at infinity. Hence, at any point q within S

$$U \leqq W \leqq W_0.$$

As the point q approaches Q the function U tends toward W_0. Therefore, the function W also tends toward W_0 and is continuous across S.

Take now the function

$$V = W - W_0 + P.$$

It is harmonic inside of S, since

$$\Delta W = 0, \quad \text{and} \quad \Delta W_0 = \Delta P;$$

and it is equal to P on S, since $W - W_0$ vanishes on S. It is, therefore, the function which was sought; and since Green's problem can be solved for a polynomial P, it can be solved for any function

$$P_1 + P_2 + P_3 + \cdots + P_n + \cdots$$

by the principles of Sec. 165.

The restriction that ΔP shall be negative everywhere within Σ is easily removed. Any polynomial, whatever its values in Σ may be, can be regarded as the difference between two polynomials,

$$P = P_2 - P_1,$$

the polynomials P_1 and P_2 being chosen so that

$$\Delta P_1 < 0, \qquad \Delta P_2 < 0,$$

everywhere within Σ. In accordance with the above analysis there exist two functions V_1 and V_2 each of which is harmonic within S, and equal respectively to P_1 and P_2 on S. The desired function V then is

$$V = V_2 - V_1.$$

Problems

1. Show directly by the method of balayage that on any given closed surface S there exists one and only one distribution of a unit mass on S which is centrobaric with respect to a given point P which lies within S.

2. Suppose the function V satisfies the following conditions:

(*a*) V is harmonic in every region that lies wholly within or wholly without a given closed surface S.

(*b*) V is regular at infinity, and acts there like a Newtonian potential.

(*c*) V and its normal derivative have definite limits at any point P of the surface both from the inside and from the outside. If these limits are denoted by

$$V_1, \qquad \frac{\partial V_1}{\partial n}, \qquad \text{and} \qquad V_2, \qquad \frac{\partial V_2}{\partial n},$$

then

$$\sigma_1 = +\frac{1}{4\pi}\left(\frac{\partial V_1}{\partial n} - \frac{\partial V_2}{\partial n}\right), \qquad \sigma_2 = -\frac{1}{4\pi}(V_1 - V_2)$$

are continuous functions on S.

Show that V is the sum of the potentials of a simple layer and of a double layer on S.

3. Given a closed surface S and a continuous function Φ, such that

$$\int_S \Phi d\omega = 0.$$

Show that there exists a function V which satisfies the conditions

$$\Delta V = 0 \qquad \text{within } S, \qquad \frac{\partial V}{\partial n} = \Phi \qquad \text{on } S.$$

4. If S is a closed, everywhere convex surface which has two finite principal radii of curvature at each point, and if R is the maximum value of the radii of curvature, show that

$$\int_S \frac{\cos \varphi}{\rho^2} d\omega < \frac{A}{4R^2},$$

where ρ is measured from a point of the surface, φ is the angle which ρ makes with the interior normal, and A is the area of the surface.

5. A shell of finite thickness separates space into three regions, A the hollow of the shell, B the space within the shell, C the space outside of the shell. If V_A is the potential due to matter within A and V_C is the potential due to matter lying in C and if at all points of B there exists a linear relation with constant coefficients $aV_A + cV_C + b = 0$, in which a, b, and c are distinct from zero, then

$$V_A = 0, \qquad V_B = -\frac{c}{b}.$$

6. Verify the following formulas for the configuration constant λ:
for the circle,

$$\lambda = \frac{1}{2};$$

for the ellipse

$$\lambda \leqq 1 - \frac{1}{2}\left(\frac{b}{a}\right)^3;$$

for any closed, convex, plane curve of length L for which R is the maximum value of the radius of curvature,

$$\lambda \leqq 1 - \frac{L}{4\pi R};$$

for any closed, convex, surface for which A is the area and R the maximum value which occurs for the radius of curvature,

$$\lambda \leqq 1 - \frac{A}{16\pi R^2}.$$

CHAPTER VII

SPHERICAL HARMONICS

168. Definitions.—A function is said to be harmonic within a region R if the function and its first derivatives are continuous in R, and if, also, it satisfies the equation of Laplace,

$$\Delta V = \frac{\partial^2 V}{\partial x^2} + \frac{\partial^2 V}{\partial y^2} + \frac{\partial^2 V}{\partial z^2} = 0.$$

There is an infinite variety of functions which satisfy these conditions, and therefore, an infinite variety of functions which are harmonic. In general, they are transcendental; that is, they cannot be expressed by means of elementary functions which are related by a finite number of combinations of the fundamental operations of arithmetic. They are frequently expressed by series; and for this purpose it is desirable to have a normal set harmonic functions in terms of which such series can be expressed.

No one set of normal harmonic functions is best adapted to every expansion, but the simplest, and therefore the best known and most commonly used, set of normalized harmonics are the Spherical Harmonics, to which the present chapter is devoted. A second normalized set of harmonic functions is the Ellipsoidal Harmonics of Lamé, and a third set is the Toroidal Harmonics of Hicks. The following chapter will be devoted to the Ellipsoidal Harmonics of Lamé.

A *spherical solid harmonic* is an harmonic function which is homogeneous in the letters x, y, z. The degree of its homogeneity, may be real or complex. Of course, it satisfies the equation of Laplace, and, since it is homogeneous, it also satisfies the equation of Euler. Hence, if V is a spherical harmonic of degree n, it satisfies the two equations

$$\frac{\partial^2 V}{\partial x^2} + \frac{\partial^2 V}{\partial y^2} + \frac{\partial^2 V}{\partial z^2} = 0,$$

$$x\frac{\partial V}{\partial x} + y\frac{\partial V}{\partial y} + z\frac{\partial V}{\partial z} = nV,$$

the first of which states that V is harmonic, and the second that it is homogeneous.

A *spherical surface harmonic* is the set of values which a solid spherical harmonic takes on the surface of a unit sphere which has its center at the origin. It is obtained as a function of the polar angles by replacing the rectangular coordinates by polar coordinates, the radius vector being taken equal to unity.

A *complete spherical harmonic* is a spherical harmonic which is finite and single valued for all finite values of the coordinates.

A *partial spherical harmonic* is a spherical harmonic which either does not satisfy the equation of Laplace everywhere, or, which is not a single valued function.

169. Examples of Spherical Harmonics.—The following examples of spherical harmonics are taken from the table given in Thompson & Tait's "Treatise on Natural Philosophy," Vol. I, p. 172.

Degree -2, $\dfrac{x}{r^3}$; $\dfrac{z}{r^3}\tan^{-1}\dfrac{y}{x}$; $\dfrac{z}{r^3}\log\dfrac{r+z}{r-z}-\dfrac{2}{r^2}$;

Degree -1, $\dfrac{1}{r}$; $\dfrac{1}{r}\tan^{-1}\dfrac{y}{x}$; $\dfrac{1}{r}\log\dfrac{r+z}{r-z}$;

Degree 0, $\log\dfrac{r+z}{r-z}$; $\tan^{-1}\dfrac{y}{x}$; $\dfrac{rz(x^2-y^2)}{(x^2+y^2)^2}$;

Degree $+1$, z; $z\tan^{-1}\dfrac{y}{x}$; $\left(\log\dfrac{r+z}{r-z}+\dfrac{2rz}{x^2+y^2}\right)x$;

Degree $+2$, x^2-y^2; $2z^2-x^2-y^2$; xy.

The functions x/r^3, $1/r$, x^2-y^2, etc. are complete spherical harmonics; while

$$\frac{z}{r^3}\tan^{-1}\frac{x}{y}, \qquad \left(\log\frac{r+z}{r-z}+\frac{2rz}{x^2+y^2}\right)x, \text{ etc.}$$

are partial spherical harmonics, since they are not single valued.

The general, homogeneous, polynomial of the second degree,

$$ax^2+by^2+cz^2+eyz+fzx+gxy,$$

is harmonic if

$$a+b+c=0.$$

170. Homogeneous, Harmonic Polynomials.—Consider the complete, homogeneous, polynomial of degree n in x, y, z. It contains $(n + 1)(n + 2)/2$ coefficients which, at the moment, can be regarded as arbitrary. If it is substituted in the equation of Laplace, there results a complete, homogeneous, polynomial of degree $n - 2$ which has $n(n - 1)/2$ coefficients, each of which must vanish if the given polynomial is harmonic. Hence the $(n + 1)(n + 2)/2$ coefficients are subject to $n(n - 1)/2$ conditions, leaving $2n + 1$ of the coefficients arbitrary. It would naturally be expected, therefore, that there exist $2n + 1$ independent spherical harmonics which are homogeneous polynomials of degree n. It will be shown in Secs. 174 and 176 that this is actually the case.

As an example, let $n = 3$. Then the polynomial is

$$P = ax^3 + by^3 + cz^3 + 3dy^2z + 3ez^2x + 3fx^2y + 3hyz^2$$
$$+ 3izx^2 + 3jxy^2 + 6kxyz;$$

and

$$\Delta P \equiv 6(a + e + j)x + 6(b + f + h)y + 6(c + d + i)z.$$

If P is harmonic, the three conditions

$$a + e + j = 0,$$
$$b + f + h = 0,$$
$$c + d + i = 0,$$

must be satisfied. After solving these equations for, say, a, b, and c, and substituting in P, there results

$$P = (3y^2z - z^3)d + (3z^2x - x^3)e + (3x^2y - y^3)f + (3yz^2 - y^3)h$$
$$+ (3zx^2 - z^3)i + (3xy^2 - x^3)j + 6kxyz.$$

since this expression is harmonic whatever $d, e, f, \ldots$ may be, each of the binomials, which are their coefficients, must be harmonic. There are seven of these binomials, and it is evident that they are linearly independent; that is, if L, M, and N are any three of these binomials, no two of which are the same, and if l, m, and n are any three constants, there does not exist a relation of the form

$$lL + mM + nN \equiv 0,$$

other than

$$l = m = n = 0.$$

Any such linear combination, however, will be a homogeneous polynomial of the third degree which is harmonic; and every homogeneous, harmonic polynomial of the third degree can be represented as a linear combination of the above seven harmonics.

171. Relation between Certain Harmonics.—Let φ_1 and φ_2 be any two functions of x, y, and z, and form the Laplacian of their product.   It is found that

$$\Delta(\varphi_1 \cdot \varphi_2) = \varphi_1 \Delta \varphi_2 + \varphi_2 \Delta \varphi_1 + 2\left(\frac{\partial \varphi_1}{\partial x}\frac{\partial \varphi_2}{\partial x} + \frac{\partial \varphi_1}{\partial y}\frac{\partial \varphi_2}{\partial y} + \frac{\partial \varphi_1}{\partial z}\frac{\partial \varphi_2}{\partial z}\right).$$

Now let

$$\varphi_1 = (x^2 + y^2 + z^2)^{\frac{m}{2}} = r^m, \qquad \varphi_2 = H_n,$$

where H_n is a spherical harmonic of degree n.   It is readily verified that

$$\Delta r^m = m(m+1)r^{m-2},$$

$$2\left(\frac{\partial \varphi_1}{\partial x}\frac{\partial \varphi_2}{\partial x} + \frac{\partial \varphi_1}{\partial y}\frac{\partial \varphi_2}{\partial y} + \frac{\partial \varphi_1}{\partial z}\frac{\partial \varphi_2}{\partial z}\right) =$$

$$2mr^{m-2}\left(x\frac{\partial H_n}{\partial x} + y\frac{\partial H_n}{\partial y} + z\frac{\partial H_n}{\partial z}\right) = 2mnr^{m-2}H_n;$$

and, since

$$\Delta H_n = 0,$$

it is seen that

$$\Delta(r^m \cdot H_n) = m(m + 2n + 1)r^{m-2}H_n. \qquad (1)$$

Aside from the trivial value $m = 0$, this expression vanishes, if and only if,

$$m = -(2n + 1).$$

That is, if H_n is a spherical harmonic, then H_n/r^{2n+1} also is a spherical harmonic.   This can be written

$$\frac{H_n}{r^{2n+1}} = H_{-(n+1)}, \qquad \text{or} \qquad \frac{H_n}{r^n} = \frac{H_{-(n+1)}}{r^{-(n+1)}};$$

or again, if $m + n = -1$,

$$\frac{H_n}{r^n} = \frac{H_m}{r^m},$$

which shows the relation between any two spherical harmonics which give rise to the same surface harmonics.

172. The Expansion of a Potential.—If $\varphi(x, y, z)$ satisfies the equation of Laplace, then $\partial\varphi/\partial x$ also satisfies it; for, on changing the order of differentiation,

$$\Delta\frac{\partial\varphi}{\partial x} = \frac{\partial}{\partial x}(\Delta\varphi) = \frac{\partial}{\partial x}(0) = 0.$$

In like manner, it is shown that every derivative of φ satisfies Laplace's equation. That is to say, if φ is a homogeneous function of degree n which satisfies the equation of Laplace,

$$\frac{\partial^{i+j+k}\varphi}{\partial x^i \partial y^j \partial z^k}$$

is a homogeneous function of degree $n - i - j - k$ (provided it does not vanish identically) which also satisfies it. In particular

$$\frac{\partial^{i+j+k}}{\partial x^i \partial y^j \partial z^k}\left(\frac{1}{\rho}\right)$$

is harmonic of degree $-(i + j + k + 1)$ outside of any small sphere about the point ξ, η, ζ, where

$$\rho = \sqrt{(x - \xi)^2 + (y - \eta)^2 + (z - \zeta)^2}.$$

The function $1/\rho$ can be expanded in powers of ξ, η, and ζ by means of Taylor's theorem, viz.

$$\left.\begin{array}{c}\dfrac{1}{\rho} = \displaystyle\sum_{i,j,k} \dfrac{(-1)^{i+j+k}}{i!\,j!\,k!} \cdot \dfrac{\partial^{i+j+k}}{\partial x^i \partial y^j \partial z^k}\left(\dfrac{1}{r}\right) \cdot \xi^i \eta^j \zeta^k, \\[2mm] r = \sqrt{x^2 + y^2 + z^2}.\end{array}\right\} \qquad (1)$$

Suppose ξ, η, ζ are the coordinates of a particle of mass dm of a body B that lies wholly within a sphere Σ which has its center at the origin of the coordinate system. If x, y, z is a point which lies outside of Σ, the series, of Eq. (1) is uniformly convergent. Hence

$$V = \int_B \frac{dm}{\rho} = \sum_{i,j,k} \frac{(-1)^{i+j+k}}{i!\,j!\,k!} \frac{\partial^{i+j+k}}{\partial x^i \partial y^j \partial z^k}\left(\frac{1}{r}\right) \int_B \xi^i \eta^j \zeta^k dm. \qquad (2)$$

The expressions

$$I_{i,j,k} = \int_B \xi^i \eta^j \zeta^k dm$$

are the inertial integrals which were discussed in Chap. II. Their coefficients in Eq. (2) are spherical harmonics of degree $-(i + j + k + 1)$. Let

$$H_{i,j,k} = \frac{(-1)^{i+j+k}}{i!\,j!\,k!} \frac{\partial^{i+j+k}}{\partial x^i \partial y^j \partial z^k}\left(\frac{1}{r}\right).$$

Then

$$V = \sum_{i,j,k} H_{i,j,k} I_{i,j,k} \qquad (3)$$

THE THEORY OF THE POTENTIAL

is an expansion of the potential function in terms of the inertial integrals and spherical harmonics. It should be noted that the spherical harmonics $H_{i,j,k}$ are altogether independent of the body B.

173. Rotation about an Imaginary Axis.—In Sec. 26 it was shown that the equation of Laplace is invariant under a rotation of the axes defined by the equations.

$$\left.\begin{array}{l} x = \alpha_1\xi + \alpha_2\eta + \alpha_3\zeta, \\ y = \beta_1\xi + \beta_2\eta + \beta_3\zeta, \\ z = \gamma_1\xi + \gamma_2\eta + \gamma_3\zeta, \end{array}\right\} \tag{1}$$

provided the following relations are satisfied by the coefficients α, β, γ:

$$\left.\begin{array}{ll} \alpha_1{}^2 + \beta_1{}^2 + \gamma_1{}^2 = 1, & \alpha_1\alpha_2 + \beta_1\beta_2 + \gamma_1\gamma_2 = 0, \\ \alpha_2{}^2 + \beta_2{}^2 + \gamma_2{}^2 = 1, & \alpha_2\alpha_3 + \beta_2\beta_3 + \gamma_2\gamma_3 = 0, \\ \alpha_3{}^2 + \beta_3{}^2 + \gamma_3{}^2 = 1, & \alpha_3\alpha_1 + \beta_3\beta_1 + \gamma_3\gamma_1 = 0. \end{array}\right\} \tag{2}$$

If α and β are two parameters and i denotes $\sqrt{-1}$, it will be found that

$$\left.\begin{array}{lll} \alpha_1 = \dfrac{1 - \alpha^2 + \beta^2}{2\beta}, & \alpha_2 = \dfrac{-1 - \alpha^2 + \beta^2}{2\beta}i, & \alpha_3 = -\dfrac{\alpha}{\beta}, \\ \beta_1 = \dfrac{1 - \alpha^2 - \beta^2}{2\beta}i, & \beta_2 = \dfrac{1 + \alpha^2 + \beta^2}{2\beta}, & \beta_3 = -\dfrac{\alpha}{\beta}i, \\ \gamma_1 = \alpha, & \gamma_2 = \alpha i, & \gamma_3 = +1, \end{array}\right\} \tag{3}$$

satisfies the six conditions of Eq. (2); and therefore, Eqs. (1) with these values of the coefficients defines a rotation of the coordinate system about an imaginary axis. The axis of the rotation is the locus of the invariant points of the transformation, and is defined by the equations

$$\xi = \alpha_1\xi + \alpha_2\eta + \alpha_3\zeta, \qquad (\alpha_1 - 1)\xi + \alpha_2\eta + \alpha_3\zeta = 0,$$
$$\eta = \beta_1\xi + \beta_2\eta + \beta_3\zeta, \qquad \beta_1\xi + (\beta_2 - 1)\eta + \beta_3\zeta = 0,$$
$$\zeta = \gamma_1\xi + \gamma_2\eta + \gamma_3\zeta, \qquad \gamma_1\xi + \gamma_2\eta + (\gamma_3 - 1)\zeta = 0.$$

Since the last set of equations is homogeneous, its determinant must vanish, and it will be found that actually it does vanish. The solution of the equations then gives

$$\xi = \frac{\alpha}{1 - \beta}\zeta, \qquad \eta = \frac{i\alpha}{1 - \beta}\zeta,$$

as the equations of the axis of rotation.

If the parameters are changed by taking

$$\alpha = \frac{\lambda\mu}{1 + \lambda}, \qquad \beta = \frac{1}{1 + \lambda},$$

so that

$$\left.\begin{aligned}
&\alpha_1 = 1 - \frac{\lambda^2(\mu^2 - 1)}{2(1 + \lambda)}, \qquad \alpha_2 = i\left[-\lambda - \frac{\lambda^2(\mu^2 - 1)}{2(1 + \lambda)}\right], \\
&\beta_1 = i\left[\lambda - \frac{\lambda^2(\mu^2 + 1)}{2(1 + \lambda)}\right], \; \beta_2 = 1 + \frac{\lambda^2(\mu^2 + 1)}{2(1 + \lambda)}, \\
&\gamma_1 = \frac{\lambda\mu}{1 + \lambda}, \qquad\qquad \gamma_2 = \frac{i\lambda\mu}{1 + \lambda}, \\
&\alpha_3 = -\lambda\mu, \qquad\quad \beta_3 = -i\lambda\mu, \qquad\quad \gamma_3 = +1,
\end{aligned}\right\} \quad (4)$$

the direction cosines of the axis of rotation

$$\mu, \qquad i\mu, \qquad +1$$

depend upon μ alone, and λ measures the amount of the rotation about this axis.

174. Harmonics Which Depend upon r and z Alone.—Suppose H is an harmonic which depends only upon r and z, where

$$r^2 = x^2 + y^2 + z^2.$$

Since it satisfies the equation of Laplace in the letters x, y, z, it will also satisfy the equation of Laplace in the letters ξ, η, ζ, after the transformation Eq. (173.3) is made. Since Eqs. (173.2) are satisfied, the function r is invariant under this transformation; that is

$$r^2 = x^2 + y^2 + z^2 = \xi^2 + \eta^2 + \zeta^2.$$

The letter z, however, must be replaced by

$$z = \zeta + \alpha(\xi + i\eta).$$

Suppose further that $H = H_n$ is a homogeneous, harmonic, polynomial of degree n in the letters x, y, z. When expressed as a function of r and z, it is a rational integral function of r^2 and z. After the transformation, it becomes

$$H_n(r^2, z) = H_n(r^2, \zeta + \alpha(\xi + i\eta)),$$

which can be arranged in powers of α, thus:

$$H_n = H_n^{(0)} + \alpha(\xi + i\eta)\frac{\partial H_n^{(0)}}{\partial \zeta} + \frac{\alpha^2}{2!}(\xi + i\eta)^2\frac{\partial^2 H_n^{(0)}}{\partial \zeta^2} + \cdots$$

$$+ \frac{\alpha^n}{n!}(\xi + i\eta)^n\frac{\partial^n H_n^{(0)}}{\partial \zeta^n}. \quad (1)$$

Since this polynomial is harmonic *whatever* α *may be*, the coefficient of each power of α separately is harmonic. But these coefficients are complex; therefore, the real part of each coefficient is harmonic by itself, and the purely imaginary part also. Therefore, the polynomial represented by Eq. (1) contains $2n + 1$ separate harmonic functions. That they are linearly independent is evident at once by taking

$$\xi + i\eta = \rho e^{i\theta},$$

so that

$$(\xi + i\eta)^k = \rho^k(\cos k\theta + i \sin k\theta),$$

and bearing in mind that H_n is homogeneous in r, ξ, η, and ζ.

It follows, therefore, that if there exists a homogeneous polynomial in x, y, z of degree n which is expressible as a function of r^2 and z alone and which also is harmonic, there exist $2n + 1$ linearly independent, homogeneous, harmonic polynomials of degree n. It will be shown in Sec. 176 that, aside from a constant factor, for every positive, integral value of n there exists one, and only one, homogeneous polynomial of degree n which is expressible as a function of r^2 and z alone.

175. The Equation of Laplace for Surface Harmonics.—
If H_n is a solid spherical harmonic of degree n, then

$$S_n = \frac{H_n}{r^n}$$

is a surface harmonic of degree n; that is, it represents the values which H_n takes on the surface of a sphere of radius unity. It is a function of the polar angles, which can be taken to be the longitude and polar distance on the sphere.

If Laplace's equation is transformed from rectangular to polar coordinates (Sec. 57) by the substitution

$$x = r \sin \varphi \cos \theta,$$

$$y = r \sin \varphi \sin \theta,$$

$$z = r \cos \varphi,$$

there results

$$r \frac{\partial^2(rV)}{\partial r^2} + \frac{1}{\sin \varphi} \frac{\partial}{\partial \varphi}\left(\sin \varphi \frac{\partial V}{\partial \varphi}\right) + \frac{1}{\sin^2 \varphi} \frac{\partial^2 V}{\partial \theta^2} = 0. \qquad (1)$$

If now

$$V = H_n = r^n S_n$$

is homogeneous of degree n, so that S_n is a function of φ and θ alone, the differentiation with respect to r in Eq. (1) can be performed; for

$$r \frac{\partial^2 (rV)}{\partial r^2} = r \frac{\partial^2 (r^{n+1} S_n)}{\partial r^2} = n(n+1) r^n S_n.$$

After removing the common factor r^n, Eq. (1) reduces to

$$\frac{1}{\sin^2 \varphi} \frac{\partial^2 S_n}{\partial \theta^2} + \frac{1}{\sin \varphi} \frac{\partial}{\partial \varphi} \left(\sin \varphi \frac{\partial S_n}{\partial \varphi} \right) + n(n+1) S_n = 0. \quad (2)$$

Every spherical surface harmonic of degree n must satisfy this differential equation; and conversely, every solution of this equation is a surface harmonic of degree n.

Since the integral over any closed surface of the normal derivative of any harmonic function is zero (Eq. (58.5)), it follows that for every k

$$\int_S \frac{\partial H_k}{\partial n} d\omega = 0.$$

On the surface of a sphere

$$H_k = r^k S_k, \qquad \text{and} \qquad \frac{\partial H_k}{\partial n} = k r^{k-1} S_k.$$

Hence

$$\int_S \frac{\partial H_k}{\partial n} d\omega = k r^{k-1} \int_S S_k d\omega = 0.$$

Therefore, if $k \neq 0$,

$$\int_S S_k d\omega = 0; \quad (3)$$

that is, the integral over the sphere of any spherical surface harmonic of degree k is zero, except when k is zero. Since S_0 is a constant,

$$\int_S S_0 d\omega = 4\pi a^2 S_0.$$

176. Zonal Harmonics.—A spherical harmonic which can be expressed as a function of r and z alone is a solid zonal harmonic. A solid zonal harmonic of degree n divided by r^n is a surface zonal harmonic of degree n. Evidently, it is independent of the longitude. Hence, if P_n is a surface zonal harmonic, it does not contain θ, and Eq. (175.2) becomes

$$\frac{1}{\sin \varphi} \frac{\partial}{\partial \varphi} \left(\sin \varphi \frac{\partial P_n}{\partial \varphi} \right) + n(n+1) P_n = 0, \quad (1)$$

which is the differential equation of a zonal harmonic of degree n.

For the sake of notation, let

$$\mu = \cos \varphi;$$

then Eq. (1) becomes

or,

$$\left. \begin{aligned} \frac{d}{d\mu}\left((1 - \mu^2)\frac{dP_n}{d\mu}\right) + n(n + 1)P_n = 0, \\ (1 - \mu^2)\frac{d^2P_n}{d\mu^2} - 2\mu\frac{dP_n}{d\mu} + n(n + 1)P_n = 0. \end{aligned} \right\} \quad (2)$$

If the solid zonal harmonic is a polynomial in r^2 and z, the corresponding surface zonal harmonic is a polynomial in $\cos \varphi$ of degree n; and therefore, a polynomial in μ of degree n. If it is assumed that

$$P_n = a_0\mu^n + a_1\mu^{n-1} + a_2\mu^{n-2} + \cdots,$$

it is found that, aside from a constant factor, the constant coefficients a_k are uniquely determined by Eq. (2). Hence, there exists one, and but one, zonal harmonic which is a polynomial in μ of degree n. In order to normalize them, it is customary to choose the constant factor in such a way that

$$P_n = +1 \quad \text{when} \quad \mu = +1.$$

With this understanding, then, every standard zonal harmonic which is a polynomial in μ is equal to $+1$ at the north pole of the sphere.

Since Eq. (2) is a differential equation of the second order, a complete solution contains two arbitrary constants; and since it is linear and homogeneous, the complete solution has the form

$$P_n = C_1P(\mu) + C_2Q(\mu),$$

where C_1 and C_2 are the two constants of integration.

If it is assumed that P is the polynomial solution, and that this solution is known, it will be found that

$$Q = P \int \frac{d\mu}{(1 - \mu^2)P^2}$$

also satisfies Eq. (2). This solution evidently contains logarithms and fractions, and is known as a zonal harmonic of the second kind.

177. The Polynomials of Legendre.—Let ρ be measured from a point on the z-axis at a distance z_0 from the origin. The function

$$\frac{1}{\rho} = \frac{1}{\sqrt{x^2 + y^2 + (z - z_0)^2}}$$

satisfies the equation of Laplace and is expressible in terms of r^2 and z alone, since

$$\rho^2 = r^2 - 2zz_0 + z_0{}^2. \tag{1}$$

On taking $V = 1/\rho$ in Eq. (175.1) and bearing in mind that $1/\rho$ does not depend upon θ, it is found that

$$r\frac{d^2}{dr^2}\left(\frac{r}{\rho}\right) + \frac{d}{d\mu}\left((1 - \mu^2)\frac{d}{d\mu}\left(\frac{1}{\rho}\right)\right) = 0. \tag{2}$$

Since

$$z = r \cos \varphi = r\mu,$$

Equation (1) can also be written

$$\rho^2 = r^2 - 2rz_0\mu + z_0{}^2.$$

After dividing through by $z_0{}^2$, and then taking

$$\frac{r}{z_0} = h, \qquad 1 - 2\mu h + h^2 = \frac{1}{H^2} = \frac{\rho^2}{z_0{}^2},$$

it is found that

$$\frac{1}{\rho} = \frac{H}{z_0}, \qquad \frac{r}{\rho} = hH, \qquad dr = z_0 dh;$$

and Eq. (2) becomes

$$h\frac{d^2(hH)}{dh^2} + \frac{d}{d\mu}\left[(1 - \mu^2)\frac{dH}{d\mu}\right] = 0. \tag{3}$$

The function

$$\begin{aligned}
H &= [1 - 2\mu h + h^2]^{-\frac{1}{2}} \\
&= [1 - (e^{i\varphi} + e^{-i\varphi})h + h^2]^{-\frac{1}{2}} \\
&= (1 - e^{i\varphi}h)^{-\frac{1}{2}}(1 - e^{-i\varphi}h)^{-\frac{1}{2}}
\end{aligned}$$

is evidently expansible as a power series in h, and since

$$|e^{i\varphi}| = |e^{-i\varphi}| = 1,$$

this expansion is convergent if $|h| < 1$. It can be written

$$H = 1 + p_1 h + p_2 h^2 + p_3 h^3 + \cdots + p_n h^n + \cdots;$$

therefore

$$hH = h + p_1h^2 + p_2h^3 + p_3h^4 + \cdots + p_nh^{n+1} + \cdots,$$

and

$$h\frac{d^2(hH)}{dh^2} = 1 \cdot 2p_1h + 2 \cdot 3p_2h^2 + \cdots + n(n+1)p_nh^n + \cdots$$

Also, since μ occurs only in the coefficients of the series,

$$\frac{d}{d\mu}\left[(1 - \mu^2)\frac{dH}{d\mu}\right] = \sum_{n=1}^{\infty}\frac{d}{d\mu}\left[(1 - \mu^2)\frac{dp_n}{d\mu}\right]h^n.$$

Hence, Eq. (3) expanded in powers of h becomes

$$\sum_{n=1}^{\infty}\left(\frac{d}{d\mu}\left[(1 - \mu^2)\frac{dp_n}{d\mu}\right] + n(n+1)p_n\right)h^n = 0. \qquad (4)$$

Since Eq. (4) holds for all values of $h < 1$, it follows that each coefficient separately is zero, and therefore,

$$\frac{d}{d\mu}\left[(1 - \mu^2)\frac{dp_n}{d\mu}\right] + n(n+1)p_n = 0. \qquad n = 1, 2, \cdots, \infty. \quad (5)$$

Equation (5), however, is identical with Eq. (176.2), and since p_n is evidently a polynomial in μ, from the definition of h, it follows that p_n and P_n can differ only by a constant multiplier. But, for $\mu = 1$,

$$H = \frac{1}{1 - h} = 1 + h + h^2 + \cdots + h^n + \cdots.$$

Therefore

$$p_n(+1) = +1 \qquad n = 1, 2, \cdots, \infty,$$

and p_n is identical with P_n, the standard zonal harmonic of degree n.

The coefficients p_n of the expansion of $(1 - 2\mu h + h^2)^{-\frac{1}{2}}$ in powers of h are known as the *polynomials of Legendre*, or, sometimes, *Legendrians*. It follows, therefore, that the standard zonal harmonics are simply the polynomials of Legendre, and

$$H = 1 + \sum_{n=1}^{\infty} P_nh^n. \qquad (6)$$

If $|h| > 1$, the function H can be expanded in powers of the reciprocal of h. Thus

$$H = \frac{1}{\sqrt{h^2 - 2\mu h + 1}} = \frac{1}{h}\frac{1}{\sqrt{1 - 2\mu\dfrac{1}{h} + \dfrac{1}{h^2}}}$$

$$= \frac{1}{h} + \sum_{n=1}^{\infty}\frac{P_n}{h^{n+1}} = \sum_{n=0}^{\infty}P_n h^{-(n+1)},$$

where P_0 is understood to be unity.

It will be observed, that if n is changed to $-(n+1)$ in Eq. (5), the equation remains unaltered, and therefore

$$P_n \equiv P_{-(n+1)}.$$

178. The Expansion in Taylor's Series.—The expansion of any function $\varphi(z - z_0)$ in powers of z_0 according to Taylor's theorem is

$$\varphi(z - z_0) = \varphi(z) + \sum_{n=1}^{\infty}(-1)^n\frac{d^n\varphi}{dz^n}\frac{z_0^n}{n!}.$$

In the present case

$$\varphi(z - z_0) = \frac{1}{\rho} = \frac{1}{\sqrt{x^2 + y^2 + (z - z_0)^2}} = \frac{1}{\sqrt{r^2 - 2\mu z_0 + z_0^2}}.$$

Therefore

$$\frac{1}{\rho} = \sum_{n=0}^{\infty}\frac{(-1)}{n!}\frac{d^n}{dz^n}\left(\frac{1}{r}\right)z_0^n,$$

or

$$\frac{1}{\rho} = \frac{1}{r}\sum_{n=0}^{\infty}(-1)^n\frac{r^{n+1}}{n!}\frac{d^n}{dz^n}\left(\frac{1}{r}\right)\left(\frac{z_0}{r}\right)^n. \tag{1}$$

Since $1/\rho$ satisfies the equation of Laplace, whatever z_0 may be, it follows that

$$\frac{d^n}{dz^n}\left(\frac{1}{r}\right)$$

is harmonic and is expressible in terms of r and z alone. Hence

$$(-1)^n\frac{r^{n+1}}{n!}\frac{d^n}{dz^n}\left(\frac{1}{r}\right) \tag{2}$$

is a zonal harmonic of degree n. Since, for $\mu = +1$,

$$\frac{1}{\rho} = \frac{1}{r}\left[1 + \left(\frac{z_0}{r}\right) + \left(\frac{z_0}{r}\right)^2 + \left(\frac{z_0}{r}\right)^3 + \cdots\right],$$

each coefficient of Eq. (1) reduces to unity for $\mu = 1$. Therefore, these coefficients are standard zonal harmonics, and

$$P_n = (-1)^n \frac{r^{n+1}}{n!} \cdot \frac{d^n}{dz^n}\left(\frac{1}{r}\right). \tag{3}$$

179. The Expansion in Lagrange's Series.—Let x be defined as a function of μ and h by the relation

$$hx = 1 - \sqrt{1 - 2\mu h + h^2}, \tag{1}$$

so that

$$\frac{dx}{d\mu} = \frac{1}{\sqrt{1 - 2\mu h + h^2}} = H. \tag{2}$$

If Eq. (1) is rationalized, it is found that

$$x = \mu + h\left(\frac{x^2 - 1}{2}\right).$$

This expression is admirably suited to expansion by a beautiful theorem of Lagrange.[1] If z is defined as a function of w by means of the equation

$$z = w + \alpha\varphi(w),$$

where α is a parameter and $\varphi(z)$ is any function which is developable in powers of $z - w$, then z can be expanded as a power series in α, and the form of this expansion is

$$z = w + \alpha\varphi(w) + \sum_{n=1}^{\infty} \frac{\alpha^{n+1}}{(n+1)!} \frac{d^n}{dw^n}(\varphi(w))^{n+1}. \tag{3}$$

By means of this formula, it is found that

$$x = \mu + h\frac{\mu^2 - 1}{2} + \sum_{n=1}^{\infty} \frac{h^{n+1}}{(n+1)!} \frac{d^n}{d\mu^n}\left(\frac{\mu^2 - 1}{2}\right)^{n+1};$$

and on differentiating with respect to μ there results

$$\frac{dx}{d\mu} = H = 1 + \sum_{n=1}^{\infty} \frac{h^n}{n!} \frac{d^n}{d\mu^n}\left(\frac{\mu^2 - 1}{2}\right)^n.$$

[1] WILLIAMSON's "Differential Calculus," p. 151, or, GOURSAT-HEDRICK, "Mathematical Analysis," Vol I, p. 404.

Since, by Eq. (177.6),

$$H = 1 + \sum_{n=1}^{\infty} P_n h^n,$$

it follows from a comparison of the coefficients of these two expressions that

$$P_n = \frac{1}{n!} \frac{d^n}{d\mu^n} \left(\frac{\mu^2 - 1}{2} \right)^n, \tag{4}$$

a formula which is due to Roderigues (1815).

It is evident from this expression that P_n contains only even powers of μ, if n is even, and only odd powers of μ, if n is odd. This is evident also from the fact that if μ is changed into $-\mu$ and h into $-h$ in the equation

$$H = \frac{1}{\sqrt{1 - 2\mu h + h^2}} = \sum P_n h^n, \tag{5}$$

the equation remains unaltered.

180. Zonal Harmonics Given Explicitly.—Although the formulas so far given are not the best ones for computing the zonal harmonics, it will add to the clarity of thought to have a few zonal harmonics, or Legendre's polynomials if preferred, set forth explicitly. The following are the values given by Eq. (186.4).

$$P_0 = 1, \qquad\qquad P_1 = \mu,$$

$$P_2 = \frac{3}{2}\mu^2 - \frac{1}{2}, \qquad P_3 = \frac{5}{2}\mu^3 - \frac{3}{2}\mu,$$

$$P_4 = \frac{7 \cdot 5}{2 \cdot 4}\mu^4 - \frac{5 \cdot 3}{2 \cdot 2}\mu^2 + \frac{3 \cdot 1}{2 \cdot 4},$$

$$P_5 = \frac{9 \cdot 7}{2 \cdot 4}\mu^5 - \frac{7 \cdot 5}{2 \cdot 2}\mu^3 + \frac{5 \cdot 3}{2 \cdot 4}\mu,$$

$$P_6 = \frac{11 \cdot 9 \cdot 7}{2 \cdot 4 \cdot 6}\mu^6 - \frac{9 \cdot 7 \cdot 5}{2 \cdot 4 \cdot 2}\mu^4 + \frac{7 \cdot 5 \cdot 3}{2 \cdot 2 \cdot 4}\mu^2 - \frac{5 \cdot 3 \cdot 1}{2 \cdot 4 \cdot 6},$$

$$P_7 = \frac{13 \cdot 11 \cdot 9}{2 \cdot 4 \cdot 6}\mu^7 - \frac{11 \cdot 9 \cdot 7}{2 \cdot 4 \cdot 2}\mu^5 + \frac{9 \cdot 7 \cdot 5}{2 \cdot 2 \cdot 4}\mu^3 - \frac{7 \cdot 5 \cdot 3}{2 \cdot 4 \cdot 6}\mu,$$

$$P_8 = \frac{15 \cdot 13 \cdot 11 \cdot 9}{2 \cdot 4 \cdot 6 \cdot 8}\mu^8 - \frac{13 \cdot 11 \cdot 9 \cdot 7}{2 \cdot 4 \cdot 6 \cdot 2}\mu^6 + \frac{11 \cdot 9 \cdot 7 \cdot 5}{2 \cdot 4 \cdot 2 \cdot 4}\mu^4$$

$$- \frac{9 \cdot 7 \cdot 5 \cdot 3}{2 \cdot 2 \cdot 4 \cdot 6}\mu^2 + \frac{7 \cdot 5 \cdot 3 \cdot 1}{2 \cdot 4 \cdot 6 \cdot 8},$$

$$P_9 = \frac{17 \cdot 15 \cdot 13 \cdot 11}{2 \cdot 4 \cdot 6 \cdot 8} \mu^9 - \frac{15 \cdot 13 \cdot 11 \cdot 9}{2 \cdot 4 \cdot 6 \cdot 2} \mu^7 + \frac{13 \cdot 11 \cdot 9 \cdot 7}{2 \cdot 4 \cdot 2 \cdot 4} \mu^5$$

$$- \frac{11 \cdot 9 \cdot 7 \cdot 5}{2 \cdot 2 \cdot 4 \cdot 6} \mu^3 + \frac{9 \cdot 7 \cdot 5 \cdot 3}{2 \cdot 4 \cdot 6 \cdot 8} \mu,$$

$$P_{10} = \frac{19 \cdot 17 \cdot 15 \cdot 13 \cdot 11}{2 \cdot 4 \cdot 6 \cdot 8 \cdot 10} \mu^{10} - \frac{17 \cdot 15 \cdot 13 \cdot 11 \cdot 9}{2 \cdot 4 \cdot 6 \cdot 8 \cdot 2} \mu^8$$

$$+ \frac{15 \cdot 13 \cdot 11 \cdot 9 \cdot 7}{2 \cdot 4 \cdot 6 \cdot 2 \cdot 4} \mu^6 - \frac{13 \cdot 11 \cdot 9 \cdot 7 \cdot 5}{2 \cdot 4 \cdot 2 \cdot 4 \cdot 6} \mu^4$$

$$+ \frac{11 \cdot 9 \cdot 7 \cdot 5 \cdot 3}{2 \cdot 2 \cdot 4 \cdot 6 \cdot 8} \mu^2 - \frac{9 \cdot 7 \cdot 5 \cdot 3 \cdot 1}{2 \cdot 4 \cdot 6 \cdot 8 \cdot 10}.$$

If the coefficients in these expressions are reduced to their lowest terms, the denominators will contain only powers of 2.

181. The Zeros of the Zonal Harmonics are All Real.—

Although Eq. (179.4) is not particularly well adapted to deriving the explicit forms of the polynomials, it is of great advantage in showing that the values of μ for which these polynomials vanish are all real and lie between -1 and $+1$.

It will be observed that the equation

$$(\mu^2 - 1)^n = 0$$

has n roots equal to $+1$ and n roots equal to -1. Its first derivative is an equation of degree $2n - 1$, which has $n - 1$ roots equal to $+1$, $n - 1$ roots equal to -1, and one root equal to zero.

The second derivative is an equation of degree $2n - 2$ which has $n - 2$ roots equal to $+1$, and $n - 2$ roots equal to -1; and since the first derivative vanishes for $\mu = 0$, the second derivative, by Rolle's theorem, must vanish at least once between $\mu = -1$ and $\mu = 0$, and at least once between $\mu = 0$ and $\mu = +1$. Since all of the $2n - 2$ roots have already been accounted for, it cannot vanish more than once in the intervals mentioned. Let these two roots be μ_2 and $-\mu_2$.

The third derivative has $2n - 3$ roots, of which $n - 3$ are equal to $+1$, $n - 3$ equal to -1, one equal to zero and one in each of the intervals $(-1, -\mu_2)$ and $(+\mu_2, +1)$. Let these last two roots be μ_3 and $-\mu_3$.

The fourth derivative has $2n - 4$ roots, of which $n - 4$ are equal to $+1$, $n - 4$ equal to -1, and one in each of the four intervals $(-1, -\mu_3)$, $(-\mu_3, 0)$, $(0, +\mu_3)$ and $(+\mu_3, +1)$.

If the $(i-1)^{th}$ derivative has $i-1$ roots $\mu_{i-1}^{(k)}$ different from ± 1, the ith derivative must vanish once in each of the i intervals into which the $i-1$ roots $\mu_{i-1}^{(k)}$ separate the interval

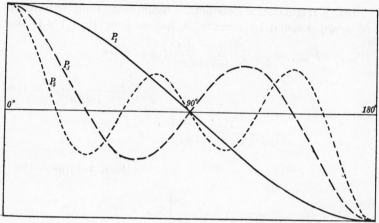

Fig. 101.

$(-1, +1)$. Since it is a polynomial of degree $2n-i$ with $n-i$ roots for $\mu = -1$, $n-i$ roots for $\mu = +1$, and i roots

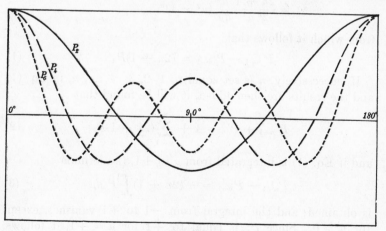

Fig. 102.

lying between these limits, all of its roots are real and lie between the limits $\mu = \pm 1$, the limits included.

Hence the nth derivative has no roots ± 1, and n roots in the interval $(-1, +1)$. There are, therefore, n distinct latitudes on the sphere for which the zonal harmonic of degree n vanishes, and these latitudes are symmetrically situated with respect to the equator.

182. Certain Useful Relations.—If differentiations with respect to μ are denoted by accents, it follows from Eq. (179.4) that

$$P'_{n+1} - P'_{n-1} = \frac{1}{2^{n+1}(n+1)!} \frac{d^{n+2}}{d\mu^{n+2}}(\mu^2 - 1)^{n+1}$$

$$- \frac{1}{2^{n-1}(n-1)!} \frac{d^n}{d\mu^n}(\mu^2 - 1)^{n-1}$$

$$= \frac{1}{2^{n+1}(n+1)!} \frac{d^n}{d\mu^n} \left[\frac{d^2}{d\mu^2}(\mu^2 - 1)^{n+1} \right.$$

$$\left. - 4n(n+1)(\mu^2 - 1)^{n-1} \right]$$

$$= \frac{1}{2^{n+1}(n+1)!} \frac{d^n}{d\mu^n} \left[2(n+1)(\mu^2 - 1)^n \right.$$

$$\left. + 4n(n+1)\mu^2(\mu^2 - 1)^{n-1} - 4n(n+1)(\mu^2 - 1)^{n-1} \right]$$

$$= \frac{2n+1}{2^n n!} \frac{d^n}{d\mu^n}(\mu^2 - 1)^n,$$

from which it follows that

$$P'_{n+1} - P'_{n-1} = (2n+1)P_n. \tag{1}$$

If, successively, n is set equal to 1, 2, 3, . . . , n, in Eq. (1) and the results are then added, it will be found that

$$P'_{n+1} + P'_n = 1 + \sum_{k=1}^{n} (2k+1)P_k; \tag{2}$$

and if Eq. (1) is integrated from μ to $+1$, the formula

$$P_{n+1} - P_{n-1} = -(2n+1)\int_{\mu}^{1} P_n d\mu \tag{3}$$

is obtained; and the integral from -1 to $+1$ vanishes, except for $n = 0$. Since P_n is equal to $+1$ for $\mu = +1$, it follows, if μ is sufficiently close to $+1$, that P_n is positive, and therefore, the right member of Eq. (3) is negative. Hence, for every n,

$$P_{n+1} < P_{n-1} < 1,$$

if μ is sufficiently close to $+1$.

From the differential equation, Eq. (176.2) there is obtained by integration

$$n(n + 1)\int_\mu^1 P_n d\mu = (1 - \mu^2)P'_n.$$

On comparing this equation with Eq. (3), it is seen that

$$P_{n+1} - P_{n-1} = -\left(\frac{1}{n} + \frac{1}{n + 1}\right)(1 - \mu^2)P'_n, \qquad (4)$$

which has a curious resemblance to Eq. (1).

183. The Zonal Harmonics are Orthogonal Functions.—It has been proved that

$$\frac{1}{\sqrt{1 - 2\mu h + h^2}} = \sum_{i = 0}^\infty P_i h^i, \qquad (1)$$

and

$$\frac{1}{\sqrt{1 - 2\mu k + k^2}} = \sum_{j = 0}^\infty P_j k^j.$$

If these two expressions are multiplied together and then integrated with respect to μ from $\mu = -1$ to $\mu = +1$, there results

$$\left. \begin{aligned} &\int_{-1}^{+1} \frac{d\mu}{\sqrt{1 - 2\mu h + h^2}\sqrt{1 - 2\mu k + k^2}} \\ &= \int_{-1}^{+1} \sum_{i = 0}^\infty \sum_{j = 0}^\infty P_i P_j h^i k^j d\mu = \sum_{i = 0}^\infty \sum_{j = 0}^\infty h^i k^j \int_{-1}^{+1} P_i P_j d\mu. \end{aligned} \right\} \quad (2)$$

The indefinite integral of the left member is

$$-\frac{1}{\sqrt{hk}} \log \left[\sqrt{k(1 - 2\mu h + h^2)} + \sqrt{h(1 - 2\mu k + k^2)}\right];$$

and the definite integral is

$$\frac{1}{\sqrt{hk}} \log \frac{(1 + h)\sqrt{k} + (1 + k)\sqrt{h}}{(1 - h)\sqrt{k} + (1 - k)\sqrt{h}}$$

$$= \frac{1}{\sqrt{hk}} \log \frac{(\sqrt{k} + \sqrt{h})(1 + \sqrt{hk})}{(\sqrt{k} + \sqrt{h})(1 - \sqrt{hk})} = \frac{1}{\sqrt{hk}} \log \frac{1 + \sqrt{hk}}{1 - \sqrt{hk}}.$$

Since

$$\frac{1}{x} \log \frac{1 + x}{1 - x} = 2\sum_{n = 0}^\infty \frac{x^{2n}}{2n + 1},$$

equation (2) can be written

$$\sum_{n=0}^{\infty} \frac{2h^n k^n}{2n+1} = \sum_{i=0}^{\infty} \sum_{j=0}^{\infty} h^i k^j \int_{-1}^{+1} P_i P_j d\mu.$$

A comparison of the coefficients of the two members of this equation shows that

$$\int_{-1}^{+1} P_i P_j d\mu = 0 \qquad i \neq j, \tag{3}$$

and

$$\int_{-1}^{+1} P_n{}^2 d\mu = \frac{2}{2n+1}. \tag{4}$$

That is, the zonal harmonics are orthogonal functions, which is a fundamental property. The method of proof here given is due to Legendre.

If the formula

$$\frac{1}{K} = \frac{1}{\sqrt{1-2\mu k + k^2}} = \sum_{j=0}^{\infty} P_j k^j$$

is differentiated with respect to μ, there results, after dividing through by k,

$$\frac{1}{K^3} = \frac{1}{(\sqrt{1-2\mu k + k^2})^3} = \sum_{j=0}^{\infty} P'_{j+1} k^i. \tag{5}$$

Also

$$\frac{1}{H} = \frac{1}{\sqrt{1-2\mu h + h^2}} = \sum_{i=0}^{\infty} P_i h^i.$$

Multiply these two expressions together, and then integrate with respect to μ. There results

$$\int_{-1}^{+1} \frac{d\mu}{HK^3} = \sum_{i=0}^{\infty} \sum_{j=0}^{\infty} h^i k^j \int_{-1}^{+1} P_i P'_{j+1} d\mu. \tag{6}$$

The indefinite integral of the left member is

$$\int \frac{d\mu}{HK^3} = \frac{1}{(k-h)(1-kh)} \cdot \frac{H}{K},$$

and the value of the definite integral is

$$\int_{-1}^{+1} \frac{d\mu}{HK^3} = \frac{2}{(1-kh)(1-k^2)} = 2 \sum_{i=0}^{\infty} \sum_{n=0}^{\infty} h^i k^{i+2n}. \tag{7}$$

A comparison of the right members of Eqs. (6) and (7) shows that

$$\left.\begin{array}{l} \int_{-1}^{+1} P_i P'_j d\mu = 0, \quad \text{if } j \leqq i, \text{ or if } i + j \text{ is even,} \\[2mm] \int_{-1}^{+1} P_i P'_j d\mu = 2, \quad \text{if } j > i, \text{ and } i + j \text{ is odd.} \end{array}\right\} \quad (8)$$

184. A Generalization of the Preceeding Formulas.—To simplify the notation, let

$$P_n^{(j)} \equiv \frac{d^j P_n}{d\mu^j}.$$

Consider the integral

$$G_j = \int_{-1}^{+1} (1 - \mu^2)^i P_m^{(j)} P_n^{(j)} d\mu. \qquad (1)$$

The function P_n satisfies the differential equation, Eq. (176.2),

$$(1 - \mu^2) P_n^{(2)} - 2\mu P_n^{(1)} + n(n + 1) P_n = 0.$$

If this equation is differentiated successively $j - 1$ times, there results

$$(1 - \mu^2) P_n^{(j+1)} - 2j\mu P_n^{(j)} + (n + j)(n - j + 1) P_n^{(j-1)} = 0,$$

which, after multiplication by $(1 - \mu^2)^{j-1}$, can be written

$$\frac{d}{d\mu}[(1 - \mu^2)^j P_n^{(j)}] = -(n + j)(n - j + 1)[(1 - \mu^2)^{j-1} P_n^{(j-1)}]. \quad (2)$$

If Eq. (1) is integrated by parts, there results

$$G_j = \left[P_m^{(j-1)} (1 - \mu^2)^j P_n^{(j)} \right]_{-1}^{+1}$$

$$- \int_{-1}^{+1} P_m^{(j-1)} \frac{d}{d\mu}[(1 - \mu^2)^j P_n^{(j)}] d\mu. \quad (3)$$

The first term in the right member vanishes, since $(1 - \mu^2)$ is zero at both limits. The second term can be transformed by Eq. (2), so that Eq. (3) becomes

$$\int_{-1}^{+1} (1 - \mu^2)^j P_m^{(j)} P_n^{(j)} d\mu =$$

$$(n + j)(n - j + 1) \int_{-1}^{+1} (1 - \mu^2)^{j-1} P_m^{(j-1)} P_n^{(j-1)} d\mu. \quad (4)$$

Equation (4) can be written

$$G_j = (n + j)(n - j + 1)G_{j-1};$$

and sequentially,

$$G_{j-1} = (n + j - 1)(n - j + 2)G_{j-2},$$

$$\cdot \quad \cdot \quad \cdot \quad \cdot \quad \cdot \quad \cdot \quad \cdot \quad \cdot \quad \cdot \quad \cdot \quad \cdot \quad \cdot \quad \cdot \quad \cdot$$

$$G_1 = (n + 1)nG_0.$$

On multiplying these equations together, it is found that

$$G_j = \frac{(n + j)!}{(n - j)!}G_0;$$

or, written out in full,

$$\int_{-1}^{+1}(1 - \mu^2)^j P_m{}^{(j)} P_n{}^{(j)} d\mu = \frac{(n + j)!}{(n - j)!}\int_{-1}^{+1} P_m P_n d\mu.$$

It follows from Eqs. (183.3) and (183.4) that, if j is any positive integer less than, or at most equal to n,

$$\int_{-1}^{+1}(1 - \mu^2)^j P_m{}^{(j)} P_n{}^{(j)} d\mu = 0 \qquad m \neq n, \tag{5}$$

$$\int_{-1}^{+1}(1 - \mu^2)^j (P_m{}^{(j)})^2 d\mu = \frac{2}{2n + 1}\frac{(n + j)!}{(n - j)!}. \tag{6}$$

These results can be regarded as a generalization of Eqs. (183.3) and (183.4).

185. A Recursion Formula for Zonal Harmonics.—If Eq. (183.1) is differentiated with respect to h, there results

$$\frac{\mu - h}{(1 - 2\mu h + h^2)^{\frac{3}{2}}} = \sum_{n=1}^{\infty} nP_n h^{n-1};$$

or, on multiplying through by $(1 - 2\mu h + h^2)$

$$(\mu - h)\left[1 + \sum_{n=1}^{\infty} P_n h^n\right] - (1 - 2\mu h + h^2)\sum_{n=1}^{\infty} nP_n h^{n-1} = 0.$$

If this expression is arranged according to powers of h, there results

$$\mu - P_1 + \sum_{n=1}^{\infty} [(2n + 1)\mu P_n - nP_{n-1} - (n + 1)P_{n+1}]h^n = 0,$$

in which, of course, $P_0 = 1$. From this expression is derived the recursion formula

$$(n + 1)P_{n+1} - (2n + 1)\mu P_n + nP_{n-1} = 0, \tag{1}$$

which holds for $n = 1, 2, 3, \cdots$.

If the same formula, Eq. (183.1), is differentiated with respect to μ, there is obtained

$$\frac{h}{(1 - 2\mu h + h^2)^{\frac{3}{2}}} = \sum_{n=0}^{\infty} P'_n h^n;$$

or,

$$h \sum_{n=0}^{\infty} P_n h^n - (1 - 2\mu h + h^2) \sum_{n=0}^{\infty} P'_n h^n = 0.$$

This expression arranged according to powers of h becomes

$$\sum_{n=1}^{\infty} [P_n - P'_{n+1} + 2\mu P'_n - P'_{n-1}]h^{n+1} = 0;$$

consequently

$$P'_{n+1} - 2\mu P'_n + P'_{n-1} = P_n. \tag{2}$$

186. The General Formula for Zonal Harmonics.—Consider the formula

$$H^{2p} = \frac{1}{(1 - 2\mu h + h^2)^p}, \tag{1}$$

in which p is any number, not necessarily an integer. It can be expressed as a power series in h,

$$H^{2p} = \sum_{n=0}^{\infty} H_n^{(p)} h^n,$$

which is convergent if $|h| < 1$. It can also be written

$$H^{2p} = \left[1 - 2h\left(\mu - \frac{1}{2}h\right) \right]^{-p},$$

and expanded by the binomial theorem in powers of $2h\left(\mu - \frac{1}{2}h\right)$, thus:

$$H^{2p} = \sum_{i=0}^{\infty} \frac{(p + i - 1)!}{i!(p - 1)!} (2h)^i \left(\mu - \frac{1}{2}h\right)^i,$$

provided, of course, p is an integer. If p is not an integer the factorials which depend upon p become gamma functions, and

$$H^{2p} = \sum_{i=0}^{\infty} \frac{\Gamma(p + i)}{i!\Gamma(p)} (2h)^i \left(\mu - \frac{1}{2}h\right)^i.$$

This formula is valid provided only that $p > 0$ and

$$| 2\mu h - h^2 | < 1.$$

This last condition is satisfied for every μ from -1 to $+1$ provided

$$| h | < \sqrt{2} - 1 = .4141 \cdots.$$

Again, by the binomial theorem,

$$\left(\mu - \frac{1}{2}h \right)^i = \sum_{j=0}^{i} (-1)^j \frac{i!}{j!(i-j)!} \mu^{i-j} \left(\frac{h}{2} \right)^j;$$

so that

$$H^{2p} = \sum_{i=0}^{\infty} 2^i \frac{\Gamma(p+i)}{i!\Gamma(p)} h^i \sum_{j=0}^{i} (-1)^j \frac{i!}{j!(i-j)!} \left(\frac{h}{2} \right)^j \mu^{i-j}$$

$$= \sum_{i=0}^{\infty} \sum_{j=0}^{i} (-1)^j 2^{i-j} \frac{\Gamma(p+i)}{j!(i-j)!\Gamma(p)} \mu^{i-j} h^{i+j}.$$

This series can be rearranged as a power series in h by taking

$$i + j = n, \qquad \text{or} \qquad i = n - j.$$

With this change it becomes

$$H^{2p} = \sum_{n=0}^{\infty} h^n \sum_{j=0}^{t} (-1)^j 2^{n-2j} \frac{\Gamma(p+n-j)}{j!(n-2j)!\Gamma(p)} \mu^{n-2j},$$

where $t = n/2$ or $(n-1)/2$, according as n is even or odd. Therefore

$$H_n^{(p)} = \sum_{j=0}^{t} (-1)^j 2^{n-2j} \frac{\Gamma(p+n-j)}{j!(n-2j)!\Gamma(p)} \mu^{n-2j}, \qquad (2)$$

which is a polynomial in μ of degree n.

For $p = \frac{1}{2}$, this gives the general expression for the zonal harmonic of degree n. If the notation

$$[2n] = 2 \cdot 4 \cdot 6 \cdots \cdots 2n,$$

$$[2n - 1] = 1 \cdot 3 \cdot 5 \cdot 7 \cdots \cdots (2n - 1),$$

is used, the gamma functions can be dispensed with, and

$$H_n^1 = P_n = \sum_{j=0}^{t} (-1)^j \frac{[2n - 2j - 1]}{(n - 2j)![2j]} \mu^{n-2j}. \qquad (3)$$

Since

$$(n - 2j)! = [n - 2j][n - 2j - 1],$$

one of the brackets in the right member containing the product of all of the even numbers and the other the product of all of the odd numbers, this expression for P_n can also be written

$$P_n = \sum_{j=0}^{t} (-1)^j \frac{[2n - 2j - 1]}{[n - 2j][n - 2j - 1][2j]} \mu^{n-2j}, \tag{4}$$

which, while not as simple in appearance as Eq. (3), is actually simpler for computing purposes. It is readily verified that this expression satisfies the recursion formula (Eq. (185.1)). It is from this formula that the explicit forms given in Sec. 180 were computed.

187. The General Expression For $H_n{}^2$.—The general expression for $H_n{}^{2p}$ becomes particularly simple for $p = 1$. Let

$$H_n{}^2 \equiv Q_n,$$

so that

$$\left. H^2 = \frac{1}{1 - 2\mu h + h^2} = \sum_{n=0}^{\infty} Q_n h^n. \right\} \tag{1}$$

If 2μ is replaced by $e^{i\varphi} + e^{-i\varphi}$, which can always be done, since $\mu = \cos \varphi$, the expression for H^2 becomes

$$H^2 = \frac{1}{(1 - he^{i\varphi})(1 - he^{-i\varphi})}$$

$$= \frac{1}{e^{i\varphi} - e^{-i\varphi}}\left(\frac{e^{i\varphi}}{1 - he^{i\varphi}} - \frac{e^{-i\varphi}}{1 - he^{-i\varphi}} \right)$$

$$= \frac{1}{2i \sin \varphi}\left[e^{i\varphi} \sum_{n=0}^{\infty} h^n e^{in\varphi} - e^{-i\varphi} \sum_{n=0}^{\infty} h^n e^{-in\varphi} \right]$$

$$= \sum_{n=0}^{\infty} \frac{\sin (n + 1)\varphi}{\sin \varphi} h^n;$$

from which it follows that

$$Q_n = \frac{\sin (n + 1)\varphi}{\sin \varphi}. \tag{2}$$

Also

$$Q_n - Q_{n-2} = \frac{\sin (n + 1)\varphi - \sin (n - 1)\varphi}{\sin \varphi},$$

which reduces to

$$Q_n - Q_{n-2} = 2 \cos n\varphi. \tag{3}$$

Likewise

$$Q_{n-1} - Q_{n-3} = 2 \cos (n - 1)\varphi,$$

. . . .

$$Q_2 - Q_0 = 2 \cos 2\varphi,$$

$$Q_1 = 2 \cos \varphi,$$

$$Q_0 = 1.$$

From these formulas it follows readily that

$$Q_{2n} = 1 + 2 \sum_{j=1}^{n} \cos 2j\varphi, \tag{4}$$

$$Q_{2n-1} = 0 + 2 \sum_{j=1}^{n} \cos (2j - 1)\varphi, \tag{5}$$

and

$$Q_{n-1} + Q_n = 1 + 2 \sum_{j=1}^{n} \cos j\varphi. \tag{6}$$

Now

$$\frac{1 + h}{1 - 2\mu h + h^2} = \sum_{n=0}^{\infty} (Q_{n-1} + Q_n)h^n \qquad (Q_{-1} = 0).$$

Therefore, the expansion explicitly is

$$\frac{1 + h}{1 - 2\mu h + h^2} = 1 + \sum_{n=1}^{\infty} h^n \left(1 + 2 \sum_{j=1}^{n} \cos j\varphi \right). \tag{7}$$

By merely squaring the series for H it is found also that

$$Q_n = \sum_{j=0}^{n} P_j P_{n-j}.$$

188. Zonal Harmonics Expressed By Cosines of Multiples of the Argument φ.—The general expression for H^{2p}, Eq. (186.1) can also be written

$$H^{2p} = (1 - he^{i\varphi})^{-p}(1 - he^{-i\varphi})^{-p}, \qquad i = \sqrt{-1}.$$

Since, by the binomial theorem,

$$(1 - he^{i\varphi})^{-p} = \sum_{j=0}^{\infty} \frac{\Gamma(p + j)}{j!\Gamma(p)} h^j e^{ji\varphi}$$

and

$$(1 - he^{-i\varphi})^{-p} = \sum_{k=0}^{\infty} \frac{\Gamma(p + k)}{k!\Gamma(p)} h^k e^{-ki\varphi},$$

there follows by multiplication

$$H^{2p} = \sum_{j=0}^{\infty} \sum_{k=0}^{\infty} \frac{\Gamma(p+j)\Gamma(p+k)}{j!\, k!\, \Gamma(p) \cdot \Gamma(p)} h^{j+k} e^{i(j-k)\varphi}.$$

This double series can be rearranged as a single power series in h by taking

$$j + k = n,$$

and therefore

$$j - k = n - 2k, \qquad j = n - k.$$

The series then becomes

$$H^{2p} = \sum_{n=0}^{\infty} \sum_{k=0}^{n} \frac{\Gamma(p+n-k) \cdot \Gamma(p+k)}{k!(n-k)!\Gamma(p) \cdot \Gamma(p)} e^{i(n-2k)\varphi} h^n.$$

Hence

$$H_n{}^{(p)} = \sum_{k=0}^{n} \frac{\Gamma(p+n-k) \cdot \Gamma(p+k)}{k!(n-k)!\, \Gamma(p) \cdot \Gamma(p)} e^{i(n-2k)\varphi}.$$

The exponent of e is $i[(n-k)-k]\varphi$. If k and $n-k$ are interchanged the exponent of e changes sign, but the coefficient of e remains unaltered. The terms can, therefore, be grouped in pairs, thus:

$$\left.\begin{array}{l} H_n{}^{(p)} = \displaystyle\sum_{k=0}^{t} \frac{\Gamma(p+n-k) \cdot \Gamma(p+k)}{k!(n-k)!\, \Gamma(p) \cdot \Gamma(p)} (e^{i(n-2k)\varphi} + e^{-i(n-2k)\varphi}) \\ \text{or} \\ H_n{}^{(p)} = 2\displaystyle\sum_{k=0}^{t} \frac{\Gamma(p+n-k)\, \Gamma(p+k)}{k!(n-k)!\, \Gamma(p)\Gamma(p)} \cos (n-2k)\varphi, \end{array}\right\} \quad (1)$$

where $t = n/2$ or $t = (n-1)/2$, according as n is even or odd. The factor 2 must be omitted from the term for which n is even and $k = n/2$. This term is independent of φ and there is only one such term, not two.

For the zonal harmonics $p = 1/2$. The gamma functions can be eliminated, just as in Sec. 186, and the general expression for the zonal harmonics can be written

$$P_n = \sum_{k=0}^{t} 2\frac{[2n-2k-1][2k-1]}{[2n-2k][2k]} \cos (n-2k)\varphi, \qquad (2)$$

with the explanation that the factor 2 is to be omitted from the term for which $2k = n$, and $[-1] = [0] = 1$. This formula gives explicitly

$$P_0 = 1, \qquad P_1 = \cos \varphi,$$

$$P_2 = 2 \cdot \frac{1 \cdot 3}{2 \cdot 4} \cos 2\varphi + \frac{1}{2 \cdot 2},$$

$$P_3 = 2 \cdot \frac{1 \cdot 3 \cdot 5}{2 \cdot 4 \cdot 6} \cos 3\varphi + 2 \cdot \frac{1 \cdot 3 \cdot 1}{2 \cdot 4 \cdot 2} \cos \varphi,$$

$$P_4 = 2 \cdot \frac{1 \cdot 3 \cdot 5 \cdot 7}{2 \cdot 4 \cdot 6 \cdot 8} \cos 4\varphi + 2 \cdot \frac{1 \cdot 3 \cdot 5 \cdot 1}{2 \cdot 4 \cdot 6 \cdot 2} \cos 2\varphi + \frac{1 \cdot 3 \cdot 1 \cdot 3}{2 \cdot 4 \cdot 2 \cdot 4},$$

$$P_5 = 2 \cdot \frac{1 \cdot 3 \cdot 5 \cdot 7 \cdot 9}{2 \cdot 4 \cdot 6 \cdot 8 \cdot 10} \cos 5\varphi + 2 \cdot \frac{1 \cdot 3 \cdot 5 \cdot 7 \cdot 1}{2 \cdot 4 \cdot 6 \cdot 8 \cdot 2} \cos 3\varphi$$
$$+ 2 \cdot \frac{1 \cdot 3 \cdot 5 \cdot 1 \cdot 3}{2 \cdot 4 \cdot 6 \cdot 2 \cdot 4} \cos \varphi,$$

$$P_6 = 2 \cdot \frac{1 \cdot 3 \cdot 5 \cdot 7 \cdot 9 \cdot 11}{2 \cdot 4 \cdot 6 \cdot 8 \cdot 10 \cdot 12} \cos 6\varphi + 2 \cdot \frac{1 \cdot 3 \cdot 5 \cdot 7 \cdot 9 \cdot 1}{2 \cdot 4 \cdot 6 \cdot 8 \cdot 10 \cdot 2} \cos 4\varphi$$
$$+ 2 \cdot \frac{1 \cdot 3 \cdot 5 \cdot 7 \cdot 1 \cdot 3}{2 \cdot 4 \cdot 6 \cdot 8 \cdot 2 \cdot 4} \cos 2\varphi + \frac{1 \cdot 3 \cdot 5 \cdot 1 \cdot 3 \cdot 5}{2 \cdot 4 \cdot 6 \cdot 2 \cdot 4 \cdot 6},$$

$$P_7 = \frac{3 \cdot 5 \cdot 7 \cdot 9 \cdot 11 \cdot 13}{4 \cdot 6 \cdot 8 \cdot 10 \cdot 12 \cdot 14} \cos 7\varphi + \frac{3 \cdot 5 \cdot 7 \cdot 9 \cdot 11 \cdot 1}{4 \cdot 6 \cdot 8 \cdot 10 \cdot 12 \cdot 2} \cos 5\varphi$$
$$+ 2 \cdot \frac{1 \cdot 3 \cdot 5 \cdot 7 \cdot 9 \cdot 1 \cdot 3}{2 \cdot 4 \cdot 6 \cdot 8 \cdot 10 \cdot 2 \cdot 4} \cos 3\varphi + 2 \cdot \frac{1 \cdot 3 \cdot 5 \cdot 7 \cdot 1 \cdot 3 \cdot 5}{2 \cdot 4 \cdot 6 \cdot 8 \cdot 2 \cdot 4 \cdot 6} \cos \varphi.$$

189. Powers of μ Expressed in Terms of Zonal Harmonics.— It is evident from the tables given in Sec. 180 that it is always possible to express a given power of μ in terms of the zonal harmonics. From this table, obviously,

$$\mu^0 = P_0, \qquad \mu^1 = P_1,$$

$$\mu^2 = \frac{2}{3}P_2 + \frac{1}{3}P_0, \qquad \mu^3 = \frac{2}{5}P_3 + \frac{3}{5}P_1,$$

and so on. From the fact that the zonal harmonics with odd subscripts are odd functions of μ, and those with even subscripts are even functions of μ, it is evident that the expression for μ^{2n} in terms of the zonal harmonics will contain only zonal harmonics with even subscripts; and the expression for μ^{2n+1} will contain only zonal harmonics with odd subscripts.

In order to obtain the general formula, let

$$\mu^n = a_0 P_0 + a_1 P_1 + a_2 P_2 + \cdots + a_n P_n,$$

where the a_k are constant coefficients which are to be determined. If this expression is multiplied through by P_m and integrated, there results

$$\int_{-1}^{+1} \mu^n P_m \, d\mu = \sum_{k=0}^{n} a_k \int_{-1}^{+1} P_k P_m \, d\mu,$$

and, by Eqs. (183.3) and (183.4), this reduces to

$$\int_{-1}^{+1} \mu^n P_m \, d\mu = \frac{2a_m}{2m+1};$$

whence

$$a_m = \frac{2m+1}{2} \int_{-1}^{+1} \mu^n P_m \, d\mu.$$

Also, by substituting the value of P_m from Eq. (179.4),

$$a_m = \frac{2m+1}{2^{m+1} m!} \int_{-1}^{+1} \mu^n \frac{d^m}{d\mu^m} (\mu^2 - 1)^m.$$

Suppose f is any function of μ and $f^{(k)}$ is the kth derivative of f with respect to μ. Then

$$\int_{-1}^{+1} \mu^n f^{(m)} d\mu$$

can be integrated by parts s times, with the result

$$\int_{-1}^{+1} \mu^n f^{(m)} d\mu = (-1)^s \frac{n!}{(n-s)!} \int_{-1}^{+1} \mu^{n-s} f^{(m-s)} d\mu,$$

provided s is less than either m or n, and provided also that $f^{(m)}$, $f^{(m-1)}$, $f^{(m-2)}$, $\cdots$ vanish at both limits. If $m > n$, the expression reduces to

$$\int_{-1}^{+1} \mu^n f^{(m)} d\mu = (-1)^n n! \int_{-1}^{+1} f^{(m-n)} d\mu$$

$$= (-1)^n n! f^{(m-n+1)} \Big|_{-1}^{+1} = 0.$$

If $m \leqq n$, it reduces to

$$\int_{-1}^{+1} \mu^n f^{(m)} d\mu = (-1)^m \frac{n!}{(n-m)!} \int_{-1}^{+1} \mu^{n-m} f \, d\mu.$$

The properties which have been assumed for the function f are possessed by the function $(\mu^2 - 1)^m$. Hence, if $m > n$,

$$a_m = \frac{2m+1}{2} \int_{-1}^{+1} \mu^n P_m \, d\mu = \frac{2m+1}{m! \, 2^{m+1}} \int_{-1}^{+1} \mu^n \frac{d^m}{d\mu^m} (\mu^2 - 1)^m d\mu = 0;$$

and if $m \leqq n$,

$$a_m = \frac{2m+1}{2} \int_{-1}^{+1} \mu^n P_m d\mu$$

$$= \frac{(2m+1)n!}{2^{m+1}m!(n-m)!} \int_{-1}^{+1} \mu^{n-m}(1-\mu^2)^m d\mu.$$

Integrating again by parts s times,

$$\int_{-1}^{+1} \mu^p (1-\mu^2)^q = \frac{2^s q! \, [p-1]}{(q-s)! \, [p+2s-1]} \int_{-1}^{+1} \mu^{p+2s}(1-\mu^2)^{q-s} d\mu.$$

By means of this formula it is seen that if $m \leqq n$,

$$a_m = \frac{2m+1}{2} \frac{n!}{(n-m)!} \frac{[n-m-1]}{[n+m-1]} \int_{-1}^{+1} \mu^{n+m} d\mu,$$

which is zero if $n+m$ is odd, but if $m+n$ is even

$$a_m = \frac{(2m+1)\, n! \, [n-m-1]}{(n-m)! \, [n+m+1]}.$$

Consequently, by setting $m = n - 2k$ and then summing with respect to k, it is seen that

$$\mu^n = \sum_{k=0}^{s} \frac{(2n-4k+1)\, n! \, [2k-1]}{[(2n-2k+1)\,(2k)!]} P_k,$$

where $s = n/2$ if n is even, and $s = (n-1)/2$ if n is odd; $[2n-1] = 1 \cdot 3 \cdot 5 \cdot \; \cdots \; (2n-1)$; and $[-1] = 1$. Since

$$(2k)! = [2k][2k-1],$$

the formula is simplified by this substitution, and becomes

$$\mu^n = \sum_{k=0}^{s} \frac{(2n-4k+1)\, n!}{[2n-2k+1]\,[2k]} P_k. \tag{1}$$

It follows, at once, that any polynomial in μ of degree m, Q_m, can be expressed in the form

$$Q_m = A_0 P_0 + A_1 P_1 + A_2 P_2 + \; \cdots \; + A_m P_m, \tag{2}$$

where the coefficients A_k are independent of μ, and are, therefore, constants.

The theorem that any function of μ which is finite and has only a finite number of discontinuities between the limits $\mu = +1$ and $\mu = -1$ can be represented in this interval by an infinite series of zonal harmonics is included in the more general theorem of Sec. 206.

190. A Definite Integral Representation of Zonal Harmonics.—
Other simple expressions for the zonal harmonics are possible.
For example, it can be represented as a definite integral. For
this purpose, consider the integral

$$I = \int_0^\pi \frac{d\omega}{a - ib \cos \omega},$$

where $i = \sqrt{-1}$, a and b are real constants, and $a > 0$. If the
numerator and denominator of the integrand are multiplied by
$a + ib \cos \omega$, the integral becomes

$$I = a \int_0^\pi \frac{d\omega}{a^2 + b^2 \cos^2 \omega} + ib \int_0^\pi \frac{\cos \omega d\omega}{a^2 + b^2 \cos^2 \omega}.$$

Since $\cos (\pi - \omega) = - \cos \omega$, it is seen that

$$\int_0^\pi \frac{\cos \omega d\omega}{a^2 + b^2 \cos^2 \omega} = 0,$$

and therefore, that

$$I = 2a \int_0^{\frac{\pi}{2}} \frac{d\omega}{a^2 + b^2 \cos^2 \omega}$$

$$= 2a \int_0^{\frac{\pi}{2}} \frac{\sec^2 \omega d\omega}{a^2 \sec^2 \omega + b^2}.$$

By means of the transformation

$$\tan \omega = s \sqrt{\frac{a^2 + b^2}{a^2}}$$

the integral reduces, since a is positive, to

$$I = \frac{2}{\sqrt{a^2 + b^2}} \int_0^\infty \frac{ds}{1 + s^2} = \frac{\pi}{\sqrt{a^2 + b^2}}.$$

Consequently, if $a > 0$,

$$\int_0^\pi \frac{d\omega}{a - ib \cos \omega} = \frac{\pi}{\sqrt{a^2 + b^2}}. \tag{1}$$

If a were negative the sign of the second member would be
reversed.

Now let

$$a = 1 - h\mu, \qquad b = h\sqrt{1 - \mu^2},$$

in Eq. (1). It then becomes

$$H = \frac{1}{\sqrt{1 - 2h\mu + h^2}} = \frac{1}{\pi} \int_0^\pi \frac{d\omega}{1 - h(\mu + i\sqrt{1 - \mu^2} \cos \omega)} \tag{2}$$

If

$$0 \leq h < 1, \qquad -1 \leq \mu \leq +1,$$

it is found that the modulus of $h(\mu + i\sqrt{1 - \mu^2}\cos\omega)$ is

$$h\sqrt{1 - (1 - \mu^2)\sin^2\omega} \leq |h| < 1.$$

The expansion of the integrand in Eq. (2) is absolutely and uniformly convergent with respect to ω. It can, therefore, be integrated term by term. Hence

$$\left.\begin{aligned}
H &= \frac{1}{\pi}\sum_{n=0}^{\infty} h^n \int_0^{\pi}(\mu + i\sqrt{1 - \mu^2}\cos\omega)^n d\omega = \sum_{n=0}^{\infty} P_n h^n, \\
P_n &= \frac{1}{\pi}\int_0^{\pi}(\mu + i\sqrt{1 - \mu^2}\cos\omega)^n d\omega,
\end{aligned}\right\} \quad (3)$$

an equation which is due to Laplace.

191. An Important Property of Zonal Harmonics.—The definite integral representation of the zonal harmonics exhibits the property that for a fixed μ the harmonic P_n tends toward zero as n increases, provided only that

$$|\mu| < 1.$$

Now

$$|P_n| < \frac{1}{\pi}\int_0^{\pi}\left|\mu + i\sqrt{1 - \mu^2}\cos\omega\right|^n d\omega;$$

or,

$$|P_n| < \frac{1}{\pi}\int_0^{\pi}\left(1 - (1 - \mu^2)\sin^2\omega\right)^{\frac{n}{2}} d\omega.$$

For brevity of notation take

$$(1 - \mu^2) = k^2 < 1,$$

and write

$$\int_0^{\pi} = \int_0^{\delta} + \int_{\delta}^{\pi - \delta} + \int_{\pi - \delta}^{\pi}.$$

Evidently

$$\int_0^{\delta}\left(1 - k^2\sin^2\omega\right)^{\frac{n}{2}} d\omega < \int_0^{\delta} d\omega = \delta;$$

$$\int_{\delta}^{\pi - \delta}\left(1 - k^2\sin^2\omega\right)^{\frac{n}{2}} d\omega < \int_{\delta}^{\pi - \delta}(1 - k^2\sin^2\delta)^{\frac{n}{2}} d\omega =$$

$$(\pi - 2\delta)(1 - k^2\sin^2\delta)^{\frac{n}{2}};$$

and

$$\int_{\pi-\delta}^{\pi} (1 - k^2 \sin^2 \omega)^{\frac{n}{2}} d\omega < \int_{\pi-\delta}^{\pi} d\omega = \delta.$$

Therefore, by taking the sum and then dividing by π,

$$\left| P_n \right| < \frac{2\delta}{\pi} + \left(1 - \frac{2\delta}{\pi}\right)(1 - k^2 \sin^2 \delta)^{\frac{n}{2}}.$$

Suppose ϵ is a positive number given in advance,

$$0 < \epsilon < 1, \quad \text{and} \quad \delta = \frac{\pi\epsilon}{4}.$$

Then

$$\frac{2\delta}{\pi} = \frac{1}{2}\epsilon;$$

and, since

$$1 - k^2 \sin^2 \delta < 1,$$

it is clear that for every $\delta > 0$, there exists an integer N_ϵ, such that for every $n > N_\epsilon$,

$$\left(1 - \frac{1}{2}\epsilon\right)\left(1 - k^2 \sin^2 \frac{\pi\epsilon}{4}\right)^{\frac{n}{2}} < \frac{1}{2}\epsilon,$$

and therefore

$$|P_n| < \epsilon.$$

It follows, therefore, that the limit of $P_n(\mu)$, for a fixed μ, as n increases is zero, if $|\mu| < 1$. If, however, $|\mu| = 1$, then $|P_n| = 1$ for every n.

Since the modulus of $\mu + i\sqrt{1 - \mu^2} \cos \omega$ is $1 - (1 - \mu^2) \sin^2 \omega$, which never exceeds unity, if $0 \leqq \mu \leqq 1$, it is evident also from Eq. (190.3),

$$P_n = \frac{1}{\pi} \int_0^{\pi} \left(\mu + i\sqrt{1 - \mu^2} \cos \omega\right)^n d\omega,$$

that

$$\left| P_n \right| \leqq \frac{1}{\pi} \int_0^{\pi} d\omega,$$

or,

$$|P_n| \leqq 1.$$

Hence the numerical value of a zonal harmonic never exceeds unity for values of μ which lie between -1 and $+1$.

192. Expansion of sin $m\varphi$ in a Series of Zonal Harmonics.—

It is proposed to represent sin $m\varphi$ by means of zonal harmonics.

Since it is an irrational function of μ, the representation will have the form of an infinite series, thus:

$$\sin m\varphi = \sum_{j=0}^{\infty} C_j P_j. \tag{1}$$

That such a representation exists is proved in Sec. 206. For the present, the validity of the series will be assumed.

If Eq. (1) is multiplied by $P_n d\mu$ and then integrated from -1 to $+1$, there results

$$\int_{-1}^{+1} P_n \sin m\varphi d\mu = \frac{2C_n}{2n+1};$$

since, by Sec. (183),

$$\int_{-1}^{+1} P_j P_n d\mu = 0, \quad \text{and} \quad \int_{-1}^{+1} P_n{}^2 d\mu = \frac{2}{2n+1}.$$

Hence

$$\left. \begin{aligned} C_n &= \frac{2n+1}{2} \int_0^{\pi} P_n \cdot \sin m\varphi \cdot \sin \varphi \cdot d\varphi, \\ \text{or,} \\ C_n &= \frac{2n+1}{4} \int_0^{\pi} P_n[\cos (m-1)\varphi - \cos (m+1)\varphi]d\varphi. \end{aligned} \right\} \tag{2}$$

On inserting the value of P_n from Eq. (188.2), this expression for C_n becomes

$$C_n = \frac{2n+1}{\cdot 4} \int_0^{\pi} [\cos (m-1)\varphi - \cos (m+1)\varphi]$$

$$\times \sum_{k=0}^{t} \frac{2[2n-2k-1][2k-1]}{[2n-2k][2k]} \cos (n-2k)\varphi d\varphi. \tag{3}$$

The product of the two factors of the integrand is a sum of a finite number of cosines of integral multiples of φ. The multiples are all odd if $m+n$ is even, and they are all even if $m+n$ is odd.

Since

$$\int_0^{\pi} \cos j\varphi d\varphi = 0, \quad \text{if } j \neq 0, \tag{4}$$

and is equal to π, if j is zero, it follows that after integration all the terms of Eq. (3) vanish except the term which carries the cosine of the zero[th] multiple of φ as a factor; and the zero[th] multiple is an even multiple. In order that such a term may exist, it is necessary that $m + n$ shall be odd. Consequently, if m is odd, Eq. (1) contains P's with even subscripts only; and if m is even, Eq. (1) contains P's with odd subscripts only.

Even though $m + n$ is odd, no such term will exist unless $n \lesseqgtr m - 1$, as is easily verified. Hence, Eq. (1) can be written

$$\sin m\varphi = \sum_{j=m-1}^{\infty} C_j P_j. \tag{5}$$

If $n = m - 1$ there is just one term in Eq. (3) that carries the cosine of the zeroth multiple of φ as a factor, namely, that one for which k is zero. Hence

$$C_{m-1} = \frac{2n+1}{4} \frac{[2n-1]}{[2n]} \pi = \frac{[2m-1]}{[2m-2]} \frac{\pi}{4}.$$

If $n > m - 1$, there are two terms in Eq. (3) that carry the cosine of the zeroth multiple of φ as a factor, namely, those for which

$$m - 1 = n - 2k \qquad \text{and} \qquad m + 1 = n - 2k.$$

For these terms

$$C_n = \frac{2n+1}{4} \left(\frac{[n+m-2][n-m]}{[n+m-1][n-m+1]} \right.$$

$$\left. - \frac{[n+m][n-m-2]}{[n+m+1][n-m-1]} \right) \pi,$$

$$= \frac{2n+1}{4} \frac{[n+m-2][n-m-2]}{[n+m-1][n-m-1]}$$

$$\left(\frac{n-m}{n-m+1} - \frac{n+m}{n+m+1} \right) \pi,$$

and therefore, finally,

$$C_n = -m\pi \frac{2n+1}{2} \frac{[n+m-2][n-m-2]}{[n+m+1][n-m+1]}.$$

The expansion for $\sin m\varphi$ as a series of zonal harmonics is therefore

$$\sin m\varphi =$$

$$\frac{[2m-1]}{[2m-2]} \frac{\pi}{4} - \frac{m\pi}{2} \sum_{n=m+1}^{\infty} \frac{[n+m-2][n-m-2]}{[n+m+1][n-m+1]} (2n+1) P_n.$$

Since, however, n is always even or always odd, it is better to set

$$n = m - 1 + 2j,$$

and then the expression becomes

$$\sin m\varphi = \tag{6}$$

$$\frac{[2m-1]}{[2m-2]}\frac{\pi}{4} - \frac{m\pi}{2}\sum_{j=1}^{\infty}\frac{[2j+2m-3][2j-3]}{[2j+2m]\,[2j]}(4j+2m-1)P_{2j+m-1};$$

where

$$[2i] = 2\cdot4\cdot6\cdots2i, \qquad [-1] = [0] = 1,$$

$$[2i+1] = 1\cdot3\cdot5\cdots(2i+1).$$

For $m = 1$, this formula reduces to

$$\sin\varphi = \frac{\pi}{4} - \frac{\pi}{2}\sum_{j=1}^{\infty}\frac{[2j-1][2j-3]}{[2j+2]\,[2j]}(4j+1)P_{2j}. \tag{7}$$

193. The Potential of a Solid of Revolution.—If the z-axis is taken as the axis of a solid of revolution, and if for a given value of z the density is a function of $x^2 + y^2$, it is evident that the potential of the body at exterior points is a function of z and r alone, where $r^2 = x^2 + y^2 + z^2$; and therefore, it can be expressed by means of the solid zonal harmonics.

If

$$Z_n = r^n P_n, \tag{1}$$

it is evident that Z_n satisfies the equation of Laplace and is a solid zonal harmonic of degree n. By Sec. 171,

$$\frac{Z_n}{r^{2n+1}} = \frac{P_n}{r^{n+1}} \tag{2}$$

also satisfies the equation of Laplace, and is a zonal harmonic which vanishes at infinity. For points in the neighborhood of the origin, provided the origin is in empty space, the potential can be expressed in the form

$$V = \sum_{n=0}^{\infty} a_n Z_n = \sum_{n=0}^{\infty} a_n r^n P_n, \tag{3}$$

and in the neighborhood of infinity in the form

$$V = \sum_{n=0}^{\infty} C_n \frac{Z_n}{r^{2n+1}} = \sum_{n=0}^{\infty} \frac{C_n}{r^{n+1}} P_n. \tag{4}$$

On the axis of revolution $P_n = 1$ for every n, and therefore, V is a function of r alone, namely,

$$V_{Axis} = \sum_{n=0}^{\infty} a_n r^n, \qquad \text{or,} \qquad V_{Axis} = \sum_{n=0}^{\infty} \frac{C_n}{r^{n+1}};$$

or, since along the axis $r = z$,

$$V_{Axis} = \sum_{n=0}^{\infty} a_n z^n, \qquad \text{or,} \qquad V_{Axis} = \sum_{n=0}^{\infty} \frac{C_n}{z^{n+1}}. \tag{5}$$

Conversely, if the expansion along the axis is known, Eq. (5), the corresponding expansion for points not lying on the axis can be derived from it merely be replacing z^n by $r^n P_n$, if the expansion is in ascending powers of z, or by replacing $z^{-(n+1)}$ by $P_n r^{-(n+1)}$ if the expansion is in descending powers of z. Since the modulus of P_n is always less than unity, or at most equal to unity, the series (3) or (4) will certainly converge if the series (5) converges. That is, if r is kept fixed, the series will converge everywhere on the sphere if it converges at the poles.

If, as is frequently the case, the expansion, Eq. (5), along the axis is easily obtained, the general expansion is obtained with equal ease.

In order to be sure that the function so determined actually represents the potential function it will be sufficient to prove the following theorem.

Theorem.—If V is an analytic function of r and z which is regular in the neighborhood of the origin (that is, is expansible in powers of r and z) and which satisfies the equation of Laplace

$$r^2 \frac{\partial^2 (rV)}{\partial r^2} + \frac{\partial}{\partial \mu}\left[(1 - \mu^2) \frac{\partial (rV)}{\partial \mu} \right] = 0,$$

where $r\mu = z$; and if V vanishes for $\mu = 1$ for all values of $r < r_0$, then V vanishes identically.

In order to prove this theorem it is convenient to change the variables by taking

$$U = rV, \qquad 1 - \mu = \nu.$$

For these new variables Laplace's equation becomes

$$r^2 \frac{\partial^2 U}{\partial r^2} + \frac{\partial}{\partial \nu}\left[\nu(2 - \nu) \frac{\partial U}{\partial \nu} \right] = 0. \tag{6}$$

Since U vanishes with r, and also with ν by hypothesis, it carries $r\nu$ as a factor; and its expansion as a power-series in r and ν has the form

$$U = \sum_{i=1}^{\infty} \sum_{j=1}^{\infty} a_{ij} r^i \nu^j,$$

where the coefficients a_{ij} are constants. It is found easily that

$$\left.\begin{array}{l} r^2 \dfrac{\partial^2 U}{\partial r^2} = \displaystyle\sum_{i=1}^{\infty} \sum_{j=1}^{\infty} i(i-1)a_{ij} r^i \nu^j, \\[4mm] \dfrac{\partial}{\partial \nu}\left[\nu(2-\nu)\dfrac{\partial U}{\partial \nu} \right] = \displaystyle\sum_{i=1}^{\infty} \sum_{j=0}^{\infty} \{2(j+1)^2 a_{i,j+1} - j(j+1)a_{ij}\} r^i \nu^j. \end{array}\right\}$$

Therefore, on taking the sum,

$$\sum_{i=1}^{\infty} \sum_{j=0}^{\infty} \{2(j+1)^2 a_{i,j+1} + [i(i-1) - j(j+1)]a_{ij}\} r_i \nu^j = 0,$$

from which it follows that

$$a_{i,j+1} = \frac{j(j+1) - i(i-1)}{2(j+1)^2} a_{ij} \qquad \begin{cases} j = 0, 1, \cdots, \infty, \\ i = 1, 2, \cdots, \infty. \end{cases}$$

Since U vanishes with ν, every $a_{i0} = 0$. Hence every coefficient $a_{i1} = 0$, and then every $a_{i2} = 0$, and so on sequentially, and $U \equiv 0$. Therefore $V \equiv 0$, since it differs from U only by the factor r.

For expansions in the neighborhood of infinity, let

$$r = \frac{1}{u}.$$

Then Laplace's equation is

$$u^2 \frac{\partial^2 V}{\partial u^2} + \frac{\partial}{\partial \nu}\left[\nu(2-\nu)\frac{\partial V}{\partial \nu} \right] = 0,$$

which has precisely the same form as Eq. (6), and the argument is repeated unaltered.

It follows, therefore, that if V and W are two functions of r and z which are harmonic in a given region through which the z-axis passes, and if they take the same values on the z-axis, then they take the same values everywhere, since $V - W$ satisfies the conditions of the above theorem. Consequently

$$V - W \equiv 0.$$

194. The Homogeneous Oblate Spheroid.—A convenient example of this mode of development is furnished by the homogeneous oblate spheroid, since its potential as a function of x, y, and z has already been given in Sec. 32, and Sec. 39. The value of the exterior potential along the axis, according to Eq. (39.2), is

$$V_{\text{Axis}} = \frac{3M}{2\sqrt{a^2 - c^2}}$$

$$\left\{ \left(1 + \frac{z^2}{a^2 - c^2}\right) \tan^{-1} \frac{\sqrt{a^2 - c^2}}{\sqrt{z^2}} - \sqrt{\frac{z^2}{a^2 - c^2}} \right\}, \quad (1)$$

where M is the mass of the spheroid, a is the equatorial axis, and c is the polar axis. The eccentricity e of a meridian section is therefore $\sqrt{a^2 - c^2}/a$.

Since

$$\tan^{-1} \lambda = \sum_{n=0}^{\infty} (-1)^n \frac{\lambda^{2n+1}}{2n + 1},$$

the expansion of Eq. (1) as a power series is

$$V_{\text{Axis}} = 3M \sum_{n=0}^{\infty} \frac{(-1)^n}{(2n + 1)(2n + 3)} \frac{(ae)^{2n}}{(\sqrt{z^2})^{2n+1}}.$$

Consequently, the expansion for the potential of a homogeneous oblate spheroid at any exterior point for which the distance from the origin is $r > a$ and for which the polar angle is φ (that is, the angle which r makes with the axis) is

$$V = 3M \sum_{n=0}^{\infty} \frac{(-1)^n}{(2n + 1)(2n + 3)} \frac{(ae)^{2n}}{r^{2n+1}} P_{2n}. \quad (2)$$

If a homogeneous shell is bounded by two concentric, co-axial, spheroids of revolution, its center lies in empty space, and the interior potential can be expanded in terms of zonal harmonics.

Let a_2 and a_1 be the equatorial radii of the outer and inner bounding surfaces, and c_2 and c_1 the corresponding polar radii. Then the potential at any interior point is, by Eq. (32.13),

$$U = (A_2 - A_1) + (B_2 - B_1)(x^2 + y^2) + (C_2 - C_1)z^2, \quad (3)$$

where A_1, B_1, C_1 are certain definite integrals which depend upon the constants a_1 and c_1, and A_2, B_2, C_2 are the same functions of the constants a_2 and c_2. The level surfaces, therefore, are also surfaces of revolution of the second order.

Along the axis the value of the potential is

$$U_{\text{Axis}} = (A_2 - A_1) + (C_2 - C_1)z^2.$$

Therefore, at any interior point the potential is

$$\left.\begin{aligned}
U &= (A_2 - A_1) + (C_2 - C_1)r^2 P_2 \\
&= (A_2 - A_1) + (C_2 - C_1)r^2\left(\frac{3}{2}\cos^2\varphi - \frac{1}{2}\right) \\
&= (A_2 - A_1) + (C_2 - C_1)\left[z^2 - \frac{1}{2}(x^2 + y^2)\right];
\end{aligned}\right\} \quad (4)$$

and the level surfaces are defined by the equation

$$z^2 - \frac{x^2 + y^2}{2} = \text{const.} \quad (5)$$

These surfaces are hyperboloids of one or two sheets according as

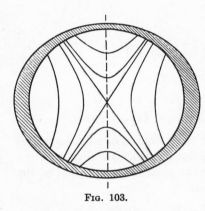

FIG. 103.

the constant is negative or positive; all of which are asymptotic to a cone whose generating angle α is defined by the relation $\tan \alpha = \sqrt{2}$, or $\alpha = 54° 45'$. It is remarkable that these hyperboloids are all of the same eccentricity, but it is more remarkable that the eccentricity is independent of the bounding surfaces, provided, of course, that they are spheroids of revolution. There is an exception only in

case both surfaces are spheres, in which case the interior potential is constant.

On comparing Eqs. (4) with (3), it is seen that

$$B_2 - B_1 = -\frac{1}{2}(C_2 - C_1). \quad (6)$$

It is a simple matter to prove this relation directly from the definitions of B_1, B_2; C_1, C_2 as definite integrals. For

$$abc\int_0^\infty \left(\frac{1}{a^2 + s} + \frac{1}{b^2 + s} + \frac{1}{c^2 + s}\right)\frac{ds}{\sqrt{(a^2 + s)(b^2 + s)(c^2 + s)}}$$

$$= -2abc\int_0^\infty \frac{\partial}{\partial s}\left(\frac{1}{\sqrt{(a^2 + s)(b^2 + s)(c^2 + s)}}\right)ds$$

$$= +2.$$

Hence, on setting b equal to a in this equation, there results

$$2a^2c \int_0^\infty \frac{ds}{(a^2+s)^2\sqrt{c^2+s}} = 2 - \int_0^\infty \frac{ds}{(a^2+s)(c^2+s)\sqrt{c^2+s}};$$

that is,

$$2B_2 = 2\pi\sigma - C_2,$$

and also

$$2B_1 = 2\pi\sigma - C_1.$$

From the difference of these two expressions, Eq. (6) follows at once.

195. The Apparent Size of a Plane Circular Disk.—It was shown in Sec. 8 that the z-component, of the attraction of any plane area in the xy-plane at any point O is proportional to the apparent size of the plane area as seen from the point O. That is, if V is the potential of the area, Z is the z-component of the attraction, and Ω is the apparent size of the area, or the solid angle subtended by the area at O, then (Eq. 18.1)),

$$Z = \frac{\partial V}{\partial z} = \sigma\Omega.$$

Since V satisfies the equation of Laplace, and all of its derivatives likewise, since

$$\Delta \frac{\partial V}{\partial z} = \frac{\partial}{\partial z}(\Delta V) = 0,$$

it follows that the apparent size Ω is an harmonic function of the coordinates of the point O.

If the plane area is a circle in the xy-plane about the origin, it is evident that the apparent size of the circle is independent of the longitude of the point O and is a function of r and z alone. It can, therefore, be expressed by means of the zonal harmonics.

It was found in Sec. 9 that the solid angle of a right circular cone, for which the generating angle is α, is

$$\Omega = 2\pi(1 - \cos\alpha).$$

If a is the radius of the circular base and $(0, 0, z)$ the coordinates of the apex, the apparent size of the base as seen from any point on the z-axis is

$$\Omega_{\text{Axis}} = 2\pi\left(1 - \sqrt{\frac{z^2}{a^2+z^2}}\right).$$

Therefore, if $z < a$,

$$\Omega_{\text{Axis}} = 2\pi\left\{1 - \frac{\sqrt{z^2}}{a} + \sum_{n=0}^{\infty}(-1)^n\frac{[2n+1]}{[2n+2]}\left(\frac{\sqrt{z^2}}{a}\right)^{2n+3}\right\};$$

and if $z > a$

$$\Omega_{\text{Axis}} = 2\pi\sum_{n=0}^{\infty}(-1)^n\frac{[2n+1]}{[2n+2]}\left(\frac{a}{z}\right)^{2n+2}.$$

Consequently, if the line r which joins the origin to the point O makes an angle φ with the z-axis, the apparent size of the disk at O is

$$\Omega = 2\pi\left\{1 - \frac{r}{a}P_1 + \sum_{n=0}^{\infty}(-1)^n\frac{[2n+1]}{[2n+2]}\left(\frac{r}{a}\right)^{2n+3}P_{2n+3}\right\},$$

if $r < a$; and if $r > a$ its value is

$$\Omega = 2\pi\sum_{n=0}^{\infty}(-1)^n\frac{[2n+1]}{[2n+2]}\left(\frac{a}{r}\right)^{2n+2}P_{2n+1}.$$

196. The Potential of a Zonal Distribution of Matter on a Spherical Surface.

—Suppose the density of a surface distribution of matter on a sphere is proportional to a zonal harmonic, so that

$$\sigma = \sigma_0 P_n(\mu).$$

The potential of this distribution at a point on the z-axis is

$$V = \int\frac{dm}{\rho} = 2\pi a\sigma_0\int_{-1}^{+1}\frac{P_n d\mu}{\rho},$$

where, Fig. 104,

$$\rho = \sqrt{z^2 - 2az\mu + a^2};$$

and the total mass is zero, except when $n = 0$.

The expansion of $1/\rho$ is

$$\frac{1}{\rho} = \frac{1}{a}\sum_{k=0}^{\infty}P_k\left(\frac{z}{a}\right)^k, \quad\text{if}\quad |z| < a,$$

and

$$\frac{1}{\rho} = \frac{1}{z}\sum_{k=0}^{\infty}P_k\left(\frac{a}{z}\right)^k, \quad\text{if}\quad |z| > a.$$

Hence

$$V = 2\pi\sigma_0 \sum_{k=0}^{\infty} \left(\frac{z}{a}\right)^k \int_{-1}^{+1} P_k P_n d\mu, \quad \text{if} \quad |z| < a,$$

or

$$V = 2\pi\sigma_0 \sum_{k=0}^{\infty} \left(\frac{a}{z}\right)^{k+1} \int_{-1}^{+1} P_k P_n d\mu, \quad \text{if} \quad |z| > a.$$

The surface integral of the product of two zonal harmonics vanishes, however, unless the two zonal harmonics are of the same degree, Eqs. (183.3) and (183.4). Hence

$$V = \frac{4\pi\sigma_0}{2n+1}\left(\frac{z}{a}\right)^n, \quad \text{or} \quad V = \frac{4\pi\sigma_0}{2n+1}\left(\frac{a}{z}\right)^{n+1},$$

according as $|z| < a$ or $|z| > a$.

In accordance with the principle of Sec. 193, the potential at any point, p, whose radius vector r makes an angle φ with the z-axis is

$$V = \frac{4\pi\sigma_0}{2n+1}\left(\frac{r}{a}\right)^n P_n, \quad \text{or} \quad V = \frac{4\pi\sigma_0}{2n+1}\left(\frac{a}{r}\right)^{2n+1} P_n,$$

according as the point p lies inside or outside of the sphere. Hence the potential of a zonal harmonic distribution of matter of degree n on the surface of a sphere is a solid zonal harmonic of degree n within the sphere, and a solid zonal harmonic of degree $-(n+1)$ outside of the sphere.

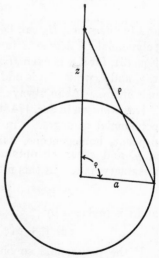

From this result and the fact that the potential of a sum of distributions is the sum of the potentials of the individual distributions, it follows that if the density on the surface of a sphere is represented by the series

$$\sigma = \sigma_0 P_0 + \sigma_1 P_1 + \sigma_2 P_2 + \sigma_3 P_3 + \cdots,$$

FIG. 104.

the potential at any point inside of the sphere is represented by the series

$$V = 4\pi \sum_{n=0}^{\infty} \frac{\sigma_n}{2n+1}\left(\frac{r}{a}\right)^n P_n,$$

and at any point outside of the sphere by the series

$$V = 4\pi \sum_{n=0}^{\infty} \frac{\sigma_n}{2n+1} \left(\frac{a}{r}\right)^n P_n.$$

If the coefficients σ_n are defined as functions of a, the density is defined over a spherical volume, and the potential of such a volume distribution can be obtained by integrating these series with respect to a.

197. Tesseral Harmonics.—The general expression for a zonal harmonic of the first kind of degree n is, Eq. (186.4),

$$P_n(\mu) = \sum_{j=0}^{t} (-1)^j \frac{[2n - 2j - 1]}{(n - 2j)! \, [2j]} \mu^{n-2j}. \tag{1}$$

There exists, therefore, one, and only one, solid zonal harmonic of degree n, aside from a constant multiplier, which is a rational integral function of r and z, namely,

$$H_n(r, z) = r^n P_n(\mu) = \sum_{j=0}^{t} (-1)^j \frac{[2n - 2j - 1]}{[2j](n - 2j)!} z^{n-2j} r^{2j}; \tag{2}$$

and furthermore, H_n can be expressed always as a homogeneous polynomial of degree n in x, y, and z. This is evident from Eqs. (2); for if n is even $H(x, y, z)$ contains only even powers of x, y, and z, while if n is odd the polynomial is odd in z, but even in x and y. It can always be written $H_n(r^2, z)$.

It was shown in Sec. 174 that if there exists such a homogeneous polynomial of degree n in r and z, then $2n + 1$ linearly independent, homogeneous, harmonic, polynomials of degree n in x, y, and z can be obtained from it by a rotation about an imaginary axis. In this rotation, r^2 is replaced by

$$r^2 = x^2 + y^2 + z^2 = \xi^2 + \eta^2 + \zeta^2,$$

and z is replaced by

$$z = \zeta + \alpha(\xi + i\eta), \qquad i = \sqrt{-1}.$$

If the polynomial so obtained is developed in powers of α it becomes, Eq. (174.1)

$$G_n = H_n^{(0)} + \alpha(\xi + i\eta)\frac{\partial H_n^{(0)}}{\partial \zeta} + \frac{\alpha^2}{2!}(\xi + i\eta)^2\frac{\partial^2 H}{\partial \zeta^2} + \cdots$$

$$+ \frac{\alpha^n}{n!}(\xi + i\eta)^n\frac{\partial^n H_n^{(0)}}{\partial \zeta^n},$$

where $H_n{}^{(0)}$ is the expression for H_n for the value $\alpha = 0$; or, returning to the letters x, y, z,

$$G_n(x, y, z) = \sum_{k=0}^{n} \frac{\alpha^k}{k!}(x + iy)^k \frac{\partial^k H_n{}^{(0)}}{\partial z^k}.$$

Now

$$\frac{\partial H_n{}^{(0)}}{\partial z} = \frac{\partial(r^n P_n)}{\partial(r\mu)} = r^{n-1}\frac{\partial P_n}{\partial \mu};$$

and, in general,

$$\frac{\partial^k H_n{}^{(0)}}{\partial z^k} = r^{n-k}\frac{\partial^k P_n}{\partial \mu^k}. \tag{3}$$

Therefore

$$G_n = \sum_{k=0}^{n} r^{n-k}(x + iy)^k \frac{\partial^k P_n}{\partial \mu^k}\frac{\alpha^k}{k!}. \tag{4}$$

Since α is an arbitrary constant, the coefficient of each power of α separately is harmonic. Consequently

$$r^{n-k}(x + iy)^k\frac{\partial^k P_n}{\partial \mu^k} \tag{5}$$

is an harmonic which is said to be of degree n and of order k.

If a change to spherical coordinates is made by the substitution

$$x = r \sin \varphi \cos \theta,$$
$$y = r \sin \varphi \sin \theta, \qquad \cos \varphi = \mu,$$
$$z = r \cos \varphi, \qquad \sin \varphi = \sqrt{1 - \mu^2};$$

and if for simplicity of notation

$$P_n{}^{(k)} \equiv \frac{\partial^k P_n}{\partial \mu^k},$$

the above harmonic, Eq. (5), becomes

$$r^n e^{ik\theta} \sin^k \varphi \, P_n{}^{(k)}.$$

On removing the factor r^n, it is seen that

$$e^{ik\theta} \sin^k \varphi \, P_n{}^{(k)}$$

is a surface harmonic of degree n and order k. Since it is complex, its real and its purely imaginary parts separately are harmonic, so that

$$\left.\begin{array}{l} C_{nk} = \sin^k \varphi \, P_n{}^{(k)} \cdot \cos k\theta, \\ S_{nk} = \sin^k \varphi \, P_n{}^{(k)} \cdot \sin k\theta, \end{array}\right\} \tag{6}$$

are two distinct types of surface harmonics of degree n and order k. These particular surface harmonics are called tesseral[1] surface harmonics, and their products by r^n are called solid tesseral harmonics. If $k = 0$, C_{n0} is simply P_n, and S_{n0} vanishes identically; so that there are $2n + 1$ tesseral harmonics of degree n. If $k = n$, $P_n^{(n)}$ is merely a constant and the corresponding harmonics

$$\left. \begin{aligned} C_{nn} &= [2n - 1] \sin^n \varphi \cos n\theta, \\ S_{nn} &= [2n - 1] \sin^n \varphi \sin n\theta, \end{aligned} \right\} \tag{7}$$

are called *sectorial* harmonics.

It will be observed that the coefficients of $\cos k\theta$ and $\sin k\theta$ in the expressions for the tesseral harmonics, (Eq. (6)), are functions of φ, or of μ, alone. If they are denoted by T_{nk}, it is seen that, explicitly,

$$\left. \begin{aligned} T_{nk} &= \sin^k \varphi P_n^{(k)} = (1 - \mu^2)^{\frac{k}{2}} \frac{d^k P_n}{d\mu^k}, \\ &= (1 - \mu^2)^{\frac{k}{2}} \sum_{j=0}^{l} (-1)^j \frac{[2n - 2j - 1]}{[2j](n - k - 2j)!} \mu^{n-k-2j}, \end{aligned} \right\} \tag{8}$$

where $l = (n - k)/2$ or $(n - k - 1)/2$ according as $n - k$ is even or odd.

It is evident now that on the surface of a unit sphere the value of any homogeneous, harmonic, polynomial of degree n in x, y, and z is represented by the formula

$$\left. \begin{aligned} H_n(\varphi, \theta) &= \sum_{k=0}^{n} (A_k C_{nk} + B_k S_{nk}) \\ &= \sum_{k=0}^{n} (A_k \cos k\theta + B_k \sin k\theta) T_{nk} \end{aligned} \right\} \tag{9}$$

or,

$$H_k(\varphi, \theta) = \sum_{k=0}^{n} D_k T_{nk} \cos (k\theta - \theta_k^{(n)}), \tag{10}$$

provided A_k and B_k, or D_k and $\theta_k^{(n)}$, are suitably chosen constants; and that its value on the surface of any other sphere of radius r can be obtained by multiplying these expressions by r^n.

---

[1] Tessera, a square or rectangle.

The Equation of Laplace for the Tesseral Harmonics.—The equation of Laplace for any surface harmonic S_n of degree n (Eq. (175.2)) is

$$\frac{d}{d\mu}\left((1 - \mu^2)\frac{dS_n}{d\mu}\right) + \frac{1}{1 - \mu^2}\frac{d^2S_n}{d\theta^2} + n(n + 1)S_n = 0.$$

If S_n is a tesseral surface harmonic,

$$S_n = T_{nk}\cos k\theta, \qquad \text{or} \qquad S_n = T_{nk}\sin k\theta.$$

In either case

$$\frac{d^2S_n}{d\theta^2} = -k^2S_n, \tag{11}$$

and the differential equation for the factor T_{nk}, which depends upon φ alone, is

$$\frac{d}{d\mu}\left((1 - \mu^2)\frac{dT_{nk}}{d\mu}\right) + \left(n(n + 1) - \frac{k^2}{1 - \mu^2}\right)T_{nk} = 0. \tag{12}$$

198.—Examples of Solid, Tesseral Harmonics.—The solid tesseral harmonics are given by Eq. (197.5) in terms of x, y, z; for it is evident from Eq. (197.1) that

$$Z_{nk} = r^{n-k}\frac{\partial^k P_n}{\partial\mu^k} = \sum_{j=0}^{l}(-1)^j\frac{[2n - 2j - 1]}{(n - k - 2j)![2j]}z^{n-k-2j}(x^2 + y^2 + z^2)^j.$$

The expansion of $(x + iy)^k$ is

$$(x + iy)^k = X_k + iY_k,$$

where

$$X_k = \sum_{s=0}^{t}(-1)^s\frac{k!}{(2s)!(k - 2s)!}x^{k-2s}y^{2s},$$

$$Y_k = \sum_{s=0}^{t}(-1)^s\frac{k!}{(2s + 1)!(k - 2s - 1)!}x^{k-2s-1}y^{2s+1}.$$

Consequently the solid tesseral harmonic, corresponding to Eq. (197.6) are

$$r^nC_{nk} = X_kZ_{nk}, \qquad \text{and} \qquad r^nS_{nk} = Y_kZ_{nk}.$$

up to and including $n = 4$ they are as follows:

$rC_{10} = z,$	$rS_{10} = 0,$
$rC_{11} = x,$	$rS_{11} = y,$

$r^2C_{20} = -\dfrac{1}{2}x^2 - \dfrac{1}{2}y^2 + z^2,$	$r^2S_{20} = 0,$
$r^2C_{21} = 3zx,$	$r^2S_{21} = 3zy,$
$r^2C_{22} = 3x^2 - 3y^2,$	$r^2S_{22} = 6xy,$

$r^3C_{30} = -\dfrac{3}{2}x^2z - \dfrac{3}{2}y^2z + z^3,$	$r^3S_{30} = 0,$
$r^3C_{31} = -\dfrac{3}{2}x^3 - \dfrac{3}{2}xy^2 + 6xz^2,$	$r^3S_{31} = -\dfrac{3}{2}x^2y - \dfrac{3}{2}y^3 + 6yz^2,$
$r^3C_{32} = 15x^2z - 15y^2z,$	$r^3S_{32} = 30xyz,$
$r^3C_{33} = 15x^3 - 45xy^2,$	$r^3S_{33} = 45x^2y - 15y^3,$

$$r^4C_{40} = \frac{3}{8}x^4 + \frac{3}{8}y^4 + z^4 + \frac{3}{4}x^2y^2 - 3y^2z^2 - 3x^2z^2,$$

$$r^4C_{41} = -\frac{15}{2}x^2z - \frac{15}{2}xy^2z + 10xz^3$$

$$r^4C_{42} = -\frac{15}{2}x^4 + \frac{15}{2}y^4 + 45x^2z^2 - 45y^2z^2,$$

$$r^4C_{43} = 105x^3z - 315xy^2z,$$

$$r^4C_{44} = 105x^4 - 630x^2y^2 + 105y^4,$$

$$r^4S_{41} = -\frac{15}{2}x^2yz - \frac{15}{2}y^3z + 10yz^3,$$

$$r^4S_{42} = -15x^3y - 15xy^3 + 90xyz^2,$$

$$r^4S_{43} = 415x^2yz - 105y^3z,$$

$$r^4S_{44} = 420x^3y - 420xy^3.$$

199. The Zeros of the Tesseral Harmonics.—It was proved in Sec. 181 that the zeros of the zonal harmonics P_n are all real and lie between $\mu = -1$ and $\mu = +1$, and that they are symmetrically situated with respect to $\mu = 0$. A continuation of the argument of Sec. 181 shows that the same statements are true also for the derivatives $P_n^{(k)}$, which have $n - k$ zeros in the interval $\mu = -1$ to $\mu = +1$, and none elsewhere It follows, therefore, that on the surface of a sphere a zonal harmonic P_n vanishes along n circles of latitude, one of which is the equator itself if n is odd, and the others are symmetrically situated with respect to the equator in the northern and southern hemispheres. Similarly $P_n^{(k)}$ vanishes along $n - k$ circles of latitude which are symmetrically situated in the two hemispheres.

The function

$$T_{nk} = (1 - \mu^2)^{\frac{k}{2}} P_n{}^{(k)}$$

obviously has zeros of order $k/2$ at each pole and $n - k$ zeros of order 1 along certain circles of latitude which are symmetrically situated with respect to the equator, making n zeros altogether in latitude.

Finally the tesseral harmonic of degree n and order k,

$$T_{nk} \cos (k\theta - \theta_k{}^{(n)}),$$

Fɪɢ. 105.

has the same zeros in latitude as the function T_{nk}, and in addition, it vanishes along the meridians, or great circles through the two poles, for which $\cos (k\theta - \theta_k{}^{(n)})$ vanishes, that is,

$$\theta = \frac{2s + 1}{k} \frac{\pi}{2} + \frac{1}{k}\theta_k{}^{(n)}, \qquad s = 0, 1, 2, \cdots 2k - 1.$$

The angle between any two successive meridians for which $\cos (k\theta - \theta_k{}^{(n)})$ vanishes is π/k, so that any tesseral harmonic of order k vanishes in longitude $2k$ times. The zeros are evenly spaced in longitude, but only symmetrically spaced in latitude. The circles of latitude and longitude for which $C_{11,6}$ vanishes are drawn in Fig. 105.

200. The Surface Integral of the Product of Two Spherical Harmonics of Different Degrees.

Let V_m and V_n be two solid spherical harmonics of degree m and n respectively, and S_m

and S_n be the two corresponding surface harmonics; so that

$$V_m = r^m S_m, \qquad V_n = r^n V_n. \tag{1}$$

Let Σ be a sphere of radius a with its center at the origin. Then since V_m and V_n and all of their derivatives are continuous within Σ, it follows from Green's theorem that

$$\int_\Sigma (V_n \Delta V_m - V_m \Delta V_n) d\tau = \int_S \left(V_n \frac{\partial V_m}{\partial n} - V_m \frac{\partial V_n}{\partial n} \right) d\omega. \tag{2}$$

Since V_m and V_n are harmonic within Σ, the left member of Eq. (1) is zero, and therefore

$$\int_S \left(V_n \frac{\partial V_m}{\partial n} - V_m \frac{\partial V_n}{\partial n} \right) d\omega = 0. \tag{3}$$

On the surface of the sphere

$$\frac{\partial V}{\partial n} = \frac{\partial V}{\partial r};$$

so that, by Eq. (1)

$$\frac{\partial V_m}{\partial n} = ma^{m-1} S_m, \qquad \frac{\partial V_n}{\partial n} = na^{n-1} S_n.$$

Furthermore

$$d\omega = a^2 d\mu d\theta;$$

therefore Eq. (3) becomes

$$(m - n)a^{m+n+1} \int_{-1}^{+1} \int_0^{2\pi} S_m S_n d\mu d\theta = 0.$$

Since, by hypothesis, $m \neq n$, it follows that

$$\int_{-1}^{+1} \int_0^{2\pi} S_m S_n d\mu d\theta = 0.$$

That is, the integral over the sphere of the product of any two spherical harmonics of different degrees is zero (compare with Eq.(183.3)).

If $m = n$, no conclusion can be drawn from this argument; another investigation is necessary.

201. The Surface Integral of the Product of Two Spherical Harmonics of the Same Degree.—Let S_n and Z_n be two spherical surface harmonics of degree n. Then, by Eq. (197.10)

$$\left. \begin{aligned} S_n &= \sum_{i=0}^n A_i \sin^i \varphi \cdot P_n^{(i)} \cos i(\theta - \theta_i^{(1)}), \\ Z_n &= \sum_{j=0}^n B_j \sin^j \varphi \cdot P_n^{(j)} \cos j(\theta - \theta_j^{(2)}), \end{aligned} \right\} \tag{1}$$

where the A_i, B_i, $\theta_i{}^{(1)}$, and $\theta_j{}^{(2)}$ are suitably chosen constants, are the expressions for S_n and Z in terms of tesseral harmonics. The surface integral of the product of these two harmonics is

$$\int_S S_n Z_n d\omega = \sum_{i=0}^{n} \sum_{j=0}^{n} A_i B_j \int_{-1}^{+1} \sin^{i+j} \varphi \cdot P_n{}^{(i)} P_n{}^{(j)} d\mu$$

$$\times \int_0^{2\pi} \cos i(\theta - \theta_i{}^{(1)}) \cos j(\theta - \theta_j{}^{(2)}) d\theta. \quad (2)$$

The integral with respect to θ is easily evaluated, for

$$\int_0^{2\pi} \cos i(\theta - \theta_i{}^{(1)}) \cos j(\theta - \theta_j{}^{(2)}) d\theta =$$

$$\begin{cases} 0, & \text{if } i \neq j, \\ \pi \cos i(\theta_i{}^{(2)} - \theta_i{}^{(1)}), & \text{if } i = j \neq 0, \\ 2\pi, & \text{if } i = j = 0. \end{cases}$$

Hence the integral reduces to those terms in Eq. (2) for which $i = j$. That is,

$$\int_S S_n Z_n d\omega = 2\pi A_0 B_0 \int_{-1}^{+1} P_n{}^2 d\mu$$

$$+ \pi \sum_{i=1}^{n} A_i B_i \cos i(\theta_i{}^{(2)} - \theta_i{}^{(1)}) \int_{-1}^{+1} (1 - \mu^2)^i (P_n{}^{(i)})^2 d\mu.$$

By Eq. (183.4),

$$\int_{-1}^{+1} P_n{}^2 d\mu = \frac{2}{2n+1},$$

and by Eq. (184.6),

$$\int_{-1}^{+1} (1 - \mu^2)^i (P_n{}^{(i)})^2 d\mu = \frac{2}{2n+1} \frac{(n+i)!}{(n-i)!},$$

hence

$$\int_S S_n Z_n d\omega = \frac{4\pi}{2n+1} A_0 B_0$$

$$+ \frac{2\pi}{2n+1} \sum_{i=1}^{n} A_i B_i \frac{(n+i)!}{(n-i)!} \cos i(\theta_i{}^{(2)} - \theta_i{}^{(1)}), \quad (2)$$

which may, or may not, vanish.

Suppose S_n and Z_n are tesseral harmonics of the same degree n but of different orders. Then either A is zero or B is zero for every index i (see Eq. (1)). Hence, the surface integral of the product of two tesseral harmonics is zero not only if they are of different degrees, by Sec. 200, but also if they are the same degree but of different orders, by Eq. (2).

If S_n and Z_n are tesseral harmonics are of the same degree n and the same order i, then Eq. (2) reduces to the single term

$$\int_S S_n Z_n d\omega = \frac{2\pi}{2n+1} A_i B_i \frac{(n+i)!}{(n-i)!} \cos i(\theta_i{}^{(2)} - \theta_i{}^{(1)}).$$

This expression vanishes if

$$i(\theta_i{}^{(2)} - \theta_i{}^{(1)}) = \frac{\pi}{2}.$$

Hence the surface integral vanishes, even though the two harmonics are of the same degree and the same order, but of different types, Eq. (197.6).

Using the notation of Sec. 197, in which the tesseral harmonics are

$$C_{ni} = \sin^i \varphi \cdot P_n{}^{(i)} \cdot \cos i\theta,$$
$$S_{ni} = \sin^i \varphi \cdot P_n{}^{(i)} \cdot \sin i\theta,$$

the above proofs can be summarized in the equations

$$\int_S C_{ni} C_{mj} d\omega = \int_S C_{ni} S_{mj} d\omega = \int S_{ni} S_{mj} d\omega = 0, \qquad m \neq n.$$

$$\int_S C_{ni} C_{nj} d\omega = \int_S C_{ni} S_{nj} d\omega = \int_S S_{ni} S_{nj} d\omega = 0, \qquad i \neq j.$$

$$\int_S C_{ni} S_{ni} d\omega = 0,$$

$$\int_S C_{ni}{}^2 d\omega = \int_S S_{ni}{}^2 d\omega = \frac{2\pi}{2n+1} \frac{(n+i)!}{(n-i)!}, \qquad i \neq 0,$$

$$\int_S C_{n0}{}^2 d\omega = \frac{4\pi}{2n+1}, \qquad \int_S S_{n0}{}^2 d\omega = 0.$$

202. The Expansion of $[(x - \xi)^2 + (y - \eta)^2 + (z - \zeta)^2]^{-\frac{1}{2}}$ **in a Series of Tesseral Harmonics.**—If x, y, z and ξ, η, ζ, are the coordinates of two points and R is the length of the line which joins them, then

$$R^2 = (x - \xi)^2 + (y - \eta)^2 + (z - \zeta)^2.$$

It is frequently desirable to have the expansion of $1/R$ as a series, and it is the purpose of the present section to show how this expansion can be obtained in terms of the tesseral harmonics.

If

$$r^2 = x^2 + y^2 + z^2,$$
$$\rho^2 = \xi^2 + \eta^2 + \zeta^2,$$

then

$$\frac{1}{R} = \frac{1}{\sqrt{(x - \xi)^2 + (y - \eta)^2 + (z - \zeta)^2}}$$

$$= \frac{1}{\sqrt{r^2 - 2r\rho \cos \lambda + \rho^2}}$$

$$= \frac{1}{r} \frac{1}{\sqrt{1 - 2h \cos \lambda + h^2}},$$

where

$$h = \frac{\rho}{r}, \qquad \cos \lambda = \frac{x\xi + y\eta + z\zeta}{r\rho}.$$

In polar coordinates

$$x = r \sin \varphi_1 \cos \theta_1, \qquad \xi = \rho \sin \varphi_2 \cos \theta_2,$$
$$y = r \sin \varphi_1 \sin \theta_1, \qquad \eta = \rho \sin \varphi_2 \sin \theta_2,$$
$$z = r \cos \varphi_1, \qquad \zeta = \rho \cos \varphi_2,$$

so that

$$\cos \lambda = \cos \varphi_1 \cos \varphi_2 + \sin \varphi_1 \sin \varphi_2 \cos (\theta_1 - \theta_2). \qquad (1)$$

The function $1/R$ is expansible in powers of h, and this expansion is convergent at all points for which $h < 1$. That is, by Eq. (180.5),

$$\frac{1}{R} = \frac{1}{r} \sum_{n=0}^{\infty} R_n h^n = \sum_{n=0}^{\infty} R_n \frac{\rho^n}{r^{n+1}},$$

in which

$$R_n = P_n(\mu) \qquad \text{for } \mu = \cos \lambda.$$

If this expression is written

$$\frac{1}{R} = \sum_{n=0}^{\infty} \frac{R_n \rho^n r^n}{r^{2n+1}}$$

it is seen that the numerator $R_n \rho^n r^n$ can be regarded as a homogeneous polynomial of degree $2n$ in the coordinates x, y, z; ξ, η, ζ; and that it is homogeneous of degree n in x, y, z and also homogeneous of degree n in ξ, η, ζ. It is obviously symmetric in these two sets of variables, and is a solid spherical harmonic in either set.

It follows, therefore, that

$$R_n = P_n(\cos \lambda)$$

when expressed in terms of φ_1, φ_2, θ_1, and θ_2, is a perfectly definite surface harmonic of degree n, and therefore, expressible in terms of the tesseral harmonics.   That is

$$R_n = \sum_{i=0}^{n} A_i \sin^i \varphi_1 \cdot P_n^{(i)}(\mu_1) \cdot \cos i(\theta_1 - \theta_i^{(1)})$$

where

$$\mu_1 = \cos \varphi_1,$$

and A_i and $\theta_i^{(i)}$ are properly chosen constants, which in this case must depend upon φ_2 and θ_2 (or $\mu_2 = \cos \varphi_2$).   It is evident, however, that when the substitution

$$\mu = \cos \varphi_1 \cos \varphi_2 + \sin \varphi_1 \sin \varphi_2 \cos (\theta_1 - \theta_2)$$

is made in $P_n(\mu)$, the function $P_n(\cos \lambda)$ is a polynomial in $\cos (\theta_1 - \theta_2)$ which, when rearranged, can contain only cosines of multiples of $(\theta_1 - \theta_2)$.   Hence $\theta_i^{(1)} = \theta_2$ for every index i. Also, since R_n is symmetric in φ_1 and φ_2, as well as in θ_1 and θ_2, its form must be

$$R_n = \sum_{i=0}^{n} B_{ni}(\sin^i \varphi_2 \cdot P_n^{(i)}(\mu_2))$$
$$(\sin^i \varphi_1 \cdot P_n^{(i)}(\mu_1)) \cos i(\theta_1 - \theta_2), \quad (2)$$

in which the B_{ni} are constants which do not depend upon φ_1, φ_2; θ_1, or θ_2.

In order to obtain the values of the constants B_{ni}, the arguments φ_1, φ_2; θ_1, and θ_2 can be given particular values.   It is convenient, then, to take

$$\theta_1 - \theta_2 = \omega, \qquad \mu_1 = \mu_2 = \mu;$$

and to denote this particular R_n by $R_n{}^*$.   Consequently

$$R_n{}^* = \sum_{i=0}^{n} B_{ni}(1 - \mu^2)^i (P_n^{(i)})^2 \cos i\omega,$$

and $\cos \lambda$ becomes

$$\cos \lambda = \mu^2 + (1 - \mu^2) \cos \omega.$$

For these particular values, it is seen that

$$\frac{1}{\sqrt{1 - 2h[\mu^2 - (1 - \mu^2) \cos \omega] + h^2}} = \sum_{n=0}^{\infty} R_n{}^* h^n. \quad (3)$$

Multiply this equation by $d\mu$, and then integrate from $\mu = -1$ to $\mu = +1$. Since

$$\int_{-1}^{+1} P_n{}^2 d\mu = \frac{2}{2n+1}, \qquad \text{by Eq. (183.4),}$$

and

$$\int_{-1}^{+1} (1 - \mu^2)^i (P_n{}^{(i)})^2 d\mu = \frac{2}{2n+1} \frac{(n+i)!}{(n-i)!} \qquad \text{by Eq. (184.6),}$$

it is found that

$$\frac{2n+1}{2} \int_{-1}^{+1} R_n{}^* d\mu = \sum_{i=0}^{n} B_{ni} \frac{(n+i)!}{(n-i)!} \cos i\omega. \tag{4}$$

The integral of the left member is

$$\int_{-1}^{+1} \frac{d\mu}{\sqrt{1 - 2h \cos \omega + h^2 - 2h(1 - \cos \omega)\mu^2}} =$$

$$\frac{2}{\sqrt{2h(1 - \cos \omega)}} \sin^{-1} \sqrt{\frac{2h(1 - \cos \omega)}{1 - 2h \cos \omega + h^2}}.$$

Therefore, the result of integrating Eq. (3) with respect to μ is

$$\frac{2}{\sqrt{2h(1 - \cos \omega)}} \sin^{-1} \sqrt{\frac{2h(1 - \cos \omega)}{1 - 2h \cos \omega + h^2}} = \sum_{n=0}^{\infty} h^n \int_{-1}^{+1} R_n{}^* d\mu.$$

Now multiply this by $\sqrt{h}$, and then differentiate with respect to h. The result is

$$\frac{1}{\sqrt{h}} \cdot \frac{1 + h}{1 - 2h \cos \omega + h^2} = \sum_{n=0}^{\infty} \frac{2n+1}{2} h^{\frac{2n-1}{2}} \int_{-1}^{+1} R_n{}^* d\mu; \tag{5}$$

or, on multiplying again by $\sqrt{h}$,

$$\frac{1 + h}{1 - 2h \cos \omega + h^2} = \sum_{n=0}^{\infty} \frac{2n+1}{2} h^n \int_{-1}^{+1} R_n{}^* d\mu. \tag{6}$$

It was shown in Eq. (187.7) that

$$\frac{1 + h}{1 - 2h \cos \omega + h^2} = 1 + \sum_{n=1}^{\infty} h^n \left(1 + 2 \sum_{i=1}^{n} \cos i\omega \right). \tag{7}$$

Hence, on substituting Eqs. (4) and (7) in Eq. (6), it is found that,

$$\sum_{n=1}^{\infty} h^n \left(1 + 2 \sum_{i=1}^{n} \cos i\omega \right) = \sum_{n=1}^{\infty} h^n \sum_{i=0}^{n} B_{ni} \frac{(n+i)!}{(n-i)!} \cos i\omega. \tag{8}$$

Since Eq. (8) is an identity in h, it follows that

$$B_{n0} = 1, \qquad B_{ni} = 2\frac{(n-i)!}{(n+i)!} \qquad i = 1, \cdots, n,$$

$$n = 1, \cdots, \infty. \quad (9)$$

These values of the coefficients B_{ni} substituted in Eq. (2) give the complete expression for the coefficients R_n, namely,

$$R_n = P_n(\mu_1) \cdot P_n(\mu_2) + 2\sum_{i=1}^{n} \frac{(n-i)!}{(n+i)!}(\sin^i \varphi_1 \cdot P_n^{(i)}(\mu_1))$$

$$\times (\sin^i \varphi_2 \cdot P_n^{(i)}(\mu_2)) \cos i(\theta_1 - \theta_2). \quad (10)$$

On expanding $\cos i(\theta_1 - \theta_2)$, viz.,

$$\cos i(\theta_1 - \theta_2) = \cos i\theta_1 \cos i\theta_2 + \sin i\theta_1 \sin i\theta_2,$$

and setting, as in Sec. 197, for the tesseral harmonics

$$C_{ni}^{(k)} = \sin^i \varphi_k \cdot P_n^{(i)}(\varphi_k) \cdot \cos i\theta_k,$$

$$S_{ni}^{(k)} = \sin^i \varphi_k \cdot P_n^{(i)}(\varphi_k) \cdot \sin i\theta_k,$$

Eq. (10) becomes Eq. (11),

$$R_n = P_n(\mu_1) \cdot P_n(\mu_2) + 2\sum_{i=1}^{n} \frac{(n-i)!}{(n+i)!}[C_{ni}^{(1)}C_{ni}^{(2)} + S_{ni}^{(1)}S_{ni}^{(2)}];$$

and, finally

$$\frac{1}{R} = \frac{1}{r} \sum_{n=0}^{\infty} R_n\left(\frac{\rho}{r}\right)^n.$$

The surface harmonics R_n are known as *Laplace's coefficients*. It is evident from the relation

$$R_n = P_n(\cos \lambda)$$

that R_n is a zonal harmonic with respect to a pole which lies on the line which joins the origin to the point x, y, z. Equation (11) is its expression in terms of the tesseral harmonics of the original pole of the sphere. In other words, Eq. (11) can be regarded merely as an equation of transformation.

203. The Expansion of the Potential of a Finite Body in a Series of Tesseral Harmonics.—The potential of any finite body B is defined as the integral

$$V = \int_B \frac{dm}{R}.$$

If, in Fig. 106, ξ, η, ζ are the coordinates of a point of the body, x, y, z the coordinates of the attracted point, and

$$R^2 = (x - \xi)^2 + (y - \eta)^2 + (z - \zeta)^2,$$
$$r^2 = x^2 + y^2 + z^2,$$
$$\rho^2 = \xi^2 + \eta^2 + \zeta^2,$$

the expression for the potential becomes, on using the results of the preceeding section,

$$V = \sum_{n=0}^{\infty} \frac{1}{r^{2n+1}} \int_B r^n \rho^n R_n dm. \tag{1}$$

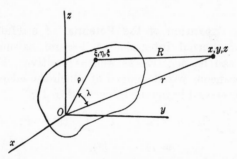

FIG. 106.

The expression for R_n is given in Eq. (202.11). Let

$$r^n P_n(\mu_1) = \mathbf{P}_n{}^{(1)}(x, y, z), \qquad \rho^n P_n(\mu_2) = \mathbf{P}_n{}^{(2)}(\xi, \eta, \zeta),$$
$$r^n C_{ni}{}^{(1)}(\varphi_1, \theta_1) = \mathbf{C}_{ni}{}^{(1)}(x, y, z), \qquad \rho^n C_{ni}{}^{(2)}(\varphi_2 \theta_2) = \mathbf{C}_{ni}{}^{(2)}(\xi, \eta, \zeta),$$
$$r^n S_{ni}{}^{(1)}(\varphi_1, \theta_1) = \mathbf{S}_{ni}{}^{(1)}(x, y, z), \qquad \rho^n S_{ni}{}^{(2)}(\varphi_2, \theta_2) = \mathbf{S}_{ni}{}^{(2)}(\xi, \eta, \zeta)$$

By Sec. 197, $\mathbf{P}_n{}^{(1)}$, $\mathbf{C}_{ni}{}^{(1)}$, $\mathbf{S}_{ni}{}^{(1)}$ and $\mathbf{P}_n{}^{(2)}$, $\mathbf{C}_{ni}{}^{(2)}$, $\mathbf{S}_{ni}{}^{(2)}$ are polynomials in x, y, z and ξ, η, ζ respectively, which are solid tesseral harmonics. Hence

$$\int_B r^n \rho^n R_n dm = \mathbf{P}_n{}^{(1)} \int_B \mathbf{P}_n{}^{(2)} dm$$

$$+ 2 \sum_{i=1}^{n} \frac{(n-i)!}{(n+i)!} \left[\mathbf{C}_{ni}{}^{(1)} \int_B \mathbf{C}_{ni}{}^{(2)} dm + \mathbf{S}_{ni}{}^{(1)} \int_B \mathbf{S}_{ni}{}^{(2)} dm \right]. \tag{2}$$

This result can be stated in words as follows: *The coefficient of the solid tesseral harmonic of degree* $-(n+1)$ *and order* i *in the expansion of the potential of a body in powers of* $1/r$ *is equal to the integral taken over the body of the corresponding solid tesseral harmonic of degree n and order i multiplied by* $2\dfrac{(n-i)!}{(n+i)!}$, *except that, when i is zero, the factor is 1 instead of 2.*

The integrals

$$\int_B C_{ni}\,dm \qquad \text{and} \qquad \int_B S_{ni}\,dm$$

will be referred to as the *tesseral harmonic integrals* of the body. The above expansion is, therefore, a series arranged according to the solid tesseral harmonics of the attracted point (x, y, z); or, equally well, according to the tesseral harmonic integrals of the body.

204. The Expansion of the Potential of a Finite Body As a Series of Inertial Integrals.—A tesseral harmonic integral of a body can be negative as well as positive. For example, for a homogeneous parallelopiped of which the edges are $2a$, $2b$, and $2c$, the tesseral harmonic integral (Sec. 198)

$$\iiint C_{22}\,dm \doteq 3\sigma \int_{-a}^{+a}\int_{-b}^{+b}\int_{-c}^{+c}(\xi^2 - \eta^2)\,d\xi\,d\eta\,d\zeta$$
$$= M(a^2 - b^2),$$

is positive or negative according as $a \gtrless b$. Every tesseral harmonic integral obviously is resolvable into the sum or difference of a number of inertial integrals (Sec. 172). As there is no direct method of computing the tesseral harmonic integrals, the general expansion in terms of the inertial integrals will be given. The formula given in Sec. 172,

$$V = \sum \frac{(-1)^{i+j+k}}{i!\,j!\,k!}\frac{\partial^{i+j+k}}{\partial x^i \partial y^j \partial z^k}\left(\frac{1}{r}\right)\int_B \xi^i \eta^j \zeta^k\,dm,$$

is symbolical only. It is desired to find the coefficients of these integrals explicitly.

Retaking the equation of Sec. 202,

$$\frac{1}{R} = \sum_{n=0}^{\infty}\frac{r^n \rho^n R_n}{r^{2n+1}}, \tag{1}$$

it will be remembered that $R_n = P_n(\cos \lambda)$ where

$$\cos \lambda = \frac{x\xi + y\eta + z\zeta}{r \cdot \rho};$$

and since, Eq. (186.3),

$$P_n(\mu) = \sum_{s=0}^{l} (-1)^s \frac{[2n - 2s - 1]}{[2s](n - 2s)!} \mu^{n-2s}$$

it is evident that

$$r^n \rho^n R_n = \sum_{s=0}^{l} (-1)^s \frac{[2n - 2s - 1]}{[2s](n - 2s)!} (x\xi + y\eta + z\zeta)^{n-2s} r^{2s} \rho^{2s}, \quad (2)$$

where l is $n/2$ or $(n - 1)/2$ according as n is even or odd. The symmetry and homogeneity with respect to the two sets of variables x, y, z and ξ, η, ζ is evident.

By the multinomial theorem of algebra

$$(a + b + c)^n = \sum_{i,j,k} \frac{n!}{i!j!k!} a^i b^j c^k, \qquad i + j + k = n.$$

Accordingly

$$\left. \begin{aligned}
(x\xi + y\eta + z\zeta)^{n-2s} &= \sum_{i,j,k} \frac{(n - 2s)!}{i!j!k!} x^i y^j z^k \cdot \xi^i \eta^j \zeta^k, \\
&\qquad\qquad i + j + k = n - 2s, \\
\rho^{2s} = (\xi^2 + \eta^2 + \zeta^2)^s &= \sum_{\alpha,\beta,\gamma} \frac{s!}{\alpha!\beta!\gamma!} \xi^{2\alpha} \eta^{2\beta} \zeta^{2\gamma}, \qquad \alpha + \beta + \gamma = s.
\end{aligned} \right\}$$

Therefore

$$(x\xi + y\eta + z\zeta)^{n-2s}(\xi^2 + \eta^2 + \zeta^2)^s =$$
$$\sum_{\alpha,\beta,\gamma} \sum_{i,j,k} \frac{(n - 2s)!s!x^i y^j z^k}{\alpha!\beta!\gamma!i!j!k!} \xi^{i+2\alpha} \eta^{j+2\beta} \zeta^{k+2\gamma}.$$

This expression can be rearranged by taking

$$i = p - 2\alpha, \quad j = q - 2\beta, \quad k = r - 2\gamma; \quad \therefore \ p + q + r = n.$$

The result is

$$(x\xi + y\eta + z\zeta)^{n-2s}(\xi^2 + \eta^2 + \zeta^2)^s$$
$$= \sum_{\alpha,\beta,\gamma} \sum_{p,q,r} \frac{(n - 2s)!s!x^{p-2\alpha} y^{q-2\beta} z^{r-2\gamma}}{\alpha!\beta!\gamma!(p - 2\alpha)!(q - 2\beta)!(r - 2\gamma)!} \xi^p \eta^q \zeta^r,$$

and this result, substituted in Eq. (2) gives

$$r^n \rho^n R_n = \sum_{s=0}^{l} (-1)^s \frac{[2n - 2s - 1]r^{2s}}{[2s](n - 2s)!}$$
$$\times \sum_{\alpha,\beta,\gamma} \sum_{p,q,r} \frac{(n - 2s)!s!x^{p-2\alpha} y^{q-2\beta} z^{r-2\gamma}}{\alpha!\beta!\gamma!(p - 2\alpha)!(q - 2\beta)!(r - 2\gamma)!} \xi^p \eta^q \zeta^r,$$

where

$$p + q + r = n, \quad \alpha + \beta + \gamma = s, \quad l = \frac{1}{2}n \quad \text{or} \quad \frac{1}{2}(n - 1),$$

$$[2n] = 2 \cdot 4 \cdot 6 \cdots 2n \qquad [2n + 1] = 1 \cdot 3 \cdot 5 \cdots (2n + 1),$$
$$\text{and} \quad [0] = 1.$$

Since $[2s] = 2^s s!$, the factors $(n - 2s)!$ and $s!$ can be cancelled, leaving

$$r^n \rho^n R_n = \sum_{s=0}^{l} \left(-\frac{1}{2}\right)^s [2n - 2s - 1] r^{2s}$$

$$\times \sum_{\alpha,\beta,\gamma} \sum_{p,q,r} \frac{x^{p-2\alpha} y^{q-2\beta} z^{r-2\gamma}}{\alpha! \beta! \gamma! (p - 2\alpha)! (q - 2\beta)! (r - 2\gamma)!} \xi^p \eta^q \zeta^r. \quad (3)$$

On substituting this result in Eq. (1), multiplying by dm, and then integrating, there results

$$V = \sum_{n=0}^{\infty} \frac{1}{r^{2n+1}} \sum_{\substack{p,q,r \\ p+q+r=n}} \left\{ \sum_{s=0}^{l} \left(-\frac{r^2}{2}\right)^s [2n - 2s - 1] \right.$$

$$\left. \times \sum_{\substack{\alpha,\beta,\gamma \\ \alpha+\beta+\gamma=s}} \frac{x^{p-2\alpha} y^{q-2\beta} z^{r-2\gamma}}{\alpha! \beta! \gamma! (p - 2\alpha)! (q - 2\beta)! (r - 2\gamma)!} \right\} \int_B \xi^p \eta^q \zeta^r dm, \quad (4)$$

which is the expansion of the potential function with respect to the series of inertial integrals. If the general expression for the inertial integrals of the given body can be given, then the general term of the expansion of its potential can be written down. This can be done for the class of bodies which is discussed in Sec. 50, and perhaps for others also.

From the symmetry relations between the two sets of variables x, y, z and ξ, η, ζ, it is possible to derive from Eq. (4) the expansion for V according to powers of $x, y,$ and z, viz.,

$$V = \sum_{n=0}^{\infty} \sum_{\substack{p,q,r \\ p+q+r=n}} \frac{x^p y^q z^r}{r^{2n+1}} \int_B \left[\sum_{s=0}^{l} \left(-\frac{\rho^2}{2}\right)^s [2n - 2s - 1] \right.$$

$$\left. \times \sum_{\substack{\alpha,\beta,\gamma \\ \alpha+\beta+\gamma=s}} \frac{\xi^{p-2\alpha} \eta^{q-2\beta} \zeta^{r-2\gamma}}{\alpha! \beta! \gamma! (p - 2\alpha)! (q - 2\beta)! (r - 2\gamma)!} \right] dm. \quad (5)$$

205. Laplace's Integral Equation.—It has already been shown (Sec. 200) that the surface integral of two spherical harmonics of different degrees is zero, and even when the degrees are the same it may vanish, as is shown in Sec. 201. A particularly interesting case when the two surface harmonics are of the same degree is that in which one of the harmonics is the Laplacian coefficient R_n, (Eq. (202.11)).

Let S_n be any surface harmonic of degree n in the variables φ_1, θ_1. Then, if A_{ni} and $\theta_i^{(1)}$ are suitably chosen constants,

$$S_n = \sum_{i=0}^{n} A_{ni} \sin^i \varphi_1 \cdot P_n^{(i)}(\mu_1) \cdot \cos i(\theta_1 - \theta_i^{(1)}). \qquad (1)$$

By its definition

$$R_n = B_{n0} \cdot P_n(\mu_1) + \sum_{i=1}^{n} B_{ni} \sin^i \varphi_1 \cdot P_n^{(i)}(\mu_1) \cdot \cos i(\theta_1 - \theta_2),$$

where

$$B_{n0} = P_n(\mu_2), \qquad B_{ni} = 2\frac{(n-i)!}{(n+i)!} \sin^i \varphi_2 P_n^{(i)}(\mu_2), \qquad (2)$$

$$\mu_2 = \cos \varphi_2, \qquad \text{and} \qquad \theta_2 \text{ is independent of } i.$$

The surface integral of the product of these two harmonics is given in Eq. (201.2),

$$\int_{-1}^{+1} \int_0^{2\pi} S_n R_n d\mu_1 d\theta_1 = \frac{4\pi}{2n+1} A_{n0} B_{n0} +$$

$$\frac{2\pi}{2n+1} \sum_{i=1}^{n} A_{ni} B_{ni} \frac{(n+i)!}{(n-i)!} \cos i(\theta_i^{(2)} - \theta_i^{(1)}).$$

If the values of B_{ni} of Eq. (2) are substituted in this formula, it becomes

$$\int_{-1}^{+1} \int_0^{2\pi} S_n R_n d\mu_1 d\theta_1 = \frac{4\pi}{2n+1} A_{n0} P_n(\mu_2) +$$

$$\frac{4\pi}{2n+1} \sum_{i=1}^{n} A_{ni} \sin^i \varphi_2 \cdot P_n^{(i)}(\mu_2) \cos i(\theta_2 - \theta_i^{(1)})$$

$$\left.\begin{array}{l} = \dfrac{4\pi}{2n+1} S_n(\mu_2, \theta_2) \qquad \text{by Eq. (1);} \\[2mm] \text{or,} \\[2mm] S_n(\mu_2, \ \theta_2) = \dfrac{2n+1}{4\pi} \displaystyle\int_{-1}^{+1} \int_0^{2\pi} R_n S_n(\mu_1, \ \theta_1) d\mu_1 d\theta_1, \end{array}\right\} \qquad (3)$$

which is one of the earliest examples of an integral equation.

Since R is symmetrical in the subscripts 1 and 2, this equation could also be written

$$S_n(\mu_1,\ \theta_1) = \frac{2n+1}{4\pi} \int_{-1}^{+1} \int_{0}^{2\pi} R_n S_n(\mu_2,\ \theta_2) d\mu_2 d\theta_2. \tag{4}$$

206. The Expansion of an Arbitrary Function in a Series of Spherical Harmonics.—Suppose there is given a function of the arguments φ and θ, which is generally continuous in the region

$$-\frac{\pi}{2} \leqq \varphi \leqq +\frac{\pi}{2}, \qquad 0 \leqq \theta \leqq 2\pi,$$

although a finite number of lines along which the given function has finite discontinuities is permissible. It was first shown by Laplace that such a function can be expanded in a convergent series of spherical harmonics, although the proof given by Laplace was lacking in rigor. The first rigorous proof was given by Dirichlet,[1] and the proof of Dirichlet's was followed by a number of others, the simplest being those of Bonnet[2] and Darboux.[3] The argument of Darboux will be followed here.

Let S_n be a general surface harmonic of degree n with $2n + 1$ arbitrary constants, and let $F(\varphi_1,\ \theta_1)$ be the given function (not necessarily harmonic). It will be remarked first of all that if F is expansible in a series of surface harmonics, S_n, then that expansion is unique. For, if,

$$F(\varphi_1,\ \theta_1) = \sum_{k=0}^{\infty} S_k, \tag{1}$$

and if $R_n(\varphi_1,\ \theta_1;\ \varphi_2,\ \theta_2)$ is Laplace's coefficient of the nth degree, then, on multiplying Eq. (1) by $R_n d\mu_1 d\theta_1$ and integrating over the sphere,

$$\int_{-1}^{+1} \int_{0}^{2\pi} R_n \cdot F d\mu_1 d\theta_1 = \sum_{k=0}^{\infty} \int_{-1}^{+1} \int_{0}^{2\pi} R_n S_k d\mu_1 d\theta_1.$$

But, since

$$\left.\begin{array}{l} \displaystyle\int_{-1}^{+1} \int_{0}^{2\pi} R_n S_k d\mu_1 d\theta_1 = 0, \qquad \text{if} \quad k \neq n, \\[3mm] \displaystyle\int_{-1}^{+1} \int_{0}^{2\pi} R_n S_n(\varphi_1, \theta_1) d\mu_1 d\theta_1 = \frac{4\pi}{2n+1} S_n(\varphi_2,\ \theta_2), \end{array}\right\}$$

---

[1] *Journal für Mathematik*, Vol. XVII, p. 35 (1837).
[2] *Journal de Liouville*, Vol. XVII (1), p. 265 (1852).
[3] *Journal de Liouville*, Vol. XIX (2), p. 1 (1874).

it is evident that

$$\int_S R_n F d\omega_1 = \frac{4\pi}{2n+1} S_n(\varphi_2, \theta_2), \qquad d\omega_1 = d\mu_1 d\theta_1;$$

and similarly

$$\int_S R_n F d\omega_2 = \frac{4\pi}{2n+1} S_n(\varphi_1, \theta_1), \qquad d\omega_2 = d\mu_2 d\theta_2.$$

But since $\int R_n F d\omega_2$ is a perfectly definite function of φ_1 and θ_1, it follows that the harmonic $S_n(\varphi_1, \theta_1)$ is a perfectly definite one, and therefore the series in Eq. (1), if it exists, is unique, and

$$F(\varphi_1, \theta_1) = \sum_{n=0}^{\infty} \frac{2n+1}{4\pi} \int_S R_n F(\varphi_2, \theta_2) d\omega_2. \qquad (2)$$

As it cannot be assumed that the series in Eq. (1) does exist, let the function F_m be defined by the finite series

$$F_m(\varphi_1, \theta_1) = \sum_{n=0}^{m} \frac{2n+1}{4\pi} \int_S R_n \cdot F(\varphi_2, \theta_2) d\omega_2, \qquad (3)$$

which is perfectly definite, and seek the limit of F_m as m increases. It will be found that the limit of F_m is F, and that the series in Eq. (1) is valid.

Let the pole where the z-axis pierces the unit sphere be denoted by the letter C, Fig. 107. Let the point whose coordinates are φ_1, θ_1 be denoted by C_1, and the point whose coordinates are φ_2, θ_2 be denoted by C_2. The angle λ is measured by the arc of the great circle which passes through C_1 and C_2, since

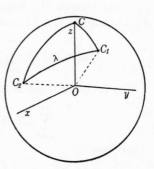

Fig. 107.

$$\cos \lambda = \cos \varphi_1 \cos \varphi_2 + \sin \varphi_1 \sin \varphi_2 \cos (\theta_2 - \theta_1);$$

and

$$R_n(\varphi_1, \theta_1; \varphi_2, \theta_2) = P_n(\cos \lambda),$$

P_n being the zonal harmonic of degree n.

If the function $F(\varphi_2, \theta_2)$ is written

$$F(\varphi_2, \theta_2) = F(C_2),$$

and $d\omega$ is a surface element in any system of coordinates, then the expression

$$F_m(\varphi_1, \theta_1) = \sum_{n=0}^{m} \frac{2n+1}{4\pi} \int_S F(C_2) P_n(\cos \lambda) d\omega$$

is independent of the coordinate system used.

Let the point C_1 be taken as the pole of a new system of coordinates, and in this new system let the coordinates of the point C_2 be φ_3 and θ_3. Then

$$\lambda = \varphi_3, \qquad \cos \lambda = \cos \varphi_3 = \mu_3,$$
$$F(C_2) = F_3(\varphi_3, \theta_3), \qquad P_n(\cos \lambda) = P_n(\mu_3).$$

Since $P_n(\mu_3)$ is independent of θ_3,

$$F_m(\varphi_1, \theta_1) = \sum_{n=0}^{m} \frac{2n+1}{4\pi} \int_{-1}^{+1} P_n(\mu_3) d\mu_3 \int_0^{2\pi} F_3(\varphi_3, \theta_3) d\theta_3. \quad (4)$$

The integral

$$G(\varphi_3) = \frac{1}{2\pi} \int_0^{2\pi} F_3(\varphi_3, \theta_3) d\theta_3$$

represents the mean value of the function $F_3(\varphi_3, \theta_3)$ along the circle of latitude φ_3. It is a perfectly well defined function of φ_3, even though the function F_3 has a finite number of finite discontinuities along the circle. Equation (4) becomes

$$F_m(\varphi_1, \theta_1) = \sum_{n=0}^{m} \frac{2n+1}{2} \int_{-1}^{+1} P_n(\mu_3) \cdot G(\mu_3) d\mu_3.$$

The function $G(\mu_3)$ is independent of n, and, by Eq. (282.2),

$$\sum_{n=0}^{m} (2n+1) P_n = P'_m + P'_{m+1}.$$

Therefore

$$F_m = \frac{1}{2} \int_{-1}^{+1} G(P_m' + P'_{m+1}) d\mu_3. \quad (5)$$

It will be assumed at first that $G(\mu_3)$ is a continuous function of μ_3 in the interval $-1 \leqq \mu_3 \leqq +1$. Then Eq. (5) can be integrated by parts, with the result

$$F_m(\varphi_1, \theta_1) = \frac{1}{2} \Big[G \cdot (P_m + P_{m+1}) \Big]_{-1}^{+1} - \frac{1}{2} \int_{-1}^{+1} (P_m + P_{m+1}) G' d\mu_3.$$

Since

$$P_m(+1) = +1 \qquad \text{and} \qquad P_m(-1) = (-1)^m,$$

it follows that

$$\frac{1}{2}[P_m(+1) + P_{m+1}(+1)] = 1,$$

and

$$\frac{1}{2}[P_m(-1) + P_{m+1}(-1)] = 0;$$

so that

$$F_m = G(+1) - \frac{1}{2}\int_{-1}^{+1}(P_m + P_{m+1})G'd\mu_3. \qquad (6)$$

Let the integral in the right member be separated into three parts

$$\int_{-1}^{+1} = \int_{-1}^{-1+\delta} + \int_{-1+\delta}^{+1-\delta} + \int_{1-\delta}^{+1},$$

and consider the sum of the first and last of these three integrals

$$\int_{-1}^{-1+\delta} + \int_{1-\delta}^{1}\left[\frac{1}{2}(P_m + P_{m+1})G'\right]d\mu_3 \leqq$$

$$\int_{-1}^{-1+\delta} + \int_{1-\delta}^{1}\left[\frac{1}{2}|P_m + P_{m+1}| \cdot |G'|\right]d\mu_3 < \int_{-1}^{-1+\delta} + \int_{1-\delta}^{1}|G'|d\mu_3.$$

Since G is continuous the discontinuities of G', if infinite, are of order less than unity; therefore, the sum of the two integrals

$$\int_{-1}^{-1+\delta} + \int_{1-\delta}^{1}|G'|d\mu_3$$

is finite and vanishes with δ. If, therefore, ϵ is given in advance, δ can be taken so small that

$$\int_{-1}^{-1+\delta} + \int_{1-\delta}^{1}\frac{1}{2}(P_m + P_{m+1})G'd\mu_3 < \frac{1}{2}\epsilon.$$

As for the remaining integral

$$\frac{1}{2}\int_{-1+\delta}^{1-\delta}(P_m + P_{m+1})G'd\mu_3,$$

let Q_m be the maximum value of $|P_m + P_{m+1}|/2$ in the interval, and

$$\overline{G} = \int_{-1+\delta}^{1-\delta}|G'|d\mu_3;$$

then

$$\frac{1}{2}\int_{-1+\delta}^{1-\delta}(P_m + P_{m+1})G'd\mu_3 \leqq \frac{1}{2}\int_{-1+\delta}^{1-\delta}|P_m + P_{m+1}| \cdot |G'|d\mu_3$$

$$\leqq \overline{G}Q_m.$$

But since, (Sec. 191),

$$\lim_{m=\infty} |P_m| = 0, \qquad \text{if} \qquad |\mu| < 1,$$

the limit of Q_m for increasing values of m also is zero. Hence m can be taken so large that

$$\frac{1}{2} \int_{-1+\delta}^{1-\delta} (P_m + P_{m+1})G' d\mu_3 < \frac{1}{2}\epsilon,$$

and therefore

$$\frac{1}{2} \int_{-1}^{+1} (P_m + P_{m+1})G' d\mu_3 < \epsilon.$$

It follows from Eq. (6), therefore, that

$$\lim_{m=\infty} F_m(\varphi_1, \theta_1) = G(+1).$$

By its definition, $G(+1)$ is the mean value of $F_3(\varphi_3, \theta_3)$ along a circle of infinitesimal radius about the pole; that is, it is the value of F at the point C_1, or $F(\varphi_1, \theta_1)$. Therefore

$$\lim_{m=\infty} F_m = F(\varphi_1, \theta_1) = \sum_{n=0}^{\infty} \frac{2n+1}{4\pi} \int_S R_n F(\varphi_2, \theta_2) d\omega_2, \qquad (7)$$

which is Eq. (2).

If the function $G(\mu_3)$ has finite discontinuities at a finite number of points, the integration of Eq. (5) by parts is still permissible. Neither the results nor the remainder of the argument is altered, but as the text books do not give the proof of the validity of integration by parts under such conditions a lengthy digression would be necessary to prove it. The proof is not difficult, however.

207. The Representation of a Rational, Integral Function.— Suppose $G(x, y, z)$ is a given homogeneous polynomial of degree n in the letters x, y, z, and assume for the moment that G can be expressed in the form

$$G(x, y, z) = \sum_{s=0}^{l} r^{2s} H_{n-2s}, \qquad (1)$$

where H_p is a solid spherical harmonic of degree p, and $2l = n$ or $n - 1$ according as n is even or odd. Form the Laplacian of both members of Eq. (1). ΔG is a homogeneous polynomial of degree $n - 2$ which is readily formed; and since

$$\Delta(r^j H_k) = j(j + 2k + 1)r^{j-2} H_k,$$

by Eq. (171.1), Eq. (1) becomes

$$\Delta G = \sum_{s=1}^{l} 2s(2n - 2s + 1)r^{2(s-1)}H_{n-2s},\qquad(2)$$

the harmonic H_n disappearing in the process, since $\Delta H_n = 0$. Aside from the constant coefficients in the right members, Eq. (2) is similar to Eq. (1), but its degree is $n - 2$. The operation can therefore be repeated

$$\Delta\Delta G = \Delta^2 G =$$

$$\sum_{s=2}^{l} 4s(s - 1)(2n - 2s + 1)(2n - 2s - 1)r^{2(s-2)}H_{n-2s},\qquad(3)$$

and Eq. (3) is of degree $n - 4$. In general, after performing the operation k times

$$\Delta^k G = \sum_{s=k}^{l} 2^k \cdot \frac{s!}{(s-k)!} \frac{[2n - 2s + 1]}{[2n - 2s - 2k + 1]}r^{2(s-k)} \cdot H_{n-2s}.$$

When k is equal to l the left member is a homogeneous polynomial of degree 1, if n is odd, or of degree zero if n is even. In either event it is harmonic, since every polynomial of degree zero or one is harmonic. The right member is reduced to a single term which contains H_1 or H_0. This equation determines H_1 or H_0, as the case may be, uniquely. The preceeding equation then determines H_3 (or H_2), and so on, back to Eq. (1) itself, which determines H_n. Thus all of the functions H_p are uniquely determined, and the representation of G in the form of Eq. (1) is possible.

If S_k is the surface harmonic corresponding to the solid harmonic H_k, so that

$$H_k = r^k S_k,$$

it is seen that Eq. (1) becomes

$$G(x, y, z) = r^n \sum_{S=0}^{l} S_{n-2s}(\varphi, \theta).$$

Hence the series of surface harmonics which represents the value of a rational, integral function on the surface of a sphere is a finite series which contains no harmonics of degree greater than n.

As an example, let the monomial xy^2z^3 be expressed in the form

$$xy^2z^3 = H_6 + r^2H_4 + r^4H_2 + r^6H_0.\qquad(a)$$

The successive operations yield the equations

$$\Delta(xy^2z^3) = 2xz^3 + 6xy^2z = 22H_4 + 36r^2H_2 + 42r^4H_0, \quad (b)$$

$$\Delta^2(xy^2z^3) = 24xz = 36 \cdot 14H_2 + 42 \cdot 20r^2H_0, \quad (c)$$

$$\Delta^3(xy^2z^3) = 0 = 42 \cdot 20 \cdot 6H_0.$$

The last equation gives $H_0 = 0$. Then

$$H_2 = \frac{xz}{21}, \quad \text{from Eq. } (c),$$

$$H_4 = \frac{1}{77}(-6x^3z + 15xy^2z + xz^3), \quad \text{from Eq. } (b),$$

and finally, from Eq. (a),

$$H_6 =$$

$$\frac{1}{3 \cdot 7 \cdot 11}(7x^5z - 56xy^4z - 14xz^5 - 49x^3y^2z + 161xy^2z^3 - 7x^3z^3).$$

Translated into the tesseral surface harmonics by means of the relations in Sec. 198, these results give

$$xy^2z^3 = \frac{r^6}{7 \cdot 9 \cdot 11}[11C_{21} + \frac{9}{10}C_{41} - \frac{9}{20}C_{43} - 2C_{61} - \frac{1}{10}C_{63}].$$

208. Green's Problem for the Sphere.—If a continuous set of values are defined on the surface of a sphere by the function $V(\xi, \eta, \zeta)$, Green's equation, Eq. (136.2), defines a function $V(x, y, z)$ which is harmonic inside (or outside, if the point x, y, z is outside) the sphere and which is equal to $V(\xi, \eta, \zeta)$ on the sphere. This equation is

$$V(x, y, z) = \frac{a(a^2 - r^2)}{4\pi} \int_S \frac{1}{\rho^3} V(\xi, \eta, \zeta)d\bar{\omega}, \quad (1)$$

where

$$\rho^2 = (x - \xi)^2 + (y - \eta)^2 + (z - \zeta)^2$$

and $d\bar{\omega}$ is an element of the surface of a unit sphere.

Suppose the function V is expanded in a series of spherical surface harmonics, Sec. 206, so that

$$V(\xi, \eta, \zeta) = \sum_{n=0}^{\infty} S_n(\varphi, \theta).$$

It was found in Eq. (183.5) that

$$\frac{1}{(\sqrt{1 - 2\mu h + h^2})^3} = \sum_{m=0}^{\infty} P'_{m+1}h^m,$$

and therefore

$$\frac{1 - h^2}{(\sqrt{1 - 2\mu h + h^2})^3} = 1 + \sum_{m=1}^{\infty} (P'_{m+1} - P'_{m-1})h^m,$$

$$= \sum_{m=0}^{\infty} (2m + 1)P_m h^m, \qquad \text{by Eq. (182.1).}$$

Since

$$\rho^2 = a^2 - 2ar \cos \lambda + r^2 \qquad \text{and} \qquad P_m(\cos \lambda) = R_m,$$

it follows that

$$\frac{a(a^2 - r^2)}{\rho^3} = \sum_{m=0}^{\infty} (2m + 1)R_m \left(\frac{r}{a}\right)^m.$$

Hence, Eq. (1) can be written

$$V(x, y, z) = \sum_{m=0}^{\infty} \left(\sum_{n=0}^{\infty} \frac{(2m + 1)}{4\pi} \int_S R_m S_n d\tilde{\omega} \right) \left(\frac{r}{a}\right)^m$$

Since R_m and S_n are surface harmonics of degree m and n respectively, it follows that, Sec. 200,

$$\int_S R_m S_n d\tilde{\omega} = 0,$$

except when $m = n$.

Suppose that in spherical coordinates

$$x = r \sin \varphi_0 \cos \theta_0,$$
$$y = r \sin \varphi_0 \sin \theta_0,$$
$$z = r \cos \varphi_0;$$

then, by Eq. (205.4), if $n = m$,

$$\frac{2m + 1}{4\pi} \int_S R_m S_m(\varphi, \theta) d\tilde{\omega} = S_m(\varphi_0, \theta_0);$$

and therefore

$$V(x, y, z) = \sum_{m=0}^{\infty} S_m(\varphi_0, \theta_0) \left(\frac{r}{a}\right)^m. \tag{2}$$

If the point x, y, z lies outside of the sphere the corresponding expression is

$$V(x, y, z) = \sum_{m=0}^{\infty} S_m(\varphi_0, \theta_0) \left(\frac{a}{r}\right)^{m+1}. \tag{3}$$

209. The Potential of a Surface Distribution of Matter on a Sphere.—Suppose there is given a surface distribution of matter of density σ on a sphere of radius a. The potential of this distribution at any interior or exterior point p (x, y, z), is

$$V = \int_S \frac{\sigma d\omega}{\rho},$$

where

$$\rho^2 = (x - \xi)^2 + (y - \eta)^2 + (z - \zeta)^2,$$

and ξ, η, ζ are the coordinates of the surface element $d\omega$. Also

$$r^2 = x^2 + y^2 + z^2,$$
$$a^2 = \xi^2 + \eta^2 + \zeta^2.$$

For points exterior to the sphere, that is $r > a$, the expansion of $1/\rho$ is, by Sec. 202,

$$\frac{1}{\rho} = \frac{1}{r} \sum_{m=0}^{\infty} R_m \left(\frac{a}{r}\right)^m ;$$

and for interior points, that is $r < a$,

$$\frac{1}{\rho} = \frac{1}{a} \sum_{m=0}^{\infty} R_m \left(\frac{r}{a}\right)^m ,$$

where R_m is the particular surface harmonic which is known as Laplace's coefficient, Eq. (202.11).

By Sec. 206, the density σ, which is assumed to be generally continuous although it may have a finite number of lines of discontinuity, can be expanded in a convergent series of surface harmonics, which, for convenience, is taken in the form

$$\sigma = \frac{1}{a} \sum_{n=0}^{\infty} \frac{2n + 1}{4\pi} S_n(\varphi, \theta).$$

Hence

$$V = \frac{1}{a^2} \sum_{m=0}^{\infty} \sum_{n=0}^{\infty} \left(\frac{a}{r}\right)^{m+1} \frac{2n + 1}{4\pi} \int_S R_m S_n d\omega ;$$

or

$$V = \frac{1}{a^2} \sum_{m=0}^{\infty} \sum_{n=0}^{\infty} \left(\frac{r}{a}\right)^m \frac{2n + 1}{4\pi} \int_S R_m S_n d\omega ,$$

according as the point p is exterior or interior to the sphere
Under the assumption that

$$x = r \sin \varphi_0 \cos \theta_0,$$
$$y = r \sin \varphi_0 \sin \theta_0,$$
$$z = r \cos \varphi_0,$$

the values of the above surface integrals are

$$\int_S R_m R_n d\omega = 0, \quad \text{if} \quad n \neq m,$$

and

$$\frac{2m+1}{4\pi a^2} \int_S R_m S_m(\varphi, \theta) d\omega = S_m(\varphi_0, \theta_0),$$

by Eq. (205.3). Hence

$$V = \sum_{m=0}^{\infty} S_m(\varphi_0, \theta_0)\left(\frac{a}{r}\right)^{m+1}, \quad \text{if } r > a, \tag{1}$$

and

$$V = \sum_{m=0}^{\infty} S_m(\varphi_0, \theta_0)\left(\frac{r}{a}\right)^{m}, \quad \text{if } r < a. \tag{2}$$

This result shows that any harmonic distribution of matter on a sphere produces the same, and none other, harmonics in both the interior and exterior potentials.

The total mass of the distribution is

$$\int_S \sigma d\omega = \int_S \sum_{n=0}^{\infty} \frac{2n+1}{4\pi a} S_n d\omega = a S_0,$$

by Eq. (175.3).

If the interior and exterior potentials are given, and if

$$\sum_{m=0}^{\infty} \frac{2m+1}{4\pi a} S_m$$

is convergent at all points of the sphere, it is readily verified that (See Eq. 126.5)

$$\sigma = +\frac{1}{4\pi}\left(\frac{\partial V_i}{\partial n_e} + \frac{\partial V_e}{\partial n_i}\right) = \sum_{m=0}^{\infty} \frac{2m+1}{4\pi a} S_m.$$

On comparing Eqs. (1) and (2) of the present section with Eqs. (2) and (3) of the preceeding section, it is seen that Green's equation for the sphere defines the interior and exterior potentials of the same distribution of matter on the sphere, a fact which, of course, was already known. The definition, however, is not by means of the surface density, but by means of the values of the potential itself on the sphere.

210. Differentiation with Respect to Poles.—It was shown in Chap. III, Sec. 54, that if α, β, γ are the direction cosines of a line and $\varphi(x, y, z)$ is a function of the rectangular coordinates, the derivative of φ in the direction of the line is

$$\frac{\partial \varphi}{\partial l} = \alpha \frac{\partial \varphi}{\partial x} + \beta \frac{\partial \varphi}{\partial y} + \gamma \frac{\partial \varphi}{\partial z},$$

and, also, that

$$dx = \alpha dl, \qquad dy = \beta dl, \qquad dz = \gamma dl.$$

Consider a sphere of radius a with its center at the origin Let α, β, γ be the direction cosines of a line, l, which starts at the origin and intersects the sphere in the point p. The point p is called the pole of the line, and differentiation in the direction of the line l is called *differentiation with respect to the pole p*, and the symbol for such differentiation is

$$\frac{\partial}{\partial l} = \alpha \frac{\partial}{\partial x} + \beta \frac{\partial}{\partial y} + \gamma \frac{\partial}{\partial z}. \tag{1}$$

The result of this differentiation is, in general, a function of x, y, and z which can be differentiated a second time with respect to the same pole, or even a different pole; and so on. Let $\alpha_1, \beta_1, \gamma_1$ be the direction cosines of the first pole, and $\alpha_2, \beta_2, \gamma_2$ be the direction cosines of the second pole. The result of two successive differentiations with respect to the two poles is

$$\frac{\partial^2}{\partial l_1 \partial l_2} = \left(\alpha_1 \frac{\partial}{\partial x} + \beta_1 \frac{\partial}{\partial y} + \gamma_1 \frac{\partial}{\partial z} \right) \left(\alpha_2 \frac{\partial}{\partial x} + \beta_2 \frac{\partial}{\partial y} + \gamma_2 \frac{\partial}{\partial z} \right)$$

$$= \alpha_1 \alpha_2 \frac{\partial^2}{\partial x^2} + \alpha_1 \beta_2 \frac{\partial^2}{\partial x \partial y} + \alpha_1 \gamma_2 \frac{\partial^2}{\partial x \partial z}$$

$$+ \beta_1 \alpha_2 \frac{\partial^2}{\partial y \partial x} + \beta_1 \beta_2 \frac{\partial^2}{\partial y^2} + \beta_1 \gamma_2 \frac{\partial^2}{\partial y \partial z}$$

$$+ \gamma_1 \alpha_2 \frac{\partial^2}{\partial z \partial x} + \gamma_1 \beta_2 \frac{\partial^2}{\partial z \partial y} + \gamma_1 \gamma_2 \frac{\partial^2}{\partial z^2}.$$

It will be observed that these differential operators obey the fundamental laws of algebra, namely, the associative law, the distributive law, and the commutative law. They can be treated in their combinations, therefore, just as though they were algebraic quantities. Accordingly

$$\frac{\partial}{\partial l_1} \frac{\partial}{\partial l_2} \frac{\partial}{\partial l_3} \cdots \frac{\partial}{\partial l_n} = \prod_{k=1}^{n} \left(\alpha_k \frac{\partial}{\partial x} + \beta_k \frac{\partial}{\partial y} + \gamma_k \frac{\partial}{\partial z} \right),$$

is the general expression for differentiation with respect to n poles, which may, or may not, be all different.

It is evident that the nth derivative of an harmonic function with respect to n poles is itself an harmonic function, for it is merely the sum of a finite number of ordinary derivatives multiplied by constants; and each ordinary derivative is harmonic (Sec. 172). If φ is an harmonic function of degree m, its nth derivative with respect to n poles is an harmonic function of degree $m - n$.

As an example of polar differentiation, consider the the fourth derivative of $1/r$ with respect to the four corners of a regular tetrahedron which has its center at the origin, one corner on the z-axis, one corner lying in the yz-plane, and one edge parallel to the x-axis. The direction cosines of the four corners are, then,

$$\alpha_1 = 0, \qquad \alpha_2 = 0, \qquad \alpha_3 = -\sqrt{\frac{2}{3}}, \qquad \alpha_4 = +\sqrt{\frac{2}{3}},$$

$$\beta_1 = 0, \qquad \beta_2 = \frac{2}{3}\sqrt{2}, \qquad \beta_3 = -\frac{1}{3}\sqrt{2}, \qquad \beta_4 = -\frac{1}{3}\sqrt{2},$$

$$\gamma_1 = 1, \qquad \gamma_2 = -\frac{1}{3}, \qquad \gamma_3 = -\frac{1}{3}, \qquad \gamma_4 = -\frac{1}{3}.$$

The fourth derivative with respect to these four poles is

$$\frac{\partial^4}{\partial l_1 \partial l_2 \partial l_3 \partial l_4} = \prod_{k=1}^{4}\left(\alpha_k\frac{\partial}{\partial x} + \beta_k\frac{\partial}{\partial y} + \gamma_k\frac{\partial}{\partial z}\right) =$$

$$\frac{\partial}{\partial z}\left(\frac{2}{3}\sqrt{2}\frac{\partial}{\partial y} - \frac{1}{3}\frac{\partial}{\partial z}\right)\left(-\sqrt{\frac{2}{3}}\frac{\partial}{\partial x} - \frac{\sqrt{2}}{3}\frac{\partial}{\partial y} - \frac{1}{3}\frac{\partial}{\partial z}\right)$$

$$\left(\sqrt{\frac{2}{3}}\frac{\partial}{\partial x} - \frac{\sqrt{2}}{3}\frac{\partial}{\partial y} - \frac{1}{3}\frac{\partial}{\partial z}\right)$$

$$= -\frac{4\sqrt{2}}{9}\frac{\partial^4}{\partial x^2\partial y\partial z} + \frac{2}{9}\frac{\partial^4}{\partial x^2\partial z^2} + \frac{4\sqrt{2}}{27}\frac{\partial^4}{\partial y^3\partial z} + \frac{2}{9}\frac{\partial^4}{\partial y^2\partial z^2} - \frac{1}{27}\frac{\partial^4}{\partial z^4}.$$

This symbol operating on the function $1/r$ gives

$$\frac{7}{9r^9}(-3x^4 - 3y^4 - 8z^4 - 6x^2y^2 + 24y^2z^2 + 24x^2z^2$$

$$- 60\sqrt{2}x^2yz + 20\sqrt{2}y^3z).$$

Since $1/r$ is symmetric with respect to all directions, the above expression is an harmonic which is symmetric with respect to the four lines which pass through the center and through the four corners of the tetrahedron respectively. This symmetry is not in evidence in the above expression, since the tetrahedron itself is not symmetrical with respect to the axes of the coordinate system.

A very simple example in which the symmetry is in evidence is the third derivative with respect to each of the coordinate axes, namely

$$\frac{\partial^3}{\partial x \partial y \partial z}\left(\frac{1}{r}\right) = -15\frac{xyz}{r^7}.$$

211. Derivation of the Tesseral Harmonics by Polar Differentiation.—It was proved in Sec. 178 that the surface zonal harmonic of degree n is

$$P_n(\mu) = (-1)^n \frac{r^{n+1}}{n!} \frac{\partial^n}{\partial z^n}\left(\frac{1}{r}\right),$$

which is the nth derivative of $1/r$ with respect to n poles multiplied by r^{n+1} and a constant factor. In this case the n poles are coincident and are all located on the z-axis; and the harmonic has but one axis of symmetry.

If, instead of lying on the z-axis, the n coincident poles of a surface harmonic of degree n lie on a line whose direction cosines are α, β, γ, it is clear from the symmetry of $1/r$ with respect to all directions that it is a zonal harmonic which has the line whose direction cosines are α, β, γ as an axis, and that its expression is

$$R_n = (-1)^n \frac{r^{n+1}}{n!}\left(\alpha\frac{\partial}{\partial x} + \beta\frac{\partial}{\partial y} + \gamma\frac{\partial}{\partial z}\right)^n\left(\frac{1}{r}\right). \tag{1}$$

This is evidently Laplace's coefficient (Sec. 202). If it is referred to its own axis, it is simply a zonal harmonic.

In the analysis which follows it will be shown that the tesseral harmonics of degree n and order k can be obtained by differentiating $1/r$ with respect to $n - k$ coincident poles which lie on the z-axis and k simple poles which lie in the xy-plane and which are uniformly distributed in longitude. The longitude of these k simple poles will be taken to be

$$p_j = \theta_0 + \frac{2j\pi}{k}, \qquad j = 1, \cdots, k;$$

the latitude, of course, being zero. The symbol for differentiation with respect to these poles, Eq. (210.1), is

$$\frac{\partial}{\partial l_j} = \cos\left(\theta_0 + \frac{2j\pi}{k}\right)\frac{\partial}{\partial x} + \sin\left(\theta_0 + \frac{2j\pi}{k}\right)\frac{\partial}{\partial y}. \tag{2}$$

Differentiation with respect to z does not occur since the direction cosine of each of these poles with respect to the z-axis is zero.

Let the variables be changed by taking

$$\xi = x + iy, \qquad \eta = x - iy, \qquad \text{where} \qquad i = \sqrt{-1},$$

so that

$$\frac{\partial}{\partial x} = \frac{\partial}{\partial \xi} + \frac{\partial}{\partial \eta}, \qquad \frac{\partial}{\partial y} = i\left(\frac{\partial}{\partial \xi} - \frac{\partial}{\partial \eta}\right).$$

The derivative with respect to the pole p_j then becomes

$$\left.\begin{aligned}
\frac{\partial}{\partial l_j} &= \left[\cos\left(\theta_0 + \frac{2j\pi}{k}\right) + i \sin\left(\theta_0 + \frac{2j\pi}{k}\right)\right]\frac{\partial}{\partial \xi} \\
&\qquad + \left[\cos\left(\theta_0 + \frac{2j\pi}{k}\right) - i \sin\left(\theta_0 + \frac{2j\pi}{k}\right)\right]\frac{\partial}{\partial \eta} \\
&= e^{i\left(\theta_0 + \frac{2j\pi}{k}\right)}\frac{\partial}{\partial \xi} + e^{-i\left(\theta_0 + \frac{2j\pi}{k}\right)}\frac{\partial}{\partial \eta}; \\
\frac{\partial}{\partial l_1}\frac{\partial}{\partial l_2} \cdots \frac{\partial}{\partial l_k} &= \prod_{j=1}^{k}\left[e^{i\left(\theta_0 + \frac{2j\pi}{k}\right)}\frac{\partial}{\partial \xi} + e^{-i\left(\theta_0 + \frac{2j\pi}{k}\right)}\frac{\partial}{\partial \eta}\right].
\end{aligned}\right\} \quad (3)$$

This somewhat complicated expression is simplified by taking

$$a = e^{i\theta_0}\frac{\partial}{\partial \xi}, \qquad b = e^{-i\theta_0}\frac{\partial}{\partial \eta},$$

and becomes

$$\left.\begin{aligned}
\frac{\partial}{\partial l_1}\frac{\partial}{\partial l_2} \cdots \frac{\partial}{\partial l_k} &= \prod_{j=1}^{k}\left(ae^{\frac{2j\pi i}{k}} + be^{-\frac{2j\pi i}{k}}\right), \\
&= \prod\left(ae^{\frac{4j\pi i}{k}} + b\right) \cdot \prod e^{-\frac{2j\pi i}{k}} \\
&= e^{-(k+1)\pi i}\prod\left(ae^{\frac{4j\pi i}{k}} + b\right).
\end{aligned}\right\} \quad (4)$$

The first factor in this expression, $e^{-(k+1)\pi i}$, is equal to $+1$ if k is odd, and is equal to -1 if k is even.

If k is odd, say $k = 2s + 1$, the derivative is

$$\frac{\partial}{\partial l_1}\frac{\partial}{\partial l_2} \cdots \frac{\partial}{\partial l_{2s+1}} = \prod_{j=1}^{2s+1}\left(ae^{\frac{4j\pi i}{2s+1}} + b\right). \quad (5)$$

The two groups of complex numbers $e^{\frac{2j\pi i}{2s+1}}$ and $e^{\frac{4j\pi i}{2s+1}}$, $j = 1$, $2, \cdots, 2s + 1$, are identical except for the order in which the numbers occur; for

$$e^{\frac{4m\pi i}{2s+1}} = e^{\frac{2n\pi i}{2s+1}},$$

if $n = 2m$ and $m \leqq s$; or, if $n = 2m - (2s + 1)$ and $s < m \leqq 2s + 1$.   Hence

$$\frac{\partial}{\partial l_1} \frac{\partial}{\partial l_2} \cdots \frac{\partial}{\partial l_{2s+1}} = \prod_{j=1}^{2s+1} \left(ae^{\frac{2j\pi i}{2s+1}} + b \right), \qquad (6)$$

since the right members of Eqs. (5) and (6) differ only in the order in which the factors occur.   It is known from the theory of equations, however, that

$$x^{2s+1} + 1 = \prod_{n=1}^{2s+1} \left(x - e^{\frac{(2n+1)\pi i}{2s+1}} \right) = \prod_{j=1}^{2s+1} \left(x + e^{\frac{2j\pi i}{2s+1}} \right).$$

On replacing x in this equation by b/a and then multiplying through by a^{2s+1}, there results

$$\prod_{j=1}^{2s+1} \left(ae^{\frac{2j\pi i}{2s+1}} + b \right) = a^{2s+1} + b^{2s+1}; \qquad (7)$$

and, therefore, from Eq. (6),

$$\left. \begin{aligned} &\frac{\partial}{\partial l_1} \frac{\partial}{\partial l_2} \cdots \frac{\partial}{\partial l_{2s+1}} = a^{2s+1} + b^{2s+1}, \\ \text{or} \\ &\frac{\partial}{\partial l_1} \frac{\partial}{\partial l_2} \cdots \frac{\partial}{\partial_k} = e^{ik\theta_0}\frac{\partial^k}{\partial \xi^k} + e^{-ik\theta_0}\frac{\partial^k}{\partial \eta^k}, \quad \text{if} \quad k = 2s + 1. \end{aligned} \right\} \quad (8)$$

If k is even, say $k = 2s$, the expression for the operator becomes

$$\frac{\partial}{\partial l_1} \frac{\partial}{\partial l_2} \cdots \frac{\partial}{\partial l_{2s}} = -\prod_{j=1}^{2s} \left(ae^{\frac{2j\pi i}{s}} + b \right);$$

and since

$$l^{\frac{2j\pi i}{s}} = e^{\frac{2(j+s)\pi i}{s}},$$

each of the factors of the right member is repeated.   Therefore,

$$\frac{\partial}{\partial l_1} \frac{\partial}{\partial l_2} \cdots \frac{\partial}{\partial l_{2s}} = -\left[\prod_{j=1}^{s} \left(ae^{\frac{2j\pi i}{s}} + b \right) \right]^2. \qquad (9)$$

If s is odd Eqs. (7) and (8) show that

$$\left. \begin{aligned} \frac{\partial}{\partial l_1} \frac{\partial}{\partial l_2} \cdots \frac{\partial}{\partial l_{2s}} &= -\left(e^{is\theta_0}\frac{\partial^s}{\partial \xi^s} + e^{-is\theta_0}\frac{\partial^s}{\partial \eta^s} \right)^2 \\ &= -e^{2is\theta_0}\frac{\partial^{2s}}{\partial \xi^{2s}} - e^{-2is\theta_0}\frac{\partial^{2s}}{\partial \eta^{2s}} - 2\frac{\partial^{2s}}{\partial \xi^s \partial \eta^s}. \end{aligned} \right\} \quad (10)$$

If s is even, so that k is a multiple of 4, say $k = 2s = 4t$, Eq. (9) becomes

$$\frac{\partial}{\partial l_1}\frac{\partial}{\partial l_2} \cdots \frac{\partial}{\partial l_{4t}} = -\left[\prod_{j=1}^{2t}\left(ae^{\frac{j\pi i}{t}} + b\right)\right]^2$$

Now

$$x^{2t} - 1 = \prod_{j=1}^{2t}\left(x - e^{\frac{j\pi i}{t}}\right) = \prod_{j=1}^{2t}\left(x + e^{\frac{j\pi i}{t}}\right),$$

the two expressions differing only in the order of the factors. Hence

$$\left.\begin{aligned}
\prod_{j=1}^{2t}\left(ae^{\frac{j\pi i}{t}} + b\right) &= b^{2t} - a^{2t}, \\
\frac{\partial}{\partial l_1}\frac{\partial}{\partial l_2} \cdots \frac{\partial}{\partial l_{4t}} &= -(a^{2t} - b^{2t})^2 \\
&= -e^{4it\theta_0}\frac{\partial^{4t}}{\partial\xi^{4t}} - e^{-4it\theta_0}\frac{\partial^{4t}}{\partial\eta^{4t}} + 2\frac{\partial^{4t}}{\partial\xi^{2t}\partial\eta^{2t}}.
\end{aligned}\right\} \quad (11)$$

It is evident from the equations of transformation from x, y to ξ, η that

$$\frac{\partial^2}{\partial x^2} + \frac{\partial^2}{\partial y^2} = 4\frac{\partial^2}{\partial\xi\partial\eta}.$$

Hence, the Laplacian operator becomes

$$\frac{\partial^2}{\partial x^2} + \frac{\partial^2}{\partial y^2} + \frac{\partial^2}{\partial z^2} \equiv 4\frac{\partial^2}{\partial\xi\partial\eta} + \frac{\partial^2}{\partial z^2}.$$

If the function operated upon is harmonic, it is clear that

$$4\frac{\partial^2}{\partial\xi\partial\eta} + \frac{\partial^2}{\partial z^2} = 0,$$

and therefore, when applied to harmonic functions,

$$\frac{\partial^2}{\partial\xi\partial\eta} = -\frac{1}{4}\frac{\partial^2}{\partial z^2}. \quad (12)$$

With the symbolism thus developed, it is now possible to differentiate $1/r$, which is certainly harmonic, with respect to n poles, $n - k$ of which are coincident and lie on the z-axis, while the remaining k are in the xy-plane and are uniformly distributed with respect to the longitude.

The differentiation with respect to the $n - k$ poles on the z-axis is given by Eq. (178.3),

$$\frac{\partial^{n-k}}{\partial z^{n-k}}\left(\frac{1}{r}\right) = (-1)^{n-k}(n-k)!\, r^{-(n-k+1)}P_{n-k}(\mu);$$

and since, Eq. (186.3),

$$P_{n-k} = \sum_{j=0}^{t} (-1)^j \frac{[2n - 2k - 2j - 1]}{[2j](n - k - 2j)!}\mu^{n-k-2j}, \tag{13}$$

where $2t$ is equal to $n - k$ or $n - k - 1$ according as $n - k$ is even or odd, it can also be expressed

$$\frac{\partial^{n-k}}{\partial z^{n-k}}\left(\frac{1}{r}\right) = (-1)^{n-k}(n-k)!\sum_{j=0}^{t} (-1)^j \frac{[2n - 2k - 2j - 1]}{[2j](n - k - 2j)!}\frac{z^{n-k-2j}}{r^{2n-2k-2j+1}}$$

The letters ξ and η enter this expression only implicitly through the letter r, and

$$r^2 = x^2 + y^2 + z^2 = \xi\eta + z^2.$$

If h is any integer, it is readily verified that

$$\frac{\partial}{\partial\xi}\left(\frac{1}{r^h}\right) = -\frac{h}{2}\cdot\frac{\eta}{r^{h+2}}, \qquad \frac{\partial^2}{\partial\xi^2}\left(\frac{1}{r^h}\right) = \frac{h}{2}\cdot\frac{h+2}{2}\cdot\frac{\eta^2}{r^{h+4}};$$

and in general,

$$\frac{\partial^m}{\partial\xi^m}\left(\frac{1}{r^h}\right) = \left(-\frac{1}{2}\right)^m\frac{[h + 2m - 2]}{[h - 2]}\frac{\eta^m}{r^{h+2m}}.$$

Likewise

$$\frac{\partial^m}{\partial\eta^m}\left(\frac{1}{r^h}\right) = \left(-\frac{1}{2}\right)^m\frac{[h + 2m - 2]}{[h - 2]}\frac{\xi^m}{r^{h+2m}}.$$

From these results it follows that

$$\left(e^{ik\theta_0}\frac{\partial^k}{\partial\xi^k} + e^{-ik\theta_0}\frac{\partial^k}{\partial\eta^k}\right)\frac{\partial^{n-k}}{\partial z^{n-k}}\left(\frac{1}{r}\right) = (-1)^n\frac{(n - k)!}{2^k} \tag{14}$$

$$\times \sum_{j=0}^{t} (-1)^j\frac{[2n - 2k - 2j - 1]}{[2j](n - k - 2j)!}\frac{[2n - 2j - 1]}{[2n - 2k - 2j - 1]}\frac{z^{n-k-2j}}{r^{2n-2j+1}}$$

$$\times (\eta^k e^{ik\theta_0} + \xi^k e^{-ik\theta_0}).$$

Now

$$\xi = x + iy = r\sin\varphi\cdot e^{i\theta},$$

and

$$\eta = x - iy = r\sin\varphi\cdot e^{-i\theta};$$

hence

$$\xi^k e^{-ik\theta_0} + \eta^k e^{ik\theta_0} = 2r^k\sin^k\varphi\cos k(\theta - \theta_0).$$

Since this expression is independent of j, Eq. (14) reduces to

$$\left(e^{ik\theta_0}\frac{\partial^k}{\partial\xi^k} + e^{-ik\theta_0}\frac{\partial^k}{\partial\eta^k}\right)\frac{\partial^{n-k}}{\partial z^{n-k}}\left(\frac{1}{r}\right)$$

$$= (-1)^n\frac{(n-k)!}{2^{k-1}r^{n+1}}\sin^k\varphi\cos k(\theta - \theta_0)$$

$$\times \sum_{j=0}^{t}(-1)^j\frac{[2n - 2j - 1]}{[2j](n - k - 2j)!}\mu^{n-k-2j}.$$

If this equation is compared with Eq. (197.8), it is seen that the right member can be written

$$(-1)^n\frac{(n-k)!}{2^{k-1}r^{n+1}}T_{nk}\cos k(\theta - \theta_0),$$

which, aside from the factor $\dfrac{(-1)^n(n-k)!}{(2^{k-1}r^{n+1})}$ is the tesseral harmonic of degree n and order k.

It follows also, if k is even, that (Eq. (12))

$$\frac{\partial^k}{\partial\xi^{\frac{k}{2}}\partial\eta^{\frac{k}{2}}} = \left(-\frac{1}{4}\right)^{\frac{k}{2}}\frac{\partial^k}{\partial z^k},$$

and

$$2\frac{\partial^k}{\partial\xi^{\frac{k}{2}}\partial\eta^{\frac{k}{2}}}\cdot\frac{\partial^{n-k}}{\partial z^{n-k}}\left(\frac{1}{r}\right) = (-1)^{\frac{k}{2}}\frac{1}{2^{k-1}}\frac{\partial^n}{\partial z^n}\left(\frac{1}{r}\right)$$

$$= (-1)^{n+\frac{k}{2}}\frac{n!}{2^{k-1}r^{n+1}}P_n(\mu).$$

If $k/2$ is odd this term occurs in Eq. (10) with a negative sign, while, if $k/2$ is even the term occurs in Eq. (11) with a positive sign. Hence, in either equation the sign of the term is $(-1)^n$.

On substituting these results in Eqs. (8), (10), and (11), it is found that

$$\frac{\partial}{\partial l_1}\frac{\partial}{\partial l_2}\cdots\frac{\partial}{\partial l_k}\cdot\frac{\partial^{n-k}}{\partial z^{n-k}}\left(\frac{1}{r}\right) = (-1)^n\frac{(n-k)!}{2^{k-1}r^{n+1}}T_{nk}\cos k(\theta - \theta_0),$$

if k is odd, and

$$\frac{\partial}{\partial l_1}\frac{\partial}{\partial l_2}\cdots\frac{\partial}{\partial l_k}\cdot\frac{\partial^{n-k}}{\partial z^{n-k}}\left(\frac{1}{r}\right) = (-1)^{n+1}\frac{(n-k)!}{2^{k-1}r^{n+1}}T_{nk}\cos k(\theta - \theta_0)$$

$$+ (-1)^n\frac{n!}{2^{k-1}r^{n+1}}P_n(\mu),$$

if k is even.

It was from the point of view of polar differentiation that tesseral harmonics were discussed by James Clerk Maxwell in his Treatise on Electricity and Magnetism.[1]

Problems

1. Show that

$$\sin^4 \varphi = \frac{8}{15}P_0 - \frac{16}{21}P_2 + \frac{8}{35}P_4.$$

2. Show that

$$\int_\mu^1 P_i P_j d\mu = \frac{(1 - \mu^2)}{(i - j)(i + j + 1)}(P_j P_i' - P_i P_j').$$

3. Show that

$$(\mu^2 - 1)^i \frac{d^{n+i}(\mu^2 - 1)^n}{d\mu^{n+i}} = \frac{(n + i)!}{(n - i)!}\frac{d^{n-i}(\mu^2 - 1)^n}{d\mu^{n-i}},$$

or symmetrically

$$\frac{(\mu^2 - 1)^{\frac{i}{2}}}{(n + i)!}\frac{d^{n+i}(\mu^2 - 1)^n}{d\mu^{n+i}} = \frac{(\mu^2 - 1)^{-\frac{i}{2}}}{(n - i)!}\frac{d^{n-i}(\mu^2 - 1)^n}{d\mu^{n-i}}.$$

4. Show that the coefficients of $4^n P_n(\mu)$ are all integers.

5. If the expansion of $f(\mu)$ in terms of the zonal harmonics is

$$f(\mu) = \sum_{j=0}^{\infty} a_j P_j,$$

show that the expansion for the function $\mu f(\mu)$ is

$$\mu f(\mu) = \sum_{j=0}^{\infty} \left(\frac{j a_{j-1}}{2j - 1} + \frac{(j + 1)a_{j+1}}{2j + 3}\right)P_j,$$

in which a_{-1} is equal to zero.

6. Show that the potential of a uniform wire in the form of a circle of radius a is

$$V = \frac{M}{a} \sum_{n=0}^{\infty} (-1)^n \frac{[2n - 1]}{[2n]}\left(\frac{r}{a}\right)^{2n} P_{2n},$$

or

$$V = \frac{M}{r} \sum_{n=0}^{\infty} (-1)^n \frac{[2n - 1]}{[2n]}\left(\frac{a}{r}\right)^{2n} P_{2n},$$

according as $r < a$ or $r > a$.

[1] Vol. I, Chap. XII.

7. Show that

$$\sqrt{1 - 2\mu h + h^2} = 1 - P_1 h - \sum_{n=1}^{\infty} \frac{P_{n+1} - P_{n-1}}{2n + 1} h^{n+1}.$$

8. A spherical cap is cut from the surface of a sphere of radius a by a cone with its apex at the center of the sphere and generating angle α, and covered uniformly with matter. Show that the potential of the cap outside of the sphere, and at a distance r from the center, is

$$V = 2\pi\sigma a \left\{ (1 - \lambda)\frac{a}{r} + \sum_{n=1}^{\infty} \frac{P_{n-1}(\lambda) - P_{n+1}(\lambda)}{2n + 1} \left(\frac{a}{r}\right)^{n+1} P_n(\mu) \right\},$$

where $\lambda = \cos \alpha$ and $\mu = \cos \varphi$; and inside of the sphere

$$V = 2\pi\sigma a \left\{ (1 - \lambda) + \sum_{n=1}^{\infty} \frac{P_{n-1}(\lambda) - P_{n+1}(\lambda)}{2n + 1} \left(\frac{r}{a}\right)^{n} P_n(\mu) \right\}.$$

9. If matter is distributed on a circular disk of radius a in such a way that the potential on the disk is constant and equal to unity, show that elsewhere

$$V = 1 + \frac{2}{\pi} \sum_{n=1}^{\infty} (-1)^n \frac{|P_{2n-1}|}{2n - 1} \left(\frac{r}{a}\right)^{2n-1} \qquad \text{if } r < a,$$

and

$$V = \frac{2}{\pi} \sum_{n=0}^{\infty} (-1)^n \frac{P_{2n}}{2n + 1} \left(\frac{a}{r}\right)^{2n+1} \qquad \text{if } r > a.$$

10. The potential of an equipotential distribution of matter on the surface of an oblate spheroid is

$$V = \frac{M}{ae} \left[\frac{\pi}{2} \sum_{n=0}^{\infty} -\frac{(-1)^n}{2n + 1} \left(\frac{r}{ae}\right)^{2n+1} |P_{2n-1}| \right] \qquad \text{if } r > ae,$$

$$V = \frac{M}{ae} \sum_{n=0}^{\infty} \frac{(-1)^n}{2n + 1} \left(\frac{ae}{r}\right)^{2n+1} P_{2n} \text{ if } r > ae.$$

11. The potential of a homogeneous hemisphere of radius a outside the sphere of radius a is

$$V = \frac{M}{a} \left(\frac{a}{r} + 3 \sum_{n=0}^{\infty} (-1)^n \frac{[2n - 1]}{[2n + 4]} \left(\frac{a}{r}\right)^{2n+2} P_{2n+1} \right).$$

Inside the sphere but outside the hemisphere, i.e., $r < a$, $\varphi > \pi/2$,

$$V = \frac{M}{a} \left(\frac{3}{2} - \frac{3}{2}\left(\frac{r}{a}\right)P_1 + \left(\frac{r}{a}\right)^2 P_2 - 3 \sum_{n=1}^{\infty} \frac{[2n - 3]}{[2n + 2]} \left(\frac{r}{a}\right)^{2n+1} P_{2n+1} \right).$$

12. Show that

$$\int_0^1 P_m d\mu = (-1)^n \frac{[2n-1]}{[2n+2]} \quad \text{if} \quad m = 2n+1,$$

and vanishes if $m = 2n$.

13. Show that

$$\int_0^1 P_m{}^2 d\mu = \frac{1}{2m+1}.$$

14. Show that

$$\int_{-1}^{+1} (P'_m)^2 d\mu = m(m+1).$$

15. Show that

$$\sum_{n=0}^{\infty} \frac{P_n}{n+1} = \log \frac{1 + \sin \frac{1}{2}\varphi}{\sin \frac{1}{2}\varphi}.$$

16. Show that, if $i + j + k = 2n$,

$$\int_{-1}^{+1} P_i P_j P_k d\mu = \frac{[2n][2n-2i-1][2n-2j-1][2n-2k-1]}{[2n+1][2n-2i][2n-2j][2n-2k]}.$$

17. If a sphere of radius r has its center at the origin, and if its density is $\sigma = a\xi + b\eta + c\zeta$, show that the potential at any exterior point x, y, z at a distance R from the center is

$$V = \frac{4\pi r^5}{15R^3}(ax + by + cz).$$

18. If k^2 is any real positive quantity

$$\int_{-1}^{+1} \frac{P_{2n+1} d\mu}{(1 + k^2\mu^2)^{n+2}} = 0,$$

and

$$\int_{-1}^{+1} \frac{P_{2n} d\mu}{(\sqrt{1 + k^2\mu^2})^{2n+3}} = (-1)^n \frac{2}{2n+1} \frac{k^{2n}}{(\sqrt{1 + k^2})^{2n+1}}.$$

19. For any given harmonic of degree n the problem of finding the n lines which pass through the poles of the harmonic has one and only one solution, but the directions which are to be regarded as positive along these lines can be reversed in pairs.

20. If $\mu = \cos \varphi$ and $\nu = \sin \varphi$, show that

$$P_n = \sum_{j=0}^{l} (-1)^j \frac{n!}{[2j]^2(n-2j)!} \mu^{n-2j}\nu^{2j},$$

where $2l = n$ or $n - 1$ according as n is even or odd.

CHAPTER VIII

ELLIPSOIDAL HARMONICS

212. Introduction.—Among the geometrical bodies the ellipsoid is second in importance only to the sphere, and many of the problems which relate to the sphere occur also for the ellipsoid, such as the attractions of surface distributions of matter, the flow of heat through the solid body, the motions of fluids around bodies of a given shape, etc. It is natural therefore to seek for harmonic functions which are related to the ellipsoid in the same manner that the spherical harmonics are related to the sphere.

The first theory which was constructed for these functions was by George Green in 1833,[1] using only rectangular and polar coordinates. For this reason, Cayley proposed the name *Greenians* for these functions.

A second theory in which elliptic coordinates were introduced was published by Lamé in the Journal de Liouville for 1839,[2] and his functions are commonly known as the *Functions of Lamé*. Both the functions of Green and the functions of Lamé reduce to spherical harmonics of Laplace when the ellipsoid becomes a sphere. The development of the theory of Lamé is much improved by the introduction of the elliptic function of Weierstrass, as was done by Poincaré,[3] and it is the theory of Lamé, according to Poincaré, that will be set forth here.

213. Definition of the Elliptic Coordinates.—The elliptic coordinates of a point x, y, z are the values, q_1, q_2, q_3, of q which satisfy the equation

$$\frac{x^2}{q - a^2} + \frac{y^2}{q - b^2} + \frac{z^2}{q - c^2} - 1 = 0. \tag{1}$$

[1] GREEN, GEORGE, "On the Determination of the Exterior and Interior Attractions of Ellipsoids of Variable Densities, *Transactions of the Cambridge Philosophical Society*, 1835. See also his collected works, p. 187.

[2] LAMÉ, "Leçons sur les Functions Inverse des Transcendantes et les Functions Isothermes." Paris, (1857).

[3] POINCARÉ, H., "Figures D'Equilibre d'une Masse Fluide," (1903).

If this equation is cleared of fractions, it becomes a cubic equation in q with the coefficient of the highest power of q equal to -1. Therefore the equation

$$
\begin{aligned}
f(q) &= \frac{x^2}{q - a^2} + \frac{y^2}{q - b^2} + \frac{z^2}{q - c^2} - 1 \\
&\equiv -\frac{(q - q_1)(q - q_2)(q - q_3)}{(q - a^2)(q - b^2)(q - c^2)}
\end{aligned}
\tag{2}
$$

is merely an identity in q. It is satisfied whatever value q may have.

The quantities q_1, q_2, q_3; a^2, b^2, c^2, arranged in the order of their magnitude, are as follows

$$
0 < c^2 < q_3 < b^2 < q_2 < a^2 < q_1.
$$

The surface $q_1 = $ const. is an ellipsoid;
The surface $q_2 = $ const. is an hyperboloid of one sheet;
The surface $q_3 = $ const. is an hyperboloid of two sheets.
If α, β, γ are the axes of the ellipsoid, then

$$
q_1 = a^2 + \alpha^2 = b^2 + \beta^2 = c^2 + \gamma^2
$$

from which it is evident that

$$
\alpha < \beta < \gamma.
$$

The x-axis coincides with shortest axis of the ellipsoid and the z-axis with the longest.

If Eq. (2) is multiplied successively by $(q - a^2)$, $(q - b^2)$, $(q - c^2)$ and q is then set equal to a^2, b^2, and c^2, there results

$$
\left.
\begin{aligned}
x^2 &= \frac{(q_1 - a^2)(q_2 - a^2)(q_3 - a^2)}{(a^2 - b^2)(a^2 - c^2)}, \\
y^2 &= \frac{(q_1 - b^2)(q_2 - b^2)(q_3 - b^2)}{(b^2 - c^2)(b^2 - a^2)}, \\
z^2 &= \frac{(q_1 - c^2)(q_2 - c^2)(q_3 - c^2)}{(c^2 - a^2)(c^2 - b^2)}.
\end{aligned}
\right\}
\tag{3}
$$

If these three equations are added, it is found that

$$
\left.
\begin{aligned}
x^2 + y^2 + z^2 &= (q_1 + q_2 + q_3) - (a^2 + b^2 + c^2), \\
r^2 &= (q_1 - a^2) + (q_2 - b^2) + (q_3 - c^2).
\end{aligned}
\right\}
\tag{4}
$$

or

Hence the equation of a sphere whose center is at the origin, in elliptic coordinates, is

$$
q_1 + q_2 + q_3 = \text{const.} = r^2 + (a^2 + b^2 + c^2).
\tag{5}
$$

If the first equation of Eq. (3) is multiplied by $(b^2 + c^2)$, the second by $(c^2 + a^2)$ and the third by $(a^2 + b^2)$, and the results are then added, it is found that

$$(b^2 + c^2)x^2 + (c^2 + a^2)y^2 + (a^2 + b^2)z^2 = (q_1q_2 + q_2q_3 + q_3q_1)$$
$$- (a^2b^2 + b^2c^2 + c^2a^2).$$

Hence the equation

$$q_1q_2 + q_2q_3 + q_3q_1 = \text{const.}, \tag{6}$$

represents a certain family of similar ellipsoids.

Finally, if the first equation is divided by a^2, the second by b^2, and the third by c^2, and the results are added, it is found that

$$\frac{x^2}{a^2} + \frac{y^2}{b^2} + \frac{z^2}{c^2} = 1 + \frac{q_1q_2q_3}{a^2b^2c^2}.$$

Hence the equation

$$q_1q_2q_3 = \text{const.} \tag{7}$$

also represents a family of similar ellipsoids. Of course, the equation

$$q_1 = \text{const.}$$

represents a family of confocal ellipsoids.

214. Differential Relations.—If the point x, y, z is given a displacement ds_1, in which q_1 varies while q_2 and q_3 remain fixed, then

$$ds_1{}^2 = \left[\left(\frac{\partial x}{\partial q_1} \right)^2 + \left(\frac{\partial y}{\partial q_1} \right)^2 + \left(\frac{\partial z}{\partial q_1} \right)^2 \right] dq_1{}^2$$

$$= R_1{}^2 dq_1{}^2,$$

where

$$R_1{}^2 = \left(\frac{\partial x}{\partial q_1} \right)^2 + \left(\frac{\partial y}{\partial q_1} \right)^2 + \left(\frac{\partial z}{\partial q_1} \right)^2$$

$$= \frac{1}{4} \left[\frac{x^2}{(q_1 - a^2)^2} + \frac{y^2}{(q_1 - b^2)^2} + \frac{z^2}{(q_1 - c^2)^2} \right] \quad \text{by Eq. (213.3)}$$

$$= -\frac{1}{4} \frac{\partial f}{\partial q} \Big|_{q = q_1} \quad \text{by Eq. (213.2).}$$

If the second expression for $f(q)$ is used, it is seen that

$$-\frac{\partial f}{\partial q} = \frac{(q - q_2)(q - q_3)}{(q - a^2)(q - b^2)(q - c^2)} + (q - q_1) \Big[\quad \Big].$$

It is not necessary to compute the terms which carry $(q - q_1)$ as a factor since they all vanish when q is set equal to q_1.

The notation is much simplified by taking

$$
\left.
\begin{aligned}
A^2 &= \frac{1}{4}(q_3 - q_2)(q_2 - q_1)(q_1 - q_3) > 0, \\
A_1{}^2 &= (q_1 - a^2)(q_1 - b^2)(q_1 - c^2) > 0, \\
A_2{}^2 &= (q_2 - a^2)(q_2 - b^2)(q_2 - c^2) < 0, \\
A_3{}^2 &= (q_3 - a^2)(q_3 - b^2)(q_3 - c^2) > 0.
\end{aligned}
\right\}
\tag{1}
$$

The quantities A, A_1, and A_3 are real, but A_2 is a pure imaginary. It is then found that

$$
\left.
\begin{aligned}
R_1{}^2 &= \frac{1}{4}\frac{(q_1 - q_2)(q_1 - q_3)}{(q_1 - a^2)(q_1 - b^2)(q_1 - c^2)} = \frac{A^2}{A_1{}^2(q_2 - q_3)}; \\
\text{and similarly,} \\
R_2{}^2 &= \frac{1}{4}\frac{(q_2 - q_1)(q_2 - q_3)}{(q_2 - a^2)(q_2 - b^2)(q_2 - c^2)} = \frac{A^2}{A_2{}^2(q_3 - q_1)}, \\
R_3{}^2 &= \frac{1}{4}\frac{(q_3 - q_1)(q_3 - q_2)}{(q_3 - a^2)(q_3 - b^2)(q_3 - c^2)} = \frac{A^2}{A_3{}^2(q_1 - q_2)}.
\end{aligned}
\right\}
\tag{2}
$$

Since the displacements

$$
ds_1 = R_1 dq_1, \qquad ds_2 = R_2 dq_2, \qquad ds_3 = R_3 dq_3, \tag{3}
$$

are mutually orthogonal, ds_1 being normal to the ellipsoid, the general displacement, or the arc-element, is

$$
ds^2 = R_1{}^2 dq_1{}^2 + R_2{}^2 dq_2{}^2 + R_3{}^2 dq_3{}^2.
$$

The surface element on the ellipsoid, $q_1 = \text{const.}$, is

$$
d\omega = R_2 R_3 dq_2 dq_3; \tag{4}
$$

and the element of volume is

$$
d\tau = R_1 R_2 R_3 dq_1 dq_2 dq_3. \tag{5}
$$

It might be observed, if p_1, p_2, p_3 are the lengths of the perpendiculars from the origin to tangent planes of the ellipsoid, hyperboloid of one sheet and hyperboloid of two sheets respectively, that

$$
p_1 = \frac{1}{2R_1}, \qquad p_2 = \frac{1}{2R_2}, \qquad p_3 = \frac{1}{2R_3}. \tag{6}
$$

215. The Equation of Laplace.—The equation of Laplace in any orthogonal system of coordinates is, Eq. (57.8),

$$
\frac{\partial}{\partial q_1}\left(\frac{R_2 R_3}{R_1}\frac{\partial V}{\partial q_1}\right) + \frac{\partial}{\partial q_2}\left(\frac{R_3 R_1}{R_2}\frac{\partial V}{\partial q_2}\right) + \frac{\partial}{\partial q_3}\left(\frac{R_1 R_2}{R_3}\frac{\partial V}{\partial q_3}\right) = 0.
$$

Using the values of R_1, R_2, and R_3 from Eq. (214.2) this expression becomes

$$\frac{\partial}{\partial q_1}\left(\frac{A_1(q_2 - q_3)}{A_2 A_3}\frac{\partial V}{\partial q_1}\right) + \frac{\partial}{\partial q_2}\left(\frac{A_2(q_3 - q_1)}{A_3 A_1}\frac{\partial V}{\partial q_2}\right)$$
$$+ \frac{\partial}{\partial q_3}\left(\frac{A_3(q_1 - q_2)}{A_1 A_2}\frac{\partial V}{\partial q_3}\right) = 0.$$

Since the product $A_i A_j$ is independent of q_k, this equation can be multiplied through by $A_1 A_2 A_3$, and written

$$A_1\frac{\partial}{\partial q_1}\left(A_1\frac{\partial V}{\partial q_1}\right) \cdot (q_2 - q_3) + A_2\frac{\partial}{\partial q_2}\left(A_2\frac{\partial V}{\partial q_2}\right) \cdot (q_3 - q_1)$$
$$+ A_3\frac{\partial}{\partial q_3}\left(A_3\frac{\partial V}{\partial q_3}\right) \cdot (q_1 - q_2) = 0;$$

or, again,

$$(q_2 - q_3)\left(A_1\frac{\partial}{\partial q_1}\right)^2 V + (q_3 - q_1)\left(A_2\frac{\partial}{\partial q_2}\right)^2 V +$$
$$(q_1 - q_2)\left(A_3\frac{\partial}{\partial q_3}\right)^2 V = 0. \quad (1)$$

If three new functions u_1, u_2, u_3 are defined by the differential relations

$$du_1 = -\frac{dq_1}{2A_1}, \qquad du_2 = -\frac{dq_2}{2A_2}, \qquad du_3 = -\frac{dq_3}{2A_3}, \qquad (2)$$

in which du_2 is a pure imaginary, Eq. (1) takes the simplified form

$$(q_2 - q_3)\frac{\partial^2 V}{\partial u_1{}^2} + (q_3 - q_1)\frac{\partial^2 V}{\partial u_2{}^2} + (q_1 - q_2)\frac{\partial^2 V}{\partial u_3{}^2} = 0. \qquad (3)$$

There exist also the following identities:

$$q_1(q_2 - q_3) + q_2(q_3 - q_1) + q_3(q_1 - q_2) \equiv 0,$$
$$(q_2 - q_3) + (q_3 - q_1) + (q_1 - q_2) \equiv 0.$$

If the first of these identities is multiplied by $-NV$ and the second by $-\overline{M}V$, where $\overline{M}$ and N are any two constants, and are then added to Eq. (3), there results

$$\sum\left[\frac{\partial^2 V}{\partial u_i{}^2} - (Nq_i + \overline{M})V\right](q_j - q_k) = 0, \qquad (4)$$

where the letters i, j, k are 1, 2, 3 and are to be permuted circularly.

Expressed wholly in terms of the letters q_i, this equation can also be written, in view of Eq. (1),

$$\sum \left[A_i{}^2 \frac{\partial^2 V}{\partial q_i{}^2} + \frac{1}{2} \frac{\partial A_i{}^2}{\partial q_i} \frac{\partial V}{\partial q_i} - (Nq_i + \overline{M})V \right](q_i - q_k) = 0. \quad (5)$$

216. The Elliptic Functions of Weierstrass.—The letters u_1, u_2, u_3 as defined in Eq. (215.2) are evidently particular values of the general function u which is defined in terms of q by the equation

$$du = \frac{-dq}{\sqrt{4(q - a^2)(q - b^2)(q - c^2)}}. \quad (1)$$

This would be the normal form of the differential equation of the elliptic $\wp$-function of Weierstrass if the sum of the roots $a^2 + b^2 + c^2$ were zero. It is a simple matter, however, to change the variables and satisfy this condition. Let s be a new variable and h, e_1, e_2, e_3 new constants, which are defined as follows:

$$q = s + h, \qquad b^2 = e_2 + h,$$
$$a^2 = e_1 + h, \qquad c^2 = e_3 + h.$$

With these letters Eq. (1) becomes

$$du = \frac{-ds}{\sqrt{4(s - e_1)(s - e_2)(s - e_3)}}; \quad (2)$$

and if

$$h = \frac{1}{3}(a^2 + b^2 + c^2),$$

it is seen that

$$e_1 + e_2 + e_3 = 0;$$

also

$$e_1 > e_2 > e_3.$$

The solution of Eq. (2) is

$$s = \wp u,$$

provided the constant of integration is chosen so that s is infinite when u is zero. Therefore

$$\left. \begin{array}{ll} q_1 = \wp u_1 + h, & q_1 - a^2 = \wp u_1 - e_1, \\ q_2 = \wp u_2 + h, & q_2 - b^2 = \wp u_2 - e_2, \\ q_3 = \wp u_3 + h, & q_3 - c^2 = \wp u_3 - e_3, \end{array} \right\} \quad (3)$$

If the derivatives of $\wp$ with respect to u are denoted by accents, Eq. (2) shows that[1]

$$\begin{aligned}\wp'^2 &= 4(\wp - e_1)(\wp - e_2)(\wp - e_3) \\ &= 4\wp^3 - g_2\wp - g_3,\end{aligned} \right\} \qquad (4)$$

where

$$g_2 = -4(e_2e_3 + e_3e_1 + e_1e_2), \qquad g_3 = +4e_1e_2e_3.$$

If Eq. (4) is differentiated with respect to u and the factor $2\wp'$ is removed, and if for brevity of notation

$$\wp_1 = \wp - e_1, \qquad \wp_2 = \wp - e_2, \qquad \wp_3 = \wp - e_3, \\ \text{it is found that} \\ \wp'^2 = 4\wp_1\wp_2\wp_3, \right\} \qquad (5)$$

and

$$\begin{aligned}\wp'' &= 2[\wp_2\wp_3 + \wp_3\wp_1 + \wp_1\wp_2] \\ &= 6\wp^2 - \frac{1}{2}g_2.\end{aligned} \right\} \qquad (6)$$

The power series expansion of $\wp u$ in the neighborhood of the value $u = 0$ is

$$\wp u = \frac{1}{u^2} + * + \frac{g_2}{20}u^2 + \frac{g_3}{28}u^4 + \cdots, \qquad (7)$$

from which it is seen that $\wp u$ has a pole of the second order at the origin. It is a doubly periodic function, the real period being $2\omega_1$ and the purely imaginary period $2\omega_3$. For convenience of notation it is customary to take

$$\omega_2 = \omega_1 + \omega_3.$$

As u increases from zero along the real axis, $\wp u$ decreases from $+\infty$ and at the half period, $u = \omega_1$, its value is $\wp\omega_1 = e_1$. If u increases to the full period $2\omega_1$, $\wp u$, of course, returns to $+\infty$. But if, instead of continuing to move along the axis of reals, u turns at the point ω_1 and moves at a right angle to it, thereby becoming complex, the function $\wp u$ continues to be real, decreases from e_1 and arrives at the value e_2 when u arrives at the point ω_2 (Fig. 108). If u turns again at ω_2 and proceeds toward ω_3 along the third side of the rectangle whose sides are the half-periods, $\wp u$ continues to be real and decreases from e_2 to e_3. Along the

---

[1] For formulas relating to the Weierstrass elliptic functions, see SCHWARZ, H. A., "Formeln und Lehrsätze zum Gebrauche der elliptischen Functionen" (1893).

fourth side of the rectangle $\wp u$ is still real and decreases from e_3 to $-\infty$ as u moves from ω_3 to the origin. Hence, $\wp u$ is real all along the rectangle whose sides are the half periods, and its derivative is always negative if u moves as is indicated in the diagram. Furthermore

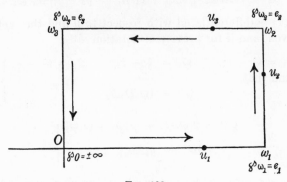

FIG. 108.

$$\wp\omega_1 = e_1, \qquad \wp\omega_2 = e_2, \qquad \wp\omega_3 = e_3.$$

Since

$$q_1 - a^2 = \wp u_1 - e_1 > 0,$$

it follows that

$$0 < u_1 < e_1;$$

that is, u_1 is real and lies on the first side of the rectangle. Also

$$q_2 - b_2 = \wp u_2 - e_2 > 0.$$

Therefore, u_2 is complex and lies on the second side of the rectangle. Lastly,

$$q_3 - c^2 = \wp u_3 - e_3 > 0,$$

and u_3, also complex, lies on the third side of the rectangle. The functions

$$\sqrt{\wp_1} = \sqrt{\wp u - e_1}, \qquad \sqrt{\wp_2} = \sqrt{\wp u - e_2},$$

$$\sqrt{\wp_3} = \sqrt{\wp u - e_3} \quad (8)$$

are the sigma quotients of Weierstrass. They also are single valued elliptic functions of u with a single pole at the origin, as is evident from Eq. (7). They are doubly periodic, but their periods are not necessarily $2\omega_1$ and $2\omega_3$. One of the periods is doubled in accordance with the following rule.[1]

but
$$
\left.
\begin{aligned}
\sqrt{\wp_i(u + 2\omega_i)} &= +\sqrt{\wp_i u} & i &= 1, 2, 3, \\
\sqrt{\wp_i(u + 2\omega_j)} &= -\sqrt{\wp_i u} & j &\neq i, \\
\sqrt{\wp_i(u + 4\omega_j)} &= +\sqrt{\wp_i u}.
\end{aligned}
\right\} \tag{9}
$$

Since
$$
q_i = \wp u_i + h,
$$

Eq. (215.4) becomes

$$
\sum \left[\frac{d^2 V}{du_i{}^2} - (N\wp u_i + M)V \right](\wp u_j - \wp u_k) = 0, \tag{10}
$$

where
$$
M = Nh + \overline{M}.
$$

The expressions for the rectangular coordinates (Eq. (213.3)) become

$$
\left.
\begin{aligned}
x^2 &= \frac{(\wp u_1 - e_1)(\wp u_2 - e_1)(\wp u_3 - e_1)}{(e_1 - e_2)(e_1 - e_3)}, \\
y^2 &= \frac{(\wp u_1 - e_2)(\wp u_2 - e_2)(\wp u_3 - e_2)}{(e_2 - e_1)(e_2 - e_3)}, \\
z_2 &= \frac{(\wp u_1 - e_3)(\wp u_2 - e_3)(\wp u_3 - e_3)}{(e_3 - e_1)(e_3 - e_2)};
\end{aligned}
\right\} \tag{11}
$$

and Eq. (213.4) gives

$$
x^2 + y^2 + z^2 = r^2 = \wp u_1 + \wp u_2 + \wp u_3. \tag{12}
$$

217. Spherical Harmonics in Elliptic Coordinates.—From the point of view of dimensions x, y, z; a, b, and c are lengths, and each has the dimension L^1; consequently q, q_1, q_2, q_3 have the dimension L^2. Any homogeneous polynomial of degree n in x^2, y^2, and z^2 can be expressed rationally and integrally in terms of the elliptic coordinates by means of Eq. (213.3). That is, a homogeneous polynomial of degree n in x^2, y^2, and z^2 becomes a non-homogeneous polynomial of degree n in each of the three letters q_1, q_2, and q_3; and is symmetric in these three letters, since x^2, y^2, and z^2 separately are symmetric.

Although not every homogeneous polynomial in x, y, and z is an integral function of x^2, y^2, and z^2, it is true that every

[1] Schwarz, §23.

polynomial can be expressed as a sum of terms each of which belongs to one of the following classes:

$$P(x^2, y^2, z^2), \tag{I}$$

$$\left.\begin{array}{ll} (a) & xP(x^2, y^2, z^2), \\ (b) & yP(x^2, y^2, z^2), \\ (c) & zP(x^2, y^2, z^2), \end{array}\right\} \tag{II}$$

$$\left.\begin{array}{ll} (a) & xyP(x^2, y^2, z^2), \\ (b) & yzP(x^2, y^2, z^2), \\ (c) & zxP(x^2, y^2, z^2), \end{array}\right\} \tag{III}$$

$$xyzP(x^2, y^2, z^2). \tag{IV}$$

In this table $P(x^2, y^2, z^2)$ means a homogeneous polynomial in x^2, y^2, and z^2.

Polynomials of even degree in x, y, and z can be resolved into polynomials of classes I and III; and polynomials of odd degree can be resolved into polynomials of classes II and IV. Only polynomials of the first class can be expressed rationally in terms of the elliptic coordinates. The other three classes become polynomials which are symmetric in q_1, q_2, and q_3 multiplied by one of the following radicals (Eq. (213.3)) which also are symmetric in q_1, q_2, and q_3:

$$\Pi\sqrt{q_i - a^2}, \qquad \Pi\sqrt{q_i - b^2)}, \qquad \Pi\sqrt{q_i - c^2},$$

$$\Pi\sqrt{(q_i - a^2)(q_i - b^2)}, \qquad \Pi\sqrt{(q_i - b^2)(q_i - c^2)},$$

$$\Pi\sqrt{(q_i - c^2)(q_i - a^2)}, \qquad \Pi\sqrt{(q_i - a^2)(q_i - b^2)(q_i - c^2)}.$$

A solid spherical harmonic which is a homogeneous polynomial in the rectangular coordinates can, therefore, be expressed in this manner in terms of the elliptic coordinates; but it does not cease to be a spherical harmonic when so expressed. The transformation gives merely another, though interesting, expression of a familiar harmonic. If, after the transformation, q_1 is kept fixed while q_2 and q_3 are varied, the new expression gives the value of the spherical harmonic on the surface of a certain ellipsoid, but the harmonic itself is in no way related to the ellipsoid.

218. The Inverse Problem.—Suppose $f(q_1)$ is a polynomial of degree n in q_1, and $f(q_2)$ is the same polynomial in the letter q_2. Expressed in terms of its factors

$$f(q_1) = (q_1 - \alpha_1)(q_1 - \alpha_2) \cdots (q_1 - \alpha_n),$$

$$f(q_2) = (q_2 - \alpha_1)(q_2 - \alpha_2) \cdots (q_2 - \alpha_n),$$
$$f(q_3) = (q_3 - \alpha_1)(q_3 - \alpha_2) \cdots (q_3 - \alpha_n).$$

The product of these three expressions is

$$f(q_1) \cdot f(q_2) \cdot f(q_3) = \prod_{i=1}^{n}[(q_1 - \alpha_i)(q_2 - \alpha_i)(q_3 - \alpha_i)].$$

If q_1, q_2, and q_3 are the elliptic coordinates of a point, then, by Eq. (213.2),

$$(q_1 - \alpha_i)(q_2 - \alpha_i)(q_3 - \alpha_i) \equiv$$
$$C_i\left(\frac{x^2}{\alpha_i - a^2} + \frac{y^2}{\alpha_i - b^2} + \frac{z^2}{\alpha_i - c^2} - 1\right),$$

where C_i is the constant

$$C_i = (\alpha_i - a^2)(\alpha_i - b^2)(\alpha_i - c^2).$$

Therefore, the product

$$f(q_1) \cdot f(q_2) \cdot f(q_3) = D\prod_{i=1}^{n}\left(\frac{x^2}{\alpha_i - a^2} + \frac{y^2}{\alpha_i - b^2} + \frac{z^2}{\alpha_i - c^2} - 1\right)$$
$$= Q_n(x^2, y^2, z^2), \tag{I}$$

where

$$D = \prod_{i=1}^{n}[(\alpha_i - a^2)(\alpha_i - b^2)(\alpha_i - c^2)],$$

is a polynomial which, expressed in the q's, is symmetric in q_1, q_2, and q_3 and of degree n in each; and expressed in rectangular coordinates is a polynomial of degree n in x^2, y^2, and z^2, which, in general, is non-homogeneous.

If the polynomial $f(q_1)$ is multiplied by one of the radicals, and

$$\varphi_a(q_1) = \sqrt{q_1 - a^2} \cdot f(q_1), \qquad \varphi_b(q_1) = \sqrt{q_1 - b^2}f(q_1),$$
$$\varphi_c(q_1) = \sqrt{q_1 - c^2}f(q_1),$$

then, by Eq. (213.3),

$$\left.\begin{array}{l}\varphi_a(q_1) \cdot \varphi_a(q_2) \cdot \varphi_a(q_3) = A_a x Q_n(x^2, y^2, z^2), \\ \varphi_b(q_1) \cdot \varphi_b(q_2) \cdot \varphi_b(q_3) = A_b y Q_n(x^2, y^2, z^2), \\ \varphi_c(q_1) \cdot \varphi_c(q_2) \cdot \varphi_c(q_3) = A_c z Q_n(x^2, y^2, z^2), \end{array}\right\} \tag{II}$$

where A_a, A_b, A_c are certain constants, are polynomials of degree $2n + 1$ in x, y, and z.

Similarly, if

$$\psi_{ab}(q_i) = \sqrt{(q_i - a^2)(q_i - b^2)}f(q_i) \qquad i = 1, 2, 3,$$

the symmetrical products

$$\left.\begin{array}{l} \psi_{ab}(q_1) \cdot \psi_{ab}(q_2) \cdot \psi_{ab}(q_3) = B_{ab}xyQ_n(x^2, y^2, z^2), \\ \psi_{bc}(q_1) \cdot \psi_{bc}(q_2) \cdot \psi_{bc}(q_3) = B_{bc}yzQ_n(x^2, y^2, z^2), \\ \psi_{ca}(q_1) \cdot \psi_{ca}(q_2) \cdot \psi_{ca}(q_3) = B_{ca}zxQ_n(x^2, y^2, z^2), \end{array}\right\} \qquad \text{(III)}$$

are polynomials in x, y, and z of degree $2n + 2$.

Finally, if

$$\omega(q_i) = \sqrt{(q_i - a^2)(q_i - b^2)(q_i - c^2)}f(q_i),$$

the symmetrical product,

$$\omega(q_1) \cdot \omega(q_2) \cdot \omega(q_3) = CxyzQ_n(x^2, y^2, z^2), \qquad \text{(IV)}$$

is a polynomial in x, y, and z of degree $2n + 3$.

The polynomials in x, y, and z of classes I and III are of even degree, while those of classes II and IV are of odd degree. In general, they are not homogeneous.

219. The Functions of Lamé.—Suppose V_i is a function of q_i alone and that it satisfies the differential equation (see Eq. (215.4))

$$\frac{d^2V_i}{du_i^2} = (Nq_i + \overline{M})V_i, \qquad i = 1, 2, 3, \qquad (1)$$

where $\overline{M}$ and N are constants, and u_i is defined in Eq. (215.2). The functions V_i which are defined by these equations are not harmonic unless $\overline{M}$ and N are zero, but the product

$$V_1V_2V_3$$

is harmonic, since it satisfies the equation of Laplace (Eq. (215.4)).

Lamé, who was interested in certain problems relating to the conduction of heat in ellipsoids, sought solutions of this type, doubtless in analogy with the spherical harmonics, which, in polar coordinates, have the form

$$R(r) \cdot \Phi(\varphi) \cdot \Theta(\theta).$$

Following the analogy further, he sought functions V_1, V_2, V_3 which are polynomials in q_1, q_2, or q_3, or polynomials multiplied by the radicals indicated in the preceeding section. It is evident that, if such functions exist, the symmetric product

$$V_1V_2V_3$$

also is a polynomial in x, y, and z, and therefore a particular combination of solid spherical harmonics. It will be shown in the following sections that such solutions exist for each of the four classes of Sec. 218.

It was proved by Moutard that the functions of Lamé present the only case in which harmonic polynomials in x, y, and z can be resolved into quadratic and linear factors.

220. Determination of the Constant N.—Omitting the subscripts, for the sake of convenience, the differential equation which is to be satisfied is Eq. (219.1), or, preferably, the form given in Eq. (216.10), namely,

$$\frac{d_2 V}{du^2} - (N\wp u + M)V = 0; \tag{1}$$

and the solutions sought are polynomials in $\wp$ or polynomials multiplied by radicals. That is, the solution must be of class I, II, III, or IV. Hence, if P is a polynomial in $\wp u$, these classes are

$$\begin{array}{ll}
\text{(I)} \quad V = P, \\
\text{(II)} \begin{cases} V = \sqrt{\wp_1}\, P, \\ V = \sqrt{\wp_2}\, P, \\ V = \sqrt{\wp_3}\, P, \end{cases} & \text{(III)} \begin{cases} V = \sqrt{\wp_1\wp_2}\, P, \\ V = \sqrt{\wp_2\wp_3}\, P, \\ V = \sqrt{\wp_3\wp_1}\, P, \end{cases} \\
& \text{(IV)} \quad V = \sqrt{\wp_1\wp_2\wp_3}\, P,
\end{array} \right\} \tag{2}$$

where

$$\wp_1 = \wp - e_1 = q - a^2, \qquad \wp_2 = \wp - e_2 = q - b^2,$$
$$\wp_3 = \wp - e_3 = q - c^2. \tag{3}$$

When expressed in terms of the rectangular coordinates, the polynomial will be assumed to be of degree m. If m is even, say $m = 2n$, only function of classes I and III can occur. In class I, the polynomial P will be of degree n in $\wp$, and in class III the polynomials will be of degree $n - 1$ in $\wp$. If m is odd, say $m = 2n + 1$, only classes II and IV occur; the polynomials P of class II will be of degree n and those of class IV will be of degree $n - 1$.

If it is borne in mind that

$$\wp = \frac{1}{u^2} + * + \frac{g_2}{20}u^2 + \frac{g_3}{28}u^4 + \cdots,$$

$$\sqrt{\wp_i} = \frac{1}{u} - \frac{e_i}{2}u + \left(\frac{g_2}{40} - \frac{e_i^2}{8}\right)u^3 + \cdots,$$

it is seen that each of the functions in Eqs. (2), if it exists, can be expanded in ascending powers of u, and that in every case V has the form

$$V = \frac{a_{-m}}{u^m} + \frac{a_{-(m-1)}}{u^{m-1}} + \cdots.$$

The differential Eq. (1) also can be arranged in powers of u, and the coefficient of each power of u separately must vanish.

The coefficient of the first term, $u^{-(m+2)}$, is $[m(m+1) - N] a_{-m}$. Therefore

$$N = m(m+1), \tag{4}$$

whatever the class may be. Expressed in terms of the letter n, however, its expressions for the several classes are

$$\left.\begin{array}{ll} \text{(I) } N = 2n(2n+1), & \text{(III) } N = 2n(2n+1), \\ \text{(II) } N = (2n+1)(2n+2), & \text{(IV) } N = (2n+1)(2n+2); \end{array}\right\} \tag{5}$$

for in classes I and III,

$$m = 2n,$$

and in classes II and IV,

$$m = 2n + 1.$$

221. Existence of Solutions for Class I.—On substituting the value of N from Eq. (220.5), the differential equation, Eq. (220.1) is

$$\frac{d^2V}{du^2} - [2n(2n+1)\wp + M]V = 0, \tag{1}$$

and V is understood to be a polynomial in $\wp$ of degree n. The constant M in Eq. (1) is still arbitrary and is available for satisfying the necessary conditions.

Since V is a polynomial in $\wp$ of degree n, it can be written

$$V = \sum_{k=0}^{n} a_k \wp^k,$$

where the coefficients a_k are constants and must be chosen so as to satisfy Eq. (1). Since V depends upon u only through $\wp$,

$$\frac{dV}{du} = \frac{\partial V}{\partial \wp} \wp' \tag{2}$$

and

$$\frac{d^2V}{du^2} = \frac{\partial^2 V}{\partial \wp^2} \wp'^2 + \frac{\partial V}{\partial \wp} \wp''. \tag{3}$$

But,

$$\wp'^2 = 4\wp^3 - g_2\wp - g_3, \quad \text{and} \quad \wp'' = 6\wp^2 - \frac{1}{2}g_2, \tag{4}$$

as is seen from Eqs. (216. 4) and (216.6). Hence Eq. (1) becomes

$$(4\wp^3 - g_2\wp - g_3) \sum_{k=0}^{n} k(k-1)a_k\wp^{k-2} + \left(6\wp^2 - \frac{1}{2}g^2\right) \sum_{k=0}^{n} ka_k\wp^{k-1}$$

$$- [2n(2n+1)\wp + M] \sum_{k=0}^{n} a_k\wp^k = 0.$$

Arranged according to powers of $\wp$, this expression gives

$$\sum_{k=-1}^{n} \left[2(n-k)(2n+2k+1)a_k + Ma_{k+1} \right. \tag{5}$$

$$\left. + \frac{1}{2}(k+2)(2k+3)g_2a_{k+2} + (k+2)(k+3)g_3a_{k+3} \right]\wp^{k+1} = 0,$$

in which the coefficients

$$a_{-1} = a_{n+1} = a_{n+2} = a_{n+3} = 0.$$

Commencing with $k = n$, it is seen that the coefficient of $\wp^{n+1}$ vanishes, and that a_n can be taken equal to $+1$. Then sequentially,

$$2 \cdot 1 \cdot (4n-1)a_{n-1} = -M,$$

$$2 \cdot 2 \cdot (4n-3)a_{n-2} = -Ma_{n-1} - \frac{1}{2}n(2n-1)g_2,$$

$$\dotfill ;$$

so that

$$\left. \begin{aligned} a_{n-1} &= \frac{-M}{2 \cdot 1 \cdot (4n-1)}, \\ a_{n-2} &= \frac{+M^2}{2^2 \cdot 2!(4n-1)(4n-3)} - \frac{n(2n-1)g_2}{2^2 \cdot 2 \cdot (4n-3)}, \end{aligned} \right\} \tag{6}$$

It is seen from this sequence that the coefficient a_{n-k} is of degree k in M, and therefore a_0 is of degree n in M. The coefficient of $\wp^0$ in Eq. (5), $(k = -1)$,

$$Ma_0 + \frac{1}{2}g_2a_1 + 2g_3a_2 = 0, \tag{7}$$

contains no undetermined coefficient a_k. It must therefore vanish by itself. This gives an equation in M of degree $n + 1$, and M must be chosen so as to satisfy it. There are $n + 1$ values of M which will do this, and for each value of M the coefficients a_k are uniquely determined.

There exist, therefore, $n + 1$ functions of Lamé of Class I.

222. Existence of Solutions for Class II.—For class II the differential equation is

$$\frac{d^2V}{du^2} - [(2n+1)(2n+2)\wp + M]V = 0, \qquad (1)$$

and, taking the first of the forms of Class II, Eq. (220.2),

$$V = \sqrt{\wp_1}\,P,$$

where P is a polynomial in $\wp$ of degree n. To simplify the notation P^* will be used to denote the first derivative of P with respect to $\wp$ and P^{**} the second derivative of P with respect to $\wp$. Then, by differentiating logarithmically, it is seen that

$$\frac{\partial V}{\partial \wp} = \left(\frac{1}{2\wp_1} + \frac{P^*}{P}\right)V = \sqrt{\wp_1}\left(\frac{1}{2\wp_1}P + P^*\right)$$

and

$$\frac{\partial^2 V}{\partial \wp^2} = \left[\left(\frac{1}{2\wp_1} + \frac{P^*}{P}\right)^2 - \frac{1}{2\wp_1{}^2} + \frac{P^{**}}{P} - \frac{P^{*2}}{P^2}\right]V$$

$$= \sqrt{\wp_1}\left(-\frac{P}{4\wp_1{}^2} + \frac{P^*}{\wp_1} + P^{**}\right).$$

It is better this time to take, Eq. (216.6),

$$\wp'^2 = 4\wp_1\wp_2\wp_3, \qquad \wp'' = 2(\wp_2\wp_3 + \wp_3\wp_1 + \wp_1\wp_2).$$

Then Eq. (1) becomes, after removing the factor $\sqrt{\wp_1}$,

$$(\wp_2 + \wp_3 - (2n+1)(2n+2)\wp - M)P$$

$$+ (6\wp_2\wp_3 + 2\wp_3\wp_1 + 2\wp_1\wp_2)P^*$$

$$+ 4\wp_1\wp_2\wp_3 P^{**} = 0,$$

or, by virtue of Eq. (220.3),

$$\left.\begin{array}{l}[-2n(2n+3)\wp + e_1 - M]P \\ \quad + [10\wp^2 + 4e_1\wp + (6e_2e_3 - 2e_1{}^2)]P^* \\ \quad + [4\wp^3 + 4(e_2e_3 - e_1{}^2)\wp - 4e_1e_2e_3]P^{**} = 0.\end{array}\right\} \quad (2)$$

On substituting

$$P = \sum_{k=0}^{n} a_k\wp^k, \qquad P^* = \sum_{k=0}^{n} ka_k\wp^{k-1}, \qquad P^{**} = \sum_{k=0}^{n} k(k-1)a_k\wp^{k-2}$$

in Eq. (2) and then arranging according to powers of $\wp$, there results

$$\sum_{k=-1}^{n} \left\{ -2(n-k)(2n+2k+3)a_k + [(4k+5)e_1 - M]a_{k+1} \right.$$
$$+ [2(k+2)(2k+5)e_2e_3 - 2(k+2)(2k+3)e_1{}^2]a_{k+2}$$
$$\left. - 4(k+2)(k+3)e_1e_2e_3a_{k+3} \right\} \wp^{k+1} = 0, \quad (3)$$

in which

$$a_n = +1, \qquad a_{-1} = a_{n+1} = a_{n+2} = a_{n+3} = 0.$$

The coefficients are determined sequentially just as before:

$$a_{n-1} = \frac{(4n+1)e_1 - M}{2(4n+1)},$$

$$a_{n-2} = \frac{[(4n+1)e_1 - M][(4n-3)e_1 - M]}{2 \cdot 4 \cdot (4n+1)(4n-1)}$$
$$+ \frac{n[(2n+1)e_2e_3 - (2n-1)e_1{}^2]}{2(4n-1)},$$

. . . .

The coefficient a_{n-k} is of degree k in M, and therefore a_0 is of degree n in M. There remains, finally, the equation for which $k = -1$, namely,

$$(e_1 - M)a_0 + (6e_2e_3 - 2e_1{}^2)a_1 - 8e_1e_2e_3a_2 = 0.$$

This equation, which determines M, is of degree $n + 1$. There exist therefore $n + 1$ functions of Lamé of the form

$$V = \sqrt{\wp_1}P;$$

and similarly, $n + 1$ functions for each of the forms

$$V = \sqrt{\wp_2}P \quad \text{and} \quad V = \sqrt{\wp_3}P.$$

There are, therefore, $3n + 3$ functions of Lamé in class II.

223. Existence of Solutions for Class III.—In class III, the function V has the form

$$V = \sqrt{\wp_1\wp_2}P,$$

where P is a polynomial in $\wp$ of degree $n - 1$. Also

$$\frac{\partial V}{\partial \wp} = \frac{\wp_1 + \wp_2}{2\sqrt{\wp_1\wp_2}} P + \sqrt{\wp_1\wp_2}P^*,$$

$$\frac{\partial^2 V}{\partial \wp^2} = \frac{-\wp_1{}^2 + 2\wp_1\wp_2 - \wp_2{}^2}{4(\wp_1\wp_2)^{\frac{3}{2}}} P + \frac{\wp_1 + \wp_2}{\sqrt{\wp_1\wp_2}}P^* + \sqrt{\wp_1\wp_2}P^{**}.$$

$$\wp'{}^2 = 4\wp_1\wp_2\wp_3, \qquad \wp'' = 2(\wp_2\wp_3 + \wp_3\wp_1 + \wp_1\wp_2).$$

Since, Eq. (220.5),

$$N = 2n(2n + 1),$$

the differential equation becomes, after removing the factor $\sqrt{\wp_1\wp_2}$,

$$[\wp_1 + \wp_2 + 4\wp_3 - 2n(2n + 1)\wp - M]P$$
$$+ [6\wp_2\wp_3 + 6\wp_3\wp_1 + 2\wp_1\wp_2]P^*$$
$$+ 4\wp_1\wp_2\wp_3 P^{**} = 0. \quad (1)$$

On setting

$$P = \sum_{k=0}^{n-1} a_k\wp^k, \quad P^* = \sum_{k=0}^{n-1} ka_k\wp^{k-1}, \quad P^{**} = \sum_{k=0}^{n-1} k(k-1)a_k\wp^{k-2},$$

replacing $\wp_1$, $\wp_2$, and $\wp_3$ by their values in terms of $\wp$, and then arranging the entire expression in powers of $\wp$, Eq. (1) becomes

$$\sum_{k=-1}^{n-1} \Bigg\{ -2(n - k - 1)(2n + 2k + 3)a_k - [(4k + 7)e_3 + M]a_{k+1}$$
$$+ [(k + 2)(4k + 6)e_1e_2 - (k + 2)(4k + 10)e_3{}^2]a_{k+2}$$
$$- 4(k + 2)(k + 3)e_1e_2e_3a_{k+3} \Bigg\}\wp^{k+1} = 0.$$

If a_{n-1} is taken equal to unity, it is found that

$$\left.\begin{aligned} a_{n-2} &= -\frac{(4n - 1)e_3 + M}{2(4n - 1)}, \\ a_{n-3} &= \frac{[M + (4n - 1)e_3][M + (4n - 5)e_3]}{2 \cdot 4 \cdot (4n - 1)(4n - 3)} \\ &+ \frac{(n - 1)(4n - 6)e_1e_2 - (n - 1)(4n - 2)e_3{}^2}{4(4n - 3)}, \end{aligned}\right\} \quad (2)$$

$$\dotfill$$

The last coefficient a_0 is of degree $n - 1$ in M, and the coefficient of $\wp^0$ gives

$$-(3e_3 + M)a_0 + (2e_1e_2 - 6e_3{}^2)a_1 - 8e_1e_2e_3a_2 = 0. \quad (3)$$

This is an equation of the nth degree in M. There exist, therefore, n functions of Lamé for each of the forms

$$V = \sqrt{\wp_1 \wp_2} P, \qquad V = \sqrt{\wp_2 \wp_3} P, \qquad V = \sqrt{\wp_1 \wp_2} P;$$

and therefore, $3n$ functions in class III. There are also $n + 1$ functions in class I. Hence, if $m = 2n$ is even, there are altogether

$$(n + 1) + 3n = 4n + 1 = 2m + 1$$

functions of Lamé.

224. Existence of Solutions for Class IV.—There is only one form in the fourth class, namely,

$$V = \sqrt{\wp_1 \wp_2 \wp_3} P,$$

in which P is a polynomial of degree $n - 1$ in $\wp$; and

$$N = (2n + 1)(2n + 2).$$

It is found that

$$\frac{\partial V}{\partial \wp} = \sqrt{\wp_1 \wp_2 \wp_3} \left[\frac{1}{2} \left(\frac{1}{\wp_1} + \frac{1}{\wp_2} + \frac{1}{\wp_3} \right) P + P^* \right],$$

$$\frac{\partial^2 V}{\partial \wp^2} = \sqrt{\wp_1 \wp_2 \wp_3} \left[-\frac{1}{4} \left(\frac{1}{\wp_1{}^2} + \frac{1}{\wp_2{}^2} + \frac{1}{\wp_3{}^2} \right) P + \right.$$

$$\left. \frac{1}{2} \left(\frac{1}{\wp_1 \wp_2} + \frac{1}{\wp_2 \wp_3} + \frac{1}{\wp_3 \wp_1} \right) P + \left(\frac{1}{\wp_1} + \frac{1}{\wp_2} + \frac{1}{\wp_3} \right) P^* + P^{**} \right].$$

Taking

$$\wp'^2 = 4\wp_1 \wp_2 \wp_3, \qquad \wp'' = 2(\wp_2 \wp_3 + \wp_3 \wp_1 + \wp_1 \wp_2),$$

and removing the factor $\sqrt{\wp_1 \wp_2 \wp_3}$, the differential equation reduces to

$$[4(\wp_1 + \wp_2 + \wp_3) - (2n + 1)(2n + 2)\wp - M]P$$
$$+ 6[\wp_2 \wp_3 + \wp_3 \wp_1 + \wp_1 \wp_2]P^*$$
$$+ 4\wp_1 \wp_2 \wp_3 P^{**} = 0;$$

and this expression, arranged in powers of $\wp$, gives

$$\sum_{k=-1}^{n-1} \left\{ -2(n - k - 1)(2n + 2k + 5)a_k - Ma_{k+1} \right.$$

$$\left. - \frac{1}{2}(k + 2)(2k + 5)g_2 a_{k+2} - (k + 2)(k + 3)g_3 a_{k+3} \right\} \wp^{k+1} = 0.$$

If a_{n-1} is taken equal to unity, the remaining coefficients are

$$a_{n-2} = \frac{-M}{2(4n+1)},$$

$$a_{n-3} = \frac{M^2}{2 \cdot 4 \cdot (4n+1)(4n-1)} - \frac{(n-1)(2n-1)g_2}{2 \cdot 4 \cdot (4n-1)},$$

. . . .

The last coefficient a_0 is of degree $n-1$ in M; and the coefficient of $\wp^0$, that is, the equation in M, is

$$2Ma_0 + 3g_2a_1 + 4g_3a_2 = 0.$$

Since this equation is of degree n, there are n functions of Lamé in class IV. But there are $3n+3$ functions in Class II. Hence, if $m = 2n+1$ is odd, there are

$$(3n+3) + n = 4n+3 = 2m+1$$

functions of Lamé.

225. The Products of Lamé.—Whether m is even or whether it is odd, there are always $2m+1$ functions of Lamé, which, when translated into rectangular coordinates, are polynomials in x, y, and z of degree m.

These functions are separable into four classes as is indicated in Eq. (220.3). Suppose, for example,

$$V = \sqrt{\wp_1}\,P(\wp)$$

is a function of Lamé, where $\wp_1 = \wp - e_1$, and P is a polynomial in $\wp$ of degree n. Let R_i be one of the roots of the polynomial, so that

$$V = \sqrt{\wp u - e_1}\, \prod_{k=1}^{n} (\wp u - R_k).$$

Then

$$\left.\begin{aligned}
V_1 &= \sqrt{\wp u_1 - e_1}\, \prod_{k=1}^{n} (\wp u_1 - R_k), \\
V_2 &= \sqrt{\wp u_2 - e_2}\, \prod_{k=1}^{n} (\wp u_2 - R_k), \\
V_3 &= \sqrt{\wp u_3 - e_3}\, \prod_{k=1}^{n} (\wp u_3 - R_k).
\end{aligned}\right\} \qquad (1)$$

The product of these three functions

$$V_1 V_2 V_3 = \sqrt{(\wp u_1 - e_1)(\wp u_2 - e_1)(\wp u_3 - e_1)}$$

$$\prod_{k=1}^{n} (\wp u_1 - R_k)(\wp u_2 - R_k)(\wp u_3 - R_k) \quad (2)$$

is called a *product of Lamé*. It is expressible as a polynomial of degree $2n + 1$ in x, y, and z, which satisfies the equation of Laplace.

By Eq. (216.11), the radical is equal to x, aside from a constant factor. As was seen in Sec. 218,

$$(q_1 - \alpha)(q_2 - \alpha)(q_3 - \alpha)$$

$$= C\left(\frac{x^2}{\alpha - a^2} + \frac{y^2}{\alpha - b^2} + \frac{z^2}{\alpha - c^2} - 1 \right), \quad (3)$$

whatever α may be. If α in this expression is taken equal to $h + R$, then, since

$$\wp = q - h, \quad h - a^2 = -e_1, \quad h - b^2 = -e_2, \quad h - c^2 = -e_3,$$

Eq. (3) becomes

$$(\wp u_1 - R)(\wp u_2 - R)(\wp u_3 - R)$$

$$= C\left(\frac{x^2}{R - e_1} + \frac{y^2}{R - e_2} + \frac{z^2}{R - e_3} - 1 \right).$$

Hence, aside from a constant factor which is not important,

$$V_1 V_2 V_3 = x \prod_{k=1}^{n} \left(\frac{x^2}{R_k - e_1} + \frac{y^2}{R_k - e_2} + \frac{z^2}{R_k - e_3} - 1 \right). \quad (4)$$

It should be remembered always, that V_1, V_2, and V_3 represent the values of the same function for the letters q_1, q_2, and q_3, or, if preferred, for u_1, u_2, and u_3.

226. Liouville's Proof That All of the Roots are Real.—The coefficients of the characteristic equations in M are real functions of the real quantities n, e_1, e_2, and e_3. Therefore if the roots are not all real, they are conjugate complexes in pairs, and the corresponding functions V likewise.

Suppose M_1 and M_2 are two distinct roots of the characteristic equation and U_1 and U_2 are the corresponding values of V. Then

$$\frac{d^2 U_1}{du^2} = (N\wp + M_1)U_1,$$

and

$$\frac{d^2U_2}{du^2} = (N\wp + M_2)U_2.$$

If the first of these equations is multiplied by U_2, the second by $-U_1$ and then added, there results

$$U_2\frac{d^2U_1}{du^2} - U_1\frac{d^2U_2}{du^2} = (M_1 - M_2)U_1U_2,$$

and therefore, by integration,

$$\left[U_2\frac{dU_1}{du} - U_1\frac{dU_2}{du} \right]_a^b = (M_1 - M_2)\int_a^b U_1U_2du. \qquad (1)$$

The left member of this equation assumes different forms according to the class to which U_1 and U_2 belong. Bearing in mind that

$$\frac{d\wp}{du} = \wp' = -2\sqrt{\wp_1\wp_2\wp_3},$$

it is seen that if V belongs to the first class

$$V = P(\wp) \qquad \text{and} \qquad \frac{dV}{du} = -2\sqrt{\wp_1\wp_2\wp_3}P^*.$$

Hence

$$U_2\frac{dU_1}{du} - U_1\frac{dU_2}{du} = -2\sqrt{\wp_1\wp_2\wp_3}[P_2P_1^* - P_1P_2^*]. \qquad (I)$$

If V belongs to class II,

$$V = \sqrt{\wp_1}P \qquad \text{and} \qquad \frac{dV}{du} = \sqrt{\wp_2\wp_3}P + 2\wp_1\sqrt{\wp_2\wp_3}P^*,$$

so that

$$U_2\frac{dU_1}{du} - U_1\frac{dU_2}{du} = -2\wp_1\sqrt{\wp_1\wp_2\wp_3}(P_2P_1^* - P_1P_2^*). \qquad (II)$$

If V belongs to class III, it is found, similarly, that

$$U_2\frac{dU_1}{du} - U_1\frac{dU_2}{du} = -2\wp_1\wp_2\sqrt{\wp_1\wp_2\wp_3}(P_2P_1^* - P_1P_2^*); \qquad (III)$$

and for class IV,

$$U_2\frac{dU_1}{du} - U_1\frac{dU_2}{du} = -2\wp_1\wp_2\wp_3\sqrt{\wp_1\wp_2\wp_3}(P_2P_1^* - P_1P_2^*). \qquad (IV)$$

Since (Sec. 216),

$$\wp_1(\omega_1) = 0, \qquad \wp_2(\omega_2) = 0, \qquad \wp_3(\omega_3) = 0,$$

and since P and its derivatives with respect to $\wp$ are finite for all finite values of $\wp$, it follows that if the limits of integration in Eq. (1) are

$$a = \omega_1, \qquad b = \omega_2, \qquad \text{or,} \qquad a = \omega_2, \qquad b = \omega_3,$$

the left member of Eq. (1) vanishes whatever the class may be. Therefore, since M_1 is different from M_2, by hypothesis,

$$\int_{\omega_1}^{\omega_2} U_1 U_2 \, du = \int_{\omega_2}^{\omega_3} U_1 U_2 \, du = 0.$$

If M_1 and M_2 are conjugate imaginaries, so also are U_1 and U_2, say

$$U_1 = W_1 + iW_2, \qquad U_2 = W_1 - iW_2,$$

where W_1 and W_2 are real. Then

$$\int_{\omega_1}^{\omega_2} U_1 U_2 \, du = \int_{\omega_1}^{\omega_2} (W_1{}^2 + W_2{}^2) \, du = 0,$$

which is impossible, since W_1 and W_2 are not both zero.

It follows that M_1 and M_2 cannot be conjugate complex numbers; therefore the roots of the equation in M are all real.

227. Particular Examples of Lamé's Functions.—It is worth while to interrupt the argument at this point for the purpose of exhibiting some of the simplest of the functions of Lamé, and a numerical computation of some of the more complicated ones.

$$m = 0.$$

In this case, in which the functions are constants it is evident that

$$V_1 = V_2 = V_3 = 1.$$

$$m = 1.$$

It is seen from Sec. 222 that

$$V = \sqrt{\wp_1}, \qquad \sqrt{\wp_2}, \qquad \text{or} \qquad \sqrt{\wp_3}.$$

Therefore, since

$$\wp_1 = q - a^2, \qquad \wp_2 = q - b^2, \qquad \wp_3 = q - c^2,$$

it is found that

$$V_1 V_2 V_3 = \sqrt{q_1 - a^2} \sqrt{q_2 - a^2} \sqrt{q_3 - a^2} = h_1 x,$$

or,

$$V_1 V_2 V_3 = \sqrt{q_1 - b^2} \sqrt{q_2 - b^2} \sqrt{q_3 - b^2} = h_2 y,$$

or,

$$V_1 V_2 V_3 = \sqrt{q_1 - c^2} \sqrt{q_2 - c^2} \sqrt{q_3 - c^2} = h_3 z,$$

where

$$h_1 = \sqrt{(a^2 - b^2)(a^2 - c^2)}, \qquad h_2 = \sqrt{(b^2 - c^2)(b^2 - a^2)},$$

$$h_3 = \sqrt{(c^2 - a^2)(c^2 - b^2)}.$$

$$m = 4.$$

In order that the numerical details may be carried out, it will be assumed in what follows, that

$$a = 5, \qquad b = 4, \qquad c = 3.$$

From the formulas of Sec. 216 there is obtained

$$q = \wp + h, \qquad e_2 = b^2 - h,$$

$$e_1 = a^2 - h, \qquad e_3 = c^2 - h,$$

$$h = \frac{1}{3}(a^2 + b^2 + c^2),$$

$$g_2 = -4(e_1 e_2 + e_2 e_3 + e_3 e_1),$$

$$g_3 = +4 e_1 e_2 e_3.$$

Hence,

$$h = 16\tfrac{2}{3}, \qquad e_1 = 8\tfrac{1}{3}, \qquad e_2 = -\tfrac{2}{3}, \qquad e_3 = -7\tfrac{2}{3};$$

$$e_1 e_2 + e_2 e_3 + e_3 e_1 = -64\tfrac{1}{3}, \qquad e_1 e_2 e_3 = \frac{1150}{27},$$

and

$$g_2 = +\frac{772}{3}, \qquad g_3 = +\frac{4600}{27}.$$

In order not to make the problem too simple nor, on the other hand, too difficult, a determination of harmonics of the fourth order will be made. That is,

$$m = 4,$$

and therefore,

$$n = 2.$$

Since m is even, only functions of Lamé of the first and third classes are possible; and, since $2m + 1$ is 9, there are altogether 9 such functions.

Functions of Class I.—Since $n + 1$ is 3, there are three functions of Lamé in this class. Using the formulas of Sec. 221, it is found that

$$a_2 = 1, \qquad a_1 = -\frac{M}{14}, \qquad a_0 = \frac{M^2}{280} - \frac{3g_2}{20},$$

The characteristic equation, Eq. (221.7),

$$Ma_0 + \frac{1}{2}g_2a_1 + 2g_3a_2 = 0,$$

becomes

$$M^3 - 52g_2M + 560g_3 = 0,$$

or

$$M^3 - \frac{40144}{3}M + \frac{2,576,000}{27} = 0,$$

the roots of which are

$$M_1 = +111.933,$$

$$M_2 = + \;\;\; 7.157,$$

$$M_3 = -119.090.$$

The polynomial in $\wp$,

$$V = \wp^2 + a_1\wp + a_0$$

$$= \wp^2 - \frac{1}{14}M\wp + \left(\frac{M^2}{280} - \frac{3g_2}{20}\right),$$

has three different expressions, one for each of the above roots. They are

$$V(M_1) = \wp^2 - 7.995\wp + 6.146 \equiv (\wp - .862)(\wp - 7.134),$$

$$V(M_2) = \wp^2 - .511\wp - 38.417 \equiv (\wp - 6.459)(\wp + 5.948),$$

$$V(M_3) = \wp^2 + 8.506\wp + 12.051 \equiv (\wp + 1.796)(\wp + 6.711).$$

The corresponding polynomials in q are obtained from these expressions by the substitution

$$\wp = q - h = q - 16\tfrac{2}{3}.$$

These are the polynomials that were denoted by $f(q)$ in Sec. 218. Hence

$$\left.\begin{array}{l} f(q, M_1) = (q - 17.529)(q - 23.801), \\ f(q, M_2) = (q - 23.126)(q - 10.719), \\ f(q, M_3) = (q - 14.871)(q - 9.956). \end{array}\right\} \tag{1}$$

It will be observed that all of the zeros of these polynomials are real and lie between $9(=c^2)$ and $25(=a^2)$. They were denoted by the letters α_i in Sec. 218.

Each of these polynomials is a function of Lamé. Taking the first one, $f(q, M_1)$,

$$\alpha_1 = 17.529, \qquad \alpha_2 = 23.801,$$
$$\alpha_1 - a^2 = -7.471, \qquad \alpha_2 - a^2 = -1.199,$$
$$\alpha_1 - b^2 = +1.529, \qquad \alpha_2 - b^2 = +7.801,$$
$$\alpha_1 - c^2 = +8.529, \qquad \alpha_2 - c^2 = +14.801.$$

The product

$$\left(-\frac{x^2}{7.471} + \frac{y^2}{1.529} + \frac{z^2}{8.529} - 1\right)\left(-\frac{x^2}{1.199} + \frac{y^2}{7.801} + \frac{z^2}{14.801} - 1\right)$$

$$\left.\begin{array}{l} = +.1116x^4 \quad + .0839y^4 \quad + .0079z^4 \\ \quad -.5627x^2y^2 + .0593y^2z^2 - .1068x^2z^2 \\ \quad +.9675x^2 \quad - .7826y^2 \quad - .1848z^2 + 1. \end{array}\right\} \qquad (2)$$

is the corresponding product of Lamé, and it is a simple matter to verify directly that it is harmonic.

The corresponding polynomials for $f(q, M_2)$ and $f(q, M_3)$ will be left to the student as an exercise.

Aside from a constant factor, the symmetric product

$$[(q_1 - 17.529)(q_1 - 23.801)][(q_2 - 17.529)(q_2 - 23.801)]$$
$$[(q_3 - 17.529)(q_3 - 23.801)] \qquad (3)$$

is the same as the polynomial in Eq. (2). For any point x, y, z the order of magnitude of the elliptic coordinates q_1, q_2, q_3 is, Sec. 213,

$$q_1 \geqq 25 \geqq q_2 \geqq 16 \geqq q_3 \geqq 9.$$

The product, Eq. (3), and therefore, Lamé's function, (Eq. (2)) also, vanishes at all points for which

$$q_2 = 17.529 \quad \text{or} \quad q_2 = 23.801; \qquad (4)$$

that is, the polynomial in Eq. (2) vanishes at every point of the two hyperboloids of one sheet which are indicated by Eq. (4), and nowhere else.

The function of Lamé corresponding to

$$f(q, M_2) = (q - 23.126)(q - 10.719)$$

vanishes only on the surfaces

$$q_2 = 23.126 \quad \text{and} \quad q_3 = 10.719,$$

the first of which is an hyperboloid of one sheet and the second an hyperboloid of two sheets.

The third function of Lamé corresponding to

$$f(q, M_3) = (q - 14.871)(q - 9.956)$$

vanishes only on the two hyperboloids of two sheets corresponding to the values

$$q_3 = 14.871 \qquad \text{and} \qquad q_3 = 9.956.$$

On any given ellipsoid, $q_1 = \text{const.}$, the lines along which the function of Lamé vanishes make certain patterns corresponding to the patterns on the sphere formed by the lines along which a tesseral harmonic vanishes, Sec. 199. In Fig. 109 the pattern is given for M_1 on the ellipsoid $q_1 = 40$ as seen from the point

$$x = 15, \qquad y = 40, \qquad z = 10,$$

and in Figs. 110 and 111 the patterns corresponding to M_2 and M_3 are given.

The student will doubtless find it interesting and profitable to sketch these patterns on the shells of eggs. They seem much less complicated when so drawn.

Functions of Class III.—It is sufficient to consider the form

$$V = \sqrt{\wp_1 \wp_2}\, P,$$

since the others can be obtained from it by a cyclical permutation of the subscripts. P is a polynomial in $\wp$ of degree $n - 1$, which in the present case is unity. Hence

$$P = \wp + a_0,$$

where, by Eq. (223.2),

$$a_1 = 1, \qquad a_0 = -\frac{M + 7e_3}{14};$$

and, by Eq. (223.3)

$$\frac{(M + 7e_3)(M + 3e_3)}{14} + 2e_1e_2 - 6e_3{}^2 = 0,$$

or

$$M^2 + 10e_3 M - 63e_3{}^2 + 28e_1e_2 = 0.$$

This reduces to

$$9M^2 - 690M - 34{,}727 = 0,$$

so that

$$M = 111.327 = M_1, \qquad \text{or} \qquad M = -34.660 = M_2.$$

Hence

$$V(M_1) = \sqrt{\wp_1 \wp_2}(\wp - 4.119),$$

and

$$V(M_2) = \sqrt{\wp_1 \wp_2}(\wp + 6.309).$$

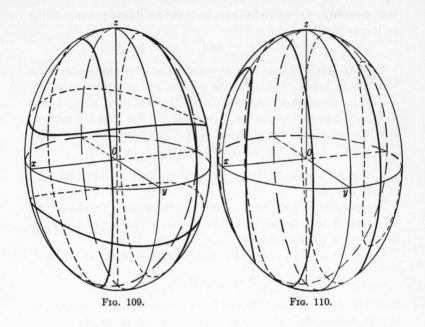

FIG. 109.

FIG. 110.

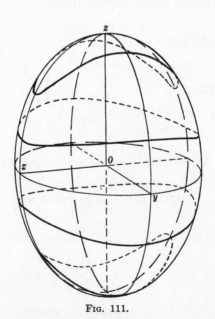

FIG. 111.

The functions in q are obtained by the substitutions

$$\wp_1 = \wp - e_1 = q - a^2, \qquad \wp_2 = \wp - e_2 = q - b^2,$$

$$\wp = q - 16\tfrac{2}{3}.$$

Hence, using the notation of Sec. 218,

$$\psi_{ab}(q) = \sqrt{(q - a^2)(q - b^2)}\,(q - 20.786)$$

for M_1, and

$$\psi_{ab}(q) = \sqrt{(q - a^2)(q - b^2)}\,(q - 10.358)$$

for the root M_2.

The corresponding polynomials in x, y, and z are

$$V = xy\left[\frac{-x^2}{4.214} + \frac{y^2}{4.786} + \frac{z^2}{11.786} - 1\right]$$

$$= -.2373x^3y + .2090xy^3 + .0849xyz^2 - xy,$$

and

$$V = xy\left[\frac{-x^2}{14.642} + \frac{-y^2}{5.642} + \frac{z^2}{1.358} - 1\right]$$

$$= -.0683x^3y - .1772xy^3 + .7366xyz^2 - xy.$$

The first of these polynomials vanishes in the yz- and the xz-planes and on the hyperboloid of one sheet for which $q_2 = 20.786$. The second polynomial vanishes in the yz- and the xz-planes and on the hyperboloid of two sheets for which $q_3 = 10.358$.

The other four functions in class III can be obtained merely by a cyclical permutation of the subscripts in the above formulas.

228. The Pattern As a Function of q_1.—In any family of triply orthogonal conicoids, the ellipsoid represented by q_1 equal to a constant increases in size as q_1 increases and its shape tends toward that of a sphere. The patterns represented in Figs. 109, 110, and 111 are the intersections on the ellipsoid of the surfaces

$$q_2 = \text{const.}, \quad \text{or} \quad q_3 = \text{const.}, \tag{1}$$

which are not altered by a change in the value of q_1. In the limit, for q_1 infinite the ellipsoid becomes a sphere whatever values the constants a^2, b^2, and c^2 may have. The surfaces represented by Eqs. (1), however, depend upon these values, and the surface

$$q_2 = \text{const.}$$

for one set, a^2, b^2, c^2, is not in general asymptotic to any one of the surfaces for another set, a^2, b^2, c^2. Hence, the limiting pattern upon the sphere for a given ellipsoidal harmonic depends upon the values of a^2, b^2, and c^2; and it cannot, in general, coincide with the pattern of some particular tesseral harmonic, as one might suspect to be the case.

229. Parametric Representations of a Sphere.—Instead of letting q_1 increase, let a^2, b^2, and c^2 be replaced everywhere by λa^2, λb^2, and λc^2; and then let λ diminish. Then, in order of magnitude,

$$q_1 > \lambda a^2 > q_2 > \lambda b^2 > q_3 > \lambda c^2.$$

The coordinate $q_1 > a^2$ can be kept fixed, but q_2 and q_3 diminish with λ. It is desirable, therefore, to take

$$q_2 = \lambda p_2 \qquad \text{and} \qquad q_3 = \lambda p_3,$$

so that, although p_2 and p_3 are functions of λ, the order of magnitudes,

$$a^2 > p_2 > b^2 > p_3 > c^2,$$

is always maintained.

Equation (213.3) becomes

$$\left. \begin{array}{l} x^2 = (q_1 - \lambda a^2) \dfrac{(p_2 - a^2)(p_3 - a^2)}{(a^2 - b^2)(a^2 - c^2)}, \\[2mm] y^2 = (q_1 - \lambda b^2) \dfrac{(p_2 - b^2)(p_3 - b^2)}{(b^2 - c^2)(b^2 - a^2)}, \\[2mm] z^2 = (q_1 - \lambda c^2) \dfrac{(p_2 - c^2)(p_3 - c^2)}{(c^2 - a^2)(c^2 - b^2)}; \end{array} \right\} \tag{2}$$

and, Eq. (213.5),

$$q_1 = r^2 + \lambda(a^2 + b^2 + c^2 - p_2 - p_3).$$

In the limit, for $\lambda = 0$, the ellipsoid. $q_1 = $ const., becomes a sphere, and

$$\left. \begin{array}{l} x^2 = r^2 \dfrac{(p_2 - a^2)(p_3 - a^2)}{(a^2 - b^2)(a^2 - c^2)}, \\[2mm] y^2 = r^2 \dfrac{(p_2 - b^2)(p_3 - b^2)}{(b^2 - c^2)(a^2 - c^2)}, \\[2mm] z^2 = r^2 \dfrac{(p_2 - c^2)(p_3 - c^2)}{(c^2 - a^2)(c^2 - b^2)}, \end{array} \right\} \tag{3}$$

which is an interesting parametric representation of a sphere, since the parameters, p_2 and p_3, enter symmetrically.

Since

$$a^2 \geqq b^2 \geqq c^2, \qquad a^2 \geqq p_2 \geqq b^2, \qquad b^2 \geqq p_3 \geqq c^2,$$

new parameters t, τ, ω_2, and ω_3 can be introduced by the relations

$$
\begin{aligned}
b^2 &= \tau a^2 + t c^2, & 0 \leqq t \leqq 1, \\
p_2 &= a^2 \sin^2 \omega_2 + b^2 \cos^2 \omega_2, & t + \tau = 1, \\
p_3 &= c^2 \sin^2 \omega_3 + b^2 \cos^2 \omega_3, & 0 \leqq \tau \leqq 1.
\end{aligned}
$$

It is found then that

$$
\left.
\begin{aligned}
x^2 &= r^2 \cos^2 \omega_2 [1 - \tau \cos^2 \omega_3], \\
y^2 &= r^2 \sin^2 \omega_2 \sin^2 \omega_3, \\
z^2 &= r^2 \cos^2 \omega_3 [1 - t \cos^2 \omega_2].
\end{aligned}
\right\} \tag{4}
$$

If b^2 coincides with a^2, t vanishes, and

$$
\begin{aligned}
x^2 &= r^2 \cos^2 \omega_2 \sin^2 \omega_3, \\
y^2 &= r^2 \sin^2 \omega_2 \sin^2 \omega_3, \\
z^2 &= r^2 \cos^2 \omega_3.
\end{aligned}
$$

If b^2 coincides with c^2, τ vanishes, and

$$
\begin{aligned}
x^2 &= r^2 \cos^2 \omega_2, \\
y^2 &= r^2 \sin^2 \omega_2 \sin^2 \omega_3, \\
z^2 &= r^2 \cos^2 \omega_3 \sin^2 \omega_2.
\end{aligned}
$$

In both of these extreme cases ω_2 and ω_3 are ordinary polar coordinates. In the first case ω_3 is the polar distance, and in the second case ω_2 is the polar distance.

It is also readily found from Eqs. (3) that

$$
\left.
\begin{aligned}
\frac{x^2}{p_2 - a^2} + \frac{y_2}{p_2 - b^2} + \frac{z^2}{p_2 - c^2} &= 0, \\
\frac{x^2}{p_3 - a^2} + \frac{y^2}{p_3 - b^2} + \frac{z^2}{p_3 - c^2} &= 0.
\end{aligned}
\right\} \tag{5}
$$

The first term in the first of these equations is negative and the other two are positive. Hence, $p_2 = $ constant, represents a cone the axis of which coincides with the x-axis. The first two terms of the second equation are negative while the third is positive. Hence $p_3 = $ const. represents a cone the axis of which coincides with the z-axis. A cross-section of either of these cones is elliptical, unless b^2 coincides with a^2 or c^2. On the sphere, therefore, either of the curves

$$p_2 = \text{const.}, \qquad \text{or}, \qquad p_3 = \text{const.}$$

is a spherical conic, and the points p_2, p_3 are the points of intersection of these spherical conics.

230. The Ellipsoidal Harmonics As Functions of λ.—If the constants a^2, b^2, and c^2 are replaced by λa^2, λb^2, and λc^2, the formulas of Sec. 216 show that e_1, e_2, and e_3 are replaced by λe_1, λe_2, and λe_3, while g_2 and g_3 are replaced by $\lambda^2 g_2$ and $\lambda^3 g_3$. If the letters q, s, and $\wp$ also are replaced by λq, λs, and $\lambda \wp$, the letter u can be replaced by $\lambda^{-\frac{1}{2}} u$, and the differential equation (Eq. (220.1)) which defines the functions of Lamé, becomes

$$\lambda \frac{d^2 V}{du^2} - (\lambda N \wp u + M) V = 0,$$

or

$$\frac{d^2 V}{du^2} - \left(N \wp u + \frac{M}{\lambda} \right) V = 0.$$

This shows that the roots of the characteristic equation in M are merely multiplied by λ, and the same is true of the roots R_i of the polynomials $P(\wp)$.   The function of Lamé, (Eq. (220.2))

$$V = \sqrt{(q - a^2)^\alpha (q - b^2)^\beta (q - c^2)^\gamma} \prod (q - \alpha_i) \qquad (1)$$

where

$$\alpha_i = R_i + h, \qquad \text{and} \qquad \alpha, \beta, \gamma = 0 \text{ or } 1,$$

becomes

$$V_1 = \sqrt{(q_1 - \lambda a^2)^\alpha (q_1 - \lambda b^2)^\beta (q_1 - \lambda c^2)^\gamma} \prod (q_1 - \lambda \alpha_i) \quad (2)$$

for $q = q_1$, an expression which is homogeneous of degree $m/2$ in q_1 and λ; and, after removing a factor $\lambda^{\frac{m}{2}}$,

$$V_i = \sqrt{(p_i - a^2)^\alpha (p_i - b^2)^\beta (p_i - c^2)^\gamma} \prod (p_i - \alpha_i), \quad i = 2, 3, \quad (3)$$

for the subscripts 2 and 3.

The product of Lamé (Sec. 218) becomes, aside from a constant factor,

$$\left. \begin{aligned} V_1 V_2 V_3 &= x^\alpha y^\beta z^\gamma \prod \left(\frac{x^2}{\alpha_i - a^2} + \frac{y^2}{\alpha_i - b^2} + \frac{z^2}{\alpha_i - c^2} - \lambda \right) \\ &= x^\alpha y^\beta z^\gamma \prod \left(\frac{x^2}{R_i - e_1} + \frac{y^2}{R_i - e_2} + \frac{z^2}{R_i - e_3} - \lambda \right) \cdot \end{aligned} \right\} \quad (4)$$

Consequently the ellipsoidal harmonic, which is of degree m when expressed in rectangular coordinates, becomes

$$V_1 V_2 V_3 = H_m(x, y, z) + \lambda H_{m-2}(x, y, z) + \lambda^2 H_{m-4}(x, y, z)$$
$$+ \cdots, \quad (5)$$

where H_k is the ensemble of terms of degree k, and therefore an harmonic polynomial, or a spherical harmonic, of degree k.

This harmonic (Eq. (5)) vanishes at every point of the surface

$$\frac{x^2}{\alpha_i - a^2} + \frac{y^2}{\alpha_i - b^2} + \frac{z^2}{\alpha_i - c^2} - \lambda = 0, \qquad (6)$$

there being $n + 1$ such surfaces for classes I and II, and n surfaces for classes III and IV. For $\lambda = 0$, the ellipsoid becomes a sphere, whatever a^2, b^2, and c^2 may be, and these zero-surfaces (Eq. (6)) reduce to elliptic cones. Hence the zeros of the surface harmonics on the sphere are spherical conics—intersection of the sphere and the cones—and not circles as they are in the case of the tesseral harmonics.

231. The Surface Harmonic $V_2 V_3$.—If the coordinate q_1 is fixed, so also is V_1 fixed, and the harmonic $V_1 V_2 V_3$, apart from a constant factor, becomes a surface harmonic on the ellipsoid $q_1 = $ const.

Consider the equations (Eqs. (229.2))

$$\left.\begin{aligned}
x^2 &= (q_1 - \lambda a^2)\frac{(p_2 - a^2)(p_3 - a^2)}{(a^2 - b^2)(a^2 - c^2)}, \\
y^2 &= (q_1 - \lambda b^2)\frac{(p_2 - b^2)(p_3 - b^2)}{(b^2 - c^2)(b^2 - a^2)}, \\
z^2 &= (q_1 - \lambda c^2)\frac{(p_2 - c^2)(p_3 - c^2)}{(c^2 - a^2)(c^2 - b^2)}, \\
r^2 &= q_1 + \lambda(p_2 + p_3 - a^2 - b^2 - c^2).
\end{aligned}\right\} \qquad (1)$$

If x, y, and z are kept fixed and λ varies, then q_1, p_2, and p_3 vary. But if p_2, p_3 and r^2 are kept fixed while λ varies, then x, y, z, and q_1 vary. Let

$$\xi = \frac{x}{\sqrt{q_1 - \lambda a^2}}, \qquad \eta = \frac{y}{\sqrt{q_1 - \lambda b^2}}, \qquad \zeta = \frac{z}{\sqrt{q_1 - \lambda c^2}}. \qquad (2)$$

Then

$$\left.\begin{aligned}
\xi^2 &= \frac{(p_2 - a^2)(p_3 - a^2)}{(a^2 - b^2)(a^2 - c^2)}, \\
\eta^2 &= \frac{(p_2 - b^2)(p_3 - b^2)}{(b^2 - c^2)(b^2 - a^2)}, \\
\zeta^2 &= \frac{(p_2 - c^2)(p_3 - c^2)}{(c^2 - a^2)(c^2 - b^2)}.
\end{aligned}\right\} \qquad (3)$$

It is evident that ξ, η, and ζ are direction cosines, since

$$\xi^2 + \eta^2 + \zeta^2 \equiv 1.$$

They are functions only of p_2 and p_3. With the same variables

$$\left.\begin{array}{l}x^2 = (r^2 - \lambda[(p_2 - b^2) + (p_3 - c^2)])\dfrac{(p_2 - a^2)(p_3 - a^2)}{(a^2 - b^2)(a^2 - c^2)}, \\[2mm] y^2 = (r^2 - \lambda[(p_2 - c^2) + (p_3 - a^2)])\dfrac{(p_2 - b^2)(p_3 - c^2)}{(b^2 - c^2)(b^2 - a^2)}, \\[2mm] z^2 = (r^2 - \lambda[(p_2 - a^2) + (p_3 - b^2)])\dfrac{(p_2 - c^2)(p_3 - c^2)}{(c^2 - a^2)(c^2 - b^2)};\end{array}\right\} \quad (4)$$

from which it is evident that ξ, η, ζ are the direction cosines, not of the point x, y, z, but of the limiting position of the point x, y, z.

The functions V_2 and V_3 depend upon p_2 and p_3 only (Eq. (230.3)) and are independent of λ. Since the limiting value of q_1 for $\lambda = 0$ is r^2, and the limiting value of V_1 is r^m (Eq. (230.2)), it is seen by taking $\lambda = 0$ in Eq. (230.5) that

$$V_2 V_3 = H_m(\xi, \eta, \zeta). \tag{5}$$

Since H_m is a homogeneous, harmonic polynomial in ξ, η, and ζ, it follows that the product of Lamé $V_2 V_3$ is a surface spherical harmonic. It is, therefore, expressible as a linear combination of tesseral harmonics of degree m.

It is a simple matter to return from the surface harmonic

$$V_2 V_3 = R(p_2) \cdot R(p_3) \prod \left(\frac{\xi^2}{\alpha_i - a^2} + \frac{\eta^2}{\alpha_i - b^2} + \frac{\zeta^2}{\alpha_i - c^2}\right), \quad (6)$$

where

$$R(p_i) = \sqrt{(p_i - a^2)^\alpha (p_i - b^2)^\beta (p_i - c^2)^\gamma},$$

Eqs. (230.3) and (230.4), to the solid harmonic $V_1 V_2 V_3$; for

$$V_1 V_2 V_3 = R(q_1 - \lambda a^2) R(p_2) R(p_3)$$

$$\times \prod (q_1 - \lambda \alpha_i) \left(\frac{\xi^2}{\alpha_i - a^2} + \frac{\eta^2}{\alpha_i - b^2} + \frac{\zeta^2}{\alpha_i - c^2}\right). \tag{7}$$

On replacing ξ, η, and ζ by their values from Eq. (2), it is found that

$$\frac{(q_1 - \lambda \alpha_i)x^2}{(\alpha_i - a^2)(q_1 - \lambda a^2)} + \frac{(q_1 - \lambda \alpha_i)y^2}{(\alpha_i - b^2)(q_1 - \lambda b^2)} + \frac{(q_1 - \lambda \alpha_i)z^2}{(\alpha_i - c^2)(q_1 - \lambda c^2)}$$

$$= \left(\frac{x^2}{\alpha_i - a^2} + \frac{y^2}{\alpha_i - b^2} + \frac{z^2}{\alpha_i - c^2}\right)$$

$$- \lambda \left(\frac{x^2}{q_1 - \lambda a^2} + \frac{y^2}{q_1 - \lambda b^2} + \frac{z^2}{q_1 - \lambda c^2}\right);$$

and since the last parenthesis is equal to 1, Eq. (7) becomes

$$V_1 V_2 V_3 = x^\alpha y^\beta z^\gamma \prod \left(\frac{x^2}{\alpha_i - a^2} + \frac{y^2}{\alpha_i - b^2} + \frac{z^2}{\alpha_i - c^2} - \lambda\right), \quad (8)$$

which is Eq. (230.4). The solid harmonics vanish on surfaces which are hyperboloids; the surface harmonics vanish on the cones to which the hyperboloids are asymptotic.

232. The Spheroidal Surface Harmonic $V_2 V_3$.—It will be of interest to see what becomes of the surface harmonic $V_2 V_3$ when b^2 tends toward a^2 or toward c^2. If b^2 tends toward a^2, the ellipsoid, $q_1 = $ constant, becomes a prolate spheroid, and q_2 ceases to play the rôle of a parameter. If b^2 tends toward c^2, the ellipsoid becomes oblate, the x-axis being the axis of revolution, and q_3 ceases to function as a parameter. In order to avoid this difficulty, the transformation of Sec. 229 will be made.

$$\left.\begin{array}{ll} b^2 = \tau a^2 + t c^2, & 0 \leq t \leq 1, \\ q_2 = a^2 - t(a^2 - c^2) \cos^2 \omega_2, & 0 \leq \tau \leq 1, \\ q_3 = c^2 + \tau(a^2 - c^2) \cos^2 \omega_3, & t + \tau = 1. \end{array}\right\} \quad (1)$$

With this transformation V_2 is a function of ω_2 alone, and V_3 is a function of ω_3 alone.

It is necessary to transform the differential equations (Eq. (215.4)),

$$\frac{d^2 V}{d u_i^2} - [m(m+1)q_i + \bar{M}]V = 0, \qquad i = 2, 3. \quad (2)$$

Since, Eqs. (215.2) and (214.1),

$$\frac{d}{du_2} = 2\sqrt{(q_2 - a^2)(q_2 - b^2)(q_2 - c^2)}\frac{d}{dq_2},$$

$$\frac{d}{du_3} = 2\sqrt{(q_3 - a^2)(q_3 - b^2)(q_3 - c^2)}\frac{d}{dq_3},$$

and

$$q_2 - a^2 = -t(a^2 - c^2)\cos^2 \omega_2,$$

$$q_2 - b^2 = +t(a^2 - c^2)\sin^2 \omega_2,$$

$$q_2 - c^2 = (a^2 - c^2)(1 - t\cos^2 \omega_2),$$

$$q_3 - a^2 = -(a^2 - c^2)(1 - \tau\cos^2 \omega_3),$$

$$q_3 - b^2 = -\tau(a^2 - c^2)\sin^2 \omega_3,$$

$$q_3 - c^2 = +\tau(a^2 - c^2)\cos^2 \omega_3,$$

it is easily verified that

$$\frac{d}{du_2} = \sqrt{-1}\sqrt{a^2 - c^2}\sqrt{1 - t\cos^2 \omega_2}\frac{d}{d\omega_2},$$

and

$$\frac{d}{du_3} = -\sqrt{a^2 - c^2}\sqrt{1 - \tau \cos^2 \omega_3}\frac{d}{d\omega_3}.$$

It must not be forgotten that du_2 is a pure imaginary. Hence, the differential equations (Eq. (2)) become

$$(a^2 - c^2)\sqrt{1 - t \cos^2 \omega_2}\frac{d}{d\omega_2}\left(\sqrt{1 - t \cos^2 \omega_2}\frac{dV_2}{d\omega_2}\right)$$

$$+ \left(m(m + 1)[a^2 - t(a^2 - c^2)\cos^2 \omega_2] + \overline{M}\right)V_2 = 0, \quad (3)$$

$$(a^2 - c^2)\sqrt{1 - \tau \cos^2 \omega_3}\frac{d}{d\omega_3}\left(\sqrt{1 - \tau \cos^2 \omega_3}\frac{dV_3}{d\omega_3}\right)$$

$$- \left(m(m + 1)[c^2 + \tau(a^2 - c^2)\cos^2 \omega_3] + \overline{M}\right)V_3 = 0.$$

If $b^2 = a^2$, the spheroid is prolate; $t = 0$, $\tau = 1$, and these equations reduce to

$$\left.\begin{array}{c}\dfrac{d^2V_2}{d\omega_2^2} + \dfrac{m(m + 1)a^2 + \overline{M}}{a^2 - c^2}V_2 = 0, \\[2mm] \dfrac{1}{\sin \omega_3}\dfrac{d}{d\omega_3}\left(\sin \omega_3\dfrac{dV_3}{d\omega_3}\right) \\[2mm] + \left(m(m + 1) - \dfrac{m(m + 1)a^2 + \overline{M}}{(a^2 - c^2)\sin^2 \omega_3}\right)V_3 = 0.\end{array}\right\} \quad (4)$$

If $b^2 = c^2$, the spheroid is oblate, the x-axis being the axis of revolution; $t = 1$, $\tau = 0$, and Eqs. (3) reduce to

$$\left.\begin{array}{c}\dfrac{1}{\sin \omega_2}\dfrac{d}{d\omega_2}\left(\sin \omega_2\dfrac{dV_2}{d\omega_2}\right) + \left(m(m + 1)\right. \\[2mm] \left. + \dfrac{m(m + 1)c^2 + \overline{M}}{(a^2 - c^2)\sin^2 \omega_2}\right)V_2 = 0 \\[2mm] \dfrac{d^2V_3}{d\omega_3^2} - \dfrac{m(m + 1)c^2 + \overline{M}}{a^2 - c^2}V_3 = 0.\end{array}\right\} \quad (5)$$

On comparing Eqs. (4) and (5) with Eq. (197.11) and (197.12), it is seen that they are the differential equations of a tesseral harmonic of degree m. In Eqs. (4), the order of the harmonic is

$$\frac{m(m + 1)a^2 + \overline{M}}{a^2 - c^2} = k^2,$$

and in Eqs. (5), the order of the harmonic is

$$-\frac{m(m + 1)c^2 + \overline{M}}{a^2 - c^2} = k^2,$$

where k is some integer not greater than m;

$$k = 0, 1, 2, \cdots, m.$$

Hence, if $b^2 = a^2$, and the spheroid is prolate, there are $m + 1$ possible values of the constant $\overline{M}$, viz.,

$$M = (a^2 - c^2)k^2 - m(m + 1)a^2, \qquad k = 0, 1, 2, \cdots, m. \quad (6)$$

If $b^2 = c^2$, and the spheroid is oblate, the values of M are

$$\overline{M} = -(a^2 - c^2)k^2 - m(m + 1)c^2, \qquad k = 0, 1, 2, \cdots, m.$$

Each of the $2m + 1$ tesseral harmonics of degree m is thus a limiting form for one of the $2m + 1$ surface harmonics V_2V_3 of Lamé, when b^2 tends toward a^2 or toward c^2. In the first case, the limits are

$$V_2 = \sin k\omega_2, \quad \text{or} \quad \cos k\omega_2, \qquad \text{and} \quad V_3 = T_{nk}(\omega_3),$$

in which ω_2 plays the rôle of the longitude θ, and ω_3 the polar distance φ. In the second case, the limits are

$$V_2 = T_{nk}(\omega_2), \qquad \text{and} \qquad V_3 = \sin k\omega_3, \quad \text{or} \quad \cos k\omega_3,$$

in which ω_2 plays the rôle of the polar distance φ, and ω_3 plays the rôle of the longitude θ.

233. The Roots of the Characteristic Equation Considered As Functions of t.

—Suppose $m = 2n$ is even. There is a characteristic equation in M, or in $\overline{M} = M - m(m + 1)h$, (Eq. (216.10)), for class I, and one for each of the cases in class III.

Consider first the roots of the characteristic equation in $\overline{M}$ for class I. These roots are functions of t, if b^2 is regarded as a function of t. There are $n + 1$ of them, and each gives rise to a polynomial of Lamé which has the form

$$V = \prod_{i=1}^{n+1} (q - \alpha_i);$$

therefore

$$V_2 = \prod_{i=1}^{n+1} (q_2 - \alpha_i) = \prod_{i=1}^{n+1} (a^2 - \alpha_i - t(a^2 - c^2) \cos^2 \omega_2).$$

The α_i, which are the roots of the polynomials of Lamé in q, also are functions of t. As was shown in the preceeding section, the limit of V_2 for $t = 0$ is $\cos k\omega_2$, or $\sin k\omega_2$, aside from a constant factor. For some values of i, at least, $a^2 - \alpha_i$ must have t as a factor, which of course, can be removed, unless V_2 reduces to a constant. In any event V_2 is a function of $\cos^2 \omega_2$, and therefore, an even function of ω_2. It could not reduce to $\sin k\omega_2$ which is an odd function of ω_2. Also, since $2\cos^2 \omega_2 = 1 + \cos 2\omega_2$, V_2 is an even function of $2\omega_2$. Hence, the limits of the $n + 1$ functions V_2 of class I are

$$\cos 0\omega_2, \qquad \cos 2\omega_2, \qquad \cos 4\omega_2, \qquad \cdots, \qquad \cos 2n\omega_2.$$

That is to say, k is an even integer if V_2 is of class I.

If V_2 belongs to class III, each of the three characteristic equations has n roots. The forms of the polynomials are

$$V_2 = \sqrt{(q_2 - b^2)(q_2 - c^2)} \prod_{i=1}^{n} (q_2 - \alpha_i), \qquad (a)$$

$$V_2 = \sqrt{-(q_2 - c^2)(q_2 - a^2)} \prod_{i=1}^{n} (q_2 - \alpha_i), \qquad (b)$$

$$V_2 = \sqrt{-(q_2 - a^2)(q_2 - b^2)} \prod_{i=1}^{n} (q_2 - \alpha_i) \qquad (c)$$

A reference to the formulas of Sec. 232 shows that these expressions become, aside from a constant factor,

$$V_2 = \sqrt{1 - t\cos^2 \omega_2} \cdot \sin \omega_2$$
$$\times \prod (a^2 - \alpha_i - t(a^2 - c^2)\cos^2 \omega_2), \quad (a)$$

$$V_2 = \sqrt{1 - t\cos^2 \omega_2} \cdot \cos \omega_2$$
$$\times \prod (a^2 - \alpha_i - t(a^2 - c^2)\cos^2 \omega_2), \quad (b)$$

$$V_3 = \sin \omega_2 \cos \omega_2 \prod (a^2 - \alpha_i - t(a^2 - c^2)\cos^2 \omega_2). \qquad (c)$$

The limiting values of these expressions are, evidently,

$$V_2 = \sin \omega_2, \qquad \sin 3\omega_2, \qquad \cdots, \qquad \sin (2n - 1)\omega_2, \quad (a)$$

$$V_2 = \cos \omega_2, \qquad \cos 3\omega_2, \qquad \cdots, \qquad \cos (2n - 1)\omega_2, \quad (b)$$

$$V_2 = \sin 2\omega_2, \qquad \sin 4\omega_2, \qquad \cdots, \qquad \sin 2n\omega_2. \qquad (c)$$

Hence, the integer k is odd for groups (a) and (b) and even for (c). All of the $2m + 1$ functions are accounted for, since

$$(n + 1) + n + n + n = 4n + 1 = 2m + 1.$$

A similar analysis holds if $m = 2n + 1$ is odd.

234. The Characteristic Equation Has No Multiple Roots.— It was shown in Sec. 226 that all of the roots of the characteristic equation are real. It is also a fundamental property that the roots are all distinct. This is evident from Eq. (232.6) when t is zero.

For brevity of notation let

$$a^2 - c^2 = A \qquad \text{and} \qquad -m(m + 1)a^2 = B.$$

For classes I and III(b), and for $t = 0$, these roots are

$$B, \quad 2A + B, \quad 4A + B, \quad \cdots, \quad 2nA + B, \tag{I}$$

$$A + B, \quad 3A + B, \cdots, \quad (2n - 1)A + B. \tag{III(b)}$$

It will be observed that the roots for III(b) lie midway between the roots for class I. As t increases from zero to one, all of these roots vary. Two of the roots of class I cannot become equal without first (or simultaneously) coinciding with one of the roots of class III(b). It will be shown that a root of class I cannot coincide with a root of class III(b).

Suppose a root of class I does coincide with a root of class III(b), and let U_1 be the corresponding polynomial of class I and U_3 be the corresponding polynomial of class III(b). Then

$$U_1 = P_1(\wp), \qquad U_3 = \sqrt{\wp_3 \wp_1}\, P_3(\wp). \tag{1}$$

Both of these expressions satisfy the same differential equation, since, by hypothesis, N and M are the same for both, namely,

$$\frac{d^2 U_1}{du^2} = (N\wp + M)U_1, \qquad \frac{d^2 U_3}{du^2} = (N\wp + M)U_3.$$

Consequently

$$U_3 \frac{d^2 U_1}{du^2} - U_1 \frac{d^2 U_3}{du^2} = 0,$$

and therefore,

$$U_3 \frac{dU_1}{du} - U_1 \frac{dU_3}{du} = \text{const.} \tag{2}$$

Since

$$\frac{dU_1}{du} = \frac{dU_1}{d\wp}\wp', \qquad \frac{dU_3}{du} = \frac{dU_3}{d\wp}\wp',$$

and

$$\wp' = -2\sqrt{\wp_1\wp_2\wp_3},$$

this result (Eq. (2)) reduces to

(Rational function of $\wp$)$\sqrt{\wp_2}$ = const.,

which is impossible unless the constant is zero. But if the constant is zero, Eq. (2) gives

$$U_3 = U_1 \times \text{const.}$$

which, also, is impossible by Eq. (1).

It follows, therefore, that the roots of the characteristic equation of class I cannot coincide with any of the roots of class III(b), and neither of the characteristic equations can have a double or multiple root.

A similar argument holds for the other classes. *The roots of a characteristic equation are all distinct.*

235. The Functions of Lamé are Linearly Independent.—

On account of the irrationalities which are involved, there is no question with respect to linear independence between the different classes. It is necessary to show, however, that for the same characteristic equation there cannot exist a relation of the form

$$V^{(i+1)} = a_1 V^{(1)} + a_2 V^{(2)} + \cdots + a_i V^{(i)},$$

where $V^{(j)}$ is the function of Lamé associated with the root M_j, $j = 1, 2, \cdots, n - 1$, or n, according to the class, and a_j is a constant different from zero. Suppose such a relation did exist, and that

$$V^{(i+1)} = \sum_{j=1}^{i} a_j V^{(j)}, \qquad i < n - 1, \text{ or } n. \tag{1}$$

The function $V^{(j)}$ satisfies the equation

$$\frac{d^2 V^{(j)}}{du^2} = N\wp V^{(j)} + M_j V^{(j)}. \tag{2}$$

Multiply this equation by the constant a_j and then sum with respect to j. There results

$$\sum a_j \frac{d^2 V^{(j)}}{du^2} = N\wp \sum a_j V^{(j)} + \sum M_j a_j V^{(j)}, \tag{3}$$

which by virtue of Eq. (1) reduces to

$$\frac{d^2 V^{(i+1)}}{du^2} = N\wp V^{(i+1)} + \sum M_j a_j V^j. \tag{4}$$

By virtue of Eq. (2)

$$\frac{d^2 V^{(i+1)}}{du^2} = N\wp V^{(i+1)} + M_{i+1} V^{(i+1)}.$$

A comparison of Eqs. (3) and (4) shows that

$$M_{i+1} V^{(i+1)} = \sum_{j=1}^{i} M_j a_j V^{(j)},$$

or

$$0 = \sum_{j=1}^{i} (M_{i+1} - M_j) a_j V^{(j)}. \tag{5}$$

Since the roots of the characteristic equation are all distinct, none of the coefficients vanishes. It follows that if such a relation as Eq. (1) existed between $i + 1$ functions of Lamé, a similar relation would exist between i functions of Lamé. A repetition of the argument would show such a relation between $i - 1$ functions of Lamé, and so on; until, finally, an equation of the form

$$0 = (M_2 - M_1) b_1 V^{(1)}$$

was reached, where b_1 is a constant different from zero. As this result is impossible, it follows that no such relation as Eq. (1) exists, and the functions of Lamé are linearly independent.

Since V_2 is a function of q_2 and V_3 is a function of q_3, it follows at once that there cannot exist a relation of the form

$$0 = \sum_{j=1}^{i} a_j V_2{}^{(j)} V_3{}^{(j)}, \qquad i \leqq n - 1, \text{ or } n.$$

Hence *the surface harmonics of Lamé are linearly independent, and they form a complete, or fundamental, system.*

236. The Expansion of an Arbitrary Function in Terms of the Ellipsoidal Harmonics.—Any given homogeneous polynomial in x, y, and z can be expressed as a linear combination of surface tesseral harmonics of degree m. Let $K_m{}^{(j)}(\varphi, \theta)$, $j = 1, 2, \cdots$, $2m + 1$, be the tesseral harmonics of degree m, and $L_m{}^{(j)} =$

$(V_2V_3)_m{}^{(j)}$, $j = 1, 2, \cdots, 2m + 1$, be the surface harmonics of Lamé of degree m. Then

$$H_m(x, y, z) = r^m \sum_{j=1}^{2m+1} A_j K_m{}^{(j)},$$

and, also,

$$H_m(x, y, z) = r^m \sum_{j=1} B_j L_m{}^{(j)}$$

where A_j and B_j are constants. Since both systems of harmonics are linearly independent it follows that there exist constants $C_i{}^{(j)}$ and $D_i{}^{(j)}$ such that

$$K_m{}^{(j)} = \sum_{i=1}^{2m+1} C_i{}^{(j)} L_m{}^{(i)},$$

and also,

$$L_m{}^{(j)} = \sum_{i=1}^{2m+1} D_i{}^{(j)} K_m{}^{(i)}.$$

That is, any harmonic in one system can be expressed linearly in terms of the other. The two systems are, therefore, equivalent.

Suppose there is given a function $F(q_2, q_3)$. By means of the relations given in Eq. (231.3) it is possible to translate this function into a function of polar coordinates φ, θ, since

$$\xi = \sin \varphi \cos \theta, \qquad \eta = \sin \varphi \sin \theta, \qquad \zeta = \cos \varphi.$$

Suppose

$$F(q_2, q_3) = \Phi(\varphi, \theta).$$

The function $\Phi(\varphi, \theta)$, under certain very general conditions, can be expanded in a series of surface harmonics in accordance with the theorem of Sec. 206,

$$\Phi(\varphi, \theta) = \sum_{m=0}^{\infty} S_m(\varphi, \theta),$$

where S_m is a surface harmonic of degree m. But, as has just been seen, S_m can be expressed in terms of the ellipsoidal harmonics,

$$S_m(\varphi, \theta) = \sum_{j=1}^{2m+1} A_m{}^{(j)} L_m{}^{(j)},$$

where the $A_m{}^{(j)}$ are constants. Hence

$$\Phi(\varphi, \theta) = F(q_2, q_3) = \sum_{m=0}^{\infty} \left(\sum_{j=1}^{2m+1} A_m{}^{(j)} L_m{}^{(j)}(q_2, q_3) \right).$$

If the function $\Phi(\varphi, \theta)$ on the sphere of radius r, when expressed in terms of the rectangular coordinates, is a polynomial of degree s in x, y, and z, the series of harmonics is finite, and

$$F(q_2, q_3) = \sum_{m=0}^{s} \left(\sum_{j=1}^{2m+1} A_m{}^{(j)} L_m{}^{(j)}(q_2 q_3) \right).$$

237. Surface Integrals.—The derivative of the harmonic function

$$V = V_1 V_2 V_3$$

normal to the ellipsoid $q_1 = $ const. is (Eq. (214.3))

$$\frac{\partial V}{\partial n} = \frac{V_2 V_3}{R_1} \frac{dV_1}{dq_1},$$

where, Eq. (214.2),

$$R_1 = \frac{\sqrt{(q_1 - q_2)(q_1 - q_3)}}{\sqrt{(q_1 - a^2)(q_1 - b^2)(q_1 - c^2)}} = \frac{A}{A_1 \sqrt{q_3 - q_2}}.$$

The surface element $d\omega$ on the ellipsoid is (Eq.(214.4))

$$d\omega = R_2 R_3 dq_2 dq_3.$$

Since the surface integral of the normal derivative of an harmonic function over any closed surface is zero (Eq. (62.2)) it follows that

$$\int \frac{\partial V}{\partial n} d\omega = \int_b^a \int_c^b V_2 V_3 \frac{dV_1}{dq_1} \frac{R_2 R_3}{R_1} dq_2 dq_3,$$

$$= \frac{A_1}{2} \frac{dV_1}{dq_1} \int \int \frac{V_2 V_3}{A_2 A_3}(q_3 - q_2) dq_2 dq_3 = 0,$$

and therefore,

$$\int_b^a \int_c^b \frac{V_2 V_3}{A_2 A_3}(q_3 - q_2) dq_2 dq_3 = 0;$$

or, since

$$\frac{dq_2}{2A_2} = du_2, \qquad \frac{dq_3}{2A_3} = du_3,$$

$$\int_{e_2}^{e_1} \int_{e_3}^{e_2} V_2 V_3 (\wp u_3 - \wp u_2) du_2 du_3 = 0.$$

Again, if U_1 and U_2 are two harmonic functions it follows from Green's theorem (Eq. (62.1)) that

$$\int\left(U_2\frac{\partial U_1}{\partial n} - U_1\frac{\partial U_2}{\partial n}\right)d\omega = 0. \tag{1}$$

Suppose that

$$U_1 = (V_1V_2V_3)_s{}^{(j)} = V_{1s}{}^{(j)}L_s{}^{(j)},$$

and

$$U_2 = (V_1V_2V_3)_t{}^{(k)} = V_{1t}{}^{(k)}L_t{}^{(k)},$$

are ellipsoidal harmonics of degrees s and t respectively. Then Eq. (1) becomes

$$\left(V_{1t}{}^{(k)}\frac{\partial V_{1s}{}^{(j)}}{\partial q_1} - V_{1s}{}^{(j)}\frac{\partial V_{1t}{}^{(k)}}{\partial q_1}\right)\int_E L_s{}^{(j)}L_t{}^{(k)}\frac{d\omega}{R_1} = 0.$$

The factor outside of the integral sign is a function of q_1 alone, and therefore constant on the ellipsoid. It is not zero, unless

$$V_{1t}{}^{(k)} = CV_{1s}{}^{(j)};$$

and in order that this should be so, it is necessary not only that $s = t$, but also $k = j$. That is U_1 differs from U_2 only by a constant factor. Assuming that U_1 and U_2 are different harmonics, though they may be of the same degree, it follows that

$$\int_E L_s{}^{(j)}L_t{}^{(k)}\frac{d\omega}{R_1} = 0,$$

or, since the denominator of R_1 is a function of q_1 alone,

$$\int_E \frac{L_s{}^{(j)}L_t{}^{(k)}d\omega}{\sqrt{(q_1 - q_2)(q_1 - q_3)}} = 0,$$

the integral being taken over the entire surface. By taking

$$\sqrt{(q_1 - q_2)(q_1 - q_3)} = \frac{1}{l},$$

this important formula can be written in the more compact form

$$\int_E lL_s{}^{(j)}L_t{}^{(k)}d\omega = 0. \tag{2}$$

It is a simple matter to show that

$$l = -\frac{du_1}{dn}; \tag{3}$$

for

$$du_1 = -\frac{dq_1}{2A_1} \qquad \text{by Eq. (215.2),}$$

and

$$dn = R_1 dq_1.$$

Hence

$$\frac{du_1}{dn} = -\frac{1}{2A_1R_1} = \frac{-1}{\sqrt{(q_1 - q_2)(q_1 - q_3)}}, \qquad \text{by Eq. (214.1),}$$

$$= -l.$$

A general formula for the integral

$$\int_E l(L_s^{(j)})^2 d\omega,$$

apparently, has not been worked out.

238. The Coefficients of an Expansion in Terms of Ellipsoidal Harmonics.—It was shown in Sec. 236 that a function $F(q_2, q_3)$ can be expanded in a series of ellipsoidal harmonics, namely,

$$F(q_2, q_3) = \sum_{m=0}^{\infty} \left(\sum_{j=1}^{2m+1} A_m^{(j)} L_m^{(j)}(q_2, q_3) \right), \tag{1}$$

where the coefficients $A_m^{(j)}$ are constants. If this expression is multiplied by $lL_m^{(j)} d\omega$ and then integrated over the ellipsoid E, there results

$$\int_E lF L_m^{(j)} d\omega = A_m^{(j)} \int_E l(L_m^{(j)})^2 d\omega,$$

all of the other terms of the expansion vanishing by Eq. (237.2). Hence

$$A_m^{(j)} = \frac{\int_E lF L_m^{(j)} d\omega}{\int_E l(L_m^{(j)})^2 d\omega}. \tag{2}$$

It will be observed that these coefficients are independent of q_1, since

$$ld\omega = lR_2R_3 dq_2 dq_3$$

$$= \frac{(q_3 - q_2)}{4\sqrt{-A_2^2 A_3^2}} dq_2 dq_3, \qquad \text{by Eq. (214.2),}$$

does not contain q_1. This expression is real since A_2^2 is negative.

If $F_m(q_2, q_3)$ is a polynomial in q_2, q_3 multiplied by the radicals

$$\sqrt{(q_2 - a^2)^{\alpha}(q_2 - b^2)^{\beta}(q_2 - c^2)^{\gamma}},$$

and

$$\sqrt{(q_3 - a^2)^{\alpha}(q_3 - b^2)^{\beta}(q_3 - c^2)^{\gamma}},$$

is symmetric with respect to the subscripts 2 and 3, and is of degree m in q_2 and q_3, its expansion in terms of the ellipsoidal harmonics terminates, and the highest degree of the harmonics which occurs is m.   Hence, if $k > m$, it is evident that

$$\int_E lF_m L_k^{(j)} d\omega = 0, \tag{3}$$

$L_k^{(j)}$ being any harmonic of degree $k > m$.

239. The Roots of Lamé's Polynomials are Real, Distinct, and Lie between a^2 and b^2.—The theorem that the roots of Lamé's polynomials (Eq. (220.2)) are real and distinct, and lie between a^2 and c^2 is analogous to the theorem that the roots of the zonal harmonics are real and distinct, and lie between $+1$ and -1. The theorem is important since these roots define the lines on the surface of the ellipsoid along which the harmonics vanish (see Figs. 109, 110, and 111).   The following proof is due to Appell.[1]

In Secs. 221 to 224 Lamé's polynomials P were regarded as polynomials in $\wp u$, but since (Eq. (216.3))

$$\wp u = q - h$$

they can be regarded also as polynomials of the same degree in q. It is as polynomials in q that the roots lie between a^2 and c^2.   It is easily verified that as polynomials in $\wp$ the roots lie between e_1 and e_3.

(a) *The Roots are All Real.*—Consider first class I, Eq. (220.2),

$$V = P(q).$$

The polynomial $P(q)$ which is of degree n can be resolved into its linear factors.   Since the coefficients of P are real, the complex factors, if any occur, will occur in pairs, the products of which are real.   The product of all of the complex factors is a real polynomial, and the product of the real factors also is a real polynomial.   Therefore,

$$P(q) = P_1(q) \cdot P_2(q)$$

can be resolved into two factors, one of which P_1 has all of its roots real, and the other P_2 has only complex roots.   The product of Lamé is

$$L_m = (V_2 V_3)_m = P_1(q_2)P_1(q_3) \cdot P_2(q_2)P_2(q_3).$$

[1] APPELL, P., "Traité de Mécanique Rationnelle," Vol. IV, p. 157.

In Eq. (238.3), let

$$F = P_1(q_2)P_1(q_3),$$

which is of degree less than m, unless P_2 is a constant.   Then

$$\int_E lFL_m d\omega = \int_E lP_1{}^2(q_2)P_1{}^2(q_3)P_2(q_2)P_2(q_3)d\omega = 0.$$

This formula is applicable, if there are any complex roots, since the degree of F is less than m.   The result obviously is impossible, since the integrand is always of the same sign.   It follows, therefore, that there are no complex roots if $V = P$ is of class I.

If V does not belong to class I, it has the form

$$V = \sqrt{(q - a^2)^\alpha(q - b^2)^\beta(q - c^2)^\gamma}P = R(q) \cdot P(q)$$

where α, β, and γ are either 0 or 1.   Also

$$L_m = (V_2V_3)_m = R(q_2)R(q_3)P_1(q_2)P_1(q_3)P_2(q_2)P_2(q_3),$$

where P_1 and P_2 have the same significance as before.   If

$$F = R(q_2)R(q_3)P_1(q_2)P_1(q_3),$$

then, if P has any complex roots,

$$\int_E lR^2(q_2)R^2(q_3)P_1{}^2(q_2)P_1{}^2(q_3)P_2(q_2)P_2(q_3)d\omega = 0.$$

Since

$$R^2(q_2) = (q_2 - a^2)^\alpha(q_2 - b^2)^\beta(q_2 - c^2)^\gamma,$$
$$R^2(q_3) = (q_3 - a^2)^\alpha(q_3 - b^2)^\beta(q_3 - c^2)^\gamma,$$

and

$$a^2 > q_2 > b^2 > q_3 > c^2,$$

it is seen again that the integrand does not change sign and the surface integral cannot vanish. It follows, therefore, that whatever class V may have, the roots of the polynomial P are all real.

(b) *The Roots are All Distinct.*—Suppose the roots of the polynomial P are not all distinct.   Conceivably, they may have any order of multiplicity, say,

$$P = \Pi(q - \alpha_i)^{n_i}.$$

The polynomial P will be resolved, just as before into the product of two polynomials

$$P = P_1P_2$$

in which P_2 contains factors which occur an even number of times and P_1 those which occur an odd number of times.   Thus, if n_i is even, the factor $(q - \alpha_i)^{n_i}$ is put in P_2, but if $n_i = 2s + 1$ is odd, the factor $(q - \alpha_i)^{2s}$ is taken into P_2 and the single factor $(q - \alpha_i)$ is included in P_1. With this resolution of the polynomial P, the polynomial P_2 does not change sign. If then F is taken equal to P_1, and if P_2 is not of degree zero, the surface integral becomes, just as before,

$$\int_E l P_1^2 P_2 d\omega = 0,$$

which also is impossible. Hence P_2 must be of degree zero, and the roots are all distinct.

(c) *All of the Roots Lie between a^2 and c^2.*—Substantially the same argument suffices to prove that all of the roots lie between a^2 and c^2. Let P_1 be the product of the factors which vanish between a^2 and c^2, and P_2 the product of all of the factors which vanish outside of these limits. If F is taken equal to P_1, and if the degree of P_2 is not zero, the surface integral again leads to a contradiction, since P_2 does not change sign within the limits of integration. It follows therefore that the degree of P_2 is zero and that all of the roots lie between a^2 and c^2.

240. Ellipsoidal Harmonics of the Second Kind.—Since, by Eq. (213.5),

$$q_1 + q_2 + q_3 = r^2 + (a^2 + b^2 + c^2)$$

and

$$a^2 > q_2 > b^2 > q_3 > c^2$$

it is evident, that if r^2 is very large, q_1 is approximately equal to r^2, and the function of Lamé V_1 of degree m is approximately equal to r^m. Consequently the ellipsoidal harmonics $(V_1 V_2 V_3)_k$ are not suitable for the expansions of potentials in the neighborhood of infinity, just as the spherical harmonics which are polynomials in x, y, and z are not suitable. The spherical harmonics were made suitable, however, merely by dividing by a certain power of r. A somewhat similar possibility exists for the ellipsoidal harmonics.

It will be remembered that the function $V_1 V_2 V_3$ of degree m is harmonic by virtue of the fact that each of the letters V satisfies the differential equation (Eq. (220.1)),

$$\frac{d^2 V}{du^2} = [m(m + 1)\wp + M]V. \tag{1}$$

But as this differential equation is of the second order, it has two solutions. Let V be the solution already determined, and U the other solution. Then, also,

$$\frac{d^2 U}{du^2} = [m(m+1)\wp + M]U. \tag{2}$$

If Eq. (1) is multiplied by $-U$ and Eq. (2) by $+V$ and the two are then added, there results

$$V\frac{d^2 U}{du^2} - U\frac{d^2 V}{du} = 0;$$

therefore, by integration

$$V\frac{dU}{du} - U\frac{dV}{du} = \text{const.} = 2m + 1. \tag{3}$$

This constant is arbitrary since, if U is a solution of Eq. (2), CU also is a solution, C being any constant. Let the constant be taken equal to $2m + 1$. By virtue of this choice U becomes a perfectly definite function U_1, which, as will be shown, satisfies the relation

$$\lim_{r=\infty} r^{m+1} U_1(q_1) = 1.$$

If Eq. (3) is divided through by $V_1{}^2$, it can be written

$$\frac{d}{du_1}\left(\frac{U_1}{V_1}\right) = \frac{2m+1}{V_1{}^2}.$$

Therefore

$$U_1 = V_1 \int_0^{u_1} \frac{2m+1}{V_1{}^2} du \tag{4}$$

The lower limit of integration, of course, is arbitrary, but it is convenient to take it to be zero. It was shown in Sec. 220 that

$$V_1 = \frac{1}{u_1{}^m} + \frac{a - (m-1)}{u_1{}^{m-1}} + \cdots,$$

and in Sec. 216 that as u_1 tends toward zero, $\wp u_1$ tends toward $+\infty$. Hence, for large values of r, $q_1 = \wp u_1 + h$, is large, and u_1 is small. Using only the principal term of the expansion of V_1, it is seen that for large values of r, approximately,

$$U_1 = \frac{1}{u_1{}^m} \int_0^{u_1} (2m+1) u^{2m} du = u_1{}^{m+1}$$

$$= \frac{1}{r^{m+1}}$$

Hence
$$\lim_{r=\infty} r^{m+1} U_1 = 1.$$

Furthermore, since U_1 satisfies the differential equation (Eq. (1)), the function $U_1V_2V_3$ is harmonic. As r tends toward infinity V_2 and V_3 remain finite, but U_1 tends toward zero like $r^{-(m+1)}$. Hence the ellipsoidal harmonics of the second kind $(U_1V_2V_3)_m$ are suitable for expansions of exterior potentials.

241. The Potential of an Ellipsoidal Harmonic Surface Distribution of Matter.—It was shown in Sec. 209 that a spherical harmonic distribution of matter on the surface of a sphere produces a similar and similarly placed harmonic in both the exterior and interior potentials of the distribution. It will be shown in the present section that an analogous theorem holds for an ellipsoidal harmonic distribution of matter on an ellipsoid.

It was shown in Sec. 126 that if W_i is harmonic inside of a closed surface S, W_e is harmonic outside of S and vanishes at infinity, and if $W_i = W_e$ on S; there exists one and only one distribution on S for which the exterior potential is W_e and the interior potential is W_i. Furthermore the density of the distribution is

$$\sigma = \frac{1}{4\pi}\left[\frac{\partial W_e}{\partial n_i} + \frac{\partial W_i}{\partial n_e}\right].$$

For the given ellipsoid let
$$W_e = V_1^{(0)} U_1 L, \qquad W_i = U_1^{(0)} V_1 L$$
be ellipsoidal harmonics of degree m, where
$$L = (V_2 V_3)_m^{(j)},$$
the superscript zero indicating the value at the surface of the ellipsoid. Thus $V_1^{(0)}$ and $U_1^{(0)}$ are constants, and $W_e = W_i$ on the surface of the ellipsoid.

Now
$$\frac{\partial W_i}{\partial n_e} = +U_1^{(0)} L \frac{\partial V_1}{\partial n_e} = -l U_1^{(0)} L \frac{\partial V_1}{\partial u_1},$$
and
$$\frac{\partial W_e}{\partial n_i} = V_1^{(0)} L \frac{\partial U_1}{\partial n_i} = +l V_1^{(0)} L \frac{\partial U_1}{\partial u_1};$$
so that
$$\sigma = \frac{1}{4\pi}\left[\frac{\partial W_i}{\partial n_e} + \frac{\partial W_e}{\partial n_i}\right] = \frac{lL}{4\pi}\left(V_1^{(0)} \frac{\partial U_1}{\partial u_1} - U_1^{(0)} \frac{\partial V_1}{\partial u_1}\right),$$

the parenthesis being evaluated on the surface. Therefore, by Eq. (240.3),

$$4\pi\sigma = (2m + 1)lL.$$

Thus the surface distribution differs from an ellipsoidal harmonic distribution only by the factor l, which however is a function of q_2 and q_3 that is independent of m.

Conversely if the surface density is given by

$$\sigma = AlL$$

where A is a constant

$$W_e = \frac{4\pi A}{2m + 1}V_1{}^{(0)}U_1 L, \quad \text{and} \quad W_i = \frac{4\pi A}{2m + 1}U_1{}^{(0)}V_1 L.$$

242. The Potential of an Ellipsoidal Homoeoid.—If m is zero,

$$V_1 = V_2 = V_3 = L = 1,$$

and, by Eq. (240.4)

$$U_1 = u_1.$$

Then

$$\sigma = Al, \quad W_e = 4\pi A u_1, \quad W_i = 4\pi A U_1{}^{(0)}. \quad\quad (1)$$

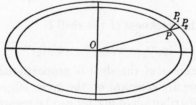

FIG. 112.

Consider the shell which is bounded by the given ellipsoid for which the axes are $q_1{}^{(0)} - a^2$, $q_1{}^{(0)} - b^2$, and $q_1{}^{(0)} - b^2$, and a similar ellipsoid which is infinitely close to it, Fig. 112. Their equations are

$$\frac{x^2}{q_1{}^{(0)} - a^2} + \frac{y^2}{q_1{}^{(0)} - b^2} + \frac{z^2}{q_1{}^{(0)} - c^2} = 1,$$

and

$$\frac{x^2}{q_1{}^{(0)} - a^2} + \frac{y^2}{q_1{}^{(0)} - b^2} + \frac{z^2}{q_1{}^{(0)} - c^2} = (1 + d\lambda)^2.$$

In the small triangle PP_1P_2,

$$PP_1 = dn, \quad PP_2 = ds, \quad OP = r.$$

Since the ellipsoids are similar

$$PP_2 = ds = rd\lambda,$$

since PP_1 is normal to both ellipsoids the angle at P_1 is a right angle, and

$$PP_1 = dn = PP_2 \cos P = r \cos P d\lambda.$$

The direction cosines of r are

$$\frac{x}{r}, \qquad \frac{y}{r}, \qquad \text{and} \qquad \frac{z}{r}.$$

The direction cosines of the normal are

$$\frac{1}{2R_1}\frac{x}{q_1^{(0)} - a^2}, \qquad \frac{1}{2R_1}\frac{y}{q_1^{(0)} - b^2}, \qquad \frac{1}{2R_1}\frac{z}{q_1^{(0)} - c^2}.$$

Hence

$$\cos P = \frac{1}{2R_1 r}\left[\frac{x^2}{q_1^{(0)} - a^2} + \frac{y^2}{q_1^{(0)} - b^2} + \frac{z^2}{q_1^{(0)} - c^2}\right] = \frac{1}{2rR_1},$$

and

$$dn = \frac{d\lambda}{2R_1};$$

or, since

$$\frac{1}{2R_1} = l\sqrt{(q_1^{(0)} - a^2)(q_1^{(0)} - b^2)(q_1^{(0)} - c^2)},$$

it results that the thickness of the shell is

$$dn = l\sqrt{(q_1^{(0)} - a^2)(q_1^{(0)} - b^2)(q_1^{(0)} - c^2)}d\lambda;$$

that is, the thickness of the shell is proportional to l, since the remaining factors are constant on the given ellipsoid.

The surface distribution of matter can be regarded as a volume distribution of constant density throughout the shell. If σ_0 is the constant volume density

$$\sigma = \sigma_0 dn$$

$$= \sigma_0 l\sqrt{(q_1^{(0)} - a^2)(q_1^{(0)} - b^2)(q_1^{(0)} - c^2)}d\lambda.$$

Consequently, if

$$A = \sigma_0\sqrt{(q_1^{(0)} - a^2)(q_1^{(0)} - b^2)(q_1^{(0)} - c^2)}d\lambda,$$

the potentials in Eq. (1) represent equally well the potentials of an ellipsoidal homoeoid, and since (Eq. (216.1))

$$u_1 = +\int_{q_1}^{\infty} \frac{dq}{\sqrt{4(q - a^2)(q - b^2)(q - c^2)}},$$

it is seen that

$$W_e = 2\pi\sigma_0 \sqrt{(q_1^{(0)} - a^2)(q_1^{(0)} - b^2)(q_1^{(0)} - c^2)}\ d\lambda$$

$$\times \int_{q_1}^{\infty} \frac{dq}{\sqrt{(q - a^2)(q - b^2)(q - c^2)}},$$

which, aside from notation, is the same result that was obtained in Sec. 123.

243. Green's Problem on an Ellipsoid.—The results already obtained with Lamé's functions furnish the solution of Green's problem (or, Dirichlet's problem, as it is often called) for an ellipsoid. Given a function F, which is defined on the surface of an ellipsoid. It is required to find a function which is harmonic within the ellipsoid and equal to F on the surface (interior problem), or, a function which is harmonic outside of the ellipsoid, equal to F on the surface, and which vanishes at infinity (exterior problem).

Let the function F be expanded in terms of the ellipsoidal harmonics in accordance with the principles of Sec. 236.

$$F = \sum_{m=0}^{\infty}\left[\sum_{j=1}^{2m+1} A_m^{(j)} L_m^{(j)}\right], \tag{1}$$

where $A_m^{(j)}$ are certain constants, which can also be written

$$A_m^{(j)} = B_m^{(j)}(V_1^{(0)} U_1^{(0)})_m^{(j)},$$

and therefore

$$F = \sum_{m=0}^{\infty}\left[\sum_{j=1}^{2m+1} B_m^{(j)}(V_1^{(0)} U_1^{(0)})_m^{(j)} L_m^{(j)}\right]. \tag{2}$$

For the interior problem take the function

$$W_i = \sum_{m=0}^{\infty}\left[\sum_{j=1}^{2m+1} B_m^{(j)}(V_1 U_1^{(0)})_m^{(j)} L_m^{(j)}\right]. \tag{3}$$

The series of Eq. (3) is convergent provided the series of Eq. (2), is convergent, since in the interior of the ellipsoid $V_1 < V_1^{(0)}$; and W_i is equal to F on the surface. Furthermore, it is harmonic, since it satisfies the equation of Laplace. It is, therefore, the function which was sought.

Similarly the function

$$W_e = \sum_{m=0}^{\infty} \left[\sum_{j=1}^{2m+1} B_m{}^{(j)} (V_1{}^{(0)} U_1)_m{}^{(j)} L_m{}^{(j)} \right]$$

satisfies all of the conditions for the exterior problem.

Therefore, W_i and W_e are the interior and exterior potentials of a certain distribution of matter on the surface of the ellipsoid. The density in this distribution is

$$\sigma = \frac{1}{4\pi} \left[\frac{\partial W_e}{\partial n_i} + \frac{\partial W_i}{\partial n_e} \right].$$

From the results of Sec. 241, it is easily seen that

$$\sigma = \frac{l}{4\pi} \sum_{m=0}^{\infty} (2n+1) \left[\sum_{j=1}^{2m+1} B_m{}^{(j)} L_m{}^{(j)} \right].$$

EXTENSION OF THE GENERAL THEORY

244. Fundamental Functions.—In addition to the spherical and ellipsoidal harmonics which are associated with the sphere and the ellipsoid, there exist other harmonic functions; for example, the Toroidal Function of Hicks[1] which are associated with the anchor ring. One concludes that there exists a corresponding set of harmonics functions associated with every closed surface.

The equation of Laplace which these functions satisfy is merely a particular case of the more general equations

$$a \frac{\partial^i U}{\partial t^i} + b \frac{\partial^2 U}{\partial x^2} + c \frac{\partial^2 U}{\partial y^2} + d \frac{\partial^2 U}{\partial z^2} + e \frac{\partial U}{\partial x} + f \frac{\partial U}{\partial y} + g \frac{\partial U}{\partial z} + h U = 0$$

in which i may have the values 1 or 2. The solution of various problems in electricity and magnetism, elasticity, acoustics and hydrodynamics depends upon the integration of such equations for which $i = 2$; and the solutions of many problems in the analytic theory of heat are reducible to the integration of such equations for $i = 1$.

For example, the vibrations of a mass of gas enclosed in a solid vessel is defined by the equation

$$\frac{\partial^2 U}{\partial x^2} + \frac{\partial^2 U}{\partial y^2} + \frac{\partial^2 U}{\partial z^2} = k^2 \frac{\partial^2 U}{\partial t^2}, \tag{1}$$

[1] Philosophical Transactions (1881).

in which k^2 is a positive constant, the solutions being subject to the conditions that

$$U = f_1(x, y, z), \qquad \frac{\partial U}{\partial n_i} = 0 \qquad \text{on } S,$$

and

$$\frac{\partial U}{\partial t} = f_2(x, y, z) \qquad \text{for} \qquad t = 0.$$

The equation of a cooling solid body leads to the equation

$$\frac{\partial^2 U}{\partial x^2} + \frac{\partial^2 U}{\partial y^2} + \frac{\partial^2 U}{\partial z^2} = k^2 \frac{\partial U}{\partial t}, \qquad (2)$$

together with the conditions that

$$U = f(x, y, z) \qquad \text{for} \qquad t = 0,$$

and

$$\frac{\partial U}{\partial n} + kU = 0 \qquad \text{on } S.$$

The time can be eliminated from Eq. (1), as was done by Cauchy, by assuming that

$$U = V_i(x, y, z)(A_j \sin \lambda_j t + B_j \cos \lambda_j t).$$

Equation (1) then reduces to

$$\Delta V_j + \lambda_j^2 k^2 V_j = 0 \qquad \text{within } S,$$

and

$$\frac{\partial V_j}{\partial n_i} = 0 \qquad \text{on } S;$$

and a similar reduction is possible for Eq. (2). The problem is then divisible into two parts.

(a) To demonstrate the existence of an infinity of simple solutions of Eq. (3), *i.e.* $j = 0, 1, 2, \cdots, \infty$.

(b) To establish the possibility of the development of a given function $f(x, y, z)$ within the given domain in a series which proceeds according to the functions V_j to which the simple functions reduce for $t = 0$.

The existence of such functions for problems of this type was established by Poincaré in his memoir Sur les Equations de la Physique Mathematique[1] in 1894, and were called Fundamental Functions. Similar sets of functions suitable for the expansions of other types of problems have been proved by other authors.

---

[1] POINCARÉ, "Acta Mathematica," Vol. XX; *American Journal of Mathematics*, Vol. XII, and "Rendiconti di Palermo," Vol. 8, p. 57 (1894).

It is of great interest to observe that all of these functions can be defined by certain integral equations of the form

$$V_i(x, y, z) = \lambda_j \int G(x, y, z; \xi, \eta, \zeta) V_i(\xi, \eta, \zeta) d\tau,$$

where λ_j is a certain constant and G is a generalized Green function, or, perhaps to a more general form

$$V_i(x, y, z) = \lambda_j \int p(\xi, \eta, \zeta) G(x, y, z; \xi, \eta, \zeta) V_i(\xi, \eta, \zeta) d\tau.$$

For an exposition of this extension of the theory the reader is referred to the works of Poincaré above mentioned and to the memoir by W. Steckloff, Theorié Generale des Fonctions Fondamentales.[1]

[1] Annales de la Faculté des Sciences de Toulouse. (1904.)

BIBLIOGRAPHY

The subject of Spherical Harmonics had its beginning in a paper of Legendre which was published in 1785, although it was written in 1782. Legendre's paper developed only the zonal harmonics, but it inspired Laplace's paper, also written in 1782, in which the general spherical harmonics, as functions of two angles, were developed, and in which also the theory of the potential was founded. Several decades elapsed before the fundamental papers of Green (1828) and Gauss (1841) appeared.

Among the volumes which are listed below that of Heine on Spherical Harmonics is the most nearly complete both as to the theory itself and also to the historical references. In some of the volumes, such as those of Neumann and of Poincaré, the author is concerned only with the theory of the potential. In others, such as those by Clerke Maxwell, Tisserand, Picard and Appell the theory of the potential is incidental to a larger field. In the articles of Burkhardt and Meyer in the German Enclyklopädie very complete references to the original memoirs will be found up to 1896, and in the article of Lichtenstein references to more recent papers up to 1918. References to certain papers which have appeared since that date will be found in a paper by O. D. Kellogg "Recent Progress with the Dirichlet Problem" in volume 32 of the Bulletin of the American Mathematical Society, p. 601.

EARLY MEMOIRS

Legendre, Sur l'attraction des spheroids, Memoirs de Mathematique et de Physique, presentes a l'Academie royale des sciences par divers savans, Tome X. (1785.)

Laplace, P. S., Theorie des attractions des spheroids et de la figure des planetes, *Mec. Cel.*, Tome III, Chap. III, Also Oeuvres, Vol. X. (1785.)

Green, George, "The Mathematical Papers of" (1828), edited by N. M. Ferrers, facsimile reprint, Paris. (1903.)

Gauss, C. F., Allgemeine Lehrsätze in Bezug auf die im verkehrten Verhältnisse des Quadrats der Entfernung wirkenden Anziehungs-und Abstossungs-Kräfte, Werke, Bde 5. (1841.)

BOOKS ON THE THEORY OF THE POTENTIAL

THOMPSON and TAIT, "Treatise on Natural Philosophy," Vol. II, Cambridge. (1867.)

MAXWELL, JAMES CLERK, "Electricity and Magnetism," Vol. I.   (1873.)

NEUMANN, C., "Untersuchungen über das Logarithmische und Newtonsche Potential," Leipsic.   (1877).

MATHIEU, E., "Theorie du Potentiel et ses Applications a l'Electrostatique et au Magnetisme," Paris.   (1886.)

PEIRCE, B. O., "The Newtonian Potential Function," Boston.   (1886.)

LEJEUNE-Dirichlet, P. G., "Vorlesungen über die im Umgekehrten Verhaltniss des Quadrats der Entfernung wirkenden Kräfte," herausgegeben von F. Grube, Leipsic.   (1887.)

NEUMANN, F., "Theorie des Potentials und der Kugelfunctionen," edited by C. Neumann.   (1887.)

TISSERAND, F., "Mecanique Celeste," Vol. II, Paris.   (1891.)

APPELL, PAUL, "Leçons sur l'attraction et la fonction potentielle," Paris.   (1892.)

POINCARÉ, HENRI, "Theorie du Potentiel Newtonien," Paris.   (1895.)

KORN, A., "Lehrbuch über das Logarithmische und Newtonsche Potential, Leipsic.   (1889.)

POINCARÉ, HENRI, "Figures d'Equilibre d'une Masse Fluide," rédigées par L. Dreyfus, Paris.   (1902.)

WEBSTER, A. G., "The Dynamics of Particles, and of Rigid, Elastic and Fluid Bodies," Leipsic.   (1904.)

PICARD, E., "Traite d'Analyse," Vol. II, Paris.   (1905.)

WANGERIN, A., "Theorie des Potentials und der Kugelfunctionen," Leipsic.   (1909.)

PLEMLJ, J., "Potentialtheoretische Untersuchungen," Leipsic.   (1911.)

OSGOOD, W. F., "Lehrbuch der Functionentheorie," Vol. I.   (1912.)

APPELL, PAUL, "Traite de Mecanique Rationelle," Vol. III.   (1908.) Vol. IV.   (1921.)

STERNBERG, W., "Potentialtheorie," two volumes, Berlin.   (1925–1926.)

EVANS, G. C., "The Logarithmic Potential, Discontinuous Dirichlet and Neumann Problems, *Colloquium Publications of the American Mathematical Society*, New York.   (1927.)

KELLOGG, O. D., "Foundations of the Potential Theory," Berlin.   (1929.)

BOOKS ON HARMONIC FUNCTIONS

LAMÉ, G., "Leçons sur les coordinees curvilignes et les diverses applications," Paris.   (1859.)

HEINE, E., "Theorie der Kugelfunctionen," 2 Ed., Berlin.   (1878.)

TODHUNTER, I., "The Functions of Laplace, Lamé, and Bessel."   (1875.)

FERRERS, N. M., "Spherical Harmonics," London.   (1877.)

BYERLY, W. E., "Fourier Series, and Spherical, Cylindrical, and Ellipsoidal Harmonics," Boston.   (1893.)

ON THE LITERATURE

BURKHARDT, H., and W. F. MEYER, Potentialtheorie, *Encyklopädie der Matematische Wissenschaften*, II A7b.

LICHTENSTEIN, L., Neuere Entwicklung der Potentialtheorie. Konforme Abbildung, *Encyklopädie*, II C3.

KELLOGG, O. D., Recent Progress with the Dirichlet Problem, *Bull. American Mathematical Society*, Vol. XXXII. (1926.)

INDEX

PARTIAL DIFFERENTIAL EQUATIONS OF MATHEMATICAL PHYSICS

by A. G. Webster

Still one of the most important treatises on partial differential equations in any language, this comprehensive work by one of America's greatest mathematical physicists covers the basic method, theory and application of partial differential equations. There are clear and full chapters on

Fourier series
integral equations
elliptic equations
spherical, cylindrical, ellipsoidal harmonics
Cauchy's method
boundary problems
method of Riemann-Volterra
and many other topics

This is a book complete in itself, developing fully the needed theory and application of every important field.

vibration
elasticity
potential theory
theory of sound
wave propagation
heat conduction
and others

Professor Webster's work is a keystone book in the library of every mature physicist, mathematical physicist, mathematician, and research engineer. It can also serve as an introduction and supplementary text for the student.

Edited by Samuel J. Plimpton. Second corrected edition. 97 illustrations. vii + 440pp. 5⅜ x 8.

S263 Paperbound **$2.00**

THEORETICAL MECHANICS: STATICS AND DYNAMICS OF A PARTICLE

by William Duncan MacMillan

Beginning with elementary concepts and postulates peculiar to mechanics, this exceptionally clear and comprehensive text carries the
student through vectors and their applications, to a thorough exposition of the statics of a particle and an intermediate level exposition of
particle dynamics. Each new concept is carefully defined and then
illustrated through the solution of hundreds of basic problems in astronomy, ballistics, transmission of power, stress and strain, elasticity, and
related topics. 340 practise problems and many examples fully worked
out in the text make it possible for anyone with a working knowledge
of calculus and differential equations to test and extend the principles
developed in the text while 200 key diagrams make the exposition
clear and explicit.

Partial Contents: PART I. Vectors, Velocity. Acceleration. Mass and
Force. Work and Energy. Center of Gravity. Moments of Inertia.
PART II. Statics of a Particle. Statics of Rigid Bodies: 1. Displacements.
2. Moments of Vectors. 4. Virtual Work. 6. Frameworks. Statics of
Deformable Bodies: 1. Funicular Polygons. 3. Elastic Solids. PART
III. Motion in a Straight Line: 1. Gravity and Gravitation. 2. Harmonic
Motion. 3. Conservative Forces in General. Curvilinear Motion. Cen-
tral Forces: 3. The Newtonian Law with a Fixed Center. 4. The Two-
body Problem. Constrained Motion: 1. Linear Constraints. 3. Tauto-
chrones and Brachistochrones. 4. Surface Constraints. The Generalized
Coordinates of Lagrange. The Canonical Equations of Hamilton. The
General Principles of Mechanics: 1. D'Alembert's Principle. 2. Prin-
ciple of Least Action. 3. Hamilton's Principle. 4. Gauss' Principle of
Least Constraint.

Complete and unabridged. 200 figures. 340 problems (about half
with answers). xvii + 430 pp. 5-3/8 x 8.

S467 Paperbound $2.00

THE FUNDAMENTAL PRINCIPLES OF QUANTUM MECHANICS, WITH ELEMENTARY APPLICATIONS
by Edwin C. Kemble

Written by the Professor of Physics at Harvard University, this volume is an inductive presentation of quantum mechanics designed for the graduate student or the specialist in some other branch of physics. While some acquaintance with advanced mathematics and the data of the physical sciences is desirable, treatment is simple, clear, and easily followed. Applications of the theory have been interwoven with the development of the basic mathematical structure.

PARTIAL CONTENTS. Introduction to dualistic theory of matter; development of Schroedinger's wave equation. Wave packets and the relation between classical mechanics and wave mechanics. One-dimensional energy-level problems. The mathematical theory of complete systems of orthogonal functions. The discrete energy spectrum of the two-particle central-field problem. The continuous spectrum and the basic properties of solutions of the many-particle problem. Dynamical variables and operators. Commutation rules and related matters. The measurement of dynamic variables. Matrix theory. Theory of perturbations which do not involve the time. Quantum statistical mechanics and the Einstein transition probabilities. Introduction to the problem of atomic structure; electron spin. The theory of the structure pf, amy-electron atoms. Appendices.

"This excellent book should be of great value to every student who desires to obtain a thorough understanding of quantum mechanics. The author has given a detailed and rigorous mathematical discussion of all of the principle quantum-mechanical methods; and he has succeeded in keeping his presentation clear and understandable," Dr. Linus Pauling, in JOURNAL OF THE AMERICAN CHEMICAL SOCIETY. Index. 611pp. 5⅜ x 8.

Paperbound $2.75

NUMERICAL INTEGRATION OF DIFFERENTIAL EQUATIONS

by A. A. Bennett, W. E. Milne, Harry Bateman

This well-known, greatly sought-after volume is an unabridged re-publication of an original monograph prepared for the National Research Council. It describes new methods of integration of differential equations developed by three leading mathematicians, and contains much material not readily available in detail elsewhere. Of special interest to mathematicians, physicists and mathematical physicists are the discussions on methods for partial differential equations, transition from difference equations to differential equations, and solution of differential equations to non-integral values of a parameter.

PARTIAL CONTENTS: "The Interpolational Polynomial," A. A. Bennett. Tabular index, arguments, values, differences. Displacements, divided differences, repeated arguments, derivation of the interpolational polynomial, integral. "Successive Approximations," A. A. Bennett. Numerical methods of successive substitutions. Approximate methods in solution of differential equations. "Step-by-Step Methods of Integration," W. E. Milne. Differential equations of the 1st order: Taylor's series, methods using ordinates, Runge-Kutta method. Systems of differential equations of the first order. Higher order differential equations. Second order equations in which first derivatives are absent. "Methods for Partial Differential Equations," Harry Bateman. Transition from solution of difference equations to solution of differential equations. Ritz's method. Least squares method. Extension of solution to nonintegral values of a parameter.

288 footnotes, mostly bibliographic; 285-item classified bibliography. Index. 108pp. 5⅜ x 8.

S305 Paperbound **$1.35**

Catalogue of Dover
SCIENCE BOOKS

BOOKS THAT EXPLAIN SCIENCE

THE NATURE OF LIGHT AND COLOUR IN THE OPEN AIR, M. Minnaert. Why is falling snow sometimes black? What causes mirages, the fata morgana, multiple suns and moons in the sky; how are shadows formed? Prof. Minnaert of U. of Utrecht answers these and similar questions in optics, light, colour, for non-specialists. Particularly valuable to nature, science students, painters, photographers. "Can best be described in one word—fascinating!" Physics Today. Translated by H. M. Kremer-Priest, K. Jay. 202 illustrations, including 42 photos. xvi + 362pp. 5⅜ x 8. T196 Paperbound **$1.95**

THE RESTLESS UNIVERSE, Max Born. New enlarged version of this remarkably readable account by a Nobel laureate. Moving from sub-atomic particles to universe, the author explains in very simple terms the latest theories of wave mechanics. Partial contents: air and its relatives, electrons and ions, waves and particles, electronic structure of the atom, nuclear physics. Nearly 1000 illustrations, including 7 animated sequences. 325pp. 6 x 9. T412 Paperbound **$2.00**

MATTER AND LIGHT, THE NEW PHYSICS, L. de Broglie. Non-technical papers by a Nobel laureate explain electromagnetic theory, relativity, matter, light, radiation, wave mechanics, quantum physics, philosophy of science. Einstein, Planck, Bohr, others explained so easily that no mathematical training is needed for all but 2 of the 21 chapters. "Easy simplicity and lucidity . . . should make this source-book of modern physcis available to a wide public," Saturday Review. Unabridged. 300pp. 5⅜ x 8. T35 Paperbound **$1.60**

THE COMMON SENSE OF THE EXACT SCIENCES, W. K. Clifford. Introduction by James Newman, edited by Karl Pearson. For 70 years this has been a guide to classical scientific, mathematical thought. Explains with unusual clarity basic concepts such as extension of meaning of symbols, characteristics of surface boundaries, properties of plane figures, vectors, Cartesian method of determining position, etc. Long preface by Bertrand Russell. Bibliography of Clifford. Corrected. 130 diagrams redrawn. 249pp. 5⅜ x 8. T61 Paperbound **$1.60**

THE EVOLUTION OF SCIENTIFIC THOUGHT FROM NEWTON TO EINSTEIN, A. d'Abro. Einstein's special, general theories of relativity, with historical implications, analyzed in non-technical terms. Excellent accounts of contributions of Newton, Riemann, Weyl, Planck, Eddington, Maxwell, Lorentz, etc., are treated in terms of space, time, equations of electromagnetics, finiteness of universe, methodology of science. "Has become a standard work," Nature. 21 diagrams. 482pp. 5⅜ x 8. T2 Paperbound **$2.00**

BRIDGES AND THEIR BUILDERS, D. Steinman, S. R. Watson. Engineers, historians, everyone ever fascinated by great spans will find this an endless source of information and interest. Dr. Steinman, recent recipient of Louis Levy Medal, is one of the great bridge architects, engineers of all time. His analysis of great bridges of history is both authoritative and easily followed. Greek, Roman, medieval, oriental bridges; modern works such as Brooklyn Bridge, Golden Gate Bridge, etc. described in terms of history, constructional principles, artistry, function. Most comprehensive, accurate semi-popular history of bridges in print in English. New, greatly revised, enlarged edition. 23 photographs, 26 line drawings. xvii + 401pp. 5⅜ x 8. T431 Paperbound **$1.95**

CONCERNING THE NATURE OF THINGS, Sir William Bragg. Christmas lectures at Royal Society by Nobel laureate, dealing with atoms, gases, liquids, and various types of crystals. No scientific background is needed to understand this remarkably clear introduction to basic processes and aspects of modern science. "More interesting than any bestseller," London Morning Post. 32pp. of photos. 57 figures. xii + 232pp. 5⅜ x 8.   T31 Paperbound **$1.35**

THE RISE OF THE NEW PHYSICS, A. d'Abro. Half million word exposition, formerly titled "The Decline of Mechanism," for readers not versed in higher mathematics. Only thorough explanation in everyday language of core of modern mathematical physical theory, treating both classical, modern views. Scientifically impeccable coverage of thought from Newtonian system through theories of Dirac, Heisenberg, Fermi's statistics. Combines history, exposition; broad but unified, detailed view, with constant comparison of classical, modern views. "A must for anyone doing serious study in the physical sciences," J. of the Franklin Inst. "Extraordinary faculty . . . to explain ideas and theories . . . in language of everyday life," Isis. Part I of set: philosophy of science, from practice of Newton, Maxwell, Poincaré, Einstein, etc. Modes of thought, experiment, causality, etc. Part II: 100 pp. on grammar, vocabulary of mathematics, discussions of functions, groups, series, Fourier series, etc. Remainder treats concrete, detailed coverage of both classical, quantum physics: analytic mechanics, Hamilton's principle, electromagnetic waves, thermodynamics, Brownian movement, special relativity, Bohr's atom, de Broglie's wave mechanics, Heisenberg's uncertainty, scores of other important topics. Covers discoveries, theories of d'Alembert, Born, Cantor, Debye, Euler, Foucault, Galois, Gauss, Hadamard, Kelvin, Kepler Laplace, Maxwell, Pauli, Rayleigh Volterra, Weyl, more than 180 others. 97 illustrations. ix + 982pp. 5⅜ x 8.
T3 Vol. 1 Paperbound **$2.00**
T4 Vol. II Paperbound **$2.00**

SPINNING TOPS AND GYROSCOPIC MOTION, John Perry. Well-known classic of science still unsurpassed for lucid, accurate, delightful exposition. How quasi-rigidity is induced in flexible, fluid bodies by rapid motions; why gyrostat falls, top rises; nature, effect of internal fluidity on rotating bodies; etc. Appendixes describe practical use of gyroscopes in ships, compasses, monorail transportation. 62 figures. 128pp. 5⅜ x 8.
T416 Paperbound **$1.00**

FOUNDATIONS OF PHYSICS, R. B. Lindsay, H. Margenau. Excellent bridge between semi-popular and technical writings. Discussion of methods of physical description, construction of theory; valuable to physicist with elementary calculus. Gives meaning to data, tools of modern physics. Contents: symbolism, mathematical equations; space and time; foundations of mechanics; probability; physics, continua; electron theory; relativity; quantum mechanics; causality; etc. "Thorough and yet not overdetailed. Unreservedly recommended," Nature. Unabridged corrected edition. 35 illustrations. xi + 537pp. 5⅜ x 8.   S377 Paperbound **$2.45**

FADS AND FALLACIES IN THE NAME OF SCIENCE, Martin Gardner. Formerly entitled "In the Name of Science," the standard account of various cults, quack systems, delusions which have masqueraded as science: hollow earth fanatics, orgone sex energy, dianetics, Atlantis, Forteanism, flying saucers, medical fallacies like zone therapy, etc. New chapter on Bridey Murphy, psionics, other recent manifestations. A fair reasoned appraisal of eccentric theory which provides excellent innoculation. "Should be read by everyone, scientist or non-scientist alike," R. T. Birge, Prof. Emeritus of Physics, Univ. of Calif; Former Pres., Amer. Physical Soc. x + 365pp. 5⅜ x 8.   T394 Paperbound **$1.50**

ON MATHEMATICS AND MATHEMATICIANS, R. E. Moritz. A 10 year labor of love by discerning, discriminating Prof. Moritz, this collection conveys the full sense of mathematics and personalities of great mathematicians. Anecdotes, aphorisms, reminiscences, philosophies, definitions, speculations, biographical insights, etc. by great mathematicians, writers: Descartes, Mill, Locke, Kant, Coleridge, Whitehead, etc. Glimpses into lives of great mathematicians, from Archimedes to Euler, Gauss, Weierstrass. To mathematicians, a superb browsing-book. To laymen, exciting revelation of fullness of mathematics. Extensive cross index. 410pp. 5⅜ x 8.   T489 Paperbound **$1.95**

GUIDE TO THE LITERATURE OF MATHEMATICS AND PHYSICS, N. G. Parke III. Over 5000 entries under approximately 120 major subject headings, of selected most important books, monographs, periodicals, articles in English, plus important works in German, French, Italian, Spanish, Russian (many recently available works). Covers every branch of physics, math, related engineering. Includes author, title, edition, publisher, place, date, number of volumes, number of pages. 40 page introduction on basic problems of research, study provides useful information on organization, use of libraries, psychology of learning, etc. Will save you hours of time. 2nd revised edition. Indices of authors, subjects. 464pp. 5⅜ x 8.   S447 Paperbound **$2.49**

THE STRANGE STORY OF THE QUANTUM, An Account for the General Reader of the Growth of Ideas Underlying Our Present Atomic Knowledge, B. Hoffmann. Presents lucidly, expertly, with barest amount of mathematics, problems and theories which led to modern quantum physics. Begins with late 1800's when discrepancies were noticed; with illuminating analogies, examples, goes through concepts of Planck, Einstein, Pauli, Schroedinger, Dirac, Sommerfield, Feynman, etc. New postscript through 1958. "Of the books attempting an account of the history and contents of modern atomic physics which have come to my attention, this is the best," H. Margenau, Yale U., in Amer. J. of Physics. 2nd edition. 32 tables, illustrations. 275pp. 5⅜ x 8.   T518 Paperbound **$1.45**

HISTORY OF SCIENCE
AND PHILOSOPHY OF SCIENCE

THE VALUE OF SCIENCE, Henri Poincaré. Many of most mature ideas of "last scientific universalist" for both beginning, advanced workers. Nature of scientific truth, whether order is innate in universe or imposed by man, logical thought vs. intuition (relating to Weierstrass, Lie, Riemann, etc), time and space (relativity, psychological time, simultaneity), Herz's concept of force, values within disciplines of Maxwell, Carnot, Mayer, Newton, Lorentz, etc. iii + 147pp. 5⅜ x 8.   S469 Paperbound **$1.35**

PHILOSOPHY AND THE PHYSICISTS, L. S. Stebbing. Philosophical aspects of modern science examined in terms of lively critical attack on ideas of Jeans, Eddington. Tasks of science, causality, determinism, probability, relation of world physics to that of everyday experience, philosophical significance of Planck-Bohr concept of discontinuous energy levels, inferences to be drawn from Uncertainty Principle, implications of "becoming" involved in 2nd law of thermodynamics, other problems posed by discarding of Laplacean determinism. 285pp. 5⅜ x 8.   T480 Paperbound **$1.65**

THE PRINCIPLES OF SCIENCE, A TREATISE ON LOGIC AND THE SCIENTIFIC METHOD, W. S. Jevons. Milestone in development of symbolic logic remains stimulating contribution to investigation of inferential validity in sciences. Treats inductive, deductive logic, theory of number, probability, limits of scientific method; significantly advances Boole's logic, contains detailed introduction to nature and methods of probability in physics, astronomy, everyday affairs, etc. In introduction, Ernest Nagel of Columbia U. says, "[Jevons] continues to be of interest as an attempt to articulate the logic of scientific inquiry." liii + 786pp. 5⅜ x 8.   S446 Paperbound **$2.98**

A HISTORY OF ASTRONOMY FROM THALES TO KEPLER, J. L. E. Dreyer. Only work in English to give complete history of cosmological views from prehistoric times to Kepler. Partial contents: Near Eastern astronomical systems, Early Greeks, Homocentric spheres of Euxodus, Epicycles, Ptolemaic system, Medieval cosmology, Copernicus, Kepler, much more. "Especially useful to teachers and students of the history of science . . . unsurpassed in its field," Isis. Formerly "A History of Planetary Systems from Thales to Kepler." Revised foreword by W. H. Stahl. xvii + 430pp. 5⅜ x 8.   S79 Paperbound **$1.98**

A CONCISE HISTORY OF MATHEMATICS, D. Struik. Lucid study of development of ideas, techniques, from Ancient Near East, Greece, Islamic science, Middle Ages, Renaissance, modern times. Important mathematicians described in detail. Treatment not anecdotal, but analytical development of ideas. Non-technical—no math training needed. "Rich in content, thoughtful in interpretations," U.S. Quarterly Booklist. 60 illustrations including Greek, Egyptian manuscripts, portraits of 31 mathematicians. 2nd edition. xix + 299pp. 5⅜ x 8.   S255 Paperbound **$1.75**

THE PHILOSOPHICAL WRITINGS OF PEIRCE, edited by Justus Buchler. A carefully balanced expositon of Peirce's complete system, written by Peirce himself. It covers such matters as scientific method, pure chance vs. law, symbolic logic, theory of signs, pragmatism, experiment, and other topics. "Excellent selection . . . gives more than adequate evidence of the range and greatness," Personalist. Formerly entitled "The Philosophy of Peirce." xvi + 368pp.   T217 Paperbound **$1.95**

SCIENCE AND METHOD, Henri Poincaré. Procedure of scientific discovery, methodology, experiment, idea-germination—processes by which discoveries come into being. Most significant and interesting aspects of development, application of ideas. Chapters cover selection of facts, chance, mathematical reasoning, mathematics and logic; Whitehead, Russell, Cantor, the new mechanics, etc. 288pp. 5⅜ x 8.   S222 Paperbound **$1.35**

SCIENCE AND HYPOTHESIS, Henri Poincaré. Creative psychology in science. How such concepts as number, magnitude, space, force, classical mechanics developed, how modern scientist uses them in his thought. Hypothesis in physics, theories of modern physics. Introduction by Sir James Larmor. "Few mathematicians have had the breadth of vision of Poincaré, and none is his superior in the gift of clear exposition," E. T. Bell. 272pp. 5⅜ x 8.   S221 Paperbound **$1.35**

ESSAYS IN EXPERIMENTAL LOGIC, John Dewey. Stimulating series of essays by one of most influential minds in American philosophy presents some of his most mature thoughts on wide range of subjects. Partial contents: Relationship between inquiry and experience; dependence of knowledge upon thought; judgments of practice, data, and meanings; stimuli of thought, etc. viii + 444pp. 5⅜ x 8.   T73 Paperbound **$1.95**

WHAT IS SCIENCE, Norman Campbell. Excellent introduction explains scientific method, role of mathematics, types of scientific laws. Contents: 2 aspects of science, science and nature, laws of chance, discovery of laws, explanation of laws, measurement and numerical laws, applications of science. 192pp. 5⅜ x 8.   S43 Paperbound **$1.25**

FROM EUCLID TO EDDINGTON: A STUDY OF THE CONCEPTIONS OF THE EXTERNAL WORLD, Sir Edmund Whittaker. Foremost British scientist traces development of theories of natural philosophy from western rediscovery of Euclid to Eddington, Einstein, Dirac, etc. 5 major divisions: Space, Time and Movement; Concepts of Classical Physics; Concepts of Quantum Mechanics; Eddington Universe. Contrasts inadequacy of classical physics to understand physical world with present day attempts of relativity, non-Euclidean geometry, space curvature, etc. 212pp. 5⅜ x 8.   T491 Paperbound **$1.35**

THE ANALYSIS OF MATTER, Bertrand Russell. How do our senses accord with the new physics? This volume covers such topics as logical analysis of physics, prerelativity physics, causality, scientific inference, physics and perception, special and general relativity, Weyl's theory, tensors, invariants and their physical interpretation, periodicity and qualitative series. "The most thorough treatment of the subject that has yet been published," The Nation. Introduction by L. E. Denonn. 422pp. 5⅜ x 8.   T231 Paperbound **$1.95**

LANGUAGE, TRUTH, AND LOGIC, A. Ayer. A clear introduction to the Vienna and Cambridge schools of Logical Positivism. Specific tests to evaluate validity of ideas, etc. Contents: function of philosophy, elimination of metaphysics, nature of analysis, a priori, truth and probability, etc. 10th printing. "I should like to have written it myself," Bertrand Russell. 160pp. 5⅜ x 8.   T10 Paperbound **$1.25**

THE PSYCHOLOGY OF INVENTION IN THE MATHEMATICAL FIELD, J. Hadamard. Where do ideas come from? What role does the unconscious play? Are ideas best developed by mathematical reasoning, word reasoning, visualization? What are the methods used by Einstein, Poincaré, Galton, Riemann? How can these techniques be applied by others? One of the world's leading mathematicians discusses these and other questions. xiii + 145pp. 5⅜ x 8.
T107 Paperbound **$1.25**

GUIDE TO PHILOSOPHY, C. E. M. Joad. By one of the ablest expositors of all time, this is not simply a history or a typological survey, but an examination of central problems in terms of answers afforded by the greatest thinkers: Plato, Aristotle, Scholastics, Leibniz, Kant, Whitehead, Russell, and many others. Especially valuable to persons in the physical sciences; over 100 pages devoted to Jeans, Eddington, and others, the philosophy of modern physics, scientific materialism, pragmatism, etc. Classified bibliography. 592pp. 5⅜ x 8.   T50 Paperbound **$2.00**

SUBSTANCE AND FUNCTION, and EINSTEIN'S THEORY OF RELATIVITY, Ernst Cassirer. Two books bound as one. Cassirer establishes a philosophy of the exact sciences that takes into consideration new developments in mathematics, shows historical connections. Partial contents: Aristotelian logic, Mill's analysis, Helmholtz and Kronecker, Russell and cardinal numbers, Euclidean vs. non-Euclidean geometry, Einstein's relativity. Bibliography. Index. xxi + 464pp. 5⅜ x 8.   T50 Paperbound **$2.00**

FOUNDATIONS OF GEOMETRY, Bertrand Russell. Nobel laureate analyzes basic problems in the overlap area between mathematics and philosophy: the nature of geometrical knowledge, the nature of geometry, and the applications of geometry to space. Covers history of non-Euclidean geometry, philosophic interpretations of geometry, especially Kant, projective and metrical geometry. Most interesting as the solution offered in 1897 by a great mind to a problem still current. New introduction by Prof. Morris Kline, N.Y. University. "Admirably clear, precise, and elegantly reasoned analysis," International Math. News. xii + 201pp. 5⅜ x 8.   S233 Paperbound **$1.60**

THE NATURE OF PHYSICAL THEORY, P. W. Bridgman. How modern physics looks to a highly unorthodox physicist—a Nobel laureate. Pointing out many absurdities of science, demonstrating inadequacies of various physical theories, weighs and analyzes contributions of Einstein, Bohr, Heisenberg, many others. A non-technical consideration of correlation of science and reality. xi + 138pp. 5⅜ x 8.   S33 Paperbound **$1.25**

EXPERIMENT AND THEORY IN PHYSICS, Max Born. A Nobel laureate examines the nature and value of the counterclaims of experiment and theory in physics. Synthetic versus analytical scientific advances are analyzed in works of Einstein, Bohr, Heisenberg, Planck, Eddington, Milne, others, by a fellow scientist. 44pp. 5⅜ x 8. S308 Paperbound **60¢**

A SHORT HISTORY OF ANATOMY AND PHYSIOLOGY FROM THE GREEKS TO HARVEY, Charles Singer. Corrected edition of "The Evolution of Anatomy." Classic traces anatomy, physiology from prescientific times through Greek, Roman periods, dark ages, Renaissance, to beginning of modern concepts. Centers on individuals, movements, that definitely advanced anatomical knowledge. Plato, Diocles, Erasistratus, Galen, da Vinci, etc. Special section on Vesalius. 20 plates. 270 extremely interesting illustrations of ancient, Medieval, enaissance, Oriental origin. xii + 209pp. 5⅜ x 8.   T389 Paperbound **$1.75**

SPACE-TIME-MATTER, Hermann Weyl. "The standard treatise on the general theory of relativity," (Nature), by world renowned scientist. Deep, clear discussion of logical coherence of general theory, introducing all needed tools: Maxwell, analytical geometry, non-Euclidean geometry, tensor calculus, etc. Basis is classical space-time, before absorption of relativity. Contents: Euclidean space, mathematical form, metrical continuum, general theory, etc. 15 diagrams. xviii + 330pp. 5⅜ x 8.   S267 Paperbound **$1.75**

4

MATTER AND MOTION, James Clerk Maxwell. Excellent exposition begins with simple particles, proceeds gradually to physical systems beyond complete analysis; motion, force, properties of centre of mass of material system; work, energy, gravitation, etc. Written with all Maxwell's original insights and clarity. Notes by E. Larmor. 17 diagrams. 178pp. 5⅜ x 8.
S188 Paperbound **$1.25**

PRINCIPLES OF MECHANICS, Heinrich Hertz. Last work by the great 19th century physicist is not only a classic, but of great interest in the logic of science. Creating a new system of mechanics based upon space, time, and mass, it returns to axiomatic analysis, understanding of the formal or structural aspects of science, taking into account logic, observation, a priori elements. Of great historical importance to Poincaré, Carnap, Einstein, Milne. A 20 page introduction by R. S. Cohen, Wesleyan University, analyzes the implications of Hertz's thought and the logic of science. 13 page introduction by Helmholtz. xlii + 274pp. 5⅜ x 8.
S316 Clothbound **$3.50**
S317 Paperbound **$1.75**

FROM MAGIC TO SCIENCE, Charles Singer. A great historian examines aspects of science from Roman Empire through Renaissance. Includes perhaps best discussion of early herbals, penetrating physiological interpretation of "The Visions of Hildegarde of Bingen." Also examines Arabian, Galenic influences; Pythagoras' sphere, Paracelsus; reawakening of science under Leonardo da Vinci, Vesalius; Lorica of Gildas the Briton; etc. Frequent quotations with translations from contemporary manuscripts. Unabridged, corrected edition. 158 unusual illustrations from Classical, Medieval sources. xxvii + 365pp. 5⅜ x 8.
T390 Paperbound **$2.00**

A HISTORY OF THE CALCULUS, AND ITS CONCEPTUAL DEVELOPMENT, Carl B. Boyer. Provides laymen, mathematicians a detailed history of the development of the calculus, from beginnings in antiquity to final elaboration as mathematical abstraction. Gives a sense of mathematics not as technique, but as habit of mind, in progression of ideas of Zeno, Plato, Pythagoras, Eudoxus, Arabic and Scholastic mathematicians, Newton, Leibniz, Taylor, Descartes, Euler, Lagrange, Cantor, Weierstrass, and others. This first comprehensive, critical history of the calculus was originally entitled "The Concepts of the Calculus." Foreword by R. Courant. 22 figures. 25 page bibliography. v + 364pp. 5⅜ x 8.
S509 Paperbound **$2.00**

A DIDEROT PICTORIAL ENCYCLOPEDIA OF TRADES AND INDUSTRY, Manufacturing and the Technical Arts in Plates Selected from "L'Encyclopédie ou Dictionnaire Raisonné des Sciences, des Arts, et des Métiers" of Denis Diderot. Edited with text by C. Gillispie. First modern selection of plates from high-point of 18th century French engraving. Storehouse of technological information to historian of arts and science. Over 2,000 illustrations on 485 full page plates, most of them original size, show trades, industries of fascinating era in such great detail that modern reconstructions might be made of them. Plates teem with men, women, children performing thousands of operations; show sequence, general operations, closeups, details of machinery. Illustrates such important, interesting trades, industries as sowing, harvesting, beekeeping, tobacco processing, fishing, arts of war, mining, smelting, casting iron, extracting mercury, making gunpowder, cannons, bells, shoeing horses, tanning, papermaking, printing, dying, over 45 more categories. Professor Gillispie of Princeton supplies full commentary on all plates, identifies operations, tools, processes, etc. Material is presented in lively, lucid fashion. Of great interest to all studying history of science, technology. Heavy library cloth. 920pp. 9 x 12.
T421 2 volume set **$18.50**

DE MAGNETE, William Gilbert. Classic work on magnetism, founded new science. Gilbert was first to use word "electricity," to recognize mass as distinct from weight, to discover effect of heat on magnetic bodies; invented an electroscope, differentiated between static electricity and magnetism, conceived of earth as magnet. This lively work, by first great experimental scientist, is not only a valuable historical landmark, but a delightfully easy to follow record of a searching, ingenious mind. Translated by P. F. Mottelay. 25 page biographical memoir. 90 figures. lix + 368pp. 5⅜ x 8.
S470 Paperbound **$2.00**

HISTORY OF MATHEMATICS, D. E. Smith. Most comprehensive, non-technical history of math in English. Discusses lives and works of over a thousand major, minor figures, with footnotes giving technical information outside book's scheme, and indicating disputed matters. Vol. I: A chronological examination, from primitive concepts through Egypt, Babylonia, Greece, the Orient, Rome, the Middle Ages, The Renaissance, and to 1900. Vol. II: The development of ideas in specific fields and problems, up through elementary calculus. "Marks an epoch . . . will modify the entire teaching of the history of science," George Sarton. 2 volumes, total of 510 illustrations, 1355pp. 5⅜ x 8. Set boxed in attractive container.
T429, 430 Paperbound, the set **$5.00**

THE PHILOSOPHY OF SPACE AND TIME, H. Reichenbach. An important landmark in development of empiricist conception of geometry, covering foundations of geometry, time theory, consequences of Einstein's relativity, including: relations between theory and observations; coordinate definitions; relations between topological and metrical properties of space; psychological problem of visual intuition of non-Euclidean structures; many more topics important to modern science and philosophy. Majority of ideas require only knowledge of intermediate math. "Still the best book in the field," Rudolf Carnap. Introduction by R. Carnap. 49 figures. xviii + 296pp. 5⅜ x 8.
S443 Paperbound **$2.00**

5

FOUNDATIONS OF SCIENCE: THE PHILOSOPHY OF THEORY AND EXPERIMENT, N. Campbell. A critique of the most fundamental concepts of science, particularly physics. Examines why certain propositions are accepted without question, demarcates science from philosophy, etc. Part I analyzes presuppositions of scientific thought: existence of material world, nature of laws, probability, etc; part 2 covers nature of experiment and applications of mathematics: conditions for measurement, relations between numerical laws and theories, error, etc. An appendix covers problems arising from relativity, force, motion, space, time. A classic in its field. "A real grasp of what science is," Higher Educational Journal. xiii + 565pp. 5⅝ x 8⅜. **S372 Paperbound $2.95**

THE STUDY OF THE HISTORY OF MATHEMATICS and THE STUDY OF THE HISTORY OF SCIENCE, G. Sarton. Excellent introductions, orientation, for beginning or mature worker. Describes duty of mathematical historian, incessant efforts and genius of previous generations. Explains how today's discipline differs from previous methods. 200 item bibliography with critical evaluations, best available biographies of modern mathematicians, best treatises on historical methods is especially valuable. 10 illustrations. 2 volumes bound as one. 113pp. + 75pp. 5⅜ x 8. **T240 Paperbound $1.25**

MATHEMATICAL PUZZLES

MATHEMATICAL PUZZLES OF SAM LOYD, selected and edited by **Martin Gardner.** 117 choice puzzles by greatest American puzzle creator and innovator, from his famous "Cyclopedia of Puzzles." All unique style, historical flavor of originals. Based on arithmetic, algebra, probability, game theory, route tracing, topology, sliding block, operations research, geometrical dissection. Includes famous "14-15" puzzle which was national craze, "Horse of a Different Color" which sold millions of copies. 120 line drawings, diagrams. Solutions. xx + 167pp. 5⅜ x 8. **T498 Paperbound $1.00**

SYMBOLIC LOGIC and THE GAME OF LOGIC, Lewis Carroll. "Symbolic Logic" is not concerned with modern symbolic logic, but is instead a collection of over 380 problems posed with charm and imagination, using the syllogism, and a fascinating diagrammatic method of drawing conclusions. In "The Game of Logic" Carroll's whimsical imagination devises a logical game played with 2 diagrams and counters (included) to manipulate hundreds of tricky syllogisms. The final section, "Hit or Miss" is a lagniappe of 101 additional puzzles in the delightful Carroll manner. Until this reprint edition, both of these books were rarities costing up to $15 each. Symbolic Logic: Index. xxxi + 199pp. The Game of Logic: 96pp. 2 vols. bound as one. 5⅜ x 8. **T492 Paperbound $1.50**

PILLOW PROBLEMS and A TANGLED TALE, Lewis Carroll. One of the rarest of all Carroll's works, "Pillow Problems" contains 72 original math puzzles, all typically ingenious. Particularly fascinating are Carroll's answers which remain exactly as he thought them out, reflecting his actual mental process. The problems in "A Tangled Tale" are in story form, originally appearing as a monthly magazine serial. Carroll not only gives the solutions, but uses answers sent in by readers to discuss wrong approaches and misleading paths, and grades them for insight. Both of these books were rarities until this edition, "Pillow Problems" costing up to $25, and "A Tangled Tale" $15. Pillow Problems: Preface and Introduction by Lewis Carroll. xx + 109pp. A Tangled Tale: 6 illustrations. 152pp. Two vols. bound as one. 5⅜ x 8. **T493 Paperbound $1.50**

NEW WORD PUZZLES, G. L. Kaufman. 100 brand new challenging puzzles on words, combinations, never before published. Most are new types invented by author, for beginners and experts both. Squares of letters follow chess moves to build words; symmetrical designs made of synonyms; rhymed crostics; double word squares; syllable puzzles where you fill in missing syllables instead of missing letter; many other types, all new. Solutions. "Excellent," Recreation. 100 puzzles. 196 figures. vi + 122pp. 5⅜ x 8. **T344 Paperbound $1.00**

MATHEMATICAL EXCURSIONS, H. A. Merrill. Fun, recreation, insights into elementary problem solving. Math expert guides you on by-paths not generally travelled in elementary math courses—divide by inspection, Russian peasant multiplication; memory systems for pi; odd, even magic squares; dyadic systems; square roots by geometry; Tchebichev's machine; dozens more. Solutions to more difficult ones. "Brain stirring stuff . . . a classic," Genie. 50 illustrations. 145pp. 5⅜ x 8. **T350 Paperbound $1.00**

THE BOOK OF MODERN PUZZLES, G. L. Kaufman. Over 150 puzzles, absolutely all new material based on same appeal as crosswords, deduction puzzles, but with different principles, techniques. 2-minute teasers, word labyrinths, design, pattern, logic, observation puzzles, puzzles testing ability to apply general knowledge to peculiar situations, many others. Solutions. 116 illustrations. 192pp. 5⅜ x 8. **T143 Paperbound $1.00**

MATHEMAGIC, MAGIC PUZZLES, AND GAMES WITH NUMBERS, R. V. Heath. Over 60 puzzles, stunts, on properties of numbers. Easy techniques for multiplying large numbers mentally, identifying unknown numbers, finding date of any day in any year. Includes The Lost Digit, 3 Acrobats, Psychic Bridge, magic squares, triangles, cubes, others not easily found elsewhere. Edited by J. S. Meyer. 76 illustrations. 128pp. 5⅜ x 8. **T110 Paperbound $1.00**

PUZZLE QUIZ AND STUNT FUN, J. Meyer. 238 high-priority puzzles, stunts, tricks—math puzzles like The Clever Carpenter, Atom Bomb, Please Help Alice; mysteries, deductions like The Bridge of Sighs, Secret Code; observation puzzlers like The American Flag, Playing Cards, Telephone Dial; over 200 others with magic squares, tongue twisters, puns, anagrams. Solutions. Revised, enlarged edition of "Fun-To-Do." Over 100 illustrations. 238 puzzles, stunts, tricks. 256pp. 5⅜ x 8.   **T337 Paperbound $1.00**

101 PUZZLES IN THOUGHT AND LOGIC, C. R. Wylie, Jr. For readers who enjoy challenge, stimulation of logical puzzles without specialized math or scientific knowledge. Problems entirely new, range from relatively easy to brainteasers for hours of subtle entertainment. Detective puzzles, find the lying fisherman, how a blind man identifies color by logic, many more. Easy-to-understand introduction to logic of puzzle solving and general scientific method. 128pp. 5⅜ x 8.   **T367 Paperbound $1.00**

CRYPTANALYSIS, H. F. Gaines. Standard elementary, intermediate text for serious students. Not just old material, but much not generally known, except to experts. Concealment, Transposition, Substitution ciphers; Vigenere, Kasiski, Playfair, multafid, dozens of other techniques. Formerly "Elementary Cryptanalysis." Appendix with sequence charts, letter frequencies in English, 5 other languages, English word frequencies. Bibliography. 167 codes. New to this edition: solutions to codes. vi + 230pp. 5⅜ x 8⅜.
                                    T97 Paperbound $1.95

CRYPTOGRAPY, L. D. Smith. Excellent elementary introduction to enciphering, deciphering secret writing. Explains transposition, substitution ciphers; codes; solutions; geometrical patterns, route transcription, columnar transposition, other methods. Mixed cipher systems; single, polyalphabetical substitutions; mechanical devices; Vigenere; etc. Enciphering Japanese; explanation of Baconian biliteral cipher; frequency tables. Over 150 problems. Bibliography. Index. 164pp. 5⅜ x 8.   **T247 Paperbound $1.00**

MATHEMATICS, MAGIC AND MYSTERY, M. Gardner. Card tricks, metal mathematics, stage mind-reading, other "magic" explained as applications of probability, sets, number theory, etc. Creative examination of laws, applications. Scores of new tricks, insights. 115 sections on cards, dice, coins; vanishing tricks, many others. No sleight of hand—math guarantees success. "Could hardly get more entertainment . . . easy to follow," Mathematics Teacher. 115 illustrations. xii + 174pp. 5⅜ x 8.   **T335 Paperbound $1.00**

AMUSEMENTS IN MATHEMATICS, H. E. Dudeney. Foremost British originator of math puzzles, always witty, intriguing, paradoxical in this classic. One of largest collections. More than 430 puzzles, problems, paradoxes. Mazes, games, problems on number manipulations, unicursal, other route problems, puzzles on measuring, weighing, packing, age, kinship, chessboards, joiners', crossing river, plane figure dissection, many others. Solutions. More than 450 illustrations. viii + 258pp. 5⅜ x 8.   **T473 Paperbound $1.25**

THE CANTERBURY PUZZLES H. E. Dudeney. Chaucer's pilgrims set one another problems in story form. Also Adventures of the Puzzle Club, the Strange Escape of the King's Jester, the Monks of Riddlewell, the Squire's Christmas Puzzle Party, others. All puzzles are original, based on dissecting plane figures, arithmetic, algebra, elementary calculus, other branches of mathematics, and purely logical ingenuity. "The limit of ingenuity and intricacy," The Observer. Over 110 puzzles, full solutions. 150 illustrations. viii + 225 pp. 5⅜ x 8.   **T474 Paperbound $1.25**

MATHEMATICAL PUZZLES FOR BEGINNERS AND ENTHUSIASTS, G. Mott-Smith. 188 puzzles to test mental agility. Inference, interpretation, algebra, dissection of plane figures, geometry, properties of numbers, decimation, permutations, probability, all are in these delightful problems. Includes the Odic Force, How to Draw an Ellipse, Spider's Cousin, more than 180 others. Detailed solutions. Appendix with square roots, triangular numbers, primes, etc. 135 illustrations. 2nd revised edition. 248pp. 5⅜ x 8.   **T198 Paperbound $1.00**

MATHEMATICAL RECREATIONS, M. Kraitchik. Some 250 puzzles, problems, demonstrations of recreation mathematics on relatively advanced level. Unusual historical problems from Greek, Medieval, Arabic, Hindu sources; modern problems on "mathematics without numbers," geometry, topology, arithmetic, etc. Pastimes derived from figurative, Mersenne, Fermat numbers: fairy chess; latruncles: reversi; etc. Full solutions. Excellent insights into special fields of math. "Strongly recommended to all who are interested in the lighter side of mathematics," Mathematical Gaz. 181 illustrations. 330pp. 5⅜ x 8.
                                    T163 Paperbound $1.75

FICTION

FLATLAND, E. A. Abbott. A perennially popular science-fiction classic about life in a 2-dimensional world, and the impingement of higher dimensions. Political, satiric, humorous, moral overtones. This land where women are straight lines and the lowest and most dangerous classes are isosceles triangles with 3° vertices conveys brilliantly a feeling for many concepts of modern science. 7th edition. New introduction by Banesh Hoffmann. 128pp. 5⅜ x 8.   **T1 Paperbound $1.00**

SEVEN SCIENCE FICTION NOVELS OF H. G. WELLS. Complete texts, unabridged, of seven of Wells' greatest novels: The War of the Worlds, The Invisible Man, The Island of Dr. Moreau, The Food of the Gods, First Men in the Moon, In the Days of the Comet, The Time Machine. Still considered by many experts to be the best science-fiction ever written, they will offer amusements and instruction to the scientific minded reader. "The great master," Sky and Telescope. 1051pp. 5⅜ x 8. **T264 Clothbound $3.95**

28 SCIENCE FICTION STORIES OF H. G. WELLS. Unabridged! This enormous omnibus contains 2 full length novels—Men Like Gods, Star Begotten—plus 26 short stories of space, time, invention, biology, etc. The Crystal Egg, The Country of the Blind, Empire of the Ants, The Man Who Could Work Miracles, Aepyornis Island, A Story of the Days to Come, and 20 others "A master . . . not surpassed by . . . writers of today," The English Journal. 915pp. 5⅜ x 8. **T265 Clothbound $3.95**

FIVE ADVENTURE NOVELS OF H. RIDER HAGGARD. All the mystery and adventure of darkest Africa captured accurately by a man who lived among Zulus for years, who knew African ethnology, folkways as did few of his contemporaries. They have been regarded as examples of the very best high adventure by such critics as Orwell, Andrew Lang, Kipling. Contents: She, King Solomon's Mines, Allan Quatermain, Allan's Wife, Maiwa's Revenge. "Could spin a yarn so full of suspense and color that you couldn't put the story down," Sat. Review. 821pp. 5⅜ x 8. **T108 Clothbound $3.95**

CHESS AND CHECKERS

LEARN CHESS FROM THE MASTERS, Fred Reinfeld. Easiest, most instructive way to improve your game—play 10 games against such masters as Marshall, Znosko-Borovsky, Bronstein, Najdorf, etc., with each move graded by easy system. Includes ratings for alternate moves possible. Games selected for interest, clarity, easily isolated principles. Covers Ruy Lopez, Dutch Defense, Vienna Game openings; subtle, intricate middle game variations; all-important end game. Full annotations. Formerly "Chess by Yourself." 91 diagrams. viii + 144pp. 5⅜ x 8. **T362 Paperbound $1.00**

REINFELD ON THE END GAME IN CHESS, Fred Reinfeld. Analyzes 62 end games by Alekhine, Flohr, Tarrasch, Morphy, Capablanca, Rubinstein, Lasker, Reshevsky, other masters. Only 1st rate book with extensive coverage of error—tell exactly what is wrong with each move you might have made. Centers around transitions from middle play to end play. King and pawn, minor pieces, queen endings; blockage, weak, passed pawns, etc. "Excellent . . . a boon," Chess Life. Formerly "Practical End Play." 62 figures. vi + 177pp. 5⅜ x 8. **T417 Paperbound $1.25**

HYPERMODERN CHESS as developed in the games of its greatest exponent, ARON NIMZOVICH, edited by Fred Reinfeld. An intensely original player, analyst, Nimzovich's approaches startled, often angered the chess world. This volume, designed for the average player, shows how his iconoclastic methods won him victories over Alekhine, Lasker, Marshall, Rubinstein, Spielmann, others, and infused new life into the game. Use his methods to startle opponents, invigorate play. "Annotations and introductions to each game . . . are excellent," Times (London). 180 diagrams. viii + 220pp. 5⅜ x 8. **T448 Paperbound $1.35**

THE ADVENTURE OF CHESS, Edward Lasker. Lively reader, by one of America's finest chess masters, including: history of chess, from ancient Indian 4-handed game of Chaturanga to great players of today; such delights and oddities as Maelzel's chess-playing automaton that beat Napoleon 3 times; etc. One of most valuable features is author's personal recollections of men he has played against—Nimzovich, Emanuel Lasker, Capablanca, Alekhine, etc. Discussion of chess-playing machines (newly revised). 5 page chess primer. 11 illustrations. 53 diagrams. 296pp. 5⅜ x 8. **S510 Paperbound $1.45**

THE ART OF CHESS, James Mason. Unabridged reprinting of latest revised edition of most famous general study ever written. Mason, early 20th century master, teaches beginning, intermediate player over 90 openings; middle game, end game, to see more moves ahead, to plan purposefully, attack, sacrifice, defend, exchange, govern general strategy. "Classic . . . one of the clearest and best developed studies," Publishers Weekly. Also included, a complete supplement by F. Reinfeld, "How Do You Play Chess?", invaluable to beginners for its lively question-and-answer method. 448 diagrams. 1947 Reinfeld-Bernstein text. Bibliography. xvi + 340pp. 5⅜ x 8. **T463 Paperbound $1.85**

MORPHY'S GAMES OF CHESS, edited by P. W. Sergeant. Put boldness into your game by flowing brilliant, forceful moves of the greatest chess player of all time. 300 of Morphy's best games, carefully annotated to reveal principles. 54 classics against masters like Anderssen, Harrwitz, Bird, Paulsen, and others. 52 games at odds; 54 blindfold games; plus over 100 others. Follow his interpretation of Dutch Defense, Evans Gambit, Giuoco Piano, Ruy Lopez, many more. Unabridged reissue of latest revised edition. New introduction by F. Reinfeld. Annotations, introduction by Sergeant. 235 diagrams. x + 352pp. 5⅜ x 8. **T386 Paperbound $1.75**

DOVER SCIENCE BOOKS

WIN AT CHECKERS, M. Hopper. (Formerly "Checkers.") Former World's Unrestricted Checker Champion discusses principles of game, expert's shots, traps, problems for beginner, standard openings, locating best move, end game, opening "blitzkrieg" moves to draw when behind, etc. Over 100 detailed questions, answers anticipate problems. Appendix. 75 problems with solutions, diagrams. 79 figures. xi + 107pp. 5⅜ x 8.   T363 Paperbound **$1.00**

HOW TO FORCE CHECKMATE, Fred Reinfeld. If you have trouble finishing off your opponent, here is a collection of lightning strokes and combinations from actual tournament play. Starts with 1-move checkmates, works up to 3-move mates. Develops ability to lock ahead, gain new insights into combinations, complex or deceptive positions; ways to estimate weaknesses, strengths of you and your opponent. "A good deal of amusement and instruction," Times, (London). 300 diagrams. Solutions to all positions. Formerly "Challenge to Chess Players." 111pp. 5⅜ x 8.   T417 Paperbound **$1.25**

A TREASURY OF CHESS LORE, edited by Fred Reinfeld. Delightful collection of anecdotes, short stories, aphorisms by, about masters; poems, accounts of games, tournaments, photographs; hundreds of humorous, pithy, satirical, wise, historical episodes, comments, word portraits. Fascinating "must" for chess players; revealing and perhaps seductive to those who wonder what their friends see in game. 49 photographs (14 full page plates). 12 diagrams. xi + 306pp. 5⅜ x 8.   T458 Paperbound **$1.75**

WIN AT CHESS, Fred Reinfeld. 300 practical chess situations, to sharpen your eye, test skill against masters. Start with simple examples, progress at own pace to complexities. This selected series of crucial moments in chess will stimulate imagination, develop stronger, more versatile game. Simple grading system enables you to judge progress. "Extensive use of diagrams is a great attraction," Chess. 300 diagrams. Notes, solutions to every situation. Formerly "Chess Quiz." vi + 120pp. 5⅜ x 8.   T433 Paperbound **$1.00**

MATHEMATICS:
ELEMENTARY TO INTERMEDIATE

HOW TO CALCULATE QUICKLY, H. Sticker. Tried and true method to help mathematics of everyday life. Awakens "number sense"—ability to see relationships between numbers as whole quantities. A serious course of over 9000 problems and their solutions through techniques not taught in schools: left-to-right multiplications, new fast division, etc. 10 minutes a day will double or triple calculation speed. Excellent for scientist at home in higher math, but dissatisfied with speed and accuracy in lower math. 256pp. 5 x 7¼.
Paperbound **$1.00**

FAMOUS PROBLEMS OF ELEMENTARY GEOMETRY, Felix Klein. Expanded version of 1894 Easter lectures at Göttingen. 3 problems of classical geometry: squaring the circle, trisecting angle, doubling cube, considered with full modern implications: transcendental numbers, pi, etc. "A modern classic . . . no knowledge of higher mathematics is required," Scientia. Notes by R. Archibald. 16 figures. xi + 92pp. 5⅜ x 8.   T298 Paperbound **$1.00**

HIGHER MATHEMATICS FOR STUDENTS OF CHEMISTRY AND PHYSICS, J. W. Mellor. Practical, not abstract, building problems out of familiar laboratory material. Covers differential calculus, coordinate, analytical geometry, functions, integral calculus, infinite series, numerical equations, differential equations, Fourier's theorem probability, theory of errors, calculus of variations, determinants. "If the reader is not familiar with this book, it will repay him to examine it," Chem. and Engineering News. 800 problems. 189 figures. xxi + 641pp. 5⅜ x 8.   S193 Paperbound **$2.25**

TRIGONOMETRY REFRESHER FOR TECHNICAL MEN, A. A. Klaf. 913 detailed questions, answers cover most important aspects of plane, spherical trigonometry—particularly useful in clearing up difficulties in special areas. Part I: plane trig, angles, quadrants, functions, graphical representation, interpolation, equations, logs, solution of triangle, use of slide rule, etc. Next 188 pages discuss applications to navigation, surveying, elasticity, architecture, other special fields. Part 3: spherical trig, applications to terrestrial, astronomical problems. Methods of time-saving, simplification of principal angles, make book most useful. 913 questions answered. 1738 problems, answers to odd numbers. 494 figures. 24 pages of formulas, functions. x + 629pp. 5⅜ x 8.   T371 Paperbound **$2.00**

CALCULUS REFRESHER FOR TECHNICAL MEN, A. A. Klaf. 756 questions examine most important aspects of integral, differential calculus. Part I: simple differential calculus, constants, variables, functions, increments, logs, curves, etc. Part 2: fundamental ideas of integrations, inspection, substitution, areas, volumes, mean value, double, triple integration, etc. Practical aspects stressed. 50 pages illustrate applications to specific problems of civil, nautical engineering, electricity, stress, strain, elasticity, similar fields. 756 questions answered. 566 problems, mostly answered. 36pp. of useful constants, formulas. v + 431pp. 5⅜ x 8.   T370 Paperbound **$2.00**

9

MONOGRAPHS ON TOPICS OF MODERN MATHEMATICS, edited by J. W. A. Young. Advanced mathematics for persons who have forgotten, or not gone beyond, high school algebra. 9 monographs on foundation of geometry, modern pure geometry, non-Euclidean geometry, fundamental propositions of algebra, algebraic equations, functions, calculus, theory of numbers, etc. Each monograph gives proofs of important results, and descriptions of leading methods, to provide wide coverage. "Of high merit," Scientific American. New introduction by Prof. M. Kline, N.Y. Univ. 100 diagrams. xvi + 416pp. 6⅛ x 9¼.
S289 Paperbound **$2.00**

MATHEMATICS IN ACTION, O. G. Sutton. Excellent middle level application of mathematics to study of universe, demonstrates how math is applied to ballistics, theory of computing machines, waves, wave-like phenomena, theory of fluid flow, meteorological problems, statistics, flight, similar phenomena. No knowledge of advanced math required. Differential equations, Fourier series, group concepts, Eigenfunctions, Planck's constant, airfoil theory, and similar topics explained so clearly in everyday language that almost anyone can derive benefit from reading this even if much of high-school math is forgotten. 2nd edition. 88 figures. viii + 236pp. 5⅜ x 8.
T450 Clothbound **$3.50**

ELEMENTARY MATHEMATICS FROM AN ADVANCED STANDPOINT, Felix Klein. Classic text, an outgrowth of Klein's famous integration and survey course at Göttingen. Using one field to interpret, adjust another, it covers basic topics in each area, with extensive analysis. Especially valuable in areas of modern mathematics. "A great mathematician, inspiring teacher, . . . deep insight," Bul., Amer. Math Soc.

Vol. I. ARITHMETIC, ALGEBRA, ANALYSIS. Introduces concept of function immediately, enlivens discussion with graphical, geometric methods. Partial contents: natural numbers, special properties, complex numbers. Real equations with real unknowns, complex quantities. Logarithmic, exponential functions, infinitesimal calculus. Transcendence of e and pi, theory of assemblages. Index. 125 figures. ix + 274pp. 5⅜ x 8.   S151 Paperbound **$1.75**

Vol. II. GEOMETRY. Comprehensive view, accompanies space perception inherent in geometry with analytic formulas which facilitate precise formulation. Partial contents: Simplest geometric manifold; line segments, Grassman determinant principles, classication of configurations of space. Geometric transformations: affine, projective, higher point transformations, theory of the imaginary. Systematic discussion of geometry and its foundations. 141 illustrations. ix + 214pp. 5⅜ x 8.   S151 Paperbound **$1.75**

A TREATISE ON PLANE AND ADVANCED TRIGONOMETRY, E. W. Hobson. Extraordinarily wide coverage, going beyond usual college level, one of few works covering advanced trig in full detail. By a great expositor with unerring anticipation of potentially difficult points. Includes circular functions; expansion of functions of multiple angle; trig tables; relations between sides, angles of triangles; complex numbers; etc. Many problems fully solved. "The best work on the subject," Nature. Formerly entitled "A Treatise on Plane Trigonometry." 689 examples. 66 figures. xvi + 383pp. 5⅜ x 8.   S353 Paperbound **$1.95**

NON-EUCLIDEAN GEOMETRY, Roberto Bonola. The standard coverage of non-Euclidean geometry. Examines from both a historical and mathematical point of view geometries which have arisen from a study of Euclid's 5th postulate on parallel lines. Also included are complete texts, translated, of Bolyai's "Theory of Absolute Space," Lobachevsky's "Theory of Parallels." 180 diagrams. 431pp. 5⅜ x 8.   S27 Paperbound **$1.95**

GEOMETRY OF FOUR DIMENSIONS, H. P. Manning. Unique in English as a clear, concise introduction. Treatment is synthetic, mostly Euclidean, though in hyperplanes and hyperspheres at infinity, non-Euclidean geometry is used. Historical introduction. Foundations of 4-dimensional geometry. Perpendicularity, simple angles. Angles of planes, higher order. Symmetry, order, motion; hyperpyramids, hypercones, hyperspheres; figures with parallel elements; volume, hypervolume in space; regular polyhedroids. Glossary. 78 figures. ix + 348pp. 5⅜ x 8.   S182 Paperbound **$1.95**

MATHEMATICS: INTERMEDIATE TO ADVANCED

GEOMETRY (EUCLIDEAN AND NON-EUCLIDEAN)

THE GEOMETRY OF RENÉ DESCARTES. With this book, Descartes founded analytical geometry. Original French text, with Descartes's own diagrams, and excellent Smith-Latham translation. Contains: Problems the Construction of Which Requires only Straight Lines and Circles; On the Nature of Curved Lines; On the Construction of Solid or Supersolid Problems. Diagrams. 258pp. 5⅜ x 8.   S68 Paperbound **$1.50**

THE WORKS OF ARCHIMEDES, edited by T. L. Heath. All the known works of the great Greek mathematician, including the recently discovered Method of Archimedes. Contains: On Sphere and Cylinder, Measurement of a Circle, Spirals, Conoids, Spheroids, etc. Definitive edition of greatest mathematical intellect of ancient world. 186 page study by Heath discusses Archimedes and history of Greek mathematics. 563pp. 5⅜ x 8.   S9 Paperbound **$2.00**

COLLECTED WORKS OF BERNARD RIEMANN. Important sourcebook, first to contain complete text of 1892 "Werke" and the 1902 supplement, unabridged. 31 monographs, 3 complete lecture courses, 15 miscellaneous papers which have been of enormous importance in relativity, topology, theory of complex variables, other areas of mathematics. Edited by R. Dedekind, H. Weber, M. Noether, W. Wirtinger. German text; English introduction by Hans Lewy. 690pp. 5⅜ x 8.   S226 Paperbound **$2.85**

THE THIRTEEN BOOKS OF EUCLID'S ELEMENTS, edited by Sir Thomas Heath. Definitive edition of one of very greatest classics of Western world. Complete translation of Heiberg text, plus spurious Book XIV. 150 page introduction on Greek, Medieval mathematics, Euclid, texts, commentators, etc. Elaborate critical apparatus parallels text, analyzing each definition, postulate, proposition, covering textual matters, refutations, supports, extrapolations, etc. This is the full Euclid. Unabridged reproduction of Cambridge U. 2nd edition. 3 volumes. 995 figures. 1426pp. 5⅜ x 8.   S88, 89, 90, 3 volume set, paperbound **$6.00**

AN INTRODUCTION TO GEOMETRY OF N DIMENSIONS, D. M. Y. Sommerville. Presupposes no previous knowledge of field. Only book in English devoted exclusively to higher dimensional geometry. Discusses fundamental ideas of incidence, parallelism, perpendicularity, angles between linear space, enumerative geometry, analytical geometry from projective and metric views, polytopes, elementary ideas in analysis situs, content of hyperspacial figures. 60 diagrams. 196pp. 5⅜ x 8.   S494 Paperbound **$1.50**

ELEMENTS OF NON-EUCLIDEAN GEOMETRY, D. M. Y. Sommerville. Unique in proceeding step-by-step. Requires only good knowledge of high-school geometry and algebra, to grasp elementary hyperbolic, elliptic, analytic non-Euclidean Geometries; space curvature and its implications; radical axes; homopethic centres and systems of circles; parataxy and parallelism; Gauss' proof of defect area theorem; much more, with exceptional clarity. 126 problems at chapter ends. 133 figures. xvi + 274pp. 5⅜ x 8.   S460 Paperbound **$1.50**

THE FOUNDATIONS OF EUCLIDEAN GEOMETRY, H. G. Forder. First connected, rigorous account in light of modern analysis, establishing propositions without recourse to empiricism, without multiplying hypotheses. Based on tools of 19th and 20th century mathematicians, who made it possible to remedy gaps and complexities, recognize problems not earlier discerned. Begins with important relationship of number systems in geometrical figures. Considers classes, relations, linear order, natural numbers, axioms for magnitudes, groups, quasi-fields, fields, non-Archimedian systems, the axiom system (at length), particular axioms (two chapters on the Parallel Axioms), constructions, congruence, similarity, etc. Lists: axioms employed, constructions, symbols in frequent use. 295pp. 5⅜ x 8.
S481 Paperbound **$2.00**

CALCULUS, FUNCTION THEORY (REAL AND COMPLEX), FOURIER THEORY

FIVE VOLUME "THEORY OF FUNCTIONS" SET BY KONRAD KNOPP. Provides complete, readily followed account of theory of functions. Proofs given concisely, yet without sacrifice of completeness or rigor. These volumes used as texts by such universities as M.I.T., Chicago, N.Y. City College, many others. "Excellent introduction . . . remarkably readable, concise, clear, rigorous," J. of the American Statistical Association.

ELEMENTS OF THE THEORY OF FUNCTIONS, Konrad Knopp. Provides background for further volumes in this set, or texts on similar level. Partial contents: Foundations, system of complex numbers and Gaussian plane of numbers, Riemann sphere of numbers, mapping by linear functions, normal forms, the logarithm, cyclometric functions, binomial series. "Not only for the young student, but also for the student who knows all about what is in it," Mathematical Journal. 140pp. 5⅜ x 8.   S154 Paperbound **$1.35**

THEORY OF FUNCTIONS, PART I, Konrad Knopp. With volume II, provides coverage of basic concepts and theorems. Partial contents: numbers and points, functions of a complex variable, integral of a continuous function, Cauchy's intergral theorem, Cauchy's integral formulae, series with variable terms, expansion and analytic function in a power series, analytic continuation and complete definition of analytic functions, Laurent expansion, types of singularities. vii + 146pp. 5⅜ x 8.   S156 Paperbound **$1.35**

THEORY OF FUNCTIONS, PART II, Konrad Knopp. Application and further development of general theory, special topics. Single valued functions, entire, Weierstrass. Meromorphic functions: Mittag-Leffler. Periodic functions. Multiple valued functions. Riemann surfaces. Algebraic functions. Analytical configurations, Riemann surface. x + 150pp. 5⅜ x 8.
S157 Paperbound **$1.35**

PROBLEM BOOK IN THE THEORY OF FUNCTIONS, VOLUME I, Konrad Knopp. Problems in elementary theory, for use with Knopp's "Theory of Functions," or any other text. Arranged according to increasing difficulty. Fundamental concepts, sequences of numbers and infinite series, complex variable, integral theorems, development in series, conformal mapping. Answers. viii + 126pp. 5⅜ x 8.   S 158 **Paperbound $1.35**

PROBLEM BOOK IN THE THEORY OF FUNCTIONS, VOLUME II, Konrad Knopp. Advanced theory of functions, to be used with Knopp's "Theory of Functions," or comparable text. Singularities, entire and meromorphic functions, periodic, analytic, continuation, multiple-valued functions, Riemann surfaces, conformal mapping. Includes section of elementary problems. "The difficult task of selecting . . . problems just within the reach of the beginner is here masterfully accomplished," AM. MATH. SOC. Answers. 138pp. 5⅜ x 8.
S159 Paperbound **$1.35**

ADVANCED CALCULUS, E. B. Wilson. Still recognized as one of most comprehensive, useful texts. Immense amount of well-represented, fundamental material, including chapters on vector functions, ordinary differential equations, special functions, calculus of variations, etc., which are excellent introductions to these areas. Requires only one year of calculus. Over 1300 exercises cover both pure math and applications to engineering and physical problems. Ideal reference, refresher. 54 page introductory review. ix + 566pp. 5⅜ x 8.
S504 Paperbound **$2.45**

LECTURES ON THE THEORY OF ELLIPTIC FUNCTIONS, H. Hancock. Reissue of only book in English with so extensive a coverage, especially of Abel, Jacobi, Legendre, Weierstrass, Hermite, Liouville, and Riemann. Unusual fullness of treatment, plus applications as well as theory in discussing universe of elliptic integrals, originating in works of Abel and Jacobi. Use is made of Riemann to provide most general theory. 40-page table of formulas. 76 figures. xxiii + 498pp. 5⅜ x 8.   S483 Paperbound **$2.55**

THEORY OF FUNCTIONALS AND OF INTEGRAL AND INTEGRO-DIFFERENTIAL EQUATIONS, Vito Volterra. Unabridged republication of only English translation. General theory of functions depending on continuous set of values of another function. Based on author's concept of transition from finite number of variables to a continually infinite number. Includes much material on calculus of variations. Begins with fundamentals, examines generalization of analytic functions, functional derivative equations, applications, other directions of theory, etc. New introduction by G. C. Evans. Biography, criticism of Volterra's work by E. Whittaker. xxxx + 226pp. 5⅜ x 8.   S502 Paperbound **$1.75**

AN INTRODUCTION TO FOURIER METHODS AND THE LAPLACE TRANSFORMATION, Philip Franklin. Concentrates on essentials, gives broad view, suitable for most applications. Requires only knowledge of calculus. Covers complex qualities with methods of computing elementary functions for complex values of argument and finding approximations by charts; Fourier series; harmonic anaylsis; much more. Methods are related to physical problems of heat flow, vibrations, electrical transmission, electromagnetic radiation, etc. 828 problems, answers. Formerly entitled "Fourier Methods." x + 289pp. 5⅜ x 8.
S452 Paperbound **$1.75**

THE ANALYTICAL THEORY OF HEAT, Joseph Fourier. This book, which revolutionized mathematical physics, has been used by generations of mathematicians and physicists interested in heat or application of Fourier integral. Covers cause and reflection of rays of heat, radiant heating, heating of closed spaces, use of trigonometric series in theory of heat, Fourier integral, etc. Translated by Alexander Freeman. 20 figures. xxii + 466pp. 5⅜ x 8.
S93 Paperbound **$2.00**

ELLIPTIC INTEGRALS, H. Hancock. Invaluable in work involving differential equations with cubics, quatrics under root sign, where elementary calculus methods are inadequate. Practical solutions to problems in mathematics, engineering, physics; differential equations requiring integration of Lamé's, Briot's, or Bouquet's equations; determination of arc of ellipse, hyperbola, lemiscate; solutions of problems in elastics; motion of a projectile under resistance varying as the cube of the velocity; pendulums; more. Exposition in accordance with Legendre-Jacobi theory. Rigorous discussion of Legendre transformations. 20 figures. 5 place table. 104pp. 5⅜ x 8.   S484 Paperbound **$1.25**

THE TAYLOR SERIES, AN INTRODUCTION TO THE THEORY OF FUNCTIONS OF A COMPLEX VARIABLE, P. Dienes. Uses Taylor series to approach theory of functions, using ordinary calculus only, except in last 2 chapters. Starts with introduction to real variable and complex algebra, derives properties of infinite series, complex differentiation, integration, etc. Covers b:uniform mapping, overconvergence and gap theorems, Taylor series on its circle of convergence, etc. Unabridged corrected reissue of first edition. 186 examples, many fully worked out. 67 figures. xii + 555pp. 5⅜ x 8.   S391 Paperbound **$2.75**

LINEAR INTEGRAL EQUATIONS, W. V. Lovitt. Systematic survey of general theory, with some application to differential equations, calculus of variations, problems of math, physics. Includes: integral equation of 2nd kind by successive substitutions; Fredholm's equation as ratio of 2 integral series in lambda, applications of the Fredholm theory, Hilbert-Schmidt theory of symmetric kernels, application, etc. Neumann, Dirichlet, vibratory problems. ix + 253pp. 5⅜ x 8.   S175 Clothbound **$3.50**
S176 Paperbound **$1.60**

DOVER SCIENCE BOOKS

DICTIONARY OF CONFORMAL REPRESENTATIONS, H. Kober. Developed by British Admiralty to solve Laplace's equation in 2 dimensions. Scores of geometrical forms and transformations for electrical engineers, Joukowski aerofoil for aerodynamics, Schwartz-Christoffel transformations for hydro-dynamics, transcendental functions. Contents classified according to analytical functions describing transformations with corresponding regions. Glossary. Topological index. 447 diagrams. 6⅛ x 9¼.   .S160 Paperbound **$2.00**

ELEMENTS OF THE THEORY OF REAL FUNCTIONS, J. E. Littlewood. Based on lectures at Trinity College, Cambridge, this book has proved extremely successful in introducing graduate students to modern theory of functions. Offers full and concise coverage of classes and cardinal numbers, well ordered series, other types of series, and elements of the theory of sets of points. 3rd revised edition. vii + 71pp. 5⅜ x 8.   S171 Clothbound **$2.85**
S172 Paperbound **$1.25**

INFINITE SEQUENCES AND SERIES, Konrad Knopp. 1st publication in any language. Excellent introduction to 2 topics of modern mathematics, designed to give student background to penetrate further alone. Sequences and sets, real and complex numbers, etc. Functions of a real and complex variable. Sequences and series. Infinite series. Convergent power series. Expansion of elementary functions. Numerical evaluation of series. v + 186pp. 5⅜ x 8.
S152 Clothbound **$3.50**
S153 Paperbound **$1.75**

THE THEORY AND FUNCTIONS OF A REAL VARIABLE AND THE THEORY OF FOURIER'S SERIES, E. W .Hobson. One of the best introductions to set theory and various aspects of functions and Fourier's series. Requires only a good background in calculus. Exhaustive coverage of: metric and descriptive properties of sets of points; transfinite numbers and order types; functions of a real variable; the Riemann and Lebesgue integrals; sequences and series of numbers; power-series; functions representable by series sequences of continuous functions; trigonometrical series; representation of functions by Fourier's series; and much more. "The best possible guide," Nature. Vol. I: 88 detailed examples, 10 figures. Index. xv + 736pp. Vol. II: 117 detailed examples, 13 figures. x + 780pp. 6⅛ x 9¼.
Vol. I: S387 Paperbound **$3.00**
Vol. II: S388 Paperbound **$3.00**

ALMOST PERIODIC FUNCTIONS, A. S. Besicovitch. Unique and important summary by a well known mathematician covers in detail the two stages of development in Bohr's theory of almost periodic functions: (1) as a generalization of pure periodicity, with results and proofs; (2) the work done by Stepanof, Wiener, Weyl, and Bohr in generalizing the theory. xi + 180pp. 5⅜ x 8.   S18 Paperbound **$1.75**

INTRODUCTION TO THE THEORY OF FOURIER'S SERIES AND INTEGRALS, H. S. Carslaw. 3rd revised edition, an outgrowth of author's courses at Cambridge. Historical introduction, rational, irrational numbers, infinite sequences and series, functions of a single variable, definite integral, Fourier series, and similar topics. Appendices discuss practical harmonic analysis, periodogram analysis, Lebesgue's theory. 84 examples. xiii + 368pp. 5⅜ x 8.
S48 Paperbound **$2.00**

SYMBOLIC LOGIC

THE ELEMENTS OF MATHEMATICAL LOGIC, Paul Rosenbloom. First publication in any language. For mathematically mature readers with no training in symbolic logic. Development of lectures given at Lund Univ., Sweden, 1948. Partial contents: Logic of classes, fundamental theorems, Boolean algebra, logic of propositions, of propositional functions, expressive languages, combinatory logics, development of math within an object language, paradoxes, theorems of Post, Goedel, Church, and similar topics. iv + 214pp. 5⅜ x 8.
S227 Paperbound **$1.45**

INTRODUCTION TO SYMBOLIC LOGIC AND ITS APPLICATION, R. Carnap. Clear, comprehensive, rigorous, by perhaps greatest living master. Symbolic languages analyzed, one constructed. Applications to math (axiom systems for set theory, real, natural numbers), topology (Dedekind, Cantor continuity explanations), physics (general analysis of determination, causality, space-time topology), biology (axiom system for basic concepts). "A masterpiece," Zentralblatt für Mathematik und Ihre Grenzgebiete. Over 300 exercises. 5 figures. xvi + 241pp. 5⅜ x 8.   S453 Paperbound **$1.85**

AN INTRODUCTION TO SYMBOLIC LOGIC, Susanne K. Langer. Probably clearest book for the philosopher, scientist, layman—no special knowledge of math required. Starts with simplest symbols, goes on to give remarkable grasp of Boole-Schroeder, Russell-Whitehead systems, clearly, quickly. Partial Contents: Forms, Generalization, Classes, Deductive System of Classes, Algebra of Logic, Assumptions of Principia Mathematica, Logistics, Proofs of Theorems, etc. "Clearest . . . simplest introduction . . . the intelligent non-mathematician should have no difficulty," MATHEMATICS GAZETTE. Revised, expanded 2nd edition. Truth-value tables. 368pp. 5⅜ 8.   S164 Paperbound **$1.75**

TRIGONOMETRICAL SERIES, Antoni Zygmund. On modern advanced level. Contains carefully organized analyses of trigonometric, orthogonal, Fourier systems of functions, with clear adequate descriptions of summability of Fourier series, proximation theory, conjugate series, convergence, divergence of Fourier series. Especially valuable for Russian, Eastern European coverage. 329pp. 5⅜ x 8.   S290 Paperbound **$1.50**

THE LAWS OF THOUGHT, George Boole. This book founded symbolic logic some 100 years ago. It is the 1st significant attempt to apply logic to all aspects of human endeavour. Partial contents: derivation of laws, signs and laws, interpretations, eliminations, conditions of a perfect method, analysis, Aristotelian logic, probability, and similar topics. xvii + 424pp. 5⅜ x 8.   S28 Paperbound **$2.00**

SYMBOLIC LOGIC, C. I. Lewis, C. H. Langford. 2nd revised edition of probably most cited book in symbolic logic. Wide coverage of entire field; one of fullest treatments of paradoxes; plus much material not available elsewhere. Basic to volume is distinction between logic of extensions and intensions. Considerable emphasis on converse substitution, while matrix system presents supposition of variety of non-Aristotelian logics. Especially valuable sections on strict limitations, existence theorems. Partial contents: Boole-Schroeder algebra; truth value systems, the matrix method; implication and deductibility; general theory of propositions; etc. "Most valuable," Times, London. 506pp. 5⅜ x 8.   S170 Paperbound **$2.00**

GROUP THEORY AND LINEAR ALGEBRA, SETS, ETC.

LECTURES ON THE ICOSAHEDRON AND THE SOLUTION OF EQUATIONS OF THE FIFTH DEGREE, Felix Klein. Solution of quintics in terms of rotations of regular icosahedron around its axes of symmetry. A classic, indispensable source for those interested in higher algebra, geometry, crystallography. Considerable explanatory material included. 230 footnotes, mostly bibliography. "Classical monograph . . . detailed, readable book," Math. Gazette. 2nd edition. xvi + 289pp. 5⅜ x 8.   S314 Paperbound **$1.85**

INTRODUCTION TO THE THEORY OF GROUPS OF FINITE ORDER, R. Carmichael. Examines fundamental theorems and their applications. Beginning with sets, systems, permutations, etc., progresses in easy stages through important types of groups: Abelian, prime power, permutation, etc. Except 1 chapter where matrices are desirable, no higher math is needed. 783 exercises, problems. xvi + 447pp. 5⅜ x 8.   S299 Clothbound **$3.95**
                                                             S300 Paperbound **$2.00**

THEORY OF GROUPS OF FINITE ORDER, W. Burnside. First published some 40 years ago, still one of clearest introductions. Partial contents: permutations, groups independent of representation, composition series of a group, isomorphism of a group with itself, Abelian groups, prime power groups, permutation groups, invariants of groups of linear substitution, graphical representation, etc. "Clear and detailed discussion . . . numerous problems which are instructive," Design News. xxiv + 512pp. 5⅜ x 8.   S38 Paperbound **$2.45**

COMPUTATIONAL METHODS OF LINEAR ALGEBRA, V. N. Faddeeva, translated by C. D. Benster. 1st English translation of unique, valuable work, only one in English presenting systematic exposition of most important methods of linear algebra—classical, contemporary. Details of deriving numerical solutions of problems in mathematical physics. Theory and practice. Includes survey of necessary background, most important methods of solution, for exact, iterative groups. One of most valuable features is 23 tables, triple checked for accuracy, unavailable elsewhere. Translator's note. x + 252pp. 5⅜ x 8.   S424 Paperbound **$1.95**

THE CONTINUUM AND OTHER TYPES OF SERIAL ORDER, E. V. Huntington. This famous book gives a systematic elementary account of the modern theory of the continuum as a type of serial order. Based on the Cantor-Dedekind ordinal theory, which requires no technical knowledge of higher mathematics, it offers an easily followed analysis of ordered classes, discrete and dense series, continuous series, Cantor's transfinite numbers. "Admirable introduction to the rigorous theory of the continuum . . . reading easy," Science Progress. 2nd edition. viii + 82pp. 5⅜ x 8.   S129 Clothbound **$2.75**
                                                             S130 Paperbound **$1.00**

THEORY OF SETS, E. Kamke. Clearest, amplest introduction in English, well suited for independent study. Subdivisions of main theory, such as theory of sets of points, are discussed, but emphasis is on general theory. Partial contents: rudiments of set theory, arbitrary sets, their cardinal numbers, ordered sets, their order types, well-ordered sets, their cardinal numbers. vii + 144pp. 5⅜ x 8.   S141 Paperbound **$1.35**

CONTRIBUTIONS TO THE FOUNDING OF THE THEORY OF TRANSFINITE NUMBERS, Georg Cantor. These papers founded a new branch of mathematics. The famous articles of 1895-7 are translated, with an 82-page introduction by P. E. B. Jourdain dealing with Cantor, the background of his discoveries, their results, future possibilities. ix + 211pp. 5⅜ x 8.
                                                             S45 Paperbound **$1.25**

NUMERICAL AND GRAPHICAL METHODS, TABLES

JACOBIAN ELLIPTIC FUNCTION TABLES, L. M. Milne-Thomson. Easy-to-follow, practical, not only useful numerical tables, but complete elementary sketch of application of elliptic functions. Covers description of principle properties; complete elliptic integrals; Fourier series, expansions; periods, zeros, poles, residues, formulas for special values of argument; cubic, quartic polynomials; pendulum problem; etc. Tables, graphs form body of book: Graph, 5 figure table of elliptic function sn (u m); cn (u m); dn (u m). 8 figure table of complete elliptic integrals K, K', E, E', nome q. 7 figure table of Jacobian zeta-function Z(u). 3 figures. xi + 123pp. 5⅜ x 8.   S194 Paperbound **$1.35**

TABLES OF FUNCTIONS WITH FORMULAE AND CURVES, E. Jahnke, F. Emde. Most comprehensive 1-volume English text collection of tables, formulae, curves of transcendent functions. 4th corrected edition, new 76-page section giving tables, formulae for elementary functions not in other English editions. Partial contents: sine, cosine, logarithmic integral; error integral; elliptic integrals; theta functions; Legendre, Bessel, Riemann, Mathieu, hypergeometric functions; etc. "Out-of-the-way functions for which we know no other source." Scientific Computing Service, Ltd. 212 figures. 400pp. 5⅝ x 8⅜.   S133 Paperbound **$2.00**

MATHEMATICAL TABLES, H. B. Dwight. Covers in one volume almost every function of importance in applied mathematics, engineering, physical sciences. Three extremely fine tables of the three trig functions, inverses, to 1000th of radian; natural, common logs; squares, cubes; hyperbolic functions, inverses; $(a^2 + b^2)$ exp: ½a; complete elliptical integrals of 1st, 2nd kind; sine, cosine integrals; exponential integrals; Ei(x) and Ei(−x); binomial coefficients; factorials to 250; surface zonal harmonics, first derivatives; Bernoulli, Euler numbers, their logs to base of 10; Gamma function; normal probability integral; over 60pp. Bessel functions; Riemann zeta function. Each table with formulae generally used, sources of more extensive tables, interpolation data, etc. Over half have columns of differences, to facilitate interpolation. viii + 231pp. 5⅜ x 8.   S445 Paperbound **$1.75**

PRACTICAL ANALYSIS, GRAPHICAL AND NUMERICAL METHODS, F. A. Willers. Immensely practical hand-book for engineers. How to interpolate, use various methods of numerical differentiation and integration, determine roots of a single algebraic equation, system of linear equations, use empirical formulas, integrate differential equations, etc. Hundreds of short-cuts for arriving at numerical solutions. Special section on American calculating machines, by T. W. Simpson. Translation by R. T. Beyer. 132 illustrations. 422pp. 5⅜ x 8.
                                                                  S273 Paperbound **$2.00**

NUMERICAL SOLUTIONS OF DIFFERENTIAL EQUATIONS, H. Levy, E. A. Baggott. Comprehensive collection of methods for solving ordinary differential equations of first and higher order. 2 requirements: practical, easy to grasp; more rapid than school methods. Partial contents: graphical integration of differential equations, graphical methods for detailed solution. Numerical solution. Simultaneous equations and equations of 2nd and higher orders. "Should be in the hands of all in research and applied mathematics, teaching," Nature. 21 figures. viii + 238pp. 5⅜ x 8.   S168 Paperbound **$1.75**

NUMERICAL INTEGRATION OF DIFFERENTIAL EQUATIONS, Bennet, Milne, Bateman. Unabridged republication of original prepared for National Research Council. New methods of integration by 3 leading mathematicians: "The Interpolational Polynomial," "Successive Approximation," A. A. Bennett, "Step-by-step Methods of Integration," W. W. Milne. "Methods for Partial Differential Equations," H. Bateman. Methods for partial differential equations, solution of differential equations to non-integral values of a parameter will interest mathematicians, physicists. 288 footnotes, mostly bibliographical. 235 item classified bibliography. 108pp. 5⅜ x 8.   S305 Paperbound **$1.35**

Write for free catalogs!

Indicate your field of interest. Dover publishes books on physics, earth sciences, mathematics, engineering, chemistry, astronomy, anthropology, biology, psychology, philosophy, religion, history, literature, mathematical recreations, languages, crafts, art, graphic arts, etc.

Write to Dept. catr
Dover Publications, Inc.
Science A   *180 Varick St., N. Y. 14, N. Y.*